NUMERICAL METHODS AND SOFTWARE FOR DYNAMIC ANALYSIS OF PLATES AND SHELLS

NUMERICAL METHODS AND SOFTWARE FOR DYNAMIC ANALYSIS OF PLATES AND SHELLS

Ernest Hinton
University College of Swansea, U.K.

Pineridge Press
Swansea, U.K.

First Published 1988 by
Pineridge Press Limited
54, Newton Road, Mumbles, Swansea, U.K.

ISBN 0–906674–66–2

Numerical methods and software for dynamic
analysis of plates and shells
I. Hinton, E.
624.1′776′0194 TA660.P6

ISBN 0–906674–66–2

Printed and bound in Great Britain by
Dotesios Printers Ltd., Bradford-on-Avon, Wiltshire

PREFACE

This book is intended as a sequel to 'Finite Element Software for Plates and Shells' which was written jointly with Roger Owen and others in 1984. It deals with the dynamic analysis of plates and shells using closed form, finite strip and finite element methods. Theory, software and applications are presented in detail and the following six FORTRAN programs are listed and documented: TRAM, FIST, VIBUK, DYNAM, VISOR and DARC3.

The book was started about three years ago and has gone through many drafts and revisions. The camera-ready manuscript reflects this history being partly type-written using an IBM golf-ball typewriter, partly produced using a scientific wordprocessing system called LEX (printed with daisy-wheel printer) and partly produced using the TEX or more precisely, Addison-Wesley's MICROTEX computer typesetting system (printed using a Hewlett Packard Laser Jet Plus). Thus, the book provides a document illustrating a rapidly changing word-processing technology.

As anyone who has developed software will testify, it is impossible to eliminate all 'bugs' from a program. Although every effort has been made to check the programs in this book, no responsibility can be accepted for their performance in practice.

To aid readers wishing to implement the programs, the complete codes together with specimen input data are available on magnetic tape or floppy disc directly from the author: Dr. E. Hinton, Dept. of Civil Engineering, University College of Swansea, Singleton Park, Swansea SA2 8PP, United Kingdom or from the publisher.

This book has been written in collaboration with several former students and colleagues to whom I am extremely grateful — they are: Djordje Vuksanovic (Belgrade), Eugenio Oñate (Barcelona), Hou Cheng Huang (Tianjin), Bahaa Al Janabi (Baghdad), Miguel Cervera (Barcelona), Javier Bonet (Barcelona) and Nenad Bićanić (Swansea). Secretaries Nancy Williams and Liz Gower provided much valued help with the typewritten sections. (On one occasion one of the chapters was inadvertantly left near an open window on a wet and windy day with catastrophic results. However, we managed to overcome this little setback – such are the perils of book writing.) Finally, I acknowledge the assistance of Dennis Morgan, Angela McGairl and Derek Gabriel in the production of the illustrations.

Swansea, South Wales *Ernest Hinton*
October 1987

CONTENTS

4. A STUDY OF THE FREE VIBRATIONS OF SQUARE PLATES WITH VARIOUS EDGE CONDITIONS

by B.S. Al Janabi and E. Hinton

5. EXPLICIT TRANSIENT DYNAMIC FINITE ELEMENT ANALYSIS OF INITIALLY STRESSED MINDLIN PLATES

by E. Hinton and Dj. Vuksanovic

6. A UNIFIED FINITE ELEMENT BASED METHOD FOR EVALUATING THE MODES OF VIBRATION OF COMPLETE SOLIDS OF REVOLUTION AND THEIR SECTORS

by E. Hinton

7. NONLINEAR TRANSIENT DYNAMIC ANALYSIS OF THREE DIMENSIONAL STRUCTURES - A FINITE ELEMENT MODEL FOR STEEL AND REINFORCED CONCRETE STRUCTURES

by M. Cervera, E. Hinton, J. Bonet and N. Bićanić

ADDITIONAL NOTES

by E. Hinton and B.S. Al Janabi

CLOSED FORM SOLUTIONS FOR DYNAMIC ANALYSIS OF SIMPLY SUPPORTED MINDLIN PLATES

E. HINTON* and Dj. VUKSANOVIC**

*** Department of Civil Engineering, University College of Swansea, U.K.**

**** Faculty of Civil Engineering, University of Belgrade, Yugoslavia**

1. INTRODUCTION

The object of this first chapter is to describe in detail some closed form solutions for dynamic analysis of simply supported rectangular Mindlin plates which rest on elastic Winkler foundations. These plates have specially orthotropic form and four different types of loading are considered, using as forcing functions: a sine pulse, a step pulse, a triangular pulse, a stepped triangular pulse or an exponential pulse. Other types of loading and forcing functions can easily by incorporated. The solutions given in this chapter include a free vibration and an initially stressed vibration analysis, as well as a buckling analysis. In Section 4 of this chapter a program called TRAM is presented for the closed form solution. The solutions obtained from this program may be used to check the accuracy of the finite strip and finite element solutions presented in Chapters 2 and 3 of this book. Some examples illustrating the use of program TRAM are given in Section 5.

2. GOVERNING EQUATIONS

Mindlin plate theory [1] allows for transverse shear deformation and thus offers an alternative to classical Kirchhoff thin plate theory [2]. The main assumptions are that:

(a) displacements are small compared with the plate thickness,

(b) the stress normal to the midplane of the plate is negligible, and

(c) normals to the midplane before deformation remain straight but not necessarily normal to the midplane after deformation.

The third assumption leads to the following displacement field,

$$\bar{u}(x,y,z) = z\theta_x(x,y) \tag{2.1a}$$

$$\bar{v}(x,y,z) = z\theta_y(x,y) \tag{2.1b}$$

$$\bar{w}(x,y,z) = w(x,y) \tag{2.1c}$$

in which x and y are the rectangular coordinates in the plane of the plate, z is the thickness-direction coordinate measured downwards from the midplane; $\bar{u}$, $\bar{v}$ and $\bar{w}$ are the displacements in the x, y and z directions respectively, w is the corresponding midplane displacement, and $\boldsymbol{\theta}_x$ and $\boldsymbol{\theta}_y$ are the normal rotations in the xz- and yz-planes respectively due to bending.

By making use of the assumption that $\sigma_z = 0$, the constitutive equations at a typical point (x, y, z) in a Mindlin plate may be expressed as

$$\boldsymbol{\sigma} = \mathbf{Q}\,\boldsymbol{\epsilon} \tag{2.2a}$$

where the stress vector $\boldsymbol{\sigma}$ has the form

$$\boldsymbol{\sigma} = [\sigma_x\,,\ \sigma_y\,,\ \tau_{xy}]^T \tag{2.2b}$$

the matrix of reduced in-plane stiffnesses for plane stress (i.e. assuming that $\sigma_z = 0$) may be written as

$$\mathbf{Q} = \begin{bmatrix} Q_{11} & Q_{12} & Q_{16} \\ Q_{12} & Q_{22} & Q_{26} \\ Q_{16} & Q_{26} & Q_{66} \end{bmatrix} \tag{2.2c}$$

the strain vector $\boldsymbol{\epsilon}$ is expressed as

$$\boldsymbol{\epsilon} = [\bar{u}_{,x}\,,\ \bar{v}_{,y}\,,\ \bar{u}_{,y} + \bar{v}_{,x}]^T \tag{2.2d}$$

Using relations (2.1), (2.2d) may be rewritten as

$$\boldsymbol{\epsilon} = z\ \boldsymbol{\epsilon}_f \tag{2.2e}$$

where

$$\boldsymbol{\epsilon}_f = [\boldsymbol{\theta}_{x,x}\,,\ \boldsymbol{\theta}_{y,y}\,,\ (\boldsymbol{\theta}_{x,y} + \boldsymbol{\theta}_{y,x})]^T \tag{2.2f}$$

Note that $\theta_{x,x} = \partial\theta_x/\partial x$ etc. The transverse shear stress-strain relations have the form

$$\boldsymbol{\tau} = \mathbf{C}\boldsymbol{\gamma} \tag{2.3a}$$

where the shear stress vector $\boldsymbol{\tau}$ is written as

$$\boldsymbol{\tau} = [\tau_{yz}\,,\ \tau_{xz}]^T \tag{2.3b}$$

The matrix of elastic constants $\mathbf{C}$ can be written as

$$\mathbf{C} = \begin{bmatrix} C_{44} & C_{45} \\ C_{45} & C_{55} \end{bmatrix} \tag{2.3c}$$

The vector of shear strains has the form

$$\boldsymbol{\gamma} = (\bar{v}_{,z} + \bar{w}_{,y}\,,\ \bar{u}_{,z} + \bar{w}_{,x})^T \tag{2.3d}$$

Again, using expressions (2.1), the shear strain vector can be rewritten as

$$\boldsymbol{\gamma} = \boldsymbol{\epsilon}_s \tag{2.3e}$$

or

$$\boldsymbol{\epsilon}_s = [\theta_y + w_{,y}\,,\ \theta_x + w_{,x}]^T \tag{2.3f}$$

For a Mindlin plate of thickness h and area A, the strain energy can be written as

$$\begin{aligned} S.E. &= 1/2 \int_A \Big(\int_{-h/2}^{h/2} \boldsymbol{\sigma}^T\, \boldsymbol{\epsilon}\, dz \Big) dA + 1/2 \int_A \Big(\int_{-h/2}^{h/2} \boldsymbol{\gamma}^T\, \boldsymbol{\tau}\, dz \Big) dA \\ &= 1/2 \int_A \Big(\int_{-h/2}^{h/2} \boldsymbol{\epsilon}_f^T\, (z^2 \mathbf{Q})\, \boldsymbol{\epsilon}_f\, dz \Big) dA + 1/2 \int_A \Big(\int_{-h/2}^{h/2} \boldsymbol{\epsilon}_s^T\, \mathbf{C}\, \boldsymbol{\epsilon}_s\, dz \Big) dA \\ &= 1/2 \int_A \boldsymbol{\epsilon}_f^T\, \mathbf{D_f}\, \boldsymbol{\epsilon}_f\, dA + 1/2 \int_A \boldsymbol{\epsilon}_s^T\, \mathbf{D_s}\, \boldsymbol{\epsilon}_s\, dA \ cr \end{aligned} \tag{2.4}$$

The plate constitutive equations can be written as

$$\boldsymbol{\sigma}_f = \mathbf{D_f}\, \boldsymbol{\epsilon}_f \tag{2.5a}$$

where the bending moments are written as

$$\boldsymbol{\sigma}_f = [M_x\,,\ M_y\,,\ M_{xy}]^T \tag{2.5b}$$

in which

$$(M_x\,,\ M_y\,,\ M_{xy}) = \int_{-h/2}^{h/2} z(\sigma_x\,,\ \sigma_y\,,\ \tau_{xy})\, dz \tag{2.5c}$$

The matrix of flexural rigidities has the form

$$\mathbf{D_f} = \begin{bmatrix} D_{11} & D_{12} & D_{16} \\ D_{12} & D_{22} & D_{26} \\ D_{16} & D_{26} & D_{66} \end{bmatrix} \tag{2.5d}$$

in which

$$D_{ij} = \int_{-h/2}^{h/2} Q_{ij}\, z^2\, dz \qquad (i,j = 1,2,6) \tag{2.5e}$$

Further, it is possible to write

$$\boldsymbol{\sigma}_s = \mathbf{D_s}\, \boldsymbol{\epsilon}_s \tag{2.6a}$$

where the shear forces may be written as

$$\boldsymbol{\sigma}_s = [Q_y\,,\ Q_x]^T \tag{2.6b}$$

and

$$(Q_y, Q_x) = \int_{-h/2}^{h/2} (\tau_{yz}, \tau_{xz})\, dz \tag{2.6c}$$

The matrix of shear rigidities can be written as

$$\mathbf{D_s} = \begin{bmatrix} S_{44} & S_{45} \\ S_{45} & S_{55} \end{bmatrix} \tag{2.6d}$$

where

$$S_{ij} = \int_{-h/2}^{h/2} C_{ij}\, dz \qquad (i,j = 4,5) \tag{2.6e}$$

Note that for specially orthotropic plates D_{16}, D_{61}, D_{26} and $D_{62} = 0$. For homogeneous plates D_{ij} and S_{ij} may be evaluated from (2.5e) and (2.6e), and for sandwich, laminated and voided plates one can use formulae which are given in Reference 3.

Note also that the strain resultants given in (2.2f) and (2.3f) are the direct curvatures $\theta_{x,x}$ and $\theta_{y,y}$ in the x and y directions respectively, the twisting curvature $(\theta_{y,x} + \theta_{x,y})$ and the shear rotations $(\theta_y + w_{,y})$ and $(\theta_x + w_{,x})$ in the yz- and xz–planes respectively.

The equations of motion for a Mindlin plate resting on an elastic Winkler foundation of modulus K, subjected due to the uniform initial stress resultants F_x and F_y may be written as

$$Q_{x,x} + Q_{y,y} + F_x w_{,xx} + F_y w_{,yy} + Kw + q = P\ddot{w} \tag{2.7a}$$

$$M_{x,x} + M_{xy,y} - Q_x + m_x = I\ddot{\theta}_x \tag{2.7b}$$

$$M_{xy,x} + M_{y,y} - Q_y + m_y = I\ddot{\theta}_y \tag{2.7c}$$

in which q, m_x and m_y are the distributed lateral loads and couples. In (2.7), differentiation with respect to x or y is denoted by a comma while differentiation with respect to time is denoted by a superposed dot, and inertias are given by

$$(P, I) = \int_{-h/2}^{h/2} \rho(1, z^2) dz \tag{2.8}$$

The closed form solution given later in the chapter is concerned with simply supported rectangular plates of uniform thickness with dimensions a and b for which the boundary conditions are given as

$$w = \theta_{x,x} = 0 \qquad x = 0, a \tag{2.9a}$$

$$w = \theta_{y,y} = 0 \qquad y = 0, b \tag{2.9b}$$

By combining (2.5a), (2.6a) and (2.7) the governing equations may be expressed as

$$S_{55}\theta_{x,x} + (S_{55} + F_x)w_{,xx} + S_{44}\theta_{y,y} + (S_{44} + F_y)w_{,yy} + Kw + q = P\ddot{w} \quad (2.10a)$$

$$D_{11}\theta_{x,xx} + D_{66}\theta_{x,yy} + (D_{12} + D_{66})\theta_{y,xy} - S_{55}\theta_x - S_{55}w_{,x} + m_x = I\ddot{\theta}_x \quad (2.10b)$$

$$(D_{12} + D_{66})\theta_{x,xy} + D_{66}\theta_{y,xx} + D_{22}\theta_{y,yy} - S_{44}\ddot{\theta}_y - S_{44}w_{,y} + m_y = I\ddot{\theta}_y \quad (2.10c)$$

For the closed form solution functions w, θ_x and θ_y are sought which satisfy (2.9) and (2.10).

3. CLOSED FORM SOLUTION

3.1 Vibration Analysis

Here the closed form solution given by Dobyns [4] is presented for a simply supported rectangular plate of uniform thickness, which has dimensions a and b, and which rests on an elastic Winkler foundation. Solutions to equations (2.10) that satisfy boundary conditions (2.9) are given as

$$\theta_x = \Phi_x^{mn} e^{i\omega_{mn}t} \quad (3.1a)$$

$$\theta_y = \Phi_y^{mn} e^{i\omega_{mn}t} \quad (3.1b)$$

$$w = W^{mn} e^{i\omega_{mn}t} \quad (3.1c)$$

where

$$\Phi_x^{mn} = A_{mn}\cos(m\pi x/a)\sin(n\pi y/b) \quad (3.2a)$$

$$\Phi_y^{mn} = B_{mn}\sin(m\pi x/a)\cos(n\pi y/b) \quad (3.2b)$$

$$W^{mn} = C_{mn}\sin(m\pi x/a)\sin(n\pi y/b) \quad (3.2c)$$

Substitution of the assumed displacements (3.1) into the equations of motion (2.10) results in

$$D_{11}\Phi^{mn}_{x,xx} + D_{66}\Phi^{mn}_{x,yy} + (D_{12} + D_{66})\Phi^{mn}_{y,xy} - S_{55}\Phi^{mn}_x - S_{55}W^{mn}_{,x} = -\omega^2_{mn}I\Phi^{mn}_x$$

$$(D_{12} + D_{66})\Phi^{mn}_{x,xy} + D_{66}\Phi^{mn}_{y,xx} + D_{22}\Phi^{mn}_{y,yy} - S_{44}\Phi^{mn}_y - S_{44}W^{mn}_{,y} = -\omega^2_{mn}I\Phi^{mn}_y$$

$$S_{55}\Phi^{mn}_{x,x} + (S_{55} + F_x)W^{mn}_{,xx} + S_{44}\Phi^{mn}_{y,y} + (S_{44} + F_y)W^{mn}_{,yy} + KW^{mn} = -\omega^2_{mn}PW^{mn} \quad (3.3)$$

Upon substitution of (3.2) into the equilibrium equations of (3.3) it is possible to obtain a set of homogeneous equations that may be solved for the natural frequencies of vibration.

$$\begin{bmatrix} (P_{11} - \omega^2_{mn}I) & P_{12} & P_{13} \\ P_{12} & (P_{22} - \omega^2_{mn}I) & P_{23} \\ P_{13} & P_{23} & (P_{33} - \omega^2_{mn}P) \end{bmatrix} \begin{bmatrix} A_{mn} \\ B_{mn} \\ C_{mn} \end{bmatrix} = \begin{bmatrix} 0 \\ 0 \\ 0 \end{bmatrix} \quad (3.4)$$

where

$$
\begin{aligned}
P_{11} &= D_{11}(m\pi/a)^2 + D_{66}(n\pi/b)^2 + S_{55} \\
P_{12} &= (D_{12} + D_{66})(m\pi/a)(n\pi/b) \\
P_{13} &= S_{55}(m\pi/a) \\
P_{22} &= D_{66}(m\pi/a)^2 + D_{22}(n\pi/b)^2 + S_{44} \\
P_{23} &= S_{44}(n\pi/b) \\
P_{33} &= (S_{55} + F_x)(m\pi/a)^2 + (S_{44} + F_y)(n\pi/b)^2 + K
\end{aligned} \tag{3.5}
$$

Three eigenvalues and their respective eigenvectors result from (3.4) for each m, n pair.

If the rotatory interia (I) is neglected (Mindlin [1] has shown that rotatory inertia has little effect in isotropic plates and it is popularly assumed that the same holds true for orthotropic plates), only one eigenvalue and its eigenvector results for each m, n. The frequency of vibration is given as

$$\omega_{mn}^2 = (QP_{33} + 2P_{12}P_{23}P_{13} - P_{22}P_{13}^2 - P_{11}P_{23}^2)/(PQ) \tag{3.6}$$

where $Q = (P_{11}P_{22} - P_{12}^2)$ and the eigenvectors associated with the natural frequency are

$$A_{mn} = C_{mn}(P_{12}P_{23} - P_{22}P_{13})/(P_{11}P_{22} - P_{12}^2) \tag{3.7a}$$

$$B_{mn} = C_{mn}(P_{12}P_{13} - P_{11}P_{23})/(P_{11}P_{22} - P_{12}^2) \tag{3.7b}$$

when normalised to C_{mn}.

The orthogonality condition for the principal modes is given by

$$(\omega_{mn}^2 - \omega_{pq}^2)\int_0^a\int_0^b (PW^{mn}W^{pq} + I\Phi_x^{mn}\Phi_x^{pq} + I\Phi_y^{mn}\Phi_y^{pq})dxdy = 0 \tag{3.9}$$

so that if $m, n \neq p, q$ then the integral is zero.

3.2 Stability Analysis

If a plate is subjected to uniform stress resultants F_x and F_y the frequency of vibration will be either increased or decreased, depending on the direction of the stress resultants. From (3.5) and (3.6) it is obvious that for the compression the frequency of vibration will be reduced. Thus, when the frequency is zero, either F_x or F_y, or a combination of both will be the critical buckling load. By putting ω_{mn} equal to zero in (3.6) the equation can be reduced to the form

$$F_x(m\pi/a)^2 + F_y(n\pi/b)^2 = R + S \tag{3.9a}$$

where

$$R = (2P_{12}P_{23}P_{13} - P_{22}P_{13}^2 - P_{11}P_{23}^2)/(P_{11}P_{22} - P_{12}^2) \tag{3.9b}$$

and

$$S = (S_{55}(m\pi/a)^2 + S_{44}(n\pi/b)^2 + K) \tag{3.9c}$$

Assuming that there are given ratios between the uniform stress resultants F_x and F_y and the critical buckling load F so that

$$F_x = \alpha F \tag{3.10}$$

$$F_y = \beta F \tag{3.11}$$

the critical buckling load is given by

$$F_{crit} = (R + S)/[\alpha(m\pi/a)^2 + \beta(n\pi/b)^2] \tag{3.12}$$

3.3 Dynamic Transient Analysis

The solution to the equations of motion can be sought as a product of two functions, a function of position and a function of time, as follows:

$$\theta_x(x,y,t) = \sum_m \sum_n \Phi_x^{mn}(x,y)T_{mn}(t) \tag{3.13a}$$

$$\theta_y(x,y,t) = \sum_m \sum_n \Phi_y^{mn}(x,y)T_{mn}(t) \tag{3.13b}$$

$$w(x,y,t) = \sum_m \sum_n W^{mn}(x,y)T_{mn}(t) \tag{3.13b}$$

where $T_{mn}(t)$ is a time dependent generalised coordination and $\sum_m$ implies a summation from $m = 1$ to ∞. Substituting equations (3.13) into the equilibrium equations (2.10) and using (3.3) gives

$$-\sum_m \sum_n \omega_{mn}^2 \Phi_x^{mn} T_{mn} + m_x/I = \sum_m \sum_n \Phi_x^{mn} \ddot{T}_{mn} \tag{3.14a}$$

$$-\sum_m \sum_n \omega_{mn}^2 \Phi_y^{mn} T_{mn} + m_y/I = \sum_m \sum_n \Phi_y^{mn} \ddot{T}_{mn} \tag{3.14b}$$

$$-\sum_m \sum_n \omega_{mn}^2 W^{mn} T_{mn} + q/P = \sum_m \sum_n W^{mn} \ddot{T}_{mn} \tag{3.14c}$$

The distributed loads m_x, m_y and q are expanded in terms of the generalised forces $Q_{mn}(t)$ as

$$m_x/I = \sum_m \sum_n Q_{mn}(t)\Phi_x^{mn}(x,y) \tag{3.15a}$$

$$m_y/I = \sum_m \sum_n Q_{mn}(t)\Phi_y^{mn}(x,y) \tag{3.15b}$$

$$q/P = \sum_m \sum_n Q_{mn}(t)W^{mn}(x,y) \tag{3.15c}$$

so that after substitution of (3.15) into (3.14) then for any m, n

$$\ddot{T}_{mn}(t) + \omega_{mn}^2 T_{mn}(t) = Q_{mn}(t) \tag{3.16}$$

The solution to (3.16), for zero initial displacement and velocity, is

$$T_{mn}(t) = (1/\omega_{mn}) \int_0^t Q_{mn}(\tau) \sin \omega_{mn}(t-\tau) d\tau \tag{3.17}$$

From (3.15), $Q_{mn}(t)$ may be obtained by multiplying the first equation by $I\Phi_x^{mn}$, the second by $I\Phi_y^{mn}$ and the third by PW^{mn}. adding all three and integrating over the plate area. Due to the orthogonality condition (3.8), the summation may be removed so that

$$Q_{mn}(t) = \int_0^a \int_0^b (m_x \Phi_x^{mn} + m_y \Phi_y^{mn} + qW^{mn}) dxdy / J_{mn} \tag{3.18a}$$

where

$$J_{mn} = \int_0^a \int_0^b ((\Phi_x^{mn})^2 I + (\Phi_y^{mn})^2 I + (W^{mn})^2 P) dxdy \tag{3.18b}$$

The solution for w, θ_x and θ_y is then obtained using (3.13), (3.2), (3.7), (3.17) and (3.18). In the cases for which rotatory inertia can be neglected, simpler relations for w, θ_x and θ_y can be achieved. When $m_x = m_y = I = 0$ and $q = \bar{q}(x,y)F(t)$, the generalised force $Q_{mn}(t)$ is

$$Q_{mn}(t) = (4F(t)/PabC_{mn}) \int_0^a \int_0^b \bar{q}(x,y) \sin(m\pi x/a) \sin(n\pi y/b) dxdy \tag{3.19}$$

By recognising that for static loading the Fourier coefficient q_{mn} [2] is given as

$$q_{mn} = (4/ab) \int_0^a \int_0^b \bar{q}(x,y) \sin(m\pi x/a) \sin(n\pi y/b) dxdy \tag{3.20}$$

then it can be seen that

$$Q_{mn}(t) = q_{mn} F(t)/PC_{mn} \tag{3.21}$$

By use of (3.21), expressions for the deformations in a plate under a transverse loading can be written as

$$w(x,y,t) = (1/P) \sum_m \sum_n q_{mn} \sin(m\pi x/a) \sin(n\pi y/b) I_d/\omega_{mn} \tag{3.22}$$

$$\theta_x(x,y,t) = (1/P) \sum_m \sum_n (A_{mn}/C_{mn}) q_{mn} \cos(m\pi x/a) \sin(n\pi y/b) I_d/\omega_{mn}$$

$$\theta_y(x,y,t) = (1/P) \sum_m \sum_n (B_{mn}/C_{mn}) q_{mn} \sin(m\pi x/a) \cos(n\pi y/b) I_d/\omega_{mn}$$

where

$$I_d = \int_0^t F(\tau) \sin \omega_{mn} (t - \tau) d\tau \tag{3.23}$$

The bending moments and the shear forces may be easily calculated at any point of the plate using (3.22) together with (2.5a) and (2.6a).

3.4 Fourier Series Representation of the Loads

The terms in the Fourier series representation of the load may be determined from (3.20). The following loading cases are considered:

(a) uniform load $q(x, y) = q$ for which

$$q_{mn} = (4q/mn\pi^2)(1 - \cos n\pi) \tag{3.24a}$$

$$\text{and so} \quad q_{mn} = (16q/mn\pi^2) \quad \text{for} \quad m, n = 1, 3, 5, \ldots \tag{3.24b}$$

$$= 0 \quad \text{for} \quad m, n = 2, 4, 6, \ldots \tag{3.24c}$$

(b) concentrated load acting at $x = \xi, y = \eta$ for which

$$q_{mn} = (4P/ab) \sin(m\pi\xi/a) \sin(n\pi\eta/b) \tag{3.25}$$

(c) a uniform load of total intensity P acting over a rectangular area $u \times v$ with its centre at $x = \xi, y = \eta$ for which

$$q = (16P/\pi^2 mnuv) \sin(m\pi\xi/a) \sin(n\pi\eta/b) \times \sin(m\pi u/2a) \sin(n\pi v/2b) \tag{3.26}$$

(d) cosine loading of total intensity P acting over a rectangular patch u, v with centre at $x = \xi, y = \eta$ for which

$$q = 4P \sin(m\pi\eta/b) \sin(m\pi\xi/a) \cos(n\pi v/2b) \cos(m\pi u/2a)/L_{mn}$$

$$\text{for} \quad (n/b \neq 1/v, m/a \neq 1/u)$$

$$= 0$$

$$\text{for} \quad (n/b = 1/v, m/a = 1/u) \tag{3.27}$$

where

$$L_{mn} = abu^2v^2(n/b - 1/v)(n/b + 1/v)(m/a - 1/u)(m/a + 1/u) \tag{3.28}$$

See Figure 3.1

3.5 The Convolution Integral

The integral in (3.23) is called the convolution integral; using this integral to compute the deformations in a plate subjected to an arbitrary loading is known

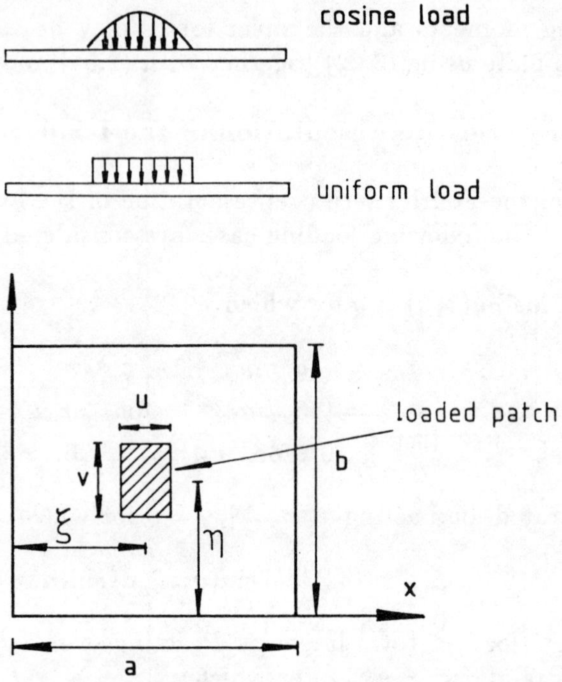

Figure 3.1 Location and shape of loaded area

as obtaining the response in the time domain. The convolution integral has been solved analytically for several commonly encountered forcing functions; a sine pulse, a step pulse, a triangular pulse, a stepped triangular pulse, and an exponential pulse, where the pulse definition is given in Figure 3.2.

The forcing function $F(t)$ and the convolution integral are:

(a) for a sine pulse

$$\begin{aligned} F(t) &= F_0 \sin(\pi t/t_1) && (0 \le t \le t_1) \\ &= 0 && (t > t_1) \\ \text{and} \quad I_d &= F_0 t_1 [\pi \sin \omega_{mn} t - \omega_{mn} t_1 \sin(\pi t/t_1)] && (0 \le t \le t_1) \\ &\quad /(\pi^2 - t_1^2 \omega_{mn}^2) \\ &= F_0 \pi t_1 [(\sin \omega_{mn} t + \sin \omega_{mn}(t - t_1))]/(\pi^2 - t_1^2 \omega_{mn}^2) && (t > t_1) \end{aligned} \tag{3.29}$$

(b) for a stepped pulse

$$F(t) = F_0 \qquad (0 \le t \le t_1)$$

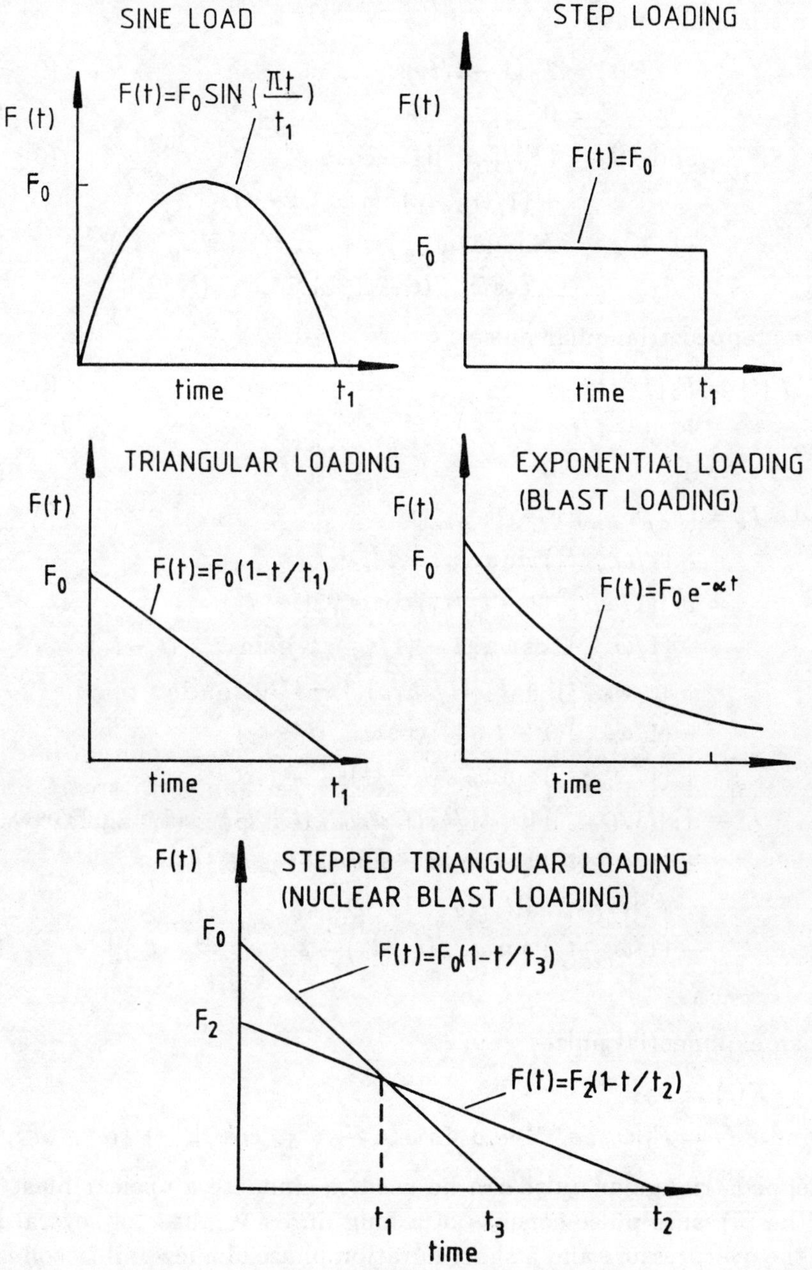

Figure 3.2 Load pulse shapes

$$= 0 \qquad (t > t_1)$$

$$\text{and} \quad I_d = (F_0/\omega_{mn})(1 - \cos\omega_{mn}t) \qquad (0 \le t \le t_1)$$

$$= (F_0/\omega_{mn})[\cos\omega_{mn}(t - t_1) - \cos\omega_{mn}t] \qquad (t > t_1)$$

$$(3.30)$$

(c) for a triangular pulse

$$F(t) = F_0(1 - t/t_1) \qquad (0 \le t \le t_1)$$

$$= 0 \qquad (t > t_1)$$

$$\text{and} \quad I_d = (F_0/\omega_{mn})[1 - \cos\omega_{mn}t + (1/\omega_{mn}t_1)\sin\omega_{mn}t - t/t_1] \qquad (0 \le t \le t_1)$$

$$= F_0[-(1/\omega_{mn})\cos\omega_{mn}t + (2/\omega_{mn}^2 t_1) \times \cos\omega_{mn}(t - t_1/2)\sin\omega_{mn}(t_1/2)] \qquad (t > t_1) \qquad (3.31)$$

(d) for a stepped triangular pulse

$$F(t) = F_0(1 - t/t_3) \qquad (0 \le t \le t_1)$$

$$= F_2(1 - t/t_2) \qquad (t_1 \le t \le t_2)$$

$$= 0 \qquad (t > t_2)$$

$$\text{and} \quad I_d = (F_0/\omega_{mn})[1 - \cos\omega_{mn}t + (1/\omega_{mn}t_3)\sin\omega_{mn}t - t/t_3] \qquad (0 \le t \le t_1)$$

$$= F_0[(1/\omega_{mn})(1 - t_1/t_3)\cos\omega_{mn}(t - t_1) - (1/\omega_{mn})\cos\omega_{mn}t - (1/\omega_{mn}^2 t_3)(\sin\omega_{mn}(t - t_1) + \sin\omega_{mn}t)] + F_2[(1/\omega_{mn})(1 - t/t_2) - (1/\omega_{mn})(1 - t_1/t_2)\cos\omega_{mn}(t - t_1) + (1/\omega_{mn}^2 t_2)\sin\omega_{mn}(t - t_1)] \qquad (t_1 \le t \le t_2)$$

$$I_d = F_0[(1/\omega_{mn})(1 - t_1/t_3)\cos\omega_{mn}(t - t_1) - (1/\omega_{mn})\cos\omega_{mn}t + (1/\omega_{mn}^2 t_3)[\sin\omega_{mn}t - \sin\omega_{mn}(t - t_1)]] + F_2[(1/\omega_{mn})(t_1/t_2 - 1)\cos\omega_{mn}(t - t_1) - (1/\omega_{mn}^2 t_2)[\sin\omega_{mn}(t - t_2) - \sin\omega_{mn}(t - t_1)]] \qquad (t > t_2)$$

$$(3.32)$$

(e) for an exponential pulse

$$F(t) = F_0 e^{-\alpha t} \qquad (3.33)$$

$$\text{and} \quad I_d = F_0[\omega_{mn}e^{-\alpha t} + \alpha\sin\omega_{mn}t - \omega_{mn}\cos\omega_{mn}t]/(\alpha^2 + \omega_{mn}^2)$$

The stepped triangular pulse can be used to simulate a nuclear blast loading where the pressure pulse consists of a long duration phase of several seconds due to the overpressure and a short duration phase of a few milliseconds due to shock wave reflection. The exponential pulse may be used to simulate a high explosive blast loading if a damping parameter α is adjusted to approximate the pressure curve from the blast test.

4. PROGRAM TRAM

4.1 Introduction

This section describes program TRAM which performs the closed form transient as well as vibration and stability analysis of simply supported, Mindlin plates as described in Section 3.

Program TRAM consists of a main segment and ten subroutines. The subroutines are now briefly described:

1. MASTER is the main segment which controls the calling of all the other subroutines.
2. DATA reads in all the input data values.
3. OUTD prints out all of the input data values with appropriate annotations.
4. INIT zeroes all initial values apart from the input values.
5. COEF calculates the coefficients P_{11}, P_{12}, P_{13}, etc.
6. EIGEN calculates eigenvalues, eigenvectors and buckling forces.
7. CONS calculates the values QMN for a given loading function.
8. CONIN calculates the convolution integral for different pulsing functions
9. SUMS sums the various Fourier series.
10. OUTP prints out the results for each time step in transient dynamic analysis.
11. OUTF prints out the results in vibration and buckling analysis.

4.2 Glossary of variable names

AA,BB: Length of plate in the x, y directions respectively

ALFA,BETA: Membrane force parameters in the x, y directions respectively

AMN1,BMN1,CMN1: The eigenvectors associated with the natural frequencies

BMX,BMY,BMXY: Bending moments M_x, M_y, M_{xy}

CX,CY,CXY: Curvatures

D11,D22,D12,D21,D66: Flexural rigidities $D_{11}, D_{22}, D_{12}, D_{21}, D_{66}$

DP: Damping parameter

ETA,ETB: x, y coordinates of centroid of load

FO,F2: Blast load parameters

FX,FY: Membrane forces in the x, y directions respectively

FCR: Buckling forces values for each pair m, n

G1: Shear modification factor

GFS: Elastic foundation modulus K

IP: = 1 for a sine pulse, = 2 for a stepped pulse, = 3 for a triangular pulse, = 4 for a stepped triangular (nuclear blast) pulse, and = 5 for an exponential (blast) pulse.

IT: = 1 for non-symmetric loads and = 2 for symmetric loads.

IQ: = 1 for uniform loads, = 2 for concentrated loads, = 3 for uniform patch loads and = 4 for cosine patch loads.

J: Number of time steps in transient dynamic analysis

KP: = 1 for vibration and buckling analysis only, = 2 for transient dynamic analysis only and = 3 for both analyses together.

LPON: Maximum number of frequencies (buckling forces) for each m, n is (20)

MPON: Maximum number of output points (140)

NPON: Number of output points

NUM: Number of Fourier terms

NUMF: Number of frequencies (buckling forces) to be calculated for each m, n

P11,P12,P13, etc.: Coefficients used to evaluate $A_{mn}, B_{mn}, C_{mn}, \omega_{mn}$ and F_{crit}

PI: π

PM: Mass density per unit of area

PZ: Load intensity

QX,QY: Shear forces

QMN: The term q_{mn} in the Fourier series representation of the load

S44,S55 Shear rigidities S_{44}, S_{55}

T1,T2,T3: Pulsing parameters

TIN: Time step length

TITLE: Problem title

U,V: Dimensions of patch load

W,WUX,WUY: w, θ_x, θ_y

WMN2: ω^2_{mn}

WMN: ω_{mn}

XCORD, YCORD: X, Y coordinates of output points

4.3 Input instructions

DATA SET 1	DATA TITLE (20A4) one record	
1- 80	TITLE	title of the problem
DATA SET 2	PLATE DIMENSIONS (2F10.5) one record	
1-10	AA	side length parallel to x axis
11-20	BB	side length parallel to y axis
DATA SET 3	FLEXURAL PROPERTIES (4F10.5) one record	
1-10	D11	flexural rigidity D_{11}
11-20	D22	flexural rigidity D_{22}
21-30	D12	coupling rigidity D_{12}
31-40	D66	torsional rigidity D_{66}
DATA SET 4	SHEAR PROPERTIES (2F10.5) one record	
1-10	S44	shear rigidity S_{44}
11-20	S55	shear rigidity S_{55}
DATA SET 5	FURTHER PLATE PARAMETERS (6F10.5) one record	
1-10	PZ	load intensity
11-20	GFS	foundation modulus
21-30	G1	shear modification factor
31-40	FX	membrane force in x-direction
41-50	FY	membrane force in y-direction
51-60	PM	mass density per unit of area

DATA SET 6	CONTROL PARAMETER (I5) one record		
1-5	KP	= 1 vibration and buckling analysis only	
		= 2 transient dynamic analysis only	
		= 3 both analyses together	

[N.B. If KP=1 next data set must be DATA SET 14.]

DATA SET 7	CONTROL DATA (2I5) one record	
1-5	NUM	number of Fourier terms
5-10	NPON	number of output points

DATA SET 8	SAMPLING POINTS (I5,2F10.5) NPON records	
1-5	JPON	point number
6-15	XCORD(.)	x-coordinate
16-25	YCORD(.)	y-coordinate

DATA SET 9	LOADING TYPE (2I5) one record	
1-5	IQ	= 1 uniform loading
		= 2 concentrated loading
		= 3 uniform loading over rectangular patch $u \times v$
		= 4 cosine loading over rectangular patch $u \times v$
6-10	IT	= 1 non-symmetric loads
		= 2 symmetric loads

DATA SET 10	LOADING POSITION (2F10.5) one record	
1-10	ETA	x-coordinate at centre of rectangular patch
11-20	ETB	y-coordinate at centre of rectangular patch

[N.B. Omit this data set if IQ< 2.]

DATA SET 11	LOAD PATCH SIZE (2F10.5) one record	
1-10	U	side length of patch parallel to x-axis
11-20	V	side length of patch parallel to y-axis

[N.B. Omit this data if IQ< 2.]

DATA SET 12	PULSING FUNCTION TYPE (I5, 6F10.5) one record	
1-5	IP	= 1 a sine pulse
		= 2 a stepped pulse
		= 3 a triangular pulse
		= 4 a stepped triangular (nuclear blast) pulse
		= 5 an exponential (blast) pulse
6-15	FO	blast load parameter
16-25	F2	blast load parameter
26-35	DP	damping parameter
36-45	T1	pulsing parameter
46-55	T2	pulsing parameter
56-65	T3	pulsing parameter

DATA SET 13	TIME STEP PARAMETERS (I5,F10.5) one record	
1-5	J	number of time steps
6-15	TIN	time step length

[N.B. Omit DATA SETS 7-13 IF KP=1.]

DATA SET 14	VIBRATION ANALYSIS PARAMETERS (I5,2F10.5) one record	
1-5	NUMF	number of frequencies to be calculated
6-15	ALFA	membrane force parameter in x-direction
16-25	BETA	membrane force parameter in y-direction

[N.B. Omit this DATA SET if KP= 2. If ALFA= 0 and BETA= 0 the buckling analysis is not considered.]

4.4 Subroutine listings

Main segment

```
C     PROGRAM TRAM
C
C     ********************************************************
C     *                                                      *
C     *            DYNAMIC ANALYSIS OF MINDLIN PLATES        *
C     *                 CLOSED FORM SOLUTION                 *
C     *                                                      *
C     ********************************************************
C
      IMPLICIT REAL*8(A-H,O-Z)
      DIMENSION  BMX(140),BMY(140),BMXY(140),CX(140),CY(140),CXY(140),
     .           FCR(20,20),QX(140),QY(140),TITLE(20),W(140),WMN(20,20),
     .           WUX(140),WUY(140),XCORD(140),YCORD(140)
      DATA MPON/140/
      DATA LPON/20/
C
      CALL DATA (AA,ALFA,BB,BETA,D11,D22,D21,D12,D66,DP,ETA,ETB,FO,F2,
     .           FX,FY,G1,GFS,IP,IQ,IT,J,KP,MPON,NPON,NUM,NUMF,PI,PM,
     .           PZ,S44,S55,T1,T2,T3,TIN,TITLE,U,V,XCORD,YCORD)
      CALL OUTD (AA,ALFA,BB,BETA,D11,D22,D21,D12,D66,DP,ETA,ETB,FO,F2,
     .           FX,FY,GFS,G1,IP,IQ,IT,J,KP,MPON,NPON,NUM,NUMF,PM,PZ,
     .           S44,S55,T1,T2,T3,TIN,TITLE,U,V,XCORD,YCORD)
      IF(KP.EQ.2) GO TO 20
C
C*** FREE VIBRATION, INITIALY STRESSED VIBRATION AND BUCKLING ANALYSIS
C
      II=0
      DO 15 M=1,NUMF
      DO 15 N=1,NUMF
      CALL COEF (AA,BB,D11,D22,D12,D66,FX,FY,G1,GFS,M,N,
     .           P11,P12,P13,P22,P23,P33,PI,S44,S55)
      CALL EIGEN(AA,ALFA,AMN1,BB,BETA,BMN1,CMN1,FCR,G1,GFS,II,LPON,M,N,
     .           PI,P11,P12,P13,P22,P23,P33,PM,S44,S55,WMN2,WMN)
   15 CONTINUE
      IF(KP.EQ.1)GO TO 30
C
C*** TRANSIENT DYNAMIC ANALYSIS
C
   20 DO 10 II=1,J
      T=FLOAT(II)*TIN
      CALL INIT(BMX,BMY,BMXY,CX,CY,CXY,MPON,NPON,QX,QY,W,WUX,WUY)
      DO 5 M=1,NUM,IT
      DO 5 N=1,NUM,IT
      CALL COEF (AA,BB,D11,D22,D12,D66,FX,FY,G1,GFS,M,N,
```

```
     .          P11,P12,P13,P22,P23,P33,PI,S44,S55)                     MAIN  45
      CALL EIGEN(AA,ALFA,AMN1,BB,BETA,BMN1,CMN1,FCR,G1,GFS,II,LPON,M,N, MAIN  46
     .          PI,P11,P12,P13,P22,P23,P33,PM,S44,S55,WMN2,WMN)          MAIN  47
      CALL CONS (AA,BB,ETA,ETB,IQ,M,N,PI,PZ,QMN,U,V)                    MAIN  48
      CALL CONIN(DP,F0,F2,IP,PI,T,T1,T2,T3,W2,WMN2)                     MAIN  49
      CALL SUMS (AA,AMN1,BB,BMN1,BMX,BMY,BMXY,CMN1,CX,CY,CXY,D11,D22,   MAIN  50
     .          D12,D66,G1,M,MPON,N,NPON,PM,QMN,QX,QY,PI,S44,S55,W,     MAIN  51
     .          W2,WMN2,WUX,WUY,XCORD,YCORD)                            MAIN  52
    5 CONTINUE                                                          MAIN  53
      CALL OUTP (BMX,BMY,BMXY,MPON,NPON,NUM,QX,QY,T,W,WUX,WUY)          MAIN  54
   10 CONTINUE                                                          MAIN  55
      IF(KP.EQ.2)GO TO 35                                               MAIN  56
   30 CALL OUTF(ALFA,BETA,FCR,LPON,NUMF,WMN)                            MAIN  57
   35 CONTINUE                                                          MAIN  58
      STOP                                                              MAIN  59
      END                                                               MAIN  60
```

Subroutine DATA

```
      SUBROUTINE DATA (AA,ALFA,BB,BETA,D11,D22,D21,D12,D66,DP,ETA,ETB,  DATA   1
     .                 F0,F2,FX,FY,G1,GFS,IP,IQ,IT,J,KP,MPON,NPON,NUM,  DATA   2
     .                 NUMF,PI,PM,PZ,S44,S55,T1,T2,T3,TIN,TITLE,U,V,    DATA   3
     .                 XCORD,YCORD)                                     DATA   4
C                                                                       DATA   5
C***  THIS SUBROUTINE READS IN ALL DATA                                 DATA   6
C                                                                       DATA   7
      IMPLICIT REAL*8(A-H,O-Z)                                          DATA   8
      DIMENSION        TITLE(20),XCORD(MPON),YCORD(MPON)                DATA   9
C                                                                       DATA  10
      READ(5,900)TITLE                                                  DATA  11
  900 FORMAT(20A4)                                                      DATA  12
      READ(5,905)AA,BB                                                  DATA  13
  905 FORMAT(2F10.5)                                                    DATA  14
      READ(5,910)D11,D22,D12,D66                                        DATA  15
  910 FORMAT(4F10.5)                                                    DATA  16
      D21=D12                                                           DATA  17
      READ(5,915)S44,S55                                                DATA  18
  915 FORMAT(2F10.5)                                                    DATA  19
      READ(5,920)PZ,GFS,G1,FX,FY,PM                                     DATA  20
  920 FORMAT(6F10.5)                                                    DATA  21
      READ(5,925)KP                                                     DATA  22
  925 FORMAT(I5)                                                        DATA  23
      IF(KP.EQ.1) GO TO 15                                              DATA  24
      READ(5,930)NUM,NPON                                               DATA  25
  930 FORMAT(2I5)                                                       DATA  26
      DO 5 IPON=1,NPON                                                  DATA  27
      READ(5,935)JPON,XCORD(IPON),YCORD(IPON)                           DATA  28
```

```
935  FORMAT(I5,2F10.5)
  5  CONTINUE
     READ(5,940)IQ,IT
940  FORMAT(2I5)
     IF(IQ.LT.2) GO TO 10
     READ(5,945)ETA,ETB
945  FORMAT(2F10.5)
     IF(IQ.LT.3) GO TO 10
     READ(5,950)U,V
950  FORMAT(2F10.5)
 10  CONTINUE
     READ(5,955) IP,FO,F2,DP,T1,T2,T3
955  FORMAT(I5,6F10.5)
     READ(5,960) J,TIN
960  FORMAT(I5,F10.5)
     IF(KP.EQ.2) GO TO 20
 15  READ(5,965)NUMF,ALFA,BETA
965  FORMAT(I5,2F10.5)
 20  CONTINUE
     PI=3.141592654
     RETURN
     END
```

Subroutine OUTD

```
      SUBROUTINE OUTD (AA,ALFA,BB,BETA,D11,D22,D21,D12,D66,DP,
     .                 ETA,ETB,FO,F2,FX,FY,GFS,G1,IP,IQ,IT,J,KP,MPON,
     .                 NPON,NUM,NUMF,PM,PZ,S44,S55,T1,T2,T3,TIN,TITLE,
     .                 U,V,XCORD,YCORD)
C
C*** PRINTS OUT THE INPUT DATA
C
      IMPLICIT REAL*8(A-H,O-Z)
      DIMENSION TITLE(20),XCORD(MPON),YCORD(MPON)
C
      WRITE(6,900)
 900  FORMAT(//,1X,'**** CLOSED FORM SOLUTION ****',/)
      WRITE(6,905)TITLE
 905  FORMAT(/,20A4)
      WRITE(6,910)
 910  FORMAT(1X,50('*'))
      WRITE(6,915)AA,BB
 915  FORMAT(//,1X,'DIMENSION OF PLATE IN X DIRECTION.','(AA)=',E12.5,
     ./,1X,'DIMENSION OF PLATE IN Y DIRECTION.','(BB)=',E12.5,/)
      WRITE(6,920)D11,D22,D21,D66
 920  FORMAT(1X,'FLEXURAL RIGIDITY....','(D11)=',E15.8,/,
     .       1X,'FLEXURAL RIGIDITY....','(D22)=',E15.8,/,
```

```
     .        1X,'COUPLING RIGIDITY....','(D12)=',E15.8,/,
     .        1X,'TORSIONAL RIGIDITY...','(D66)=',E15.8,/)
      WRITE(6,925)S44,S55
  925 FORMAT(1X,'TRANSVERSE SHEAR RIGIDITY.....','(S44)=',E15.8,/,
     .        1X,'TRANSVERSE SHEAR RIGIDITY.....','(S55)=',E15.8,/)
      WRITE(6,930)G1,GFS,PZ,FX,FY,PM,KP
  930 FORMAT(1X,'SHEAR CORRECTION FACTOR.........','(G1)=',E15.8,/,
     .        1X,'MODULUS FOR ELASTIC FOUNDATION.','(GFS)=',E15.8,/,
     .        1X,'DISTRIBUTED LOADING.............','(PZ)=',E15.8,/,
     .        1X,'MEMBRANE FORCE IN X DIREC.......','(FX)=',E15.8,/,
     .        1X,'MEMBRANE FORCE IN Y DIREC.......','(FY)=',E15.8,/,
     .        1X,'MASS DENSITY PER UNIT AREA......','(PM)=',E15.8,//,
     .        1X,'CONTROL PARAMETER...............','(KP)=',I5,/)
      IF(KP.EQ.2) GO TO 45
      WRITE(6,890)NUMF,ALFA,BETA
  890 FORMAT(1X,'NUMB. OF FREQ. TO BE CALCULAT.','(NUMF)=',I5,/,
     .        1X,'MEMB. FORCE PARAM. IN X DIR...','(ALFA)=',E15.8,/,
     .        1X,'MEMB. FORCE PARAM. IN Y DIR...','(BETA)=',E15.8,/)
   45 IF(KP.EQ.1) GO TO 40
      WRITE(6,935)NUM,NPON
  935 FORMAT(1X,'THE NO. OF TERMS IN FOURIER SERIES',1X,' (NUM)=',I5,
     ./,1X,'THE NO. OF POINTS ON PLATE',8X,' (NPON)=',I5)
      IF (IQ .EQ. 1) GO TO 5
      WRITE(6,940)ETA,ETB
  940 FORMAT(1X,'X-COORD.',5X,'(ETA)=',E15.8,
     ./,1X,'Y-COORD.',5X,'(ETB)=',E15.8)
      IF (IQ .EQ. 2) GO TO 5
      WRITE(6,945)U,V
  945 FORMAT(1X,'DIMENS. OF LOADED AREA IN X DIRECT.',2X,'(U)=',E15.8,
     ./,1X,'DIMENS. OF LOADED AREA IN Y DIRECT.',2X,'(V)=',E15.8)
    5 WRITE(6,950)
  950 FORMAT(//,50('*'))
      WRITE(6,955)
  955 FORMAT(///,1X,'TABLE SHOWS THE COMPUTED VALUES FOR'/,
     .1X,'SPECIFIED X AND Y COORDINATES.')
      IF (IQ .NE. 1) GO TO 10
      WRITE(6,960)
  960 FORMAT(/,1X,'FOR UNIFORM LOADING.')
   10 IF (IQ .NE. 2) GO TO 15
      WRITE(6,965)
  965 FORMAT(/,1X,'FOR CONCENTRATED LOADING.')
   15 IF (IQ .NE. 3) GO TO 20
      WRITE(6,970)
  970 FORMAT(/,1X,'FOR UNIFORM LOADING OVER RECTANGULAR AREAS (U.V).')
   20 IF (IQ .NE. 4) GO TO 25
      WRITE(6,975)
  975 FORMAT(/,1X,'FOR COSINE LOADING.')
```

```
 25  IF(IT.GT.1) GO TO 30
     WRITE(6,980)
980  FORMAT(/,1X,'NON-SYMMETRIC LOADING.')
 30  IF (IT .NE. 2) GO TO 35
     WRITE(6,985)
985  FORMAT(/,1X,'SYMMETRIC LOADING.')
 35  WRITE(6,990) IP,FO,F2,DP,T1,T2,T3
990  FORMAT(1X,'PULSING FUNCTION PARAMETER......','(IP)=',I5,/,
    .       1X,'BLAST LOAD PARAMETER...........','(FO)=',E15.8,/,
    .       1X,'BLAST LOAD PARAMETER...........','(F2)=',E15.8,/,
    .       1X,'DAMPING PARAMETER..............','(DP)=',E15.8,/,
    .       1X,'PULSING PARAMETER..............','(T1)=',E15.8,/,
    .       1X,'PULSING PARAMETER..............','(T2)=',E15.8,/,
    .       1X,'PULSING PARAMETER..............','(T3)=',E15.8,/)
     WRITE(6,995) J,TIN
995  FORMAT(1X,'NUMBER OF TIME STEPS...........','(J)=',I5,/,
    .       1X,'TIME STEP LENGTH...............','(TIN)=',E15.8,/)
     WRITE(6,1000)
1000 FORMAT(///,6X,'POINT',7X,'X',13X,'Y',/)
     DO 40 IPON=1,NPON
     WRITE(6,1005)IPON,XCORD(IPON),YCORD(IPON)
1005 FORMAT(6X,I3,1X,2E14.5)
 40  CONTINUE
     RETURN
     END
```

Subroutine COEF

```
      SUBROUTINE COEF (AA,BB,D11,D22,D12,D66,FX,FY,G1,GFS,M,
     .                 N,P11,P12,P13,P22,P23,P33,PI,S44,S55)
      IMPLICIT REAL*8(A-H,O-Z)
C
C*** THIS SUBROUTINE CALCULATES THE COEFFICIENTS
C*** (P11,P12,P13,P22,P23,P33)
C
      P11=D11*(FLOAT(M)*PI/AA)*(FLOAT(M)*PI/AA)
     .+D66*(FLOAT(N)*PI/BB)*(FLOAT(N)*PI/BB)+G1*S55
      P12=(D12+D66)*(FLOAT(M)*PI/AA)*(FLOAT(N)*PI/BB)
      P13=G1*S55*(FLOAT(M)*PI/AA)
      P22=D66*(FLOAT(M)*PI/AA)*(FLOAT(M)*PI/AA)
     .+D22*(FLOAT(N)*PI/BB)*(FLOAT(N)*PI/BB)+G1*S44
      P23=G1*S44*(FLOAT(N)*PI/BB)
      P33=(G1*S55+FX)*(FLOAT(M)*PI/AA)*(FLOAT(M)*PI/AA)
     .+(G1*S44+FY)*(FLOAT(N)*PI/BB)*(FLOAT(N)*PI/BB)+GFS
      RETURN
      END
```

Subroutine EIGEN

```
      SUBROUTINE EIGEN(AA,ALFA,AMN1,BB,BETA,BMN1,CMN1,FCR,G1,GFS,II,
     .                 LPON,M,N,PI,P11,P12,P13,P22,P23,P33,PM,S44,S55,
     .                 WMN2,WMN)
C
C*** EVALUATES EIGENVALUES, EIGENVECTORS AND BUCKLING FORCES
C
      IMPLICIT REAL*8(A-H,O-Z)
      DIMENSION FCR(LPON,LPON),WMN(LPON,LPON)
C
      Q=(P11*P22)-(P12*P12)
      WMN2=((Q*P33)+(2.0*P12*P23*P13)-(P22*P13*P13)-(P11*P23*
     .P23))/(PM*Q)
      IF(II.EQ.0) GO TO 5
C
C*** EIGENVECTORS
C
      CMN1=1.0
      AMN1=(((P12*P23)-(P22*P13))/((P11*P22)-(P12*P12)))*CMN1
      BMN1=(((P12*P13)-(P11*P23))/((P11*P22)-(P12*P12)))*CMN1
      GO TO 10
C
C*** EIGENVALUES
C
    5 WMN(M,N)=SQRT(WMN2)
      IF(ALFA.NE.0.0) GO TO 15
      IF(BETA.EQ.0.0) GO TO 10
C
C*** BUCKLING FORCES
C
   15 FCR(M,N)=-(((2.0*P12*P23*P13)-(P22*P13*P13)-(P11*P23*P23))/Q+
     .((G1*S55*(FLOAT(M)*PI/AA)*(FLOAT(M)*PI/AA))+
     .(G1*S44*(FLOAT(N)*PI/BB)*(FLOAT(N)*PI/BB))+GFS))/
     .((ALFA*(FLOAT(M)*PI/AA)*(FLOAT(M)*PI/AA))+
     .(BETA*(FLOAT(N)*PI/BB)*(FLOAT(N)*PI/BB)))
   10 CONTINUE
      RETURN
      END
```

Subroutine INIT

```
      SUBROUTINE INIT (BMX,BMY,BMXY,CX,CY,CXY,MPON,
     .                 NPON,QX,QY,W,WUX,WUY)
C
C*** THIS SUBROUTINE INITIALISES VARIOUS ARRAYS
C
```

```
      IMPLICIT REAL*8(A-H,O-Z)
      DIMENSION           BMX(MPON),BMY(MPON),BMXY(MPON),
     .                    CX(MPON),CY(MPON),CXY(MPON),
     .                    QX(MPON),QY(MPON),WUX(MPON),
     .                    WUY(MPON),W(MPON)
C
      DO 5 IPON=1,NPON
      W(IPON)=0.0
      WUX(IPON)=0.0
      WUY(IPON)=0.0
      CX(IPON)=0.0
      CY(IPON)=0.0
      CXY(IPON)=0.0
      BMX(IPON)=0.0
      BMY(IPON)=0.0
      BMXY(IPON)=0.0
      QX(IPON)=0.0
      QY(IPON)=0.0
    5 CONTINUE
      RETURN
      END
```

Subroutine CONS

```
      SUBROUTINE CONS (AA,BB,ETA,ETB,IQ,M,N,PI,PZ,QMN,U,V)
      IMPLICIT REAL*8(A-H,O-Z)
C
C*** THIS SUBROUTINE CALCULATES THE VALUES
C*** QMN FOR A GIVEN LOADING FUNCTION
C
      GO TO(5,10,15,20),IQ
 5    QMN=(16.0*PZ)/(PI*PI*FLOAT(M)*FLOAT(N))
      GO TO 25
10    QMN=((4.0*PZ)/(AA*BB))*SIN((FLOAT(M)*PI*ETA)/AA)*
     .SIN((FLOAT(N)*PI*ETB)/BB)
      GO TO 25
15    QMN=((16.0*PZ)/(PI*PI*FLOAT(M)*FLOAT(N)*U*V))*
     .SIN((FLOAT(M)*PI*ETA)/AA)*
     .SIN((FLOAT(N)*PI*ETB)/BB)*SIN((FLOAT(M)*PI*U)/(2.0*AA))*
     .SIN((FLOAT(N)*PI*V)/(2.0*BB))
      GO TO 25
20    QMN=(4.0*PZ*SIN((FLOAT(N)*PI*ETB)/BB)*SIN((FLOAT(M)*PI*ETA)/AA)
     .*COS((FLOAT(N)*PI*V)/(2.0*BB))*COS((FLOAT(M)*PI*U)/(2.0*AA)))/
     .((AA*BB*U*U*V*V)*((FLOAT(N)/BB)-(1.0/V))*
     .((FLOAT(N)/BB)+(1.0/V))*
     .((FLOAT(M)/AA)-(1.0/U))*((FLOAT(M)/AA)+(1.0/U)))
25    CONTINUE
```

```
      RETURN
      END
```

Subroutine CONIN

```
      SUBROUTINE CONIN(DP,F0,F2,IP,PI,T,T1,T2,T3,W2,WMN2)
C
C*** SOLVES THE CONVOLUTION INTEGRAL FOR FIVE DIFFERENT
C*** PULSING FUNCTIONS
C
      IMPLICIT REAL*8(A-H,O-Z)
      WMN=SQRT(WMN2)
      GO TO(290,300,310,320,340)IP
C
C***  FOR SINE PULSE
C
  290 IF(T.GT.T1)GO TO 295
      W2=F0*T1*(((PI*SIN(WMN*T))-(WMN*T1
     .*SIN((PI*T)/T1)))/((PI*PI)-(T1*T1*WMN2)))
      GO TO 950
C
  295 W2=(F0*PI*T1)*((SIN(WMN*T)+SIN(WMN
     .*(T-T1)))/((PI*PI)-(T1*T1*WMN2)))
      GO TO 950
C
C***  FOR STEPPED PULSE
C
  300 IF(T.GT.T1)GO TO 305
      W2=(F0/WMN)*(1.0-COS(WMN*T))
      GO TO 950
C
  305 W2=(F0/WMN)*(COS(WMN*(T-T1))-COS
     .(WMN*T))
      GO TO 950
C
C***  FOR TRIANGULAR PULSE
C
  310 IF(T.GT.T1)GO TO 315
      W2=(F0/WMN)*((1.0-COS(WMN*T))+((1.0/
     .(WMN*T1))*SIN(WMN*T))-(T/T1))
      GO TO 950
C
  315 W2=F0*(((2.0/(WMN2*T1))*COS(WMN*(T-T1/2.0))
     .*SIN(WMN*(T1/2.0)))-((1.0/WMN)*COS
     .(WMN*T)))
      GO TO 950
C
```

```
C***  FOR STEPPED TRIANGULAR(NUCLEAR BLAST) PULSE
C
  320 IF(T.GE.T1.OR.T.LE.T2)GO TO 325
      IF(T.GT.T2)GO TO 330
      W2=(FO/WMN)*((1.0-COS(WMN*T))+
     .((1.0/(WMN*T3))*SIN(WMN*T))-T/T3)
      GO TO 950
C
  325 W2=FO*(((1.0/WMN)*(1.0-T1/T3)*COS(WMN*
     .(T-T1)))-((1.0/WMN)*COS(WMN*T))
     .-((1.0/(WMN2*T3))*SIN(WMN*(T-T1)))+
     .((1.0/(WMN2*T3))*SIN(WMN*T)))+
     .F2*(((1.0/WMN)*(1.0-T/T2))-((1.0/WMN)*(1.0-T1/T2)
     .*COS(WMN*(T-T1)))+((1.0/(WMN2*T2))*
     .SIN(WMN*(T-T1))))
      GO TO 950
C
  330 W2=FO*(((1.0/WMN)*(1.0-T1/T3)*COS(WMN*
     .(T-T1)))-((1.0/WMN)*COS(WMN*T))
     .+((1.0/(WMN2*T3))*(SIN(WMN*T)-
     .SIN(WMN*(T-T1)))))+F2*(((1.0/WMN)*(T1/T2-1.0)
     .*COS(WMN*(T-T1)))-((1.0/(WMN2*T2))*(SIN(WMN
     .*(T-T2))-SIN(WMN*(T-T1)))))
      GO TO 950
C
C***  FOR EXPONENTIAL(BLAST)PULSE
C
  340 W2=FO*(((WMN*(2.7182818**(-DP*T)))+(DP*
     .SIN(WMN*T))-(WMN*COS(WMN*T)))/
     .(DP*DP+WMN2))
  950 RETURN
      END
```

Subroutine SUMS

```
      SUBROUTINE SUMS (AA,AMN1,BB,BMN1,BMX,BMY,BMXY,CMN1,CX,CY,CXY,D11,
     .                 D22,D12,D66,G1,M,MPON,N,NPON,PM,QMN,QX,QY,PI,
     .                 S44,S55,W,W2,WMN2,WUX,WUY,XCORD,YCORD)
C
C*** THIS SUBROUTINE SUMS THE VARIOUS FOURIER SERIES
C
      IMPLICIT REAL*8(A-H,O-Z)
      DIMENSION        BMX(MPON),BMY(MPON),BMXY(MPON),CX(MPON),CY(MPON),
     .                 CXY(MPON),QX(MPON),QY(MPON),W(MPON),WUX(MPON),
     .                 WUY(MPON),XCORD(MPON),YCORD(MPON)
C
      DO 5 IPON=1,NPON
```

```
      X=XCORD(IPON)
      Y=YCORD(IPON)
      XMULT=W2*QMN/(SQRT(WMN2)*PM)
C
C*** DEFLECTION W(IPON)
C
      W(IPON)=W(IPON)+CMN1*SIN((FLOAT(M)*PI*X)/AA)*
     .SIN((FLOAT(N)*PI*Y)/BB)*XMULT
C
C*** SLOPE WUX(IPON)
C
      WUX(IPON)=WUX(IPON)+AMN1*COS((FLOAT(M)*PI*X)/AA)*
     .SIN((FLOAT(N)*PI*Y)/BB)*XMULT
C
C*** SLOPE WUY(IPON)
C
      WUY(IPON)=WUY(IPON)+BMN1*SIN((FLOAT(M)*PI*X)/AA)*
     .COS((FLOAT(N)*PI*Y)/BB)*XMULT
C
C*** CURVATURE CX(IPON)
C
      CX(IPON)=CX(IPON)+AMN1*(FLOAT(M)*PI/AA)*SIN((FLOAT(M)*PI*X)/AA)*
     .SIN((FLOAT(N)*PI*Y)/BB)*XMULT
C
C*** CURVATURE CY(IPON)
C
      CY(IPON)=CY(IPON)+BMN1*(FLOAT(N)*PI/BB)*SIN((FLOAT(M)*PI*X)/AA)*
     .SIN((FLOAT(N)*PI*Y)/BB)*XMULT
C
C*** CURVATURE CXY(IPON)
C
      CXY(IPON)=CXY(IPON)+((AMN1*(FLOAT(N)*PI/BB))+
     .(BMN1*(FLOAT(M)*PI/AA)))*
     .COS((FLOAT(M)*PI*X)/AA)*COS((FLOAT(N)*PI*Y)/BB)*XMULT
C
C*** BENDING MOMENT BMX(IPON)
C
      BMX(IPON)=-D11*CX(IPON)-D12*CY(IPON)
C
C*** BENDING MOMENT BMY(IPON)
C
      BMY(IPON)=-D22*CY(IPON)-D12*CX(IPON)
C
C*** TWISTING MOMENT BMXY(IPON)
C
      BMXY(IPON)=D66*CXY(IPON)
C
```

```
C*** SHEAR FORCE QX(IPON)
C
      QX(IPON)=QX(IPON)+G1*S55*((CMN1*FLOAT(M)*PI/AA)+AMN1)*
     .COS((FLOAT(M)*PI*X)/AA)*SIN((FLOAT(N)*PI*Y)/BB)*XMULT
C
C*** SHEAR FORCE QY(IPON)
C
      QY(IPON)=QY(IPON)+G1*S44*((CMN1*FLOAT(N)*PI/BB)+BMN1)*
     .SIN((FLOAT(M)*PI*X)/AA)*COS((FLOAT(N)*PI*Y)/BB)*XMULT
    5 CONTINUE
      RETURN
      END
```

Subroutine OUTP

```
      SUBROUTINE OUTP(BMX,BMY,BMXY,MPON,NPON,NUM,QX,QY,T,W,WUX,WUY)
C
C*** OUTPUTS THE DISPLACEMENTS, BENDING MOMENTS AND SHEAR FORCES
C*** FOR EACH TIME STEP
C
      IMPLICIT REAL*8(A-H,O-Z)
      DIMENSION BMX(MPON),BMY(MPON),BMXY(MPON),
                QX(MPON),QY(MPON),W(MPON),WUX(MPON),WUY(MPON)
C
      WRITE(6,985) T
  985 FORMAT(////,1X,'SOLUTION AT TIME.................','T=',E15.8,/)
      WRITE(6,990)
  990 FORMAT(//,3X,'POINT',5X,'W',12X,'WUX',11X,'WUY',/)
      DO 40 IPON=1,NPON
      WRITE(6,995)IPON,W(IPON),WUX(IPON),WUY(IPON)
  995 FORMAT(3X,I3,3E14.5)
   40 CONTINUE
      WRITE(6,1000)
 1000 FORMAT(//,3X,'POINT',5X,'MX',12X,'MY',11X,'MXY',12X,'QX',
     .        12X,'QY',/)
      DO 45 IPON=1,NPON
      WRITE(6,1005)IPON,BMX(IPON),BMY(IPON),BMXY(IPON),
     .QX(IPON),QY(IPON)
 1005 FORMAT(3X,I3,5E14.5)
   45 CONTINUE
      RETURN
      END
```

Subroutine OUTF

```
      SUBROUTINE OUTF(ALFA,BETA,FCR,LPON,NUMF,WMN)
C
```

```
C*** OUTPUTS THE FREQUENCIES WMN AND BUCKLING FORCES FCR                OUTF
C*** CALCULATED FOR EACH PAIR OF MODES                                  OUTF
C                                                                       OUTF
      IMPLICIT REAL*8(A-H,O-Z)                                          OUTF
      DIMENSION FCR(LPON,LPON),WMN(LPON,LPON)                           OUTF
C                                                                       OUTF
      WRITE(6,900)                                                      OUTF
  900 FORMAT(//,50('*'))                                                OUTF
      IF(ALFA.NE.0.0) GO TO 15                                          OUTF
      IF(BETA.NE.0.0) GO TO 15                                          OUTF
      WRITE(6,905)                                                      OUTF
  905 FORMAT(///,1X,'TABLE SHOWS THE COMPUTED VALUES FOR'/,             OUTF
     .       1X,'THE FREQUENCIES FOR EACH PAIR OF MODES'/)              OUTF
      WRITE(6,910)                                                      OUTF
  910 FORMAT(6X,'M',5X,'N',8X,'WMN',/1X,30('*'))                        OUTF
      DO 5 I=1,NUMF                                                     OUTF
      DO 5 J=1,NUMF                                                     OUTF
    5 WRITE(6,915)I,J,WMN(I,J)                                          OUTF
  915 FORMAT(1X,2I6,2X,E14.6)                                           OUTF
      GO TO 20                                                          OUTF
   15 WRITE(6,920)                                                      OUTF
  920 FORMAT(///,1X,'TABLE SHOWS THE COMPUTED VALUES FOR THE'/,         OUTF
     .              1X,'FREQUENCIES AND BUCKLING FORCES FOR EACH'/,     OUTF
     .              1X,'PAIR OF MODES'/)                                OUTF
      WRITE(6,925)                                                      OUTF
  925 FORMAT(6X,'M',5X,'N',8X,'WMN',11X,'FCR',/1X,45('*'))              OUTF
      DO 10 I=1,NUMF                                                    OUTF
      DO 10 J=1,NUMF                                                    OUTF
   10 WRITE(6,930)I,J,WMN(I,J),FCR(I,J)                                 OUTF
  930 FORMAT(1X,2I6,2X,2E14.6)                                          OUTF
   20 CONTINUE                                                          OUTF
      RETURN                                                            OUTF
      END                                                               OUTF
```

5. SAMPLE SOLUTIONS

5.1 Introduction

Some numerical examples are now presented using program TRAM. They can be divided into three groups:

(a) the free vibration of plates,

(b) the initially stressed vibration and buckling of plates, and

(c) the transient dynamic analysis of plates.

Results obtained using program TRAM are compared with results obtained from various sources.

5.2 Free Vibrations of Plates

Results from the analysis of plates with different thickness and aspect ratios are now presented. Table 5.1 summarises the results for a thin square plate of $h/a = 0.01$, and typical input and output data for this example are given in Figures 5.1 and 5.2 respectively.

Table 5.1 Natural frequencies ω_{mn} for a thin square plate with $h/a = 0.01$

m	n	closed form solution	finite strip solution [5]	thin plate theory [5]
1	1	19.73	19.74	19.74
1	2	49.32	49.32	49.35
2	2	78.88	78.91	78.95
1	3	98.58	98.64	98.69
2	3	128.11	128.17	128.30

(ω_{mn} in radians per second)

As can be seen from Table 5.1, excellent agreement is obtained with other solutions [5].

Table 5.2 summarises the results for a moderately thick square plate of $h/a = 0.1$, and typical input and output data for this example are given in Figures 5.3 and 5.4 respectively.

```
  A THIN SQUARE PLATE H/A=0.01
1.        1.
1.        1.        0.166     0.417
41683.3   41683.3
0.        0.        1.        0.        0.        1.
   1
   3
```

Figure 5.1 Typical input data for a thin plate

```
 **** CLOSED FORM SOLUTION ****
  A THIN SQUARE PLATE H/A=0.01
 ********************************************
 DIMENSION OF PLATE IN X DIRECTION.(AA)= 0.10000E+01
 DIMENSION OF PLATE IN Y DIRECTION.(BB)= 0.10000E+01
 FLEXURAL RIGIDITY....(D11)= 0.10000000E+01
 FLEXURAL RIGIDITY....(D22)= 0.10000000E+01
 COUPLING RIGIDITY....(D12)= 0.16600000E+00
 TORSIONAL RIGIDITY...(D66)= 0.41700000E+00
 TRANSVERSE SHEAR RIGIDITY.....(S44)= 0.41683300E+05
 TRANSVERSE SHEAR RIGIDITY.....(S55)= 0.41683300E+05
 SHEAR CORRECTION FACTOR.........(G1)= 0.10000000E+01
 MODULUS FOR ELASTIC FOUNDATION.(GFS)= 0.00000000E+00
 DISTRIBUTED LOADING.............(PZ)= 0.00000000E+00
 MEMBRANE FORCE IN X DIREC.......(FX)= 0.00000000E+00
 MEMBRANE FORCE IN Y DIREC.......(FY)= 0.00000000E+00
 MASS DENSITY PER UNIT AREA......(PM)= 0.10000000E+01
 CONTROL PARAMETER...............(KP)=    1
 NUMB. OF FREQ. TO BE CALCULAT.(NUMF)=    3
 MEMB. FORCE PARAM. IN X DIR...(ALFA)= 0.00000000E+00
 MEMB. FORCE PARAM. IN Y DIR...(BETA)= 0.00000000E+00
********************************************
 TABLE SHOWS THE COMPUTED VALUES FOR
 THE FREQUENCIES FOR EACH PAIR OF MODES
      M     N       WMN
 ***************************
      1     1    0.197345E+02
      1     2    0.493188E+02
      1     3    0.985794E+02
      2     1    0.493188E+02
      2     2    0.788822E+02
      2     3    0.128108E+03
      3     1    0.985794E+02
      3     2    0.128108E+03
      3     3    0.177276E+03
```

Figure 5.2 Typical output for a thin square plate

```
  A MODERATELY THICK SQUARE PLATE H/A=0.1
1.        1.
1.        1.        0.3       0.35
350.      350.
0.        0.        1.        0.        0.        10.
   1
   3
```

Figure 5.3 Typical input data for a thick square plate

```
 **** CLOSED FORM SOLUTION ****
  A MODERATELY THICK SQUARE PLATE H/A=0.1
 ***********************************************
 DIMENSION OF PLATE IN X DIRECTION.(AA)= 0.10000E+01
 DIMENSION OF PLATE IN Y DIRECTION.(BB)= 0.10000E+01
 FLEXURAL RIGIDITY....(D11)= 0.10000000E+01
 FLEXURAL RIGIDITY....(D22)= 0.10000000E+01
 COUPLING RIGIDITY....(D12)= 0.30000000E+00
 TORSIONAL RIGIDITY...(D66)= 0.35000000E+00
 TRANSVERSE SHEAR RIGIDITY.....(S44)= 0.35000000E+03
 TRANSVERSE SHEAR RIGIDITY.....(S55)= 0.35000000E+03
 SHEAR CORRECTION FACTOR.........(G1)= 0.10000000E+01
 MODULUS FOR ELASTIC FOUNDATION.(GFS)= 0.00000000E+00
 DISTRIBUTED LOADING.............(PZ)= 0.00000000E+00
 MEMBRANE FORCE IN X DIREC.......(FX)= 0.00000000E+00
 MEMBRANE FORCE IN Y DIREC.......(FY)= 0.00000000E+00
 MASS DENSITY PER UNIT AREA......(PM)= 0.10000000E+02
 CONTROL PARAMETER...............(KP)=    1
 NUMB. OF FREQ. TO BE CALCULAT.(NUMF)=    3
 MEMB. FORCE PARAM. IN X DIR...(ALFA)= 0.00000000E+00
 MEMB. FORCE PARAM. IN Y DIR...(BETA)= 0.00000000E+00
***********************************************
 TABLE SHOWS THE COMPUTED VALUES FOR
 THE FREQUENCIES FOR EACH PAIR OF MODES
      M     N        WMN
 *****************************
      1     1     0.607318E+01
      1     2     0.146093E+02
      1     3     0.275650E+02
      2     1     0.146093E+02
      2     2     0.225537E+02
      2     3     0.347076E+02
      3     1     0.275650E+02
      3     2     0.347076E+02
      3     3     0.457543E+02
```

Figure 5.4 Typical output for a thick square plate

Table 5.2 Non-dimensional frequencies $\lambda = \omega_{mn}(\rho h^2 G)^{-1/2}$ for a thick square plate $h/a = 0.1$

m	n	closed form solution	linear 3-D elasticity theory [5]	thin plate theory [5]
1	1	0.0937	0.0932	0.0963
2	1	0.2254	0.2226	0.2408
2	2	0.3480	0.3421	0.3853
3	1	0.4253	0.4171	0.4816
3	2	0.5355	0.5239	0.6261
3	3	0.7060	0.6889	0.8686

Table 5.3 shows the results for thin isotropic rectangular plates of different aspect ratios. The plates considered have the following properties:

$$h = 0.01, D_{11} = D_{22} = 1.0, D_{12} = 0.3, D_{66} = 0.35, S_{44} = S_{55}, = 35000.0,$$

$$\nu = 0.3 \text{ and } \rho = 100.0$$

Table 5.3 Natural frequencies ω_{mn} for thin rectangular plates with different aspect ratios

		a=1	b=2	a=2	b=5
m	n	closed form solution	thin plate theory [6]	closed form solution	thin plate theory [6]
1	1	12.335	12.337	2.862	2.862
1	2	19.734	19.739	4.046	4.046
1	3	32.062	32.076	6.020	6.020
2	1	41.921	41.946	10.263	10.264
2	2	49.313	49.348	11.447	11.449
2	3	61.631	61.685	13.420	13.423
3	1	91.175	91.294	22.594	22.601
3	2	98.557	98.696	23.778	23.786
3	3	110.857	111.033	25.750	25.760

(ω_{mn} in radians per second)

5.3 Examples of initially stressed vibration and buckling of plates

The first example is presented to illustrate the variation of the frequency of vibration of a plate subjected to biaxial tensile stresses which are equal in both directions. Table 5.4 shows the results for a moderately thick square plate $h/a = 0.1$, and input, output data for this example are given in Figures 5.5 and 5.6 respectively.

Table 5.4 Frequencies ω_{mn} for a thick square plate $h/a = 0.1$ under uniform biaxial tension

$Fa^2/\pi^2 D_{11}$	closed form solution	thin plate theory [6]
5	36.646	36.928
10	48.135	48.350
15	57.368	57.549
20	65.308	65.467
30	78.825	78.960
50	100.547	100.650
100	140.892	140.960
200	198.324	198.380

(ω_{mn} in radians per second)

The second example is concerned with a thin square plate of thickness-to-span ratio $h/a = 0.01$ subjected to uniform, biaxial compressive stresses.

Table 5.5 shows the resulting frequency factor $\lambda_{mn} = \omega_{mn}^2 a^2 b^2/\pi^2 D_{11}$ depending on the in-plane load intensity coefficient $c = Fb^2/\pi^2 D_{11}$. The plate considered has the following properties:

$$a = b = 1, D_{11} = D_{22} = 1.0, D_{12} = 0.3, D_{66} = 0.35, S_{44} = S_{55} = 35000.0,$$

$$\nu = 0.3 \text{ and } \rho = 10.0$$

Excellent agreement between the various solutions is again obtained.

```
 A THICK SQUARE PLATE H/A=0.1 UNDER TENSION IN BOTH DIR.
1.        1.
1.        1.        0.3       0.35
350.      350.
0.        0.        1.        49.348022 49.348022 1.
   1
   1
```

Figure 5.5 Input data for a thick square plate under biaxial tension

```
**** CLOSED FORM SOLUTION ****
 A THICK SQUARE PLATE H/A=0.1 UNDER TENSION IN BOTH DIR.
************************************************
DIMENSION OF PLATE IN X DIRECTION.(AA)= 0.10000E+01
DIMENSION OF PLATE IN Y DIRECTION.(BB)= 0.10000E+01
FLEXURAL RIGIDITY....(D11)= 0.10000000E+01
FLEXURAL RIGIDITY....(D22)= 0.10000000E+01
COUPLING RIGIDITY....(D12)= 0.30000000E+00
TORSIONAL RIGIDITY...(D66)= 0.35000000E+00
TRANSVERSE SHEAR RIGIDITY.....(S44)= 0.35000000E+03
TRANSVERSE SHEAR RIGIDITY.....(S55)= 0.35000000E+03
SHEAR CORRECTION FACTOR.........(G1)= 0.10000000E+01
MODULUS FOR ELASTIC FOUNDATION.(GFS)= 0.00000000E+00
DISTRIBUTED LOADING.............(PZ)= 0.00000000E+00
MEMBRANE FORCE IN X DIREC.......(FX)= 0.49348022E+02
MEMBRANE FORCE IN Y DIREC.......(FY)= 0.49348022E+02
MASS DENSITY PER UNIT AREA......(PM)= 0.10000000E+01
CONTROL PARAMETER...............(KP)=    1
NUMB. OF FREQ. TO BE CALCULAT.(NUMF)=    1
MEMB. FORCE PARAM. IN X DIR...(ALFA)= 0.00000000E+00
MEMB. FORCE PARAM. IN Y DIR...(BETA)= 0.00000000E+00
************************************************
TABLE SHOWS THE COMPUTED VALUES FOR
THE FREQUENCIES FOR EACH PAIR OF MODES
    M     N        WMN
*****************************
    1     1    0.366460E+02
```

Figure 5.6 Output for a thick square plate under biaxial tension

Table 5.5 Relationship between frequency factors λ_{mn} and load intensity coefficient c for a simply supported plate under biaxial compression

m	n	load intensity coefficient c	closed form solution	finite strip solution [7]	thin plate theory [6]
1	1	0.	3.9456	3.99994	4.0
		0.5	2.9586	2.99992	3.0
		1.0	1.9717	1.99999	2.0
		1.5	0.9847	1.00001	1.0
1	2	0.	24.6392	24.9997	25.0
		0.5	22.1718	22.4996	22.5
		1.0	19.7044	19.9998	20.0
		1.5	17.2370	17.4998	17.5
2	2	0.	63.0232	64.0246	64.0
		0.5	59.0757	60.0244	60.0
		1.0	55.1277	56.0246	56.0
		1.5	51.1799	52.0246	52.0
1	3	0.	98.4184	99.9993	100.0
		0.5	93.4836	94.9991	95.0
		1.0	88.5488	89.9994	90.0
		1.5	83.6143	84.9994	85.0

Other examples presented here are concerned with the buckling of the plates. Table 5.6 gives the closed form solutions for a square simply supported plate of various thicknesses under uniaxial stress.

Table 5.6 Buckling factors $K_b = a^2 F_{crit}/\pi^2 D_{11}$ for a simply supported square plate under uniaxial initial stress

h/a	closed form solution	exact 3-D solution [8]	finite element solution [9]	thin plate theory [10]
0.001	4.000	4.000	4.000	4.000
0.05	3.944	3.911	3.944	4.000
0.10	3.786	3.741	3.787	4.000
0.20	3.264	3.150	3.263	4.000

It is obvious from Table 5.6 that the thin plate solutions appear to overestimate the buckling loads. Closed form solution results are compared with an exact three dimensional solution given by Srinivas and Rao [8] in Figure 5.7

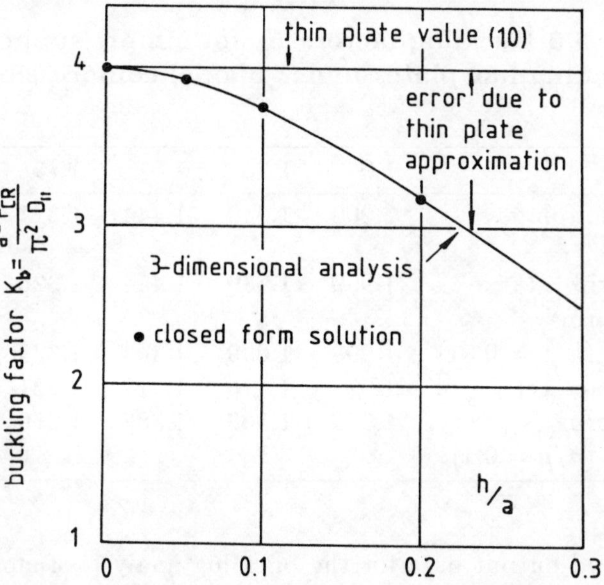

Figure 5.7 Buckling factors for initially stressed simply supported square plates of various thickness-span ratios($\nu = 0.3$)

Table 5.7 shows the results for a thin rectangular plate, compressed in the x-direction, with the following properties:

$$h/a = 0.01, \nu = 0.3$$

Table 5.7 Buckling factors K_b for plates with various aspect ratios

a/b	closed form solution	thick finite strip solution [5]	thin plate theory [2]
0.2	26.84	27.04	27.04
0.4	8.39	8.41	8.41
0.6	5.13	5.14	5.14
0.8	4.20	4.20	4.20
1.0	4.00	4.00	4.00
1.2	4.13	4.13	4.13
1.4	4.47	4.47	4.47

Table 5.8 shows buckling factors for simply supported rectangular plates under biaxial stress obtained using classical thin plate theory [10]. These results are compared with closed form solutions and finite strip solutions [11] involving thickness-to-span ratios of 0.01 and 0.1 respectively.

Table 5.8 Buckling factors K_b for simply supported rectangular plates under biaxial compression

a/b	1.0	1.25	1.5	1.75	2.0
exact thin plate [10]	2.000	1.640	1.444	1.327	1.250
finite strip [11]	1.999	1.639	1.444	1.326	1.250
closed form solution ($h/a = 0.01$)	1.999	1.639	1.444	1.326	1.250
finite strip [11]	1.777	1.475	1.317	1.221	1.159
closed form solution ($h/a = 0.1$)	1.893	1.568	1.388	1.279	1.207

Typical input and output data for the buckling analysis of simply supported Mindlin plates are shown in Figures 5.8 and 5.9 respectively.

5.4 Examples of transient dynamic analysis of plates

The next example is concerned with the dynamic analysis of rectangular simply supported plates of various thickness-to-span ratios which are subjected to a step pulse acting as uniformly distributed load over a rectangular area, as shown in Figure 3.1. The following parameters are used in this example:

$$\alpha = h/a, \beta = b/a, \xi = a/2, \eta = b/2, u = 2\alpha \text{ and } v = 2\alpha$$

Figures 5.10 - 5.13 show the time history of the centre deflection and bending moment for a centrally-loaded rectangular plate of $\beta = \sqrt{2}$ with thickness ratios $\alpha = 0.2$ and 0.1. All the results are presented in dimensionless form and are compared with those of Reismann and Lee [12]. Figures 5.10 to 5.13 show the deviation between Mindlin plate theory and classical plate theory. As expected, the difference between the two theories increases with the plate thickness. Typical input and output data for this example are given on Figures 5.14 and 5.15 respectively.

The influence of prestress on the dynamic behaviour of simply supported rectangular plate is presented in the next example. The parameters, used earlier, are again used to describe the plate and loading properties. Figures 5.16 and 5.17 show the time history of the plate centre deflection and bending moment with $\alpha = 0.1$, respectively, for several prestress conditions. The results are pre-

```
  BUCKLING FORCES FOR A THIN SQUARE PLATE H/A=0.01
1.        1.
1.        1.        0.3       0.35
35000.    35000.
0.        0.        1.        0.        0.        1.
   1
   3 1.
```

Figure 5.8 Typical input data for buckling analysis of a thin square plate

```
 **** CLOSED FORM SOLUTION ****
  BUCKLING FORCES FOR A THIN SQUARE PLATE H/A=0.01
 ************************************************
 DIMENSION OF PLATE IN X DIRECTION.(AA)= 0.10000E+01
 DIMENSION OF PLATE IN Y DIRECTION.(BB)= 0.10000E+01
 FLEXURAL RIGIDITY....(D11)= 0.10000000E+01
 FLEXURAL RIGIDITY....(D22)= 0.10000000E+01
 COUPLING RIGIDITY....(D12)= 0.30000000E+00
 TORSIONAL RIGIDITY...(D66)= 0.35000000E+00
 TRANSVERSE SHEAR RIGIDITY.....(S44)= 0.35000000E+05
 TRANSVERSE SHEAR RIGIDITY.....(S55)= 0.35000000E+05
 SHEAR CORRECTION FACTOR.........(G1)= 0.10000000E+01
 MODULUS FOR ELASTIC FOUNDATION.(GFS)= 0.00000000E+00
 DISTRIBUTED LOADING.............(PZ)= 0.00000000E+00
 MEMBRANE FORCE IN X DIREC.......(FX)= 0.00000000E+00
 MEMBRANE FORCE IN Y DIREC.......(FY)= 0.00000000E+00
 MASS DENSITY PER UNIT AREA......(PM)= 0.10000000E+01
 CONTROL PARAMETER...............(KP)=     1
 NUMB. OF FREQ. TO BE CALCULAT.(NUMF)=     3
 MEMB. FORCE PARAM. IN X DIR...(ALFA)= 0.10000000E+01
 MEMB. FORCE PARAM. IN Y DIR...(BETA)= 0.00000000E+00
************************************************
 TABLE SHOWS THE COMPUTED VALUES FOR THE
 FREQUENCIES AND BUCKLING FORCES FOR EACH
 PAIR OF MODES
     M     N          WMN            FCR
 ********************************************
     1     1    0.197336E+02 -0.394562E+02
     1     2    0.493133E+02 -0.246393E+03
     1     3    0.985572E+02 -0.984185E+03
     2     1    0.493133E+02 -0.615982E+02
     2     2    0.788679E+02 -0.157558E+03
     2     3    0.128070E+03 -0.415468E+03
     3     1    0.985572E+02 -0.109354E+03
     3     2    0.128070E+03 -0.184652E+03
     3     3    0.177204E+03 -0.353511E+03
```

Figure 5.9 Typical output data for buckling analysis of a thin square plate

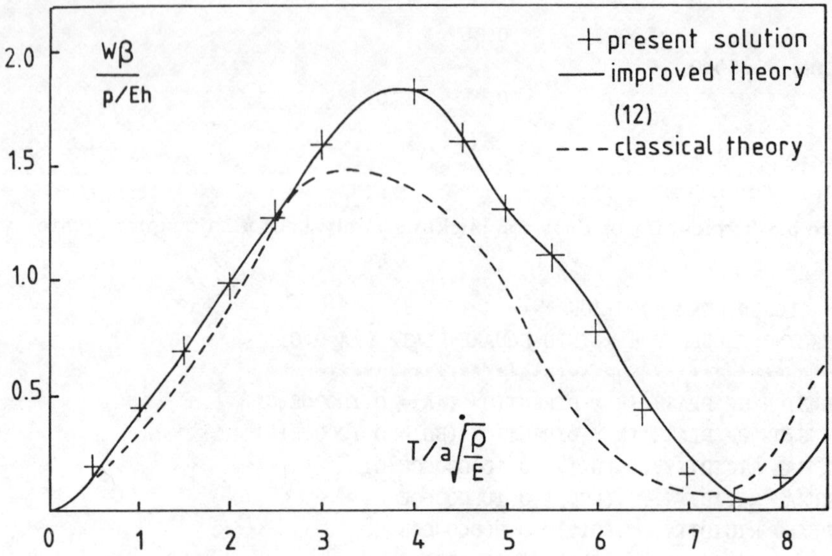

Figure 5.10 Central deflection time history for $\alpha = 0.2$

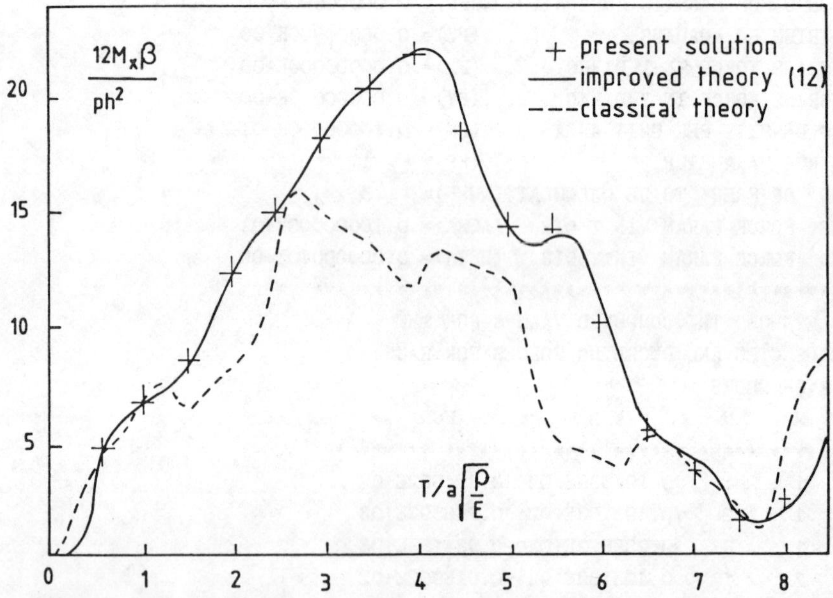

Figue 5.11 Central bending moment history for $\alpha = 0.2$

sented in dimensionless form and are compared with those of Reismann and Tendorf [13]. Finally, Figures 5.18 and 5.19 show the maximum values (attained at different times) for the central plate deflection and bending moment, respectively, as a function of prestress.

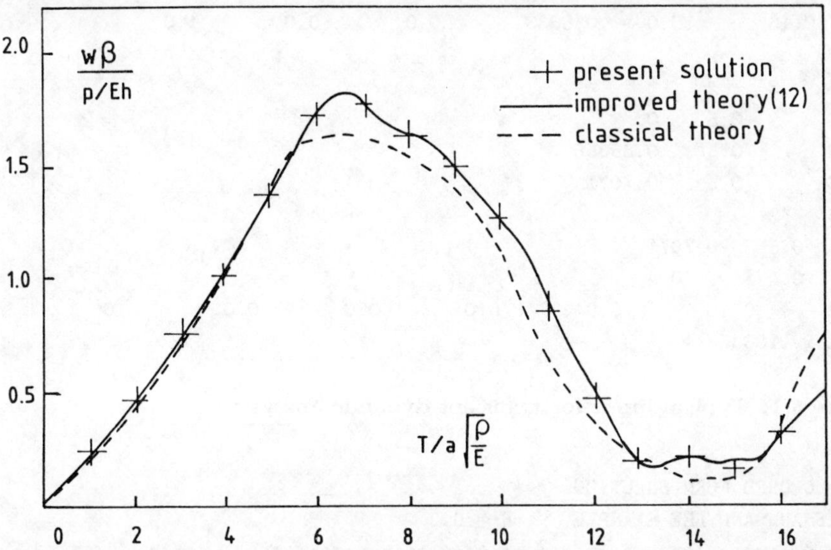

Figure 5.12 Central deflection time history for $\alpha = 0.1$

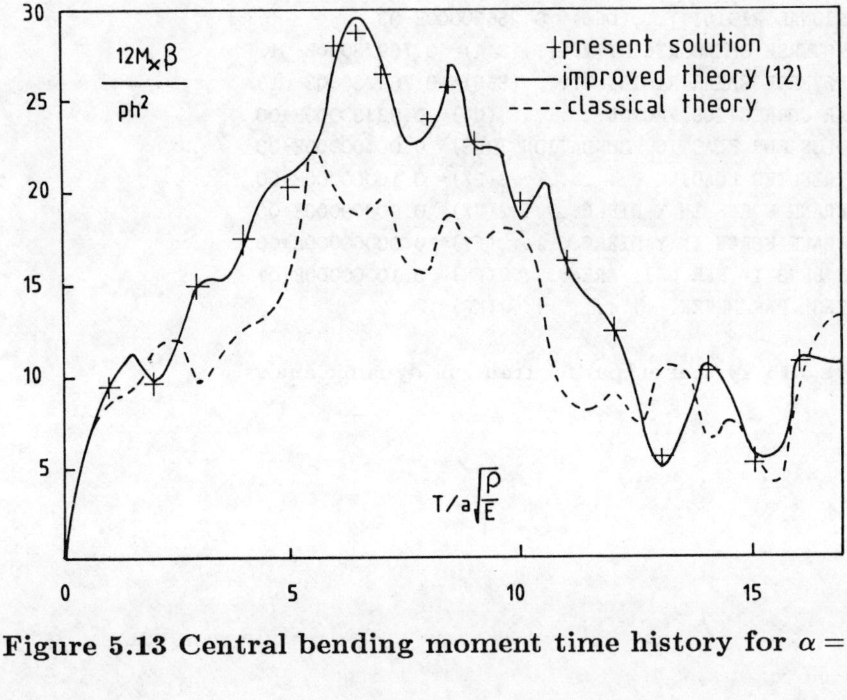

Figure 5.13 Central bending moment time history for $\alpha = 0.1$

```
 REISMANN AND LEE EXAMPLE     H = 0.2
      1.0      1.414
0.0007326 0.0007326   0.00022 0.0002565
 0.076923  0.076923
     0.16       0.0    0.8333        0.0        0.0        1.0
   2
  51    3
   1       0.5    0.
   2       0.5    0.35355
   3       0.5    0.7071
   3    2
      0.5     0.7071
      0.4          0.4
   2      0.16         0.0         0.0     100.0        0.0        0.0
   2 1.118035
```

Figure 5.14 Typical input for transient dynamic analysis

```
**** CLOSED FORM SOLUTION ****
 REISMANN AND LEE EXAMPLE     H = 0.2
**********************************************
DIMENSION OF PLATE IN X DIRECTION.(AA)= 0.10000E+01
DIMENSION OF PLATE IN Y DIRECTION.(BB)= 0.14140E+01
FLEXURAL RIGIDITY....(D11)= 0.73260000E-03
FLEXURAL RIGIDITY....(D22)= 0.73260000E-03
COUPLING RIGIDITY....(D12)= 0.22000000E-03
TORSIONAL RIGIDITY...(D66)= 0.25650000E-03
TRANSVERSE SHEAR RIGIDITY.....(S44)= 0.76923000E-01
TRANSVERSE SHEAR RIGIDITY.....(S55)= 0.76923000E-01
SHEAR CORRECTION FACTOR.........(G1)= 0.83330000E+00
MODULUS FOR ELASTIC FOUNDATION.(GFS)= 0.00000000E+00
DISTRIBUTED LOADING.............(PZ)= 0.16000000E+00
MEMBRANE FORCE IN X DIREC.......(FX)= 0.00000000E+00
MEMBRANE FORCE IN Y DIREC.......(FY)= 0.00000000E+00
MASS DENSITY PER UNIT AREA......(PM)= 0.10000000E+01
CONTROL PARAMETER...............(KP)=    2
```

Figure 5.15 Typical output for transient dynamic analysis

```
THE NO. OF TERMS IN FOURIER SERIES  (NUM)=   51
THE NO. OF POINTS ON PLATE         (NPON)=    3
X-COORD.      (ETA)= 0.50000000E+00
Y-COORD.      (ETB)= 0.70710000E+00
DIMENS. OF LOADED AREA IN X DIRECT.  (U)= 0.40000000E+00
DIMENS. OF LOADED AREA IN Y DIRECT.  (V)= 0.40000000E+00
************************************************
TABLE SHOWS THE COMPUTED VALUES FOR
SPECIFIED X AND Y COORDINATES.
FOR UNIFORM LOADING OVER RECTANGULAR AREAS (U.V).
SYMMETRIC LOADING.
PULSING FUNCTION PARAMETER......(IP)=    2
BLAST LOAD PARAMETER...........(F0)= 0.16000000E+00
BLAST LOAD PARAMETER...........(F2)= 0.00000000E+00
DAMPING PARAMETER..............(DP)= 0.00000000E+00
PULSING PARAMETER..............(T1)= 0.10000000E+03
PULSING PARAMETER..............(T2)= 0.00000000E+00
PULSING PARAMETER..............(T3)= 0.00000000E+00
NUMBER OF TIME STEPS............(J)=    2
TIME STEP LENGTH..............(TIN)= 0.11180350E+01
     POINT        X            Y
        1    0.50000E+00  0.00000E+00
        2    0.50000E+00  0.35350E+00
        3    0.50000E+00  0.70710E+00
SOLUTION AT TIME.................T= 0.11180350E+01
  POINT     W            WUX          WUY
    1  0.00000E+00  0.00000E+00  -0.28133E-02
    2  0.63603E-02  0.19577E-10  -0.12836E+00
    3  0.10366E+00  0.10583E-09   0.16224E-03
  POINT     MX           MY           MXY           QX           QY
    1  0.00000E+00  0.00000E+00   0.18365E-14   0.00000E+00  -0.43217E-03
    2  0.34983E-04 -0.54908E-03   0.10965E-12  -0.20556E-12   0.27382E-02
    3  0.15445E-02  0.15452E-02  -0.16964E-15  -0.72845E-11  -0.12449E-04
SOLUTION AT TIME.................T= 0.22360700E+01
  POINT     W            WUX          WUY
    1  0.00000E+00  0.00000E+00  -0.34875E-01
    2  0.69611E-01  0.72281E-10  -0.41562E+00
    3  0.24716E+00  0.17177E-09   0.27068E-03
  POINT     MX           MY           MXY           QX           QY
    1  0.00000E+00  0.00000E+00   0.47850E-13   0.00000E+00  -0.65322E-02
    2  0.59211E-03 -0.48562E-03   0.18932E-12  -0.17509E-11   0.10937E-01
    3  0.25230E-02  0.25618E-02  -0.11604E-15  -0.53720E-11  -0.85263E-05
```

Figure 5.15 .... continued

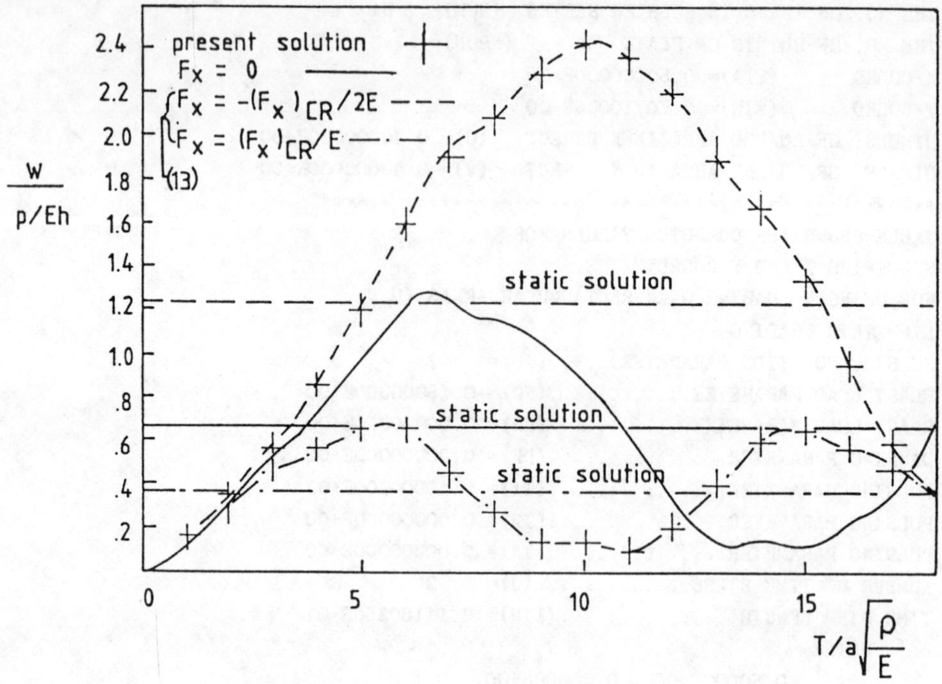

Figure 5.16 Central deflection time history

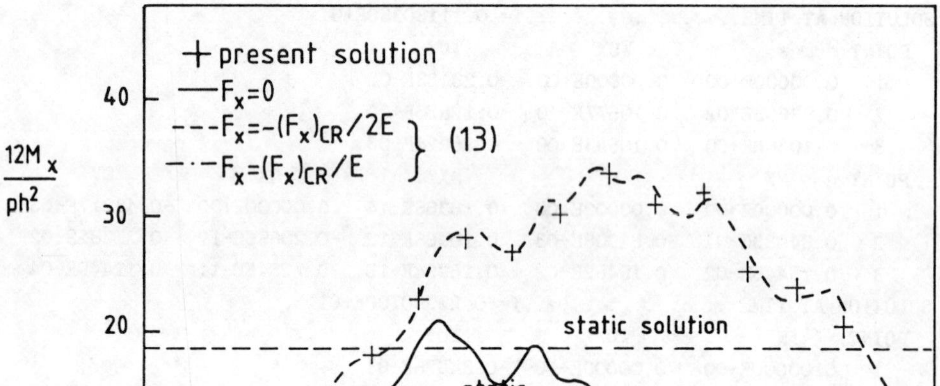

Figure 5.17 Central bending moment time history

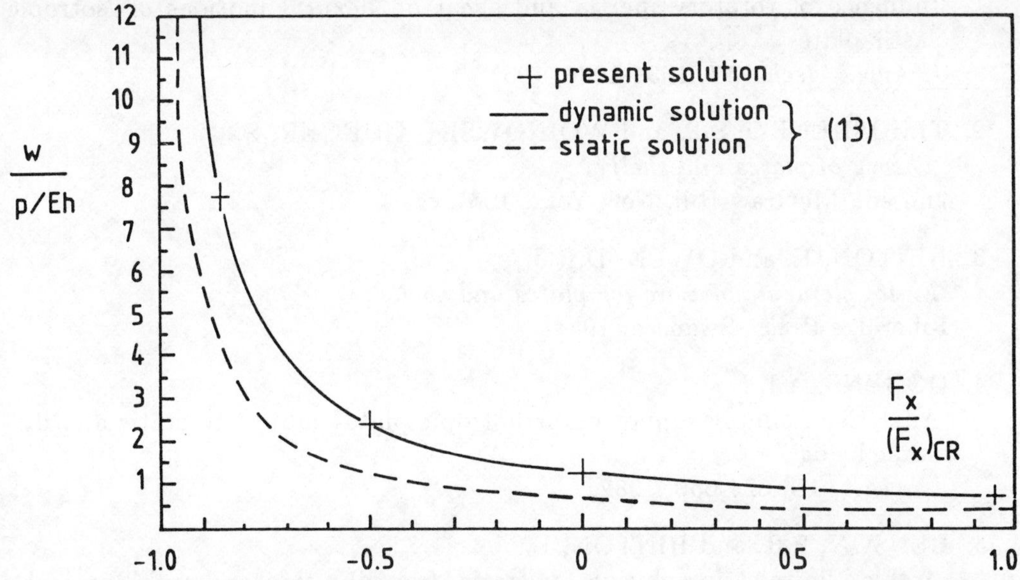

Figure 5.18 Maximum central deflection versus prestress

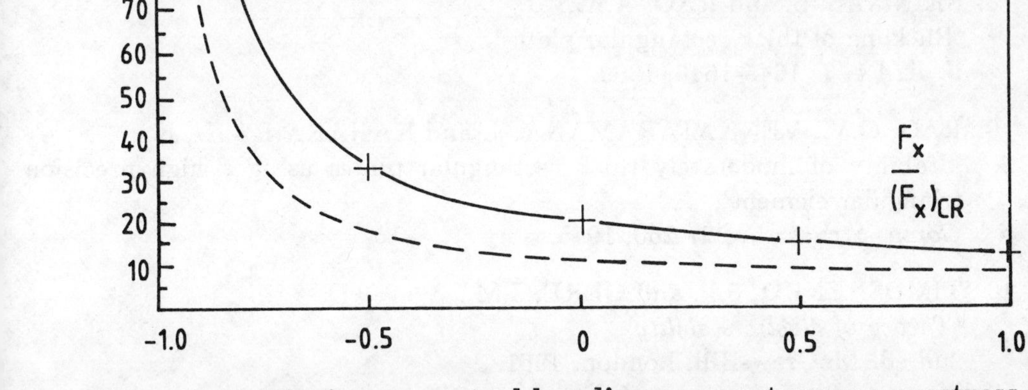

Figure 5.19 Maximum central bending moment versus prestress

REFERENCES

1. MINDLIN, R.D.,
'Influence of rotatory inertia and shear on flexural motions of isotropic elastic plates',
J. Appl. Mech., **37**, 1031-1036, 1951.

2. TIMOSHENKO, S.P. and WOINOWSKI-KRIEGER, S.,
'*Theory of plates and shells*',
2nd ed., McGraw-Hill, New York, 1961.

3. HINTON, E. and OWEN, D.R.J.,
'*Finite element software for plates and shells*',
Pineridge Press, Swansea, 1984.

4. DOBYNS, A.L.,
'Analysis of simply-supported orthotropic plates subject to static and dynamic loads',
J. AIAA, **19**, 624-650, 1982.

5. BENSON, P.R. and HINTON, E.,
'A thick finite strip solution for static, free vibration and stability problems',
Int. J. Num. Meth. Engng., **10**, 665-678, 1976.

6. LEISSA, A.W.,
'*Vibration of plates*',
NASA SP-160, Washington, D.C., 1969.

7. CHAN, H.C. and FOO, O.,
'Vibration of rectangular plates subjected to inplane forces by the finite strip method',
J. Sound and Vibration, **67**, 683-688, 1979.

8. SRINIVAS, S. and RAO, A.K.,
'Buckling of thick rectangular plates',
J. AIAA, **7**, 1645-1646, 1969.

9. RAO, G.V., VENKATARAMANA, J. and KANAKA RAJU, K.,
'Stability of moderately thick rectangular plates using a high precision triangular element',
Comp. Struct., **5**, 257-260, 1975.

10. TIMOSHENKO, S.P. and GERE, J.M.,
'*Theory of elastic stability*',
2nd ed. McGraw-Hill, London, 1961.

11. HINTON, E.,
'Buckling of initially stressed Mindlin plates using a finite strip method',
Comp. Struct., **8**, 99-105, 1978.

12. REISMANN, H. and LEE, Y.C.,
'Forced motion of rectangular plates',
Proc. 4th Biennial South-Eastern Conf. Th. App. Mech., Tulane University, New Orleans, Pergamon Press, New York, 1968.

13. REISMANN, H. and TENDORF, Z.A.,
'Dynamics of initially stressed plates',
J. Appl. Mech., **43**, 304-308, 1976.

FREE VIBRATION ANALYSIS OF PLATES USING THE FINITE STRIP METHOD

E. OÑATE* and E. HINTON**

* Universidad Politecnica de Cataluna, Barcelona, Spain.

** University College of Swansea, U.K.

1. INTRODUCTION

In this chapter a finite strip formulation [1] is presented for the free vibration analysis of plates of curved or rectangular planform and with two opposite ends simply supported. Software for a two-noded plate bending strip with reduced integration is given in which the stiffness and mass matrices and load vectors are given explicitly.

The finite strip method for the analysis of prismatic structures combines the use of Fourier expansions and one dimensional finite elements to model the longitudinal and transverse structural behaviour respectively. The finite strip method was initialy developed by Cheung [1 - 5] and Loo and Cusens [6, 7] who presented a wide range of solutions for static and dynamic analysis of plates using Kirchhoff's thin plate theory [8]. Extensions of the method to include Reissner-Mindlin plate theory have been reported by Hinton [9], Benson and Hinton [10], Dawe [11], Oñate [12], and Oñate and Suarez [13, 14].

In Section 2 of this chapter the governing equations for the vibration of plates with rectangular or curved planform are presented. Reissner-Mindlin assumptions are adopted. Section 3 provides general background for the Mindlin plate, finite strip formulation and in Section 4 the stiffness and mass matrices for a two-noded strip are given in explicit form. In Section 5, details of a computer program for the free vibration analysis of rectangular and curved plates are provided together with some examples illustrating the use of the program.

2. BASIC EQUATIONS

In this section the governing equations for the free vibrations of Mindlin plates with rectangular and curved planforms is presented.

2.1 Mindlin plates with rectangular planforms

For the rectangular plate shown in Figure 2.1, the deformed shape of the plate can be defined by the displacement fields

$$\mathbf{u} = [\, w,\ \theta_x,\ \theta_y \,]^T \tag{1}$$

where w is the lateral plate displacement and θ_x and θ_y are the normal rotations in the xz- and yz-planes respectively.

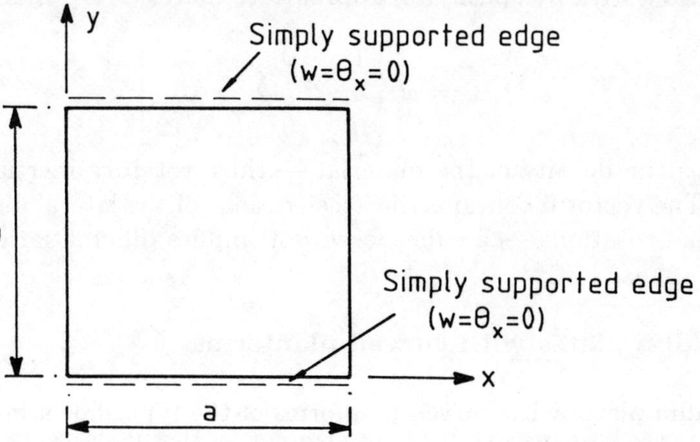

Figure 2.1 Mindlin plate with rectangular planform

In the absence of external loads, the virtual work expression for dynamic analysis can be written as

$$\int_A \delta\boldsymbol{\epsilon}_b{}^T \mathbf{D}_b\ \boldsymbol{\epsilon}_b\ dA + \int_A \delta\boldsymbol{\epsilon}_s{}^T \mathbf{D}_s\ \boldsymbol{\epsilon}_s\ dA + \int_A \delta\mathbf{u}^T \mathbf{P}\ \ddot{\mathbf{u}}\ dA = 0 \tag{2}$$

where the vector of curvatures is

$$\boldsymbol{\epsilon}_b = \begin{bmatrix} \partial\theta_x/\partial x \\ \partial\theta_y/\partial y \\ \partial\theta_x/\partial y + \partial\theta_y/\partial x \end{bmatrix} \tag{3}$$

and the vector of shear strains is

$$\boldsymbol{\epsilon}_s = \begin{bmatrix} \theta_x + \partial w/\partial x \\ \theta_y + \partial w/\partial y \end{bmatrix} \tag{4}$$

For an isotropic material, the matrix of flexural rigidities is written as

$$\mathbf{D}_b = Et^3/12(1-\nu^2) \begin{bmatrix} 1 & \nu & 0 \\ \nu & 1 & 0 \\ 0 & 0 & (1-\nu)/2 \end{bmatrix} \tag{5}$$

and the matrix of shear rigidities has the form

$$\mathbf{D}_s = Et\beta/2(1+\nu) \begin{bmatrix} 1 & 0 \\ 0 & 1 \end{bmatrix} \tag{6}$$

where E is the Young modulus, ν is the Poisson's ratio, t is the plate thickness and β is a coefficient to take into account the warping of the section (N.B. $\beta = 5/6$ for homogeneous, isotropic solid sections). Orthotropic materials can also be dealt with by specifying appropriate matrices $\mathbf{D}_b$ and $\mathbf{D}_s$. Note also that

$$\mathbf{P} = \rho t \begin{bmatrix} 1 & 0 & 0 \\ 0 & t^2/12 & 0 \\ 0 & 0 & t^2/12 \end{bmatrix} \tag{7}$$

where ρ is the density of the material — thus, rotatory inertia effects are included. The vector $\ddot{\mathbf{u}}$ contains the accelerations of the lateral displacement and the normal rotations — a superposed dot implies differentiation with respect to time.

2.2 Mindlin plates with curved planforms

For Mindlin plates with curved planforms of the type shown in Figure 2.2, the deformed shape of the plate can be defined by the displacement fields

$$\mathbf{u} = [\, w,\ \theta_r,\ \theta_\phi \,]^T \tag{8}$$

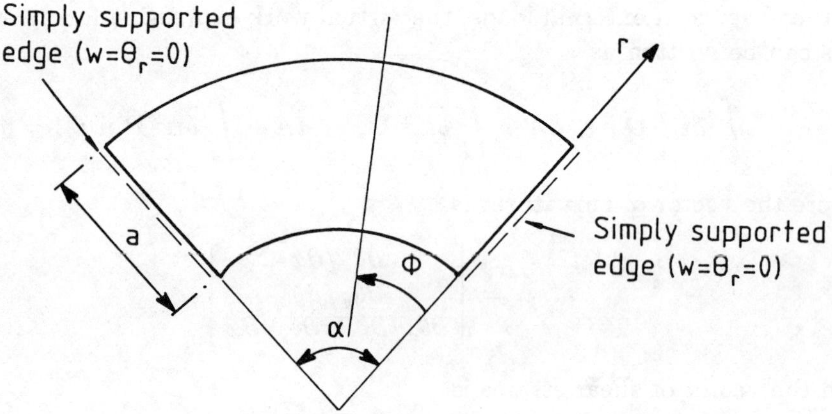

Figure 2.2 Mindlin plate with curved planform

where w is the lateral displacement and θ_r and θ_ϕ are the normal rotations in the rz- and ϕz-planes respectively (i.e. the radial plane and the plane which is tangential to the circumferential direction).

In the absence of external loads, the virtual work expression for dynamic analysis can be written as

$$\int_A \delta\boldsymbol{\epsilon}_b{}^T \mathbf{D}_b\ \boldsymbol{\epsilon}_b\ r d\phi + \int_A \delta\boldsymbol{\epsilon}_s{}^T \mathbf{D}_s\ \boldsymbol{\epsilon}_s\ r d\phi + \int_A \delta\mathbf{u}^T \mathbf{P}\ \ddot{\mathbf{u}}\ r d\phi = 0 \tag{9}$$

where

$$\epsilon_b = \begin{bmatrix} \partial\theta_r/\partial r \\ 1/r(\partial\theta_\phi/\partial\phi) + \theta_r/r \\ \partial\theta_\phi/\partial r + 1/r(\partial\theta_r/\partial\phi) - \theta_\phi/r \end{bmatrix} \tag{10}$$

$$\epsilon_s = \begin{bmatrix} \theta_r + \partial w/\partial r \\ \theta_\phi + 1/r(\partial w/\partial\phi) \end{bmatrix} \tag{11}$$

3. MINDLIN PLATE FINITE STRIP FORMULATION

Figure 3.1 shows a curved plate with circular planform, which is formed by an assembly of curved finite strips. The formulation for a rectangular plate can be considered as a particular case of the formulation presented below.

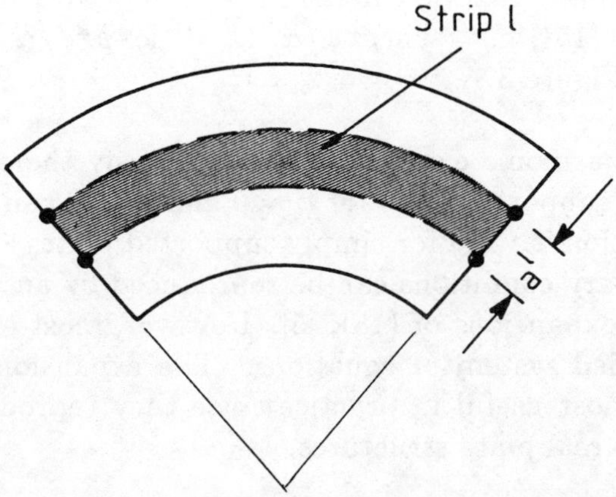

Figure 3.1 Curved Mindlin finite strips

3.1 Basic finite strip equations for curved strips

For the finite strip analysis, the plate is divided into curved , k-noded strips as shown in Figure 3.1. The displacement field inside a typical strip l can be expressed as products of polynomial one-dimensional shape functions in the radial direction of the structure and Fourier expansions in the circumferential direction. Thus, the displacements can be expressed as

$$\mathbf{u} = \sum_{p=1}^{n}\sum_{i=1}^{k} \mathbf{N}_i^p \ \mathbf{a}_i^p \tag{12}$$

where

$$\mathbf{u} = [w,\ \theta_r,\ \theta_\phi]^T \tag{13}$$

is the local displacement vector of a strip point in which w is the lateral displacement of the strip midsurface and θ_r and θ_ϕ are the two rotations of the midsurface normal.

The vector of local nodal displacement amplitudes for node i and the p-th harmonic term may be written as

$$\mathbf{a}_\mathrm{i}^\mathrm{p} = [w_i^p,\ \theta_{ri}^p,\ \theta_{\phi i}^p]^T \tag{14}$$

and the matrix of shape functions may be written as

$$\mathbf{N}_\mathrm{i}^\mathrm{p} = \begin{bmatrix} N_i S_p & 0 & 0 \\ 0 & N_i S_p & 0 \\ 0 & 0 & N_i C_p \end{bmatrix} \tag{15}$$

is the generalised shape function matrix associated with node i for the p-th harmonic term. In (15), $S_p = \sin p\pi\phi/\alpha$, $C_p = \cos p\pi\phi/\alpha$ and α is the plate angle as shown in Figure 3.1.

The fact that the harmonic expansions chosen satisfy the end boundary conditions of a simply supported strip for $\phi = 0$ and $\phi = \alpha$ can be easily checked. Thus, this formulation is valid for simply supported plates at the two opposite ends. Other boundary conditions can be reproduced by an appropriate choice of the Fourier-like expansions of (15), [5]. However, most expansions will not lead to an uncoupled system of equations. The expansions chosen here are the simplest and most useful in practice since they reproduce the boundary conditions of many real plate structures.

The generalised strain vectors can be written as

$$\boldsymbol{\epsilon}_b = \sum_{p=1}^{n} \sum_{i=1}^{k} \mathbf{B}_\mathrm{bi}^\mathrm{p}\, \mathbf{a}_\mathrm{i}^\mathrm{p} \tag{16}$$

and

$$\boldsymbol{\epsilon}_s = \sum_{p=1}^{n} \sum_{i=1}^{k} \mathbf{B}_\mathrm{si}^\mathrm{p}\, \mathbf{a}_\mathrm{i}^\mathrm{p} \tag{17}$$

where $\mathbf{B}_\mathrm{bi}^\mathrm{p}$ and $\mathbf{B}_\mathrm{si}^\mathrm{p}$ are the generalised bending and shear strain-displacement matrices, respectively associated with node i and harmonic p. These matrices may be written as

$$\mathbf{B}_\mathrm{bi}^\mathrm{p} = \begin{bmatrix} 0 & (\partial N_i/\partial r) S_p & 0 \\ 0 & N_i S_p / r & -N_i \gamma S_p / r \\ 0 & N_i \gamma C_p / r & (\partial N_i/\partial r - N_i/r) C_p \end{bmatrix} \tag{18}$$

$$\mathbf{B}^{\mathbf{p}}_{\mathbf{si}} = \begin{bmatrix} (\partial N_i/\partial r)S_p & N_i S_p & 0 \\ N_i \gamma C_p / r & 0 & N_i C_p \end{bmatrix} \tag{19}$$

with $\gamma = p\pi/\alpha$.

By substituting (12-19) into (2) and by taking into account the orthogonality properties of the trigonometric functions chosen, i.e.

$$\begin{aligned} \int_0^\alpha \sin\frac{p\pi\phi}{\alpha}\sin\frac{m\pi\phi}{\alpha}d\phi &= \alpha/2 \quad if \quad p = m \\ &= 0 \quad if \quad p \neq m \end{aligned} \tag{20a}$$

$$\begin{aligned} \int_0^\alpha \cos\frac{p\pi\phi}{\alpha}\cos\frac{m\pi\phi}{\alpha}d\phi &= \alpha/2 \quad if \quad p = m \\ &= 0 \quad if \quad p \neq m \end{aligned} \tag{20b}$$

the following system of equations can be obtained:

$$\mathbf{Ka} + \mathbf{M\ddot{a}} = \mathbf{0} \tag{21}$$

where the stiffness matrix is block-diagonal and has the form

$$\mathbf{K} = \begin{bmatrix} \mathbf{K}^{11} & \mathbf{0} & \dots & \mathbf{0} \\ \mathbf{0} & \mathbf{K}^{22} & \dots & \mathbf{0} \\ \vdots & \vdots & \ddots & \vdots \\ \mathbf{0} & \mathbf{0} & \dots & \mathbf{K}^{nn} \end{bmatrix} \tag{22}$$

the mass matrix is also block-diagonal and has the form

$$\mathbf{M} = \begin{bmatrix} \mathbf{M}^{11} & \mathbf{0} & \dots & \mathbf{0} \\ \mathbf{0} & \mathbf{M}^{22} & \dots & \mathbf{0} \\ \vdots & \vdots & \ddots & \vdots \\ \mathbf{0} & \mathbf{0} & \dots & \mathbf{M}^{nn} \end{bmatrix} \tag{23}$$

the vector of displacements is given as

$$\mathbf{a} = ([\mathbf{a}^1]^T, [\mathbf{a}^2]^T, \cdots, [\mathbf{a}^n]^T)^T \tag{24}$$

and the vector of accelerations is given as

$$\ddot{\mathbf{a}} = ([\ddot{\mathbf{a}}^1]^T, [\ddot{\mathbf{a}}^2]^T, \cdots, [\ddot{\mathbf{a}}^n]^T)^T \tag{25}$$

Details of matrices $\mathbf{K}^{\mathbf{pp}}$ and $\mathbf{M}^{\mathbf{pp}}$ will be given later in this section. Equation (24) is an uncoupled system of matrix equations which can be solved independently for each harmonic term. Thus for the p-th harmonic

$$\mathbf{K}^{\mathbf{pp}}\,\mathbf{a}^{\mathbf{p}} + \mathbf{M}^{\mathbf{pp}}\,\ddot{\mathbf{a}}^{\mathbf{p}} = \mathbf{0} \tag{26}$$

The solution of each uncoupled matrix equation is obtained using standard procedures of structural dynamics. Thus, the general solution of (26) is written as

$$\mathbf{a}^{\mathrm{p}} = \bar{\mathbf{a}}^{\mathrm{p}}\ e^{i\omega_p t} \tag{27}$$

where $e^{i\omega_p t} = cos\omega_p t + isin\omega_p t$ and ω_p and $\bar{\mathbf{a}}^{\mathrm{p}}$ are the natural frequency and vibration mode (eigen-vector) for the p-th harmonic term. Upon substitution of (27) into (26) the following classical eigenvalue equation is obtained

$$[\mathbf{K}^{\mathrm{pp}} - \omega_p^2\, \mathbf{M}^{\mathrm{pp}}]\, \bar{\mathbf{a}}^{\mathrm{p}} = \mathbf{0} \tag{28}$$

The non-trivial solution of (28) implies

$$\det\, [\mathbf{K}^{\mathrm{pp}} - \omega_p^2\, \mathbf{M}^{\mathrm{pp}}] = \mathbf{0} \tag{29}$$

from which the natural frequencies can be obtained. Finally, the corrersponding eigenvectors $\bar{\mathbf{a}}^{\mathrm{p}}$ for each frequency are obtained from (28).

In conclusion, the free vibration analysis of plates using the finite strip method requires the solution of n uncoupled eigenvalue problems, n being the number of harmonic terms used in the analysis. The natural frequencies and the corresponding vibration modes for each harmonic term are obtained from (28).

The stiffness and mass matrices of a typical curved strip are given by the expressions

$$[\mathbf{K}^{\mathrm{pp}}_{\mathrm{bij}}]^l = \alpha/2 \int_{a^l} [\mathbf{B}^{\mathrm{p}}_{\mathrm{bi}}]^T \mathbf{D}_{\mathrm{b}} \mathbf{B}^{\mathrm{p}}_{\mathrm{bj}}\ rdr \tag{30}$$

$$[\mathbf{K}^{\mathrm{pp}}_{\mathrm{sij}}]^l = \alpha/2 \int_{a^l} [\mathbf{B}^{\mathrm{p}}_{\mathrm{si}}]^T \mathbf{D}_{\mathrm{s}} \mathbf{B}^{\mathrm{p}}_{\mathrm{sj}}\ rdr \tag{31}$$

and

$$[\mathbf{M}^{\mathrm{pp}}_{\mathrm{ij}}]^l = \alpha/2 \int_{a^l} [\mathbf{N}^{\mathrm{p}}_{\mathrm{i}}]^T \mathbf{P} \mathbf{N}^{\mathrm{p}}_{\mathrm{j}}\ rdr \tag{32}$$

Note that

$$[\mathbf{K}^{\mathrm{pm}}_{\mathrm{bij}}]^l = [\mathbf{K}^{\mathrm{pm}}_{\mathrm{sij}}]^l = [\mathbf{M}^{\mathrm{pm}}_{\mathrm{ij}}]^l = \mathbf{0} \quad for \quad p \neq m \tag{33}$$

where a^l is the width of strip l and $\mathbf{B}^{\mathrm{p}}_{\mathrm{bi}}$, $\mathbf{B}^{\mathrm{p}}_{\mathrm{si}}$ and $\mathbf{N}_{\mathrm{i}}$ are directly obtained from (17), (18) and (15) by making $S_p = C_p = 1$. Note that matrix $\mathbf{M}^{\mathrm{pp}}_{\mathrm{ij}}$ is independent of the harmonic number p and, therefore, the same matrix can be used for all the different harmonic equations.

3.2 Formulation for rectangular strips

For the finite strip analysis, the plate is divided into rectangular, k-noded strips as shown in Figure 3.2

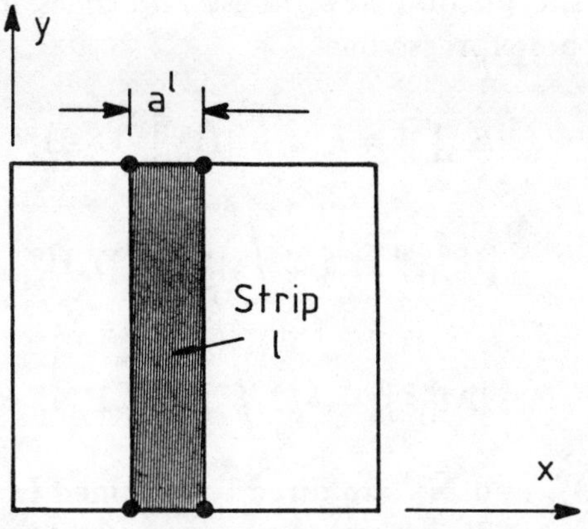

Figure 3.2 Rectangular strips

The displacement field inside typical strip l can be expressed as products od polynomial one-dimensional shape functions in the x-direction and Fourier expansions in the longitudinal, y-direction. Thus, the displacements can be expressed as

$$\mathbf{u} = \sum_{p=1}^{n} \sum_{i=1}^{k} \mathbf{N}_i^p \, \mathbf{a}_i^p \tag{34}$$

where

$$\mathbf{u} = [w, \theta_x, \theta_y]^T \tag{35}$$

The vector of nodal displacement amplitudes for node i and the p-th harmonic may be written as

$$\mathbf{a}_i^p = [w_i^p, \theta_{xi}^p, \theta_{yi}^p]^T \tag{36}$$

The matrix of shape functions $\mathbf{N}_i^p$ has the same form as the one in (15) used for the curved strips. However, for rectangular strips, $S_p = \sin p\pi y/b$ and $C_p = \cos p\pi y/b$.

The generalised strain-displacement relations have the same form as those given in (16) and (17). For rectangular strips, $\mathbf{B}_{bi}^p$ and $\mathbf{B}_{si}^p$ may be written as

$$\mathbf{B}_{bi}^p = \begin{bmatrix} 0 & (\partial N_i/\partial x)S_p & 0 \\ 0 & 0 & -N_i\bar{\gamma}S_p \\ 0 & N_i\bar{\gamma}C_p & (\partial N_i/\partial x)C_p \end{bmatrix} \tag{37}$$

$$\mathbf{B}_{si}^p = \begin{bmatrix} (\partial N_i/\partial x)S_p & N_i S_p & 0 \\ N_i\bar{\gamma}C_p & 0 & N_i C_p \end{bmatrix} \tag{38}$$

with $\bar{\gamma} = p\pi/b$.

Again, by taking advantage of orthogonality properties of the type given in (20a) and (20b), the uncoupled stiffness and mass matrices for the p-th harmonic term ,may be expressed as

$$[\mathbf{K}_{\mathrm{bij}}^{\mathrm{pp}}]^l = b/2 \int_{a^l} [\bar{\mathbf{B}}_{\mathrm{bi}}^{\mathrm{p}}]^T \mathbf{D}_\mathrm{b} \bar{\mathbf{B}}_{\mathrm{bj}}^{\mathrm{p}} \, dx \tag{39}$$

$$[\mathbf{K}_{\mathrm{sij}}^{\mathrm{pp}}]^l = b/2 \int_{a^l} [\bar{\mathbf{B}}_{\mathrm{si}}^{\mathrm{p}}]^T \mathbf{D}_\mathrm{s} \bar{\mathbf{B}}_{\mathrm{sj}}^{\mathrm{p}} \, dx \tag{40}$$

and

$$[\mathbf{M}_{\mathrm{ij}}^{\mathrm{pp}}]^l = b/2 \int_{a^l} [\bar{\mathbf{N}}_{\mathrm{i}}^{\mathrm{p}}]^T \mathbf{P} \bar{\mathbf{N}}_{\mathrm{j}}^{\mathrm{p}} \, dx \tag{41}$$

In (36-37), $\bar{\mathbf{B}}_{\mathrm{bi}}^{\mathrm{p}}$, $\bar{\mathbf{B}}_{\mathrm{si}}^{\mathrm{p}}$ and $\bar{\mathbf{N}}_{\mathrm{i}}^{\mathrm{p}}$ are directly obtained from (37), (38) and (34) by making $S_p = C_p = 1$. The other matrices in (39-41) are identical to those for the curved formulation.

4. STIFFNESS AND MASS MATRICES FOR LINEAR STRIPS

4.1 The linear strip with reduced integration

For practical applications of the above strip formulation any of the well known one dimensional Lagrangian finite elements can be used. However, the success of the Reissner-Mindlin formulation presented, for thick and thin shell/plate analysis, lays in the use of reduced integration techniques for the numerical computation of the stiffness matrix. This simply implies that the shear terms contributing to the stiffness matrix are numerically integrated with a lower order Gaussian quadrature than that needed for their exact computation, whereas the rest of the stiffness matrix is exactly calculated. Details of this technique can be found in Reference [13].

It has been recently shown by Oñate and Suarez [13], [14] that the simple two-noded linear strip element with a single integrating point for the numerical computation of all terms of the stiffness matrix has an excellent behaviour for both thin and thick plate and shell analysis and the performances compare favourably with other elements of higher order. In addition, the single point integration implies that a direct explicit form of the element matices can be directly obtained by simply evaluating the terms of all integrals at the element mid point. Thus, for curved strips, the stiffness and mass matrices may be obtained by use of (30)-(32). They have the form

$$[\mathbf{K}_{\mathrm{bij}}^{\mathrm{pp}}]^l = a^l \alpha/2([\bar{\mathbf{B}}_{\mathrm{bi}}^{\mathrm{p}}]^T \mathbf{D}_\mathrm{b} \bar{\mathbf{B}}_{\mathrm{bj}}^{\mathrm{p}} r)_0 \tag{42}$$

$$[\mathbf{K}_{\mathrm{sij}}^{\mathrm{pp}}]^l = a^l \alpha/2([\bar{\mathbf{B}}_{\mathrm{si}}^{\mathrm{p}}]^T \mathbf{D}_\mathrm{s} \bar{\mathbf{B}}_{\mathrm{sj}}^{\mathrm{p}} r)_0 \tag{43}$$

and

$$[\mathbf{M}_{\mathrm{ij}}]^l = a^l \alpha/2(\bar{\mathbf{N}}_{\mathrm{i}}^{\mathrm{T}} \mathbf{P} \bar{\mathbf{N}}_{\mathrm{j}} r)_0 \tag{44}$$

where the index $(.)_0$ implies that all the terms inside the brackets are evaluated at the strip mid point.

For rectangular strips

$$[\mathbf{K}^{pp}_{bij}]^l = a^l b/2([\bar{\mathbf{B}}^p_{bi}]^T \mathbf{D}_b \bar{\mathbf{B}}^p_{bj})_0 \tag{45}$$

$$[\mathbf{K}^{pp}_{sij}]^l = a^l b/2([\bar{\mathbf{B}}^p_{si}]^T \mathbf{D}_s \bar{\mathbf{B}}^p_{sj})_0 \tag{46}$$

$$[\mathbf{M}_{ij}]^l = a^l b/2([\bar{\mathbf{N}}_i]^T \mathbf{P} \bar{\mathbf{N}}_j)_0 \tag{47}$$

The explicit form of the stiffness and mass matrices is simply obtained by noting that in $\bar{\mathbf{B}}^p_{bi}$, $\bar{\mathbf{B}}^p_{si}$ and $\bar{\mathbf{N}}_i$, the terms $(\bar{\mathbf{N}}_i)_0 = 1/2$ and $(\partial N_i/\partial r)_0$ or $(\partial N_i/\partial x)_0 = (-1)^i/a^l$, $S_p = C_p = 1$.

4.2 Explicit form for the stiffness and lumped mass matrix

The explicit form of the stiffness matrix for the linear, two-noded strip with reduced one-point, reduced integration is coded in subroutine STIFFS in Section 5.9. Alternatively, a one-point Gauss-Legendre rule may be used to evaluate the stiffness matrices of (42), (43), (45) and (46) numerically.

The lumped mass matrix adopted may be written as

$$\mathbf{M}^l = \begin{bmatrix} \bar{a} & 0 & 0 & 0 & 0 & 0 \\ 0 & \bar{b} & 0 & 0 & 0 & 0 \\ 0 & 0 & \bar{b} & 0 & 0 & 0 \\ 0 & 0 & 0 & \bar{a} & 0 & 0 \\ 0 & 0 & 0 & 0 & \bar{b} & 0 \\ 0 & 0 & 0 & 0 & 0 & \bar{b} \end{bmatrix} \tag{48}$$

where, for a curved strip,

$$\bar{a} = \rho t \bar{r} \alpha a^l/4 \tag{49}$$

and

$$\bar{b} = \rho t^3 \bar{r} \alpha a^l/48 \tag{50}$$

and for a rectangular strip,

$$\bar{a} = \rho t a^l b/4 \tag{51}$$

and

$$\bar{b} = \rho t^3 a^l b/48 \tag{52}$$

5. PROGRAM FIST

5.1 Introduction

This section describes FIST which is a program for the free vibration analysis of Mindlin plates. In order to make all of the subroutines in FIST modular in form we have adopted a type of dynamic dimensioning. Dimensions are fixed in the main routine and all necessary information is transmitted between routines by the use of arguments. This approach has the advantage that the maximum dimensions can be updated in a very simple manner. Only the DIMENSION statements in the main segment which sets the maximum dimension sizes need modification.

Program FIST consists of four main modules:

(1) INPFS which reads in most of the input data,

(2) STIFFS which evaluates the stiffness and mass matrices for Mindlin plate strips,

(3) BERKEL which is an eigenvalue solver, and

(4) OUTFS which outputs the results.

Program FIST is written in a modular form in such a way that users can easily implement their own modules for eigenvalue solution and for output. Thus, BERKEL and OUTFS are not compulsory routines in the program. Thet are routines which illustrate the implementation of the eigenvalue solver, described and coded by Bathe and Wilson [15], which employs a subspace iteration method with Sturm sequence checks.

5.2 Glossary of variable names

Main arrays

Array name: description

COORD(MPOIN,1): x-coordinate of nodal line

ESTIF(6,6): strip stiffness matrix for a given harmonic

EMASS(6,6): strip mass matrix

IFPRE(MVFIX,NDOFN): fixity code matrix, 0=free, 1=fixed

LNODS(MELEM,2): strip nodal connectivities

MATNO(MELEM): material set numbers for each strip

NOFIX(MVFIX): nodes with at least one prescribed variable

PROPS(MMATS,5): properties for each material set

Main variables

Array name: description

DENSE: density

IHARM: counter for harmonic terms

MELEM: maximum number of strips

MEVAB: = 6, maximum number of strip variables

MMATS: maximum number of material sets

MPOIN: maximum number of nodal points

MVFIX: maximum number of restrained nodes

NDOFN: = 3, number of degrees of freedom per nodal line

NEVAB: = 6, number of degrees of freedom per strip

NELEM: number of strips

NHARM: number of harmonic terms to be used

NMATS: number of different material properties

NMODE: number of eigenvalues required

NNODE: = 2, number of nodal lines per strip

NPOIN: number of nodal lines

NTYPE: indicator = 0 for curved plates, = 1 for rectangular plates

POISS: Poisson's ratio

THICK: plate thickness

TLENG: plate length or angle

YOUNG: Young's modulus

5.3 Main segment

The main segment which controls the calling of the major subroutines is now described.

1. Initialise variables in DATA statements [MAIN 27-40].
2. Call INPFS to read in most of the data [MAIN 44-47].
3. Loop over each harmonic [MAIN 48].
   3.1 Call STIFFS to evaluate **K** and **M** [MAIN 52-54].
   3.2 Call BERKEL to find eigen values [MAIN 58-62].
   3.3 Call OUTFS to print the results [MAIN 66-67] .

5.4 Input module - Subroutine INPFS

The main function of INPFS is to read most of the input data. The basic structure of INPFS is of the following form.

1. Read and write problem title [INPF 16-17].
2. Read and write control data [INPF 23-29].
3. Read and write strip connections and property set numbers [INPF 33-38].
4. Initialise array COORD [INPF 42-44].
5. Read and write nodal coordinates [INPF 48-57].
6. Read and write fixity conditions [INPF 61-68].
7. Read and write strip properties [INPF 72-81].

5.5 Stiffness module - Subroutine STIFFS

The main function of STIFFS is to evaluate stiffness and mass matrices for Mindlin plate strips. Subroutine STIFFS has the following structure.

1. Rewind files 1 and 7 ready for writing **K** and **M** [STIF 14-15].
2. Loop over each strip [STIF 19].
   - 2.1 Initialise **K** and **M** arrays [STIF 23-26].
   - 2.2 Extract strip material set number, nodal coordinates and properties [STIF 40-60].
   - 2.3 Make stiffness matrix symmetric [STIF 106-110].
   - 2.4 Calculate diagonal mass matrix [STIF 114-125].
   - 2.5 Write **K** and **M** to files 1 and 7 respectively [STIF 129-130].

5.6 Eigenvalue extraction module - Subroutine BERKEL

Subroutine BERKEL is the interface routine for the eigenvalue solver. It prepares all necessary data for subspace iteration coded in subroutine SSPACE.

BERKEL calls subroutine COLHT to calculate column heights and subroutine ADDRES to calculate addresses of diagonal elements in a banded matrix whose column heights are known. From files 1 and 7 BERKEL reads and rewrites in vector form strip stiffness and mass matrices, then calls ADDBAN to assemble the upper triangular part of those strip matices into the compacted global matrices.

BERKEL reads two indicators for subspace iteration as input data:

- IFSS - indicator for Sturm sequence check and
- IFPR - indicator for printing during iteration

NOTE: The following subroutines are fully described and listed in ' Numerical Methods in Finite Element Analysis' by K.J. Bathe and E.L. Wilson, Prentice-Hall, New Jersey, 1976:

COLHT, ADDRES AND ADDBAN	pages 227 - 229
SSPACE	pages 509 - 517

To match subroutine BERKEL with subroutine OUTFS it is necessary to do some modifications in SSPACE and they are:

1. Input DATA statement - DATA IOUT1/4/

2. Substitute IOUT with IOUT1 in the following lines:

SPCE0292 and SPCE 0269 page 511

SPCE0292 page 512

5.7 Output module - Subroutine OUTFS

Subroutine OUTFS simply prints out eigenvalues, modes and error norms after reading from file 4. If printing during iteration is required (IFPR=1) then corresponding results are stored in file 3.

5.8 Input instructions

DATA SET 1	DATA TITLE (20A4) one record	
1- 72	TITLE	title of the problem

DATA SET 2	PROBLEM PARAMETERS (6I5) one record	
1 - 5	NPOIN	number of nodal lines
6 -10	NELEM	number of strips
11-15	NVFIX	number of prescribed nodes
16-20	NMATS	number of different materials
21-25	NMODE	number of modes required per harmonic
26-30	NHARM	number of harmonics
31-35	NTYPE	= 0 curved plate, = 1 rectangular plate

DATA SET 3	NODAL CONNECTIONS (4I5) NELEM records	
1 - 5	NUMEL	strip number
6 -10	MATNO (NUMEL)	material number for the strip
11-15	LNODS (NUMEL, 1)	global number of nodal line 1
16-20	LNODS (NUMEL, 2)	global number of nodal line 2

DATA SET 4	NODAL COORDINATES (I5, F10.5) NPOIN records	
1 - 5	IPOIN	number of nodal line
6 -15	COORD (IPOIN)	x- or r- coordinate of nodal line

DATA SET 5	FIXED VALUES (I5, 2X, 3I1) NVFIX records	
1 - 5	NOFIX (IVFIX)	number of fixed nodal line
8	IFPRE (IVFIX,1)	indicator for constraint in w
9	IFPRE (IVFIX,2)	indicator for constraint in θ_x or θ_r
10	IFPRE (IVFIX,3)	indicator for constraint in θ_y or θ_ϕ
	indicator = 1 constrained, = 0	

Note : NVFIX = 0 implies that the plate is simply supported at both ends. Also a constraint in a degree of freedom implies that the displacement associated with that degree of freedom is zero along the nodal line between the plate ends. Other non-zero constraints are not allowed in this program.

DATA SET 6	MATERIAL SET NUMBER (I5)	
1 - 5	NUMAT	number associated with material set

DATA SET 7	MATERIAL PROPERTIES (5F10.5)	
1 -10	PROPS (NUMAT, 1)	Young's modulus
11-20	PROPS (NUMAT, 2)	Poisson's ratio
21-30	PROPS (NUMAT, 3)	plate thickness
31-40	PROPS (NUMAT, 4)	density
41-50	PROPS (NUMAT, 5)	plate length or angle

N.B. Data sets 6 and 7 are repeated for each separate material set.

DATA SET 8	STURM SEQUENCE INDICATORS (2I5) one record	
1 - 5	IFSS	indicator for Sturm sequence check = 0 no check, = 1 check applied
6 -10	IFPR	indicator for printing during iteration = 0 no printing, = 1 printing

5.9 Subroutine listings

Main segment

```
C**********************************************************************MAIN
C*                                                                    *MAIN
C*    FINITE STRIP PROGRAM FOR THE FREE VIBRATION ANALYSIS             MAIN
C*    OF PLATES USING MINDLIN THEORY                                   MAIN
C*                                                                    *MAIN
C**********************************************************************MAIN
      IMPLICIT REAL*8(A-H,O-Z)                                         MAIN
C                                                                      MAIN
C*** DIMENSIONS ASSOCIATED WITH SUBROUTINES INPUT AND STIFPS           MAIN
C                                                                      MAIN
      DIMENSION COORD(50,1),ESTIF(6,6),EMASS(6,6),                     MAIN
     .          IFPRE(2,3),LNODS(25,2),MATNO(25),NOFIX(2),             MAIN
     .          PROPS(10,5)                                            MAIN
C                                                                      MAIN
C*** DIMENSIONS ASSOCIATED WITH SUBROUTINES BERKEL AND OUTPS           MAIN
C                                                                      MAIN
      DIMENSION A(900),AD(3,50),AR(171),B(900),BR(171),BS(21),         MAIN
     .          BUP(18),BLO(18),BUPC(18),D(18),ER(150,18),EIGV(18),    MAIN
     .          ID(3,50),LM(6,25),MHT(150),MAXA(151),R(150,18),        MAIN
     .          RTOLV(18),S(21),TT(150),VEC(18,18),W(150)              MAIN
C**********************************************************************MAIN
C                                                                      MAIN
C                 DYNAMIC  DIMENSIONING                                MAIN
C                                                                      MAIN
C**********************************************************************MAIN
C                                                                      MAIN
      DATA MPOIN/50/,MVFIX/2/,MELEM/25/,MMATS/10/,                     MAIN
     .     NDIME/1/,NNODE/2/,NDOFN/3/                                  MAIN
C                                                                      MAIN
      DATA MAHAM/21/,MAXNN/150/,MANNM/151/,MMODE/10/,MNEBS/900/,       MAIN
     .     MITEV/18/,MDISV/171/                                        MAIN
C                                                                      MAIN
C                                                                      MAIN
C**  NDISV=MITEV*(MITEV+1)/2                                           MAIN
C**  MAHAM=MEVAB*(MEVAB+1)/2                                           MAIN
C**  MAXNN=MPOIN*NDOFN                                                 MAIN
C**  MANNM=MAXNN+1                                                     MAIN
C**  MNEBS=APPROX. MAXNN*MEVAB                                         MAIN
C                                                                      MAIN
      MEVAB=NDOFN*NNODE                                                MAIN
C                                                                      MAIN
C*** CALL SUBROUTINE WHICH READS IN MOST OF THE DATA                   MAIN
C                                                                      MAIN
      CALL  INPFS    (COORD,IFPRE,LNODS,MATNO,                         MAIN
```

```
     .              MVFIX,MMATS,MPOIN,MELEM,NPOIN,NELEM,
     .              NVFIX,NNODE,NDOFN,NMATS,NDIME,NEVAB,NHARM,
     .              NMODE,NOFIX,NTYPE,PROPS)
      DO 30 IHARM = 1,NHARM
C
C*** FORM THE ELEMENT STIFFNESS AND MASS MATRICES
C
      CALL  STIFFS   (COORD,IHARM,LNODS,MATNO,MELEM,MEVAB,
     .                MMATS,MPOIN,NELEM,NEVAB,
     .                NNODE,NTYPE,PROPS)
C
C*** SUBSPACE ITERATION
C
   10 CALL  BERKEL   (A,AR,B,BR,BS,BUP,BLO,BUPC,D,ER,EIGV,
     .               ID,IFPRE,LM,LNODS,MHT,MAXA,MAHAM,MAXNN,MANNM,
     .               MITEV,MDISV,MNEBS,MPOIN,MELEM,MVFIX,NMODE,
     .               NPOIN,NEQ,NVFIX,NOFIX,NDOFN,NELEM,NEVAB,
     .               NNODE,RTOLV,S,TT,VEC,W)
C
C*** CALL SUBROUTINE WHICH OUTPUTS THE RESULTS
C
      CALL  OUTFS   (AD,D,EIGV,ID,IHARM,MPOIN,MAXNN,MITEV,NDOFN,
     .               NMODE,NEQ,NPOIN,R)
   30 CONTINUE
      STOP
      END
```

Subroutine INPFS

```
      SUBROUTINE INPFS   (COORD,IFPRE,LNODS,MATNO,
     .                    MVFIX,MMATS,MPOIN,MELEM,NPOIN,NELEM,
     .                    NVFIX,NNODE,NDOFN,NMATS,NDIME,NEVAB,NHARM,
     .                    NMODE,NOFIX,NTYPE,PROPS)
C************************************************************************
C
C***  INPUT MAIN DATA FOR MINDLIN STRIPS
C
C************************************************************************
      IMPLICIT REAL*8(A-H,O-Z)
C
      DIMENSION COORD(MPOIN,NDIME),IFPRE(MVFIX,NDOFN),
     .          LNODS(MELEM,NNODE),MATNO(MELEM),NOFIX(MVFIX),
     .          PROPS(MMATS,5),TITLE(20)
C
      READ(5,870) TITLE
      WRITE(6,875)TITLE
  870 FORMAT(20A4)
```

```
  875 FORMAT(///,1X,20A4)
C
C*** READ THE FIRST DATA CARD, AND ECHO IT IMMEDIATELY.
C
    8 READ(5,900) NPOIN,NELEM,NVFIX,NMATS,NMODE,NHARM,NTYPE
  900 FORMAT(7I5)
      NEVAB=NDOFN*NNODE
      WRITE(6,905) NPOIN,NELEM,NVFIX,NMATS,NMODE,NHARM,NTYPE
  905 FORMAT(//8H NPOIN =,I4,4X,8H NELEM =,I4,4X,8H NVFIX =,I4,4X,
     .8H NMATS =,I4/8H NMODE =,I4,4X,8H NHARM =,I4,4X,
     .8H NTYPE =,I4)
C
C*** READ THE ELEMENT NODAL CONNECTIONS, AND THE PROPERTY NUMBERS.
C
      WRITE(6,910)
  910 FORMAT(//6H ELEM.,2X,7HMAT.SET,2X,12HNODE NUMBERS)
      DO 10 IELEM=1,NELEM
      READ(5,900)NUMEL,MATNO(NUMEL),(LNODS(NUMEL,INODE),INODE=1,NNODE)
   10 WRITE(6,915)NUMEL,MATNO(NUMEL),(LNODS(NUMEL,INODE),INODE=1,NNODE)
  915 FORMAT(1X,I3,5X,I3,1X,2I5)
C
C*** ZERO ALL THE NODAL COORDINATES, PRIOR TO READING SOME OF THEM.
C
      DO 20 IPOIN=1,NPOIN
      DO 20 IDIME=1,NDIME
   20 COORD(IPOIN,IDIME)=0.0
C
C*** READ SOME NODAL COORDINATES, FINISHING WITH THE LAST NODE OF ALL.
C
      WRITE(6,920)
  920 FORMAT(//25H  NODAL POINT COORDINATES)
      WRITE(6,925)
  925 FORMAT(6H  NODE,7X,1HX,9X,1HY)
   30 READ(5,930) IPOIN,(COORD(IPOIN,IDIME),IDIME=1,NDIME)
  930 FORMAT(I5,F10.5)
      IF(IPOIN.NE.NPOIN) GO TO 30
      DO 50 IPOIN=1,NPOIN
   50 WRITE(6,935) IPOIN,(COORD(IPOIN,IDIME),IDIME=1,NDIME)
  935 FORMAT(1X,I5,F10.3)
C
C*** READ THE FIXED VALUES.
C
      WRITE(6,940)
  940 FORMAT(//17H RESTRAINED NODES)
      WRITE(6,945)
  945 FORMAT(5H NODE,1X,4HCODE)
   70 DO 80 IVFIX=1,NVFIX
```

```
      READ(5,950) NOFIX(IVFIX),(IFPRE(IVFIX,IDOFN),IDOFN=1,NDOFN)
   80 WRITE(6,950) NOFIX(IVFIX),(IFPRE(IVFIX,IDOFN),IDOFN=1,NDOFN)
  950 FORMAT(1X,I4,2X,3I1)
C
C*** READ THE AVAILABLE SELECTION OF ELEMENT PROPERTIES.
C
      WRITE(6,960)
  960 FORMAT(//21H  MATERIAL PROPERTIES)
      WRITE(6,965)
  965 FORMAT(8H  NUMBER,7X,10HPROPERTIES)
      DO 100 IMATS=1,NMATS
      READ(5,900)NUMAT
      READ(5,970) (PROPS(NUMAT,IPROP),IPROP=1,5)
  970 FORMAT(5F10.5)
  100 WRITE(6,980) NUMAT,(PROPS(NUMAT,IPROP),IPROP=1,5)
  980 FORMAT(1X,I5,7X,3E14.6/13X,2E14.6)
      RETURN
      END
```

Subroutine STIFFS

```
      SUBROUTINE STIFFS  (COORD,IHARM,LNODS,MATNO,MELEM,
     .                    MEVAB,MMATS,MPOIN,NELEM,NEVAB,
     .                    NNODE,NTYPE,PROPS)
C*********************************************************************
C
C***  EVALUATE STIFFNESS MATRICES
C***  FOR ELASTIC MINDLIN PLATE STRIPS
C
C*********************************************************************
      IMPLICIT REAL*8(A-H,O-Z)
      DIMENSION
     .          COORD(MPOIN,1),ESTIF(6,6),EMASS(6,6),LNODS(MELEM,NNODE),
     .          MATNO(MELEM),PROPS(MMATS,5)
      REWIND 1
      REWIND 7
C
C*** LOOP OVER EACH ELEMENT
C
      DO 80 IELEM=1,NELEM
C
C*** INITIALIZE THE ELEMENT STIFFNESS AND MASS MATRIX
C
      DO 20 IEVAB=1,NEVAB
      DO 20 JEVAB=1,NEVAB
      EMASS(IEVAB,JEVAB)=0.0
   20 ESTIF(IEVAB,JEVAB)=0.0
```

```
C
C*** EVALUATE STIFFNESS MATRIX
C
C
      LPROP=MATNO(IELEM)
      YOUNG=PROPS(LPROP,1)
      POISS=PROPS(LPROP,2)
      THICK=PROPS(LPROP,3)
      DENSE=PROPS(LPROP,4)
      TLENG=PROPS(LPROP,5)
C
C***  CALCULATE LENGTH OF STRIP
C
      NODE1=LNODS(IELEM,1)
      NODE2=LNODS(IELEM,2)
      DLENG=ABS(COORD(NODE2,1)-COORD(NODE1,1))
      GPCOD=0.5*(COORD(NODE1,1)+COORD(NODE2,1))
      PI=DATAN(.1D+01)*.4D+01
      RADIAN=180./PI
      TLANG=TLENG
      IF(NTYPE.EQ.0)TLANG=TLENG/RADIAN
C
C*** EXPLICIT CALCULATION OF STIFFNESS MATRIX
C
      COLPA=FLOAT(IHARM)*PI
      RINVE=1./GPCOD
      IF(NTYPE.EQ.1) RINVE=0
      RALFH=GPCOD*TLANG
      IF(NTYPE.EQ.1) RALFH=TLANG
      COAET=DLENG*YOUNG*THICK*RALFH/(2.*(1.+POISS))
      THIC2=THICK*THICK
      DLEN2=DLENG*DLENG
      COLP2=COLPA*COLPA
      RALF2=RALFH*RALFH
C
C*** UPPER TRIANGULAR PART OF STIFFNESS MATRIX
C
      ESTIF(1,1)=1./(2.4*DLEN2)+COLP2/(RALF2*9.6)
      ESTIF(1,2)=-1./(4.8*DLENG)
      ESTIF(1,3)=COLPA/(9.6*RALFH)
      ESTIF(1,4)=-1./(2.4*DLEN2)+COLP2/(RALF2*9.6)
      ESTIF(1,5)=ESTIF(1,2)
      ESTIF(1,6)=ESTIF(1,3)
      ESTIF(2,2)=THIC2/(12.*DLEN2*(1.-POISS))-
     .          THIC2*POISS*RINVE/(12.*DLENG*(1.-POISS))+
     .          THIC2*RINVE*RINVE/(48.*(1.-POISS))+
     .          THIC2*COLP2/(96.*RALF2)+1./9.6
```

```
      ESTIF(2,3)=-COLPA*THIC2/(RALFH*24.*(1.-POISS))*
     .           ((1.-3.*POISS)/(2.*DLENG)+RINVE*(3.-POISS)/4.)
      ESTIF(2,4)=-ESTIF(1,2)
      ESTIF(2,5)=-THIC2/(12.*DLEN2*(1.-POISS))+
     .           THIC2*RINVE*RINVE/(48.*(1.-POISS))+
     .           THIC2*COLP2/(96.*RALF2)+1./9.6
      ESTIF(2,6)=COLPA*THIC2/(RALFH*24.*(1.-POISS))*
     .           ((1.+POISS)/(2.*DLENG)-RINVE*(3.-POISS)/4.)
      ESTIF(3,3)=THIC2/(24.*DLEN2)+THIC2*RINVE/(24.*DLENG)+
     .           THIC2*COLP2/(48.*RALF2*(1.-POISS))+
     .           THIC2*RINVE*RINVE/96.+1./9.6
      ESTIF(3,4)=COLPA/(9.6*RALFH)
      ESTIF(3,5)=-COLPA*THIC2/(RALFH*24.*(1.-POISS))*
     .           ((1.+POISS)/(2.*DLENG)+RINVE*(3.-POISS)/4.)
      ESTIF(3,6)=-THIC2/(24.*DLEN2)+
     .           THIC2*COLP2/(48.*RALF2*(1.-POISS))+
     .           THIC2*RINVE*RINVE/96.+1./9.6
      ESTIF(4,4)=ESTIF(1,1)
      ESTIF(4,5)=-ESTIF(1,2)
      ESTIF(4,6)=ESTIF(1,3)
      ESTIF(5,5)=THIC2/(12.*DLEN2*(1.-POISS))+
     .           THIC2*POISS*RINVE/(12.*DLENG*(1.-POISS))+
     .           THIC2*RINVE*RINVE/(48.*(1.-POISS))+
     .           THIC2*COLP2/(96.*RALF2)+1./9.6
      ESTIF(5,6)=+COLPA*THIC2/(RALFH*24.*(1.-POISS))*
     .           ((1.-3.*POISS)/(2.*DLENG)-RINVE*(3.-POISS)/4.)
      ESTIF(6,6)=THIC2/(24.*DLEN2)-THIC2*RINVE/(24.*DLENG)+
     .           THIC2*COLP2/(48.*RALF2*(1.-POISS))+
     .           THIC2*RINVE*RINVE/96.+1./9.6
C
C*** USE SYMMETRY TO EVALUATE WHOLE MATRIX
C
      DO 30 I=1,6
      DO 30 J=I,6
      ESTIF(I,J)=ESTIF(I,J)*COAET
      ESTIF(J,I)=ESTIF(I,J)
   30 CONTINUE
C
C*** CALCULATE DIAGONAL MASS MATRIX
C
      IF(NTYPE.EQ.1) AMIN=TLANG
      IF(NTYPE.EQ.0.) AMIN=GPCOD*TLANG
      XMAS1=0.5*DLENG*THICK*DENSE*
     .AMIN*0.5
      XMAS2=XMAS1*THICK**2./12.
C
      EMASS(1,1)=XMAS1
```

```
      EMASS(2,2)=XMAS2
      EMASS(3,3)=XMAS2
      EMASS(4,4)=XMAS1
      EMASS(5,5)=XMAS2
      EMASS(6,6)=XMAS2
C
C*** STORE THE STIFFNESS AND MASS MATRIX ON DISC FILE
C
      WRITE(1) ESTIF
      WRITE(7) EMASS
   80 CONTINUE
      RETURN
      END
```

Subroutine BERKEL

```
      SUBROUTINE BERKEL (A,AR,B,BR,BS,BUP,BLO,BUPC,D,ER,EIGV,
     .                   ID,IFPRE,LM,LNODS,MHT,MAXA,MAHAM,MAXNN,MANNM,
     .                   MITEV,MDISV,MNEBS,MPOIN,MELEM,MVFIX,NMODE,
     .                   NPOIN,NEQ,NVFIX,NOFIX,NDOFN,NELEM,NEVAB,
     .                   NNODE,RTOLV,S,TT,VEC,W)
C**********************************************************************
C
C*** INTERFACE ROUTINE FOR BERKELEY SOLVER AND SUBSPACE ITERATION
C
C**********************************************************************
      IMPLICIT REAL*8(A-H,O-Z)
C
      DIMENSION ESTIF(6,6),EMASS(6,6),
     .          IFPRE(MVFIX,NDOFN),LNODS(MELEM,2),NOFIX(MVFIX)
      DIMENSION A(MNEBS),AR(MDISV),B(MNEBS),BR(MDISV),BS(MAHAM),
     .          BUP(MITEV),BLO(MITEV),BUPC(MITEV),D(MITEV),
     .          ER(MAXNN,MITEV),EIGV(MITEV),ID(NDOFN,MPOIN),
     .          LM( 6,MELEM),MHT(MAXNN),MAXA(MANNM),RTOLV(MITEV),
     .          S(MAHAM),TT(MAXNN),VEC(MITEV,MITEV),W(MAXNN)
      DATA IOUT/3/,NSTIF/8/,NITEM/16/,RTOL/0.000001/
      REWIND 1
      REWIND 7
      NROOT=NMODE
C
C***  CREATION OF ID ARRAY
C
      DO 10 IPOIN=1,NPOIN
      DO 20 IVFIX=1,NVFIX
      IF(IPOIN.NE.NOFIX(IVFIX)) GO TO 20
      DO 30 IDOFN=1,NDOFN
   30 D(IDOFN,IPOIN)=IFPRE(IVFIX,IDOFN)
```

```
      GO TO 11
   20 CONTINUE
      DO 40 IDOFN=1,NDOFN
   40 ID(IDOFN,IPOIN)=0
   11 CONTINUE
   10 CONTINUE
C
C***  NUMBER OF UNKNOWNS
C
      NEQ=0
      DO 100 IPOIN=1,NPOIN
      DO 60 IDOFN=1,NDOFN
      IF(ID(IDOFN,IPOIN)) 110,120,110
  120 NEQ=NEQ+1
      ID(IDOFN,IPOIN)=NEQ
      GO TO 60
  110 ID(IDOFN,IPOIN)=0
 60   CONTINUE
  100 CONTINUE
C
C***  ZERO A AND B
C
      DO 65 INEBS=1,MNEBS
      A(INEBS)=0.0
      B(INEBS)=0.0
   65 CONTINUE
C
C***  CONNECTIVITY ARRAY LM
C
      DO 50 IELEM=1,NELEM
      DO 70 IEVAB=1,NEVAB
   70 LM(IEVAB,IELEM)=0
      IEVAB=1
      DO 80 INODE=1,NNODE
      IDENT=LNODS(IELEM,INODE)
      DO 80 IDOFN=1,NDOFN
      LM(IEVAB,IELEM)=ID(IDOFN,IDENT)
   80 IEVAB=IEVAB+1
   50 CONTINUE
C
C***  LOOP OVER ALL ELEMENTS
C
      DO 90 IELEM=1,NELEM
      CALL COLHT(MHT,NEVAB,LM(1,IELEM))
   90 CONTINUE
C
C***  ADDRESES OF DIAGONAL ELEMENTS - MAXA ARRAY
```

```
C
      CALL ADDRES(MAXA,MHT,NEQ,NWK,MK)
C
C*** REWRITING OF ELEMENT STIFFNESS, ELEMENT MASS MATRIX AND
C*** GEOMETRIC STIFFNESS MATRIX IN VECTOR FORM
C
      DO 200 IELEM=1,NELEM
      READ(1) ESTIF
      READ(7) EMASS
  140 KOUNT=1
      DO 145 IEVAB=1,NEVAB
      DO 145 JEVAB=IEVAB,NEVAB
      S(KOUNT)=ESTIF(IEVAB,JEVAB)
      BS(KOUNT)=EMASS(IEVAB,JEVAB)
  145 KOUNT=KOUNT+1
C
C***  COMPACTED GLOBAL STIFFNESS MATRIX
C
  170 CALL ADDBAN(A,MAXA,S,LM(1,IELEM),NEVAB)
C
C***  COMPACTED GLOBAL MASS MATRIX
C
      CALL ADDBAN(B,MAXA,BS,LM(1,IELEM),NEVAB)
  200 CONTINUE
C
C***  PARAMETERS FOR SUBSPACE ITERATION
C
      NNM=1+NEQ
      NWM=NWK
      NN=NEQ
      READ(5,9)  IFSS,IFPR
    9 FORMAT(16I5)
      WRITE(6,3) IFSS,IFPR
    3 FORMAT(//,1X,20H*STURM SEQUENCE FLAG,I5,21H*ITERATION PRINT FLAG,
     .      I5)
      NC=2*NROOT
      NC2=NROOT+8
      IF(NC.GT.NC2) NC=NC2
      NNC=NC*(NC+1)/2
C
C***  SUBSPACE ITERATION
C
      CALL SSPACE (A,B,MAXA,ER,EIGV,TT,W,AR,BR,VEC,D,RTOLV,BUP,
     .BLO,BUPC,NN,NNM,NWK,NWM,NROOT,RTOL,NC,NNC,NITEM,IFSS,
     .IFPR,NSTIF,IOUT)
C
C***  EXIT OF SUBSPACE
```

```
C
      RETURN
      END
```

Subroutine OUTFS

```
      SUBROUTINE OUTFS (AD,D,EIGV,ID,IHARM,MPOIN,MAXNN,MITEV,NDOFN,
     .                  NMODE,NEQ,NPOIN,R)
C***********************************************************************
C
C*** OUTPUTS THE RESULTS FOR MINDLIN STRIPS
C
C***********************************************************************
      IMPLICIT REAL*8(A-H,O-Z)
C
      DIMENSION AD(NDOFN,MPOIN),D(MITEV),EIGV(MITEV),ID(NDOFN,MPOIN),
     .          R(MAXNN,MITEV)
C
      REWIND 4
C
      READ(4,100)(EIGV(I),I=1,NMODE)
  100 FORMAT(1H0,6E22.14)
      DO 10 J=1,NMODE
   10 READ(4,110)(R(K,J),K=1,NEQ)
  110 FORMAT(1H ,12E11.4)
      READ(4,100)(D(I),I=1,NMODE)
      WRITE(6,120) IHARM
  120 FORMAT(///,1X,'THE CALCULATED VALUES FOR HARMONIC',I4,' ARE')
      WRITE(6,125)
  125 FORMAT(/,4X,'EIGENVALUES',5X,'FREQUENCIES',6X,'ERROR NORMS',/)
      DO 15 I=1,NMODE
      FREQ=SQRT(EIGV(I))
   15 WRITE(6,130)EIGV(I),FREQ,D(I)
  130 FORMAT(1X,3E16.7)
   26 WRITE(6,140)
  140 FORMAT(//,1X,'THE CALCULATED MODES ARE')
C
      DO 30 IMODE=1,NMODE
      DO 40 IPOIN=1,NPOIN
      DO 50 IDOFN=1,NDOFN
      IF(ID(IDOFN,IPOIN)) 60,70,60
   70 AD(IDOFN,IPOIN)=0.0
      GO TO 80
   60 M=ID(IDOFN,IPOIN)
      AD(IDOFN,IPOIN)=R(M,IMODE)
   80 CONTINUE
   50 CONTINUE
```

```
   40 CONTINUE
C
      WRITE(6,150)IMODE
  150 FORMAT(/,6H MODE=I3)
      WRITE(6,170)
  170 FORMAT(/,12X,'W',8X,'THETA-X',5X,'THETA-Y',/)
      DO 90 IPOIN=1,NPOIN
   90 WRITE(6,160)IPOIN,(AD(IDOFN,IPOIN),IDOFN=1,NDOFN)
  160 FORMAT(1X,I5,3E12.4)
   30 CONTINUE
      REWIND 4
      RETURN
      END
```

5.10 Sample solutions

We now present two examples which show the applicability of the strip formulation used in program FIST for the free vibration analysis of plates.

5.10.1 Example 1: Square plate with three simply supported edges and one clamped edge

In this first example a square plate is analysed. The plate is simply supported on three edges and has the fourth edge clamped. The geometry of the plate and material properties are shown in Figure 5.1.

Twenty linear strips were used for this analysis as shown in the same figure. The modal amplitudes and natural frequencies for the first mode and the first three harmonic terms are also presented in Figure 5.1 where numerical results for the natural frequencies obtained in Reference 16 are also shown. Good agreement between both sets of results is obtained. Input data according to the input instructions of Section 5.8 are listed in Figure 5.2. Figure 5.3 contains a listing of output obtained from the program.

5.10.2 Example 2: Simply supported triangular plate with circular curved edge

The second example analyzed is a triangular plate with a circular curved edge. The plate is simply supported on the three edges. The problem is analysed with the curved plate formulation. The geometric and material properties of the plate are shown in Figure 5.4.

Twenty linear strips were again used in this analysis. Figure 5.4 also shows a plot of the modal amplitudes for the first three harmonic terms N = 1 to 3 of the first vibration modes with M = 1 together with the corresponding natural frequencies. Input and output for this problem are listed in Figures 5.5 and 5.6 respectively.

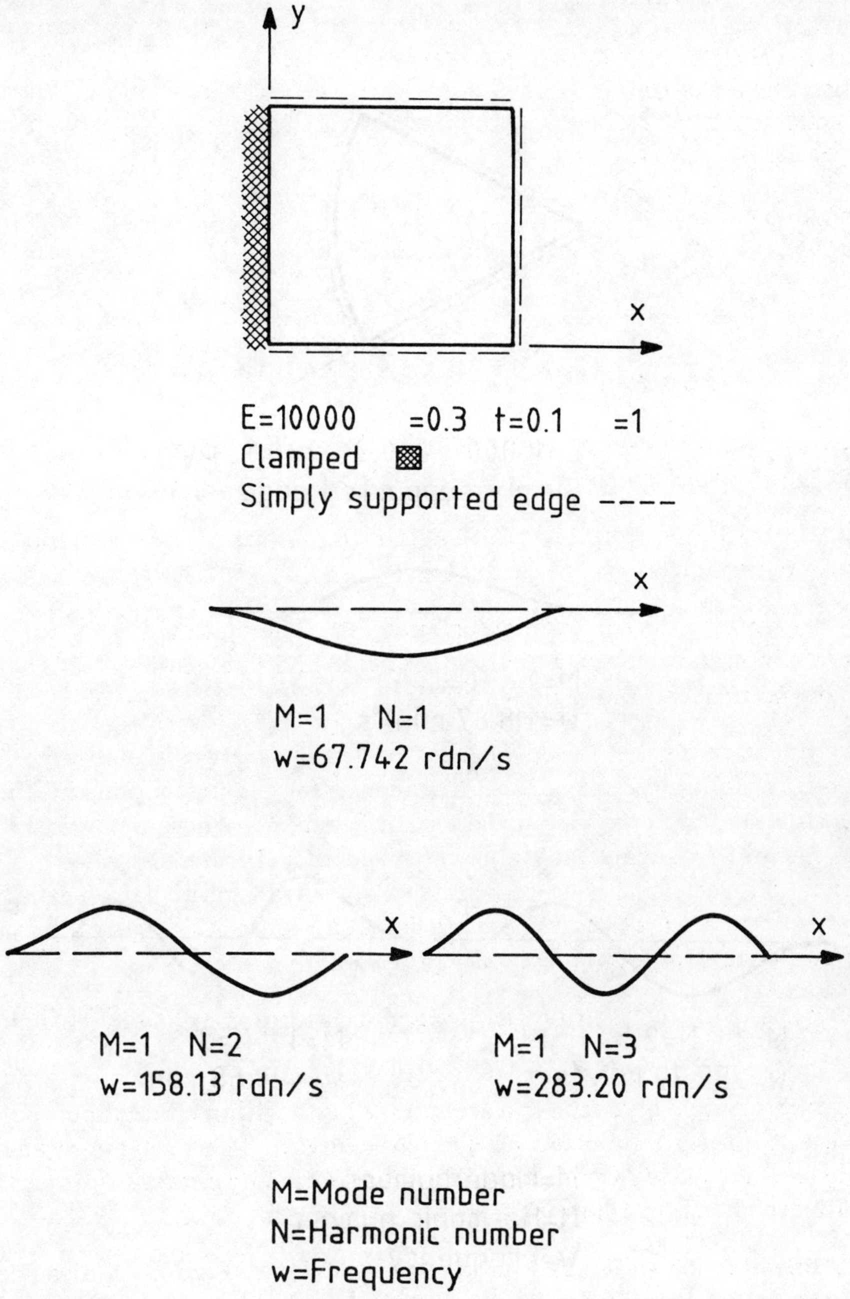

Figure 5.1 Example 1 – Square plate with three simply supported edges and one edge clamped – various modes and frequencies

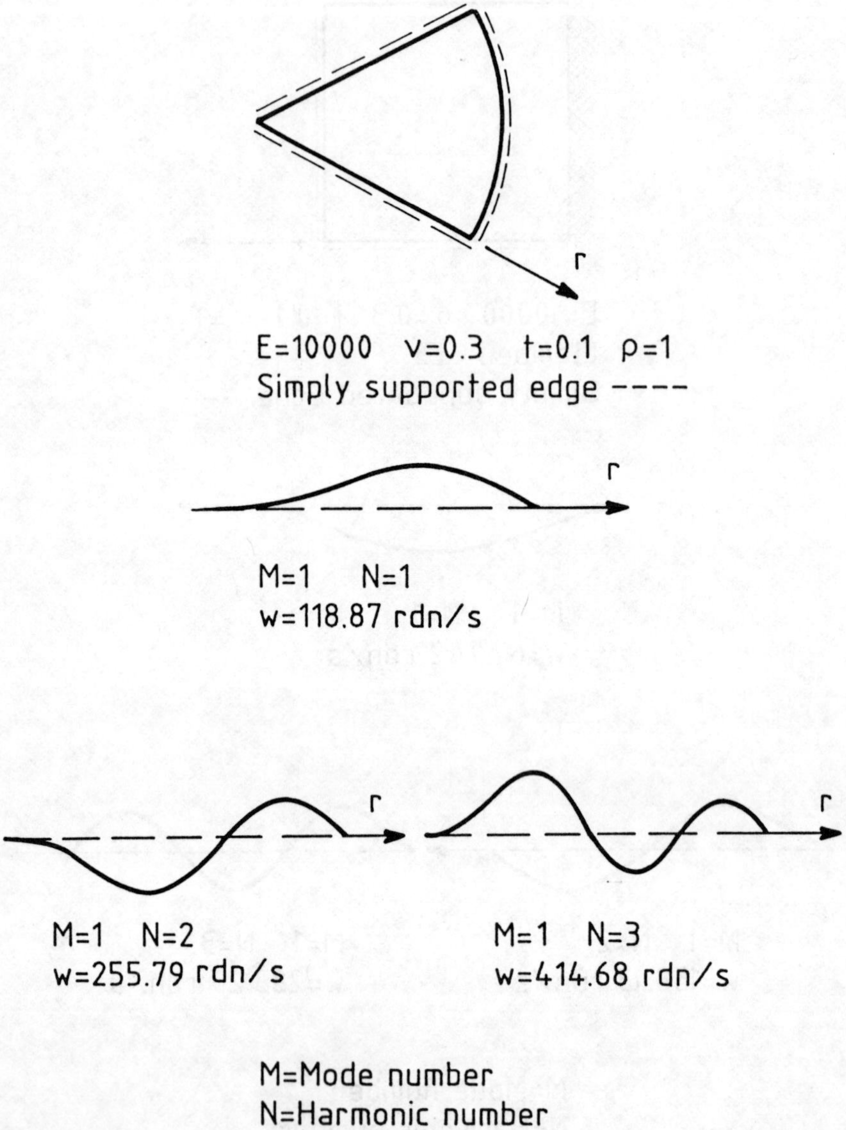

Figure 5.4 Example 2 – Simply supported triangular plate with curved edge – various modes and frequencies

```
SQUARE PLATE WITH THREE SIMPLY SUPPORTED EDGES AND ONE CLAMPED EDGE
21   20    2    1    3    3    1
 1    1    1    2
 2    1    2    3
 3    1    3    4
 4    1    4    5
 5    1    5    6
 6    1    6    7
 7    1    7    8
 8    1    8    9
 9    1    9   10
10    1   10   11
11    1   11   12
12    1   12   13
13    1   13   14
14    1   14   15
15    1   15   16
16    1   16   17
17    1   17   18
18    1   18   19
19    1   19   20
20    1   20   21
  1 0.0
  2 0.05
  3 0.1
  4 0.15
  5 0.2
  6 0.25
  7 0.3
  8 0.35
  9 0.4
 10 0.45
 11 0.5
 12 0.55
 13 0.6
 14 0.65
 15 0.7
 16 0.75
 17 0.8
 18 0.85
 19 0.9
 20 0.95
 21 1.0
  1  111
 21  101
  1
10000.        0.3        0.1        1.0        1.0
```

Figure 5.2 Input data for Example 1

```
0   1
0   1
0   1
```

Figure 5.2 Input data for Example 1

```
 SQUARE PLATE WITH THREE SIMPLY SUPPORTED EDGES AND ONE CLAMPED EDGE
NPOIN =  21      NELEM =  20      NVFIX =   2      NMATS =   1
NMODE =   3      NHARM =   3      NTYPE =   1
ELEM.  MAT.SET  NODE NUMBERS
  1        1     1   2
  2        1     2   3
  3        1     3   4
  4        1     4   5
  5        1     5   6
  6        1     6   7
  7        1     7   8
  8        1     8   9
  9        1     9  10
 10        1    10  11
 11        1    11  12
 12        1    12  13
 13        1    13  14
 14        1    14  15
 15        1    15  16
 16        1    16  17
 17        1    17  18
 18        1    18  19
 19        1    19  20
 20        1    20  21
 NODAL POINT COORDINATES
 NODE        X           Y
    1      0.000
    2      0.050
    3      0.100
    4      0.150
    5      0.200
    6      0.250
    7      0.300
    8      0.350
    9      0.400
   10      0.450
   11      0.500
   12      0.550
   13      0.600
   14      0.650
```

Figure 5.3 Output data for Example 1

```
   15      0.700
   16      0.750
   17      0.800
   18      0.850
   19      0.900
   20      0.950
   21      1.000
RESTRAINED NODES
NODE CODE
   1  111
  21  101
 MATERIAL PROPERTIES
 NUMBER        PROPERTIES
    1          0.100000E+05  0.300000E+00  0.100000E+00
               0.100000E+01  0.100000E+01
*STURM SEQUENCE FLAG     0*ITERATION PRINT FLAG     1
THE CALCULATED VALUES FOR HARMONIC    1 ARE
   EIGENVALUES       FREQUENCIES       ERROR NORMS
   0.4589039E+04    0.6774245E+02    0.5835842E-11
   0.2500413E+05    0.1581269E+03    0.3029301E-07
   0.8020451E+05    0.2832040E+03    0.4081971E-05
THE CALCULATED MODES ARE
MODE=  1
            W          THETA-X       THETA-Y
    1  0.0000E+00  0.0000E+00  0.0000E+00
    2  0.2747E+00 -0.6374E+01 -0.1649E+01
    3  0.8187E+00 -0.1098E+02 -0.3143E+01
    4  0.1546E+01 -0.1398E+02 -0.5118E+01
    5  0.2379E+01 -0.1556E+02 -0.7439E+01
    6  0.3253E+01 -0.1591E+02 -0.9911E+01
    7  0.4108E+01 -0.1518E+02 -0.1235E+02
    8  0.4893E+01 -0.1354E+02 -0.1461E+02
    9  0.5566E+01 -0.1114E+02 -0.1655E+02
   10  0.6091E+01 -0.8125E+01 -0.1806E+02
   11  0.6440E+01 -0.4666E+01 -0.1906E+02
   12  0.6595E+01 -0.9169E+00 -0.1950E+02
   13  0.6546E+01  0.2963E+01 -0.1934E+02
   14  0.6289E+01  0.6820E+01 -0.1857E+02
   15  0.5830E+01  0.1051E+02 -0.1721E+02
   16  0.5183E+01  0.1388E+02 -0.1530E+02
   17  0.4366E+01  0.1683E+02 -0.1288E+02
   18  0.3407E+01  0.1924E+02 -0.1005E+02
   19  0.2336E+01  0.2102E+02 -0.6891E+01
   20  0.1187E+01  0.2211E+02 -0.3503E+01
   21  0.0000E+00  0.2248E+02  0.0000E+00
MODE=  2
            W          THETA-X       THETA-Y
```

Figure 5.3 Output data for Example 1

```
    1  0.0000E+00  0.0000E+00  0.0000E+00
    2 -0.8108E+00  0.1489E+02  0.4095E+01
    3 -0.2166E+01  0.2270E+02  0.7385E+01
    4 -0.3704E+01  0.2407E+02  0.1110E+02
    5 -0.5107E+01  0.1999E+02  0.1456E+02
    6 -0.6113E+01  0.1178E+02  0.1706E+02
    7 -0.6541E+01  0.9678E+00  0.1806E+02
    8 -0.6296E+01 -0.1080E+02  0.1729E+02
    9 -0.5376E+01 -0.2186E+02  0.1472E+02
   10 -0.3870E+01 -0.3075E+02  0.1059E+02
   11 -0.1939E+01 -0.3629E+02  0.5325E+01
   12  0.1994E+00 -0.3774E+02 -0.4890E+00
   13  0.2300E+01 -0.3489E+02 -0.6194E+01
   14  0.4120E+01 -0.2802E+02 -0.1113E+02
   15  0.5449E+01 -0.1792E+02 -0.1474E+02
   16  0.6134E+01 -0.5749E+01 -0.1660E+02
   17  0.6094E+01  0.7068E+01 -0.1650E+02
   18  0.5336E+01  0.1903E+02 -0.1445E+02
   19  0.3950E+01  0.2875E+02 -0.1070E+02
   20  0.2098E+01  0.3508E+02 -0.5682E+01
   21  0.0000E+00  0.3727E+02  0.0000E+00
MODE=   3
           W          THETA-X     THETA-Y
    1  0.0000E+00  0.0000E+00  0.0000E+00
    2 -0.1603E+01  0.2242E+02  0.6757E+01
    3 -0.3796E+01  0.2786E+02  0.1129E+02
    4 -0.5673E+01  0.1906E+02  0.1504E+02
    5 -0.6542E+01  0.9548E+00  0.1662E+02
    6 -0.6046E+01 -0.2028E+02  0.1510E+02
    7 -0.4218E+01 -0.3836E+02  0.1050E+02
    8 -0.1450E+01 -0.4817E+02  0.3701E+01
    9  0.1617E+01 -0.4687E+02 -0.3764E+01
   10  0.4251E+01 -0.3453E+02 -0.1016E+02
   11  0.5821E+01 -0.1401E+02 -0.1397E+02
   12  0.5951E+01  0.9780E+01 -0.1430E+02
   13  0.4614E+01  0.3107E+02 -0.1109E+02
   14  0.2141E+01  0.4467E+02 -0.5145E+01
   15 -0.8594E+00  0.4730E+02  0.2078E+01
   16 -0.3652E+01  0.3830E+02  0.8801E+01
   17 -0.5551E+01  0.1991E+02  0.1337E+02
   18 -0.6090E+01 -0.3371E+01  0.1467E+02
   19 -0.5138E+01 -0.2583E+02  0.1238E+02
   20 -0.2928E+01 -0.4197E+02  0.7053E+01
   21  0.0000E+00 -0.4783E+02  0.0000E+00
*STURM SEQUENCE FLAG     0*ITERATION PRINT FLAG     1
THE CALCULATED VALUES FOR HARMONIC    2 ARE
   EIGENVALUES      FREQUENCIES      ERROR NORMS
```

Figure 5.3 Output data for Example 1

```
   0.2023030E+05   0.1422333E+03   0.7349236E-08
   0.4991246E+05   0.2234110E+03   0.6178890E-06
   0.1155003E+06   0.3398534E+03   0.2455628E-04
THE CALCULATED MODES ARE
MODE=  1
            W          THETA-X      THETA-Y
     1  0.0000E+00  0.0000E+00  0.0000E+00
     2  0.3950E+00 -0.7210E+01 -0.3808E+01
     3  0.1065E+01 -0.1174E+02 -0.7072E+01
     4  0.1885E+01 -0.1410E+02 -0.1116E+02
     5  0.2765E+01 -0.1487E+02 -0.1572E+02
     6  0.3635E+01 -0.1446E+02 -0.2032E+02
     7  0.4444E+01 -0.1315E+02 -0.2466E+02
     8  0.5151E+01 -0.1116E+02 -0.2848E+02
     9  0.5725E+01 -0.8653E+01 -0.3159E+02
    10  0.6141E+01 -0.5770E+01 -0.3386E+02
    11  0.6385E+01 -0.2643E+01 -0.3518E+02
    12  0.6445E+01  0.6093E+00 -0.3550E+02
    13  0.6318E+01  0.3874E+01 -0.3480E+02
    14  0.6008E+01  0.7043E+01 -0.3308E+02
    15  0.5521E+01  0.1002E+02 -0.3040E+02
    16  0.4873E+01  0.1270E+02 -0.2683E+02
    17  0.4082E+01  0.1502E+02 -0.2248E+02
    18  0.3172E+01  0.1690E+02 -0.1746E+02
    19  0.2168E+01  0.1829E+02 -0.1193E+02
    20  0.1100E+01  0.1913E+02 -0.6056E+01
    21  0.0000E+00  0.1942E+02  0.0000E+00
MODE=  2
            W          THETA-X      THETA-Y
     1  0.0000E+00  0.0000E+00  0.0000E+00
     2 -0.9614E+00  0.1494E+02  0.8305E+01
     3 -0.2415E+01  0.2184E+02  0.1473E+02
     4 -0.3958E+01  0.2195E+02  0.2168E+02
     5 -0.5272E+01  0.1697E+02  0.2780E+02
     6 -0.6126E+01  0.8498E+01  0.3180E+02
     7 -0.6371E+01 -0.1873E+01  0.3284E+02
     8 -0.5950E+01 -0.1260E+02  0.3057E+02
     9 -0.4893E+01 -0.2226E+02  0.2509E+02
    10 -0.3304E+01 -0.2964E+02  0.1694E+02
    11 -0.1357E+01 -0.3383E+02  0.6967E+01
    12  0.7364E+00 -0.3431E+02 -0.3735E+01
    13  0.2744E+01 -0.3100E+02 -0.1399E+02
    14  0.4443E+01 -0.2425E+02 -0.2267E+02
    15  0.5644E+01 -0.1482E+02 -0.2881E+02
    16  0.6215E+01 -0.3732E+01 -0.3172E+02
    17  0.6090E+01  0.7764E+01 -0.3109E+02
    18  0.5286E+01  0.1839E+02 -0.2698E+02
```

Figure 5.3 Output data for Example 1

```
    19  0.3890E+01  0.2696E+02 -0.1986E+02
    20  0.2060E+01  0.3251E+02 -0.1052E+02
    21  0.0000E+00  0.3444E+02  0.0000E+00
MODE=   3
             W          THETA-X      THETA-Y
     1  0.0000E+00  0.0000E+00  0.0000E+00
     2 -0.1729E+01  0.2146E+02  0.1299E+02
     3 -0.3940E+01  0.2565E+02  0.2145E+02
     4 -0.5710E+01  0.1610E+02  0.2812E+02
     5 -0.6395E+01 -0.1677E+01  0.3040E+02
     6 -0.5706E+01 -0.2151E+02  0.2676E+02
     7 -0.3740E+01 -0.3757E+02  0.1748E+02
     8 -0.9279E+00 -0.4540E+02  0.4446E+01
     9  0.2078E+01 -0.4280E+02 -0.9408E+01
    10  0.4571E+01 -0.3019E+02 -0.2087E+02
    11  0.5961E+01 -0.1049E+02 -0.2726E+02
    12  0.5917E+01  0.1165E+02 -0.2708E+02
    13  0.4454E+01  0.3095E+02 -0.2039E+02
    14  0.1923E+01  0.4282E+02 -0.8800E+01
    15 -0.1070E+01  0.4442E+02  0.4903E+01
    16 -0.3807E+01  0.3537E+02  0.1744E+02
    17 -0.5633E+01  0.1785E+02  0.2580E+02
    18 -0.6109E+01 -0.3950E+01  0.2798E+02
    19 -0.5123E+01 -0.2481E+02  0.2346E+02
    20 -0.2910E+01 -0.3972E+02  0.1333E+02
    21  0.0000E+00 -0.4512E+02  0.0000E+00
*STURM SEQUENCE FLAG      0*ITERATION PRINT FLAG      1
THE CALCULATED VALUES FOR HARMONIC    3 ARE
   EIGENVALUES        FREQUENCIES        ERROR NORMS
   0.6716433E+05    0.2591608E+03    0.1202370E-06
   0.1076781E+06    0.3281434E+03    0.1635319E-05
   0.1859471E+06    0.4312158E+03    0.3543894E-04
THE CALCULATED MODES ARE
MODE=   1
             W          THETA-X      THETA-Y
     1  0.0000E+00  0.0000E+00  0.0000E+00
     2  0.5110E+00 -0.7445E+01 -0.5945E+01
     3  0.1278E+01 -0.1155E+02 -0.1083E+02
     4  0.2151E+01 -0.1320E+02 -0.1670E+02
     5  0.3038E+01 -0.1333E+02 -0.2295E+02
     6  0.3879E+01 -0.1247E+02 -0.2903E+02
     7  0.4635E+01 -0.1096E+02 -0.3456E+02
     8  0.5273E+01 -0.8976E+01 -0.3925E+02
     9  0.5772E+01 -0.6660E+01 -0.4294E+02
    10  0.6115E+01 -0.4116E+01 -0.4548E+02
    11  0.6292E+01 -0.1435E+01 -0.4678E+02
    12  0.6297E+01  0.1298E+01 -0.4682E+02
```

Figure 5.3 Output data for Example 1

13	0.6129E+01	0.4002E+01	-0.4557E+02
14	0.5794E+01	0.6599E+01	-0.4307E+02
15	0.5299E+01	0.9016E+01	-0.3939E+02
16	0.4658E+01	0.1119E+02	-0.3463E+02
17	0.3890E+01	0.1305E+02	-0.2892E+02
18	0.3015E+01	0.1456E+02	-0.2241E+02
19	0.2057E+01	0.1566E+02	-0.1529E+02
20	0.1043E+01	0.1634E+02	-0.7753E+01
21	0.0000E+00	0.1657E+02	0.0000E+00

MODE= 2

	W	THETA-X	THETA-Y
1	0.0000E+00	0.0000E+00	0.0000E+00
2	-0.1126E+01	0.1453E+02	0.1215E+02
3	-0.2671E+01	0.2036E+02	0.2123E+02
4	-0.4203E+01	0.1938E+02	0.3067E+02
5	-0.5422E+01	0.1388E+02	0.3852E+02
6	-0.6130E+01	0.5643E+01	0.4312E+02
7	-0.6216E+01	-0.3824E+01	0.4354E+02
8	-0.5654E+01	-0.1320E+02	0.3953E+02
9	-0.4494E+01	-0.2132E+02	0.3140E+02
10	-0.2857E+01	-0.2724E+02	0.1996E+02
11	-0.9166E+00	-0.3028E+02	0.6406E+01
12	0.1121E+01	-0.3009E+02	-0.7818E+01
13	0.3039E+01	-0.2669E+02	-0.2120E+02
14	0.4630E+01	-0.2043E+02	-0.3230E+02
15	0.5724E+01	-0.1198E+02	-0.3993E+02
16	0.6205E+01	-0.2254E+01	-0.4329E+02
17	0.6021E+01	0.7716E+01	-0.4200E+02
18	0.5191E+01	0.1686E+02	-0.3621E+02
19	0.3804E+01	0.2419E+02	-0.2654E+02
20	0.2010E+01	0.2893E+02	-0.1402E+02
21	0.0000E+00	0.3057E+02	0.0000E+00

MODE= 3

	W	THETA-X	THETA-Y
1	0.0000E+00	0.0000E+00	0.0000E+00
2	-0.1878E+01	0.2011E+02	0.1824E+02
3	-0.4107E+01	0.2305E+02	0.2975E+02
4	-0.5759E+01	0.1302E+02	0.3838E+02
5	-0.6250E+01	-0.3903E+01	0.4054E+02
6	-0.5369E+01	-0.2179E+02	0.3449E+02
7	-0.3276E+01	-0.3550E+02	0.2099E+02
8	-0.4376E+00	-0.4135E+02	0.2880E+01
9	0.2493E+01	-0.3773E+02	-0.1575E+02
10	0.4835E+01	-0.2539E+02	-0.3063E+02
11	0.6042E+01	-0.7160E+01	-0.3830E+02
12	0.5835E+01	0.1272E+02	-0.3699E+02
13	0.4261E+01	0.2962E+02	-0.2701E+02

Figure 5.3 Output data for Example 1

```
14  0.1689E+01  0.3957E+02 -0.1071E+02
15 -0.1278E+01  0.4026E+02  0.8102E+01
16 -0.3946E+01  0.3153E+02  0.2502E+02
17 -0.5690E+01  0.1541E+02  0.3608E+02
18 -0.6103E+01 -0.4310E+01  0.3869E+02
19 -0.5087E+01 -0.2302E+02  0.3225E+02
20 -0.2881E+01 -0.3635E+02  0.1826E+02
21  0.0000E+00 -0.4117E+02  0.0000E+00
```

Figure 5.3 Output from Example 1

```
  TRIANGULAR PLATE PROBLEM
21    20    2    1    3    3    0
 1     1    1    2
 2     1    2    3
 3     1    3    4
 4     1    4    5
 5     1    5    6
 6     1    6    7
 7     1    7    8
 8     1    8    9
 9     1    9   10
10     1   10   11
11     1   11   12
12     1   12   13
13     1   13   14
14     1   14   15
15     1   15   16
16     1   16   17
17     1   17   18
18     1   18   19
19     1   19   20
20     1   20   21
 1 0.0
 2 0.05
 3 0.1
 4 0.15
 5 0.2
 6 0.25
 7 0.3
 8 0.35
 9 0.4
10 0.45
11 0.5
12 0.55
13 0.6
```

Figure 5.5 Input data for Example 2

```
   14 0.65
   15 0.7
   16 0.75
   17 0.8
   18 0.85
   19 0.9
   20 0.95
   21 1.0
    1  111
   21  101
    1
 10000.        0.3        0.1        1.0        57.2958
    0    1
    0    1
    0    1
```

Figure 5.5 Input for Example 2

```
    TRIANGULAR PLATE PROBLEM
NPOIN =  21       NELEM =  20       NVFIX =    2       NMATS =    1
NMODE =   3       NHARM =   3       NTYPE =   0
ELEM.  MAT.SET  NODE NUMBERS
  1        1      1    2
  2        1      2    3
  3        1      3    4
  4        1      4    5
  5        1      5    6
  6        1      6    7
  7        1      7    8
  8        1      8    9
  9        1      9   10
 10        1     10   11
 11        1     11   12
 12        1     12   13
 13        1     13   14
 14        1     14   15
 15        1     15   16
 16        1     16   17
 17        1     17   18
 18        1     18   19
 19        1     19   20
 20        1     20   21
 NODAL POINT COORDINATES
 NODE        X          Y
   1       0.000
   2       0.050
```

Figure 5.6 Output for Example 2

```
   3      0.100
   4      0.150
   5      0.200
   6      0.250
   7      0.300
   8      0.350
   9      0.400
  10      0.450
  11      0.500
  12      0.550
  13      0.600
  14      0.650
  15      0.700
  16      0.750
  17      0.800
  18      0.850
  19      0.900
  20      0.950
  21      1.000
RESTRAINED NODES
NODE CODE
   1  111
  21  101
 MATERIAL PROPERTIES
 NUMBER        PROPERTIES
   1           0.100000E+05  0.300000E+00  0.100000E+00
               0.100000E+01  0.572958E+02
*STURM SEQUENCE FLAG     0*ITERATION PRINT FLAG     1
THE CALCULATED VALUES FOR HARMONIC   1 ARE
   EIGENVALUES      FREQUENCIES       ERROR NORMS
   0.1413010E+05   0.1188701E+03   0.1302930E-12
   0.6542949E+05   0.2557919E+03   0.6378819E-08
   0.1719600E+06   0.4146806E+03   0.8776808E-05
THE CALCULATED MODES ARE
MODE=  1
            W          THETA-X      THETA-Y
    1  0.0000E+00  0.0000E+00  0.0000E+00
    2  0.1333E-02 -0.3532E+00 -0.2902E+00
    3  0.6681E-01 -0.2166E+01 -0.2250E+01
    4  0.2696E+00 -0.5200E+01 -0.5389E+01
    5  0.6654E+00 -0.9061E+01 -0.9669E+01
    6  0.1288E+01 -0.1328E+02 -0.1477E+02
    7  0.2141E+01 -0.1730E+02 -0.2031E+02
    8  0.3197E+01 -0.2051E+02 -0.2588E+02
    9  0.4396E+01 -0.2238E+02 -0.3105E+02
   10  0.5650E+01 -0.2248E+02 -0.3540E+02
   11  0.6855E+01 -0.2056E+02 -0.3859E+02
```

Figure 5.6 Output for Example 2

12	0.7895E+01	-0.1656E+02	-0.4036E+02
13	0.8658E+01	-0.1064E+02	-0.4053E+02
14	0.9048E+01	-0.3174E+01	-0.3905E+02
15	0.8993E+01	0.5299E+01	-0.3600E+02
16	0.8457E+01	0.1410E+02	-0.3155E+02
17	0.7442E+01	0.2249E+02	-0.2598E+02
18	0.5992E+01	0.2975E+02	-0.1962E+02
19	0.4189E+01	0.3524E+02	-0.1286E+02
20	0.2147E+01	0.3847E+02	-0.6121E+01
21	0.0000E+00	0.3917E+02	0.0000E+00

MODE= 2

	W	THETA-X	THETA-Y
1	0.0000E+00	0.0000E+00	0.0000E+00
2	-0.5439E-02	0.1513E+01	0.1231E+01
3	-0.2955E+00	0.8438E+01	0.8832E+01
4	-0.1134E+01	0.1851E+02	0.1997E+02
5	-0.2615E+01	0.2855E+02	0.3339E+02
6	-0.4636E+01	0.3531E+02	0.4667E+02
7	-0.6899E+01	0.3600E+02	0.5742E+02
8	-0.8971E+01	0.2912E+02	0.6369E+02
9	-0.1038E+02	0.1496E+02	0.6426E+02
10	-0.1072E+02	-0.4402E+01	0.5886E+02
11	-0.9786E+01	-0.2543E+02	0.4822E+02
12	-0.7591E+01	-0.4393E+02	0.3391E+02
13	-0.4424E+01	-0.5595E+02	0.1801E+02
14	-0.7839E+00	-0.5871E+02	0.2809E+01
15	0.2710E+01	-0.5125E+02	-0.9677E+01
16	0.5446E+01	-0.3474E+02	-0.1798E+02
17	0.6947E+01	-0.1224E+02	-0.2141E+02
18	0.6972E+01	0.1188E+02	-0.2014E+02
19	0.5570E+01	0.3292E+02	-0.1509E+02
20	0.3067E+01	0.4683E+02	-0.7729E+01
21	0.0000E+00	0.5112E+02	0.0000E+00

MODE= 3

	W	THETA-X	THETA-Y
1	0.0000E+00	0.0000E+00	0.0000E+00
2	-0.1375E-01	0.3989E+01	0.3202E+01
3	-0.8057E+00	0.1974E+02	0.2092E+02
4	-0.2886E+01	0.3813E+02	0.4380E+02
5	-0.6048E+01	0.4840E+02	0.6642E+02
6	-0.9419E+01	0.4291E+02	0.8144E+02
7	-0.1176E+02	0.1987E+02	0.8402E+02
8	-0.1198E+02	-0.1504E+02	0.7293E+02
9	-0.9609E+01	-0.5051E+02	0.5089E+02
10	-0.5060E+01	-0.7381E+02	0.2358E+02
11	0.4336E+00	-0.7579E+02	-0.2158E+01
12	0.5235E+01	-0.5468E+02	-0.2045E+02

Figure 5.6 Output for Example 2

```
   13  0.7882E+01 -0.1713E+02 -0.2802E+02
   14  0.7629E+01  0.2407E+02 -0.2494E+02
   15  0.4729E+01  0.5462E+02 -0.1429E+02
   16  0.3477E+00  0.6408E+02 -0.9150E+00
   17 -0.3862E+01  0.4979E+02  0.1028E+02
   18 -0.6370E+01  0.1777E+02  0.1587E+02
   19 -0.6330E+01 -0.1959E+02  0.1479E+02
   20 -0.3866E+01 -0.4834E+02  0.8417E+01
   21  0.0000E+00 -0.5831E+02  0.0000E+00
*STURM SEQUENCE FLAG    0*ITERATION PRINT FLAG    1
THE CALCULATED VALUES FOR HARMONIC   2 ARE
   EIGENVALUES      FREQUENCIES        ERROR NORMS
   0.7270313E+05    0.2696352E+03    0.7822725E-09
   0.2030948E+06    0.4506604E+03    0.1468370E-05
   0.4023602E+06    0.6343187E+03    0.7688248E-04
THE CALCULATED MODES ARE
MODE=  1
            W           THETA-X      THETA-Y
    1  0.0000E+00  0.0000E+00  0.0000E+00
    2  0.1010E-04 -0.4044E-03 -0.2347E-03
    3 -0.6637E-04  0.2491E-02  0.2186E-02
    4  0.1176E-02 -0.5752E-01 -0.5909E-01
    5  0.1386E-01 -0.3847E+00 -0.4003E+00
    6  0.6560E-01 -0.1318E+01 -0.1406E+01
    7  0.2075E+00 -0.3241E+01 -0.3582E+01
    8  0.5120E+00 -0.6430E+01 -0.7437E+01
    9  0.1061E+01 -0.1087E+02 -0.1332E+02
   10  0.1920E+01 -0.1610E+02 -0.2128E+02
   11  0.3113E+01 -0.2122E+02 -0.3088E+02
   12  0.4592E+01 -0.2495E+02 -0.4125E+02
   13  0.6224E+01 -0.2589E+02 -0.5110E+02
   14  0.7793E+01 -0.2288E+02 -0.5891E+02
   15  0.9026E+01 -0.1533E+02 -0.6323E+02
   16  0.9643E+01 -0.3549E+01 -0.6291E+02
   17  0.9412E+01  0.1118E+02 -0.5743E+02
   18  0.8213E+01  0.2671E+02 -0.4701E+02
   19  0.6083E+01  0.4041E+02 -0.3267E+02
   20  0.3227E+01  0.4965E+02 -0.1613E+02
   21  0.0000E+00  0.5241E+02  0.0000E+00
MODE=  2
            W           THETA-X      THETA-Y
    1  0.0000E+00  0.0000E+00  0.0000E+00
    2 -0.8745E-04  0.2025E-02  0.1149E-02
    3  0.5454E-03 -0.1426E-01 -0.1238E-01
    4 -0.8943E-02  0.3964E+00  0.4054E+00
    5 -0.9847E-01  0.2324E+01  0.2465E+01
    6 -0.4279E+00  0.6990E+01  0.7850E+01
```

Figure 5.6 Output for Example 2

```
    7 -0.1221E+01  0.1475E+02  0.1794E+02
    8 -0.2664E+01  0.2413E+02  0.3281E+02
    9 -0.4759E+01  0.3172E+02  0.5059E+02
   10 -0.7207E+01  0.3303E+02  0.6748E+02
   11 -0.9400E+01  0.2451E+02  0.7870E+02
   12 -0.1057E+02  0.5551E+01  0.8002E+02
   13 -0.1004E+02 -0.2026E+02  0.6941E+02
   14 -0.7572E+01 -0.4559E+02  0.4812E+02
   15 -0.3522E+01 -0.6167E+02  0.2062E+02
   16  0.1151E+01 -0.6159E+02 -0.6508E+01
   17  0.5148E+01 -0.4346E+02 -0.2664E+02
   18  0.7267E+01 -0.1183E+02 -0.3520E+02
   19  0.6860E+01  0.2338E+02 -0.3117E+02
   20  0.4107E+01  0.5033E+02 -0.1739E+02
   21  0.0000E+00  0.5967E+02  0.0000E+00
MODE=   3
           W           THETA-X      THETA-Y
    1  0.0000E+00  0.0000E+00  0.0000E+00
    2 -0.4271E-03  0.4265E-02  0.2346E-02
    3  0.2550E-02 -0.4133E-01 -0.3572E-01
    4 -0.3857E-01  0.1530E+01  0.1558E+01
    5 -0.3901E+00  0.7691E+01  0.8390E+01
    6 -0.1525E+01  0.1961E+02  0.2376E+02
    7 -0.3815E+01  0.3331E+02  0.4734E+02
    8 -0.7052E+01  0.3972E+02  0.7314E+02
    9 -0.1018E+02  0.2949E+02  0.9100E+02
   10 -0.1160E+02  0.3087E+00  0.9118E+02
   11 -0.9979E+01 -0.3856E+02  0.7003E+02
   12 -0.5231E+01 -0.6878E+02  0.3309E+02
   13  0.1091E+01 -0.7253E+02 -0.6535E+01
   14  0.6336E+01 -0.4394E+02 -0.3405E+02
   15  0.8099E+01  0.5181E+01 -0.4023E+02
   16  0.5612E+01  0.5012E+02 -0.2594E+02
   17  0.3272E+00  0.6667E+02 -0.1411E+01
   18 -0.4779E+01  0.4566E+02  0.1938E+02
   19 -0.6855E+01 -0.7449E+00  0.2610E+02
   20 -0.4819E+01 -0.4558E+02  0.1714E+02
   21  0.0000E+00 -0.6297E+02  0.0000E+00
*STURM SEQUENCE FLAG     0*ITERATION PRINT FLAG     1
THE CALCULATED VALUES FOR HARMONIC    3 ARE
   EIGENVALUES       FREQUENCIES        ERROR NORMS
   0.1982759E+06    0.4452818E+03    0.6043761E-08
   0.4279783E+06    0.6542005E+03    0.5805406E-05
   0.7240960E+06    0.8509383E+03    0.7907267E-04
THE CALCULATED MODES ARE
MODE=   1
           W           THETA-X      THETA-Y
```

Figure 5.6 Output for Example 2

1	0.0000E+00	0.0000E+00	0.0000E+00
2	0.4359E-07	0.1537E-04	0.7716E-05
3	-0.8535E-07	-0.6144E-04	-0.4468E-04
4	-0.2482E-06	0.2196E-03	0.2086E-03
5	0.7829E-05	-0.1515E-02	-0.1559E-02
6	0.1234E-02	-0.4164E-01	-0.4313E-01
7	0.1102E-01	-0.2589E+00	-0.2756E+00
8	0.5330E-01	-0.9682E+00	-0.1070E+01
9	0.1824E+00	-0.2667E+01	-0.3090E+01
10	0.4919E+00	-0.5889E+01	-0.7243E+01
11	0.1107E+01	-0.1090E+02	-0.1445E+02
12	0.2148E+01	-0.1727E+02	-0.2521E+02
13	0.3670E+01	-0.2364E+02	-0.3917E+02
14	0.5590E+01	-0.2770E+02	-0.5475E+02
15	0.7639E+01	-0.2678E+02	-0.6913E+02
16	0.9367E+01	-0.1882E+02	-0.7879E+02
17	0.1023E+02	-0.3458E+01	-0.8036E+02
18	0.9747E+01	0.1719E+02	-0.7177E+02
19	0.7694E+01	0.3856E+02	-0.5316E+02
20	0.4243E+01	0.5474E+02	-0.2731E+02
21	0.0000E+00	0.6021E+02	0.0000E+00

MODE= 2

	W	THETA-X	THETA-Y
1	0.0000E+00	0.0000E+00	0.0000E+00
2	-0.3373E-06	-0.1791E-03	-0.8583E-04
3	0.2731E-06	0.7270E-03	0.5085E-03
4	0.5380E-05	-0.2656E-02	-0.2445E-02
5	-0.1037E-03	0.1873E-01	0.1891E-01
6	-0.1284E-01	0.3746E+00	0.3913E+00
7	-0.1023E+00	0.1965E+01	0.2170E+01
8	-0.4357E+00	0.6158E+01	0.7328E+01
9	-0.1288E+01	0.1380E+02	0.1815E+02
10	-0.2928E+01	0.2365E+02	0.3570E+02
11	-0.5382E+01	0.3138E+02	0.5799E+02
12	-0.8188E+01	0.3059E+02	0.7918E+02
13	-0.1036E+02	0.1629E+02	0.9091E+02
14	-0.1067E+02	-0.1083E+02	0.8584E+02
15	-0.8340E+01	-0.4212E+02	0.6189E+02
16	-0.3587E+01	-0.6338E+02	0.2467E+02
17	0.2106E+01	-0.6178E+02	-0.1366E+02
18	0.6502E+01	-0.3402E+02	-0.3933E+02
19	0.7664E+01	0.9645E+01	-0.4348E+02
20	0.5056E+01	0.4892E+02	-0.2676E+02
21	0.0000E+00	0.6382E+02	0.0000E+00

MODE= 3

	W	THETA-X	THETA-Y
1	0.0000E+00	0.0000E+00	0.0000E+00

Figure 5.6 Output for Example 2

2	-0.4407E-06	-0.1056E-02	-0.4803E-03
3	-0.5085E-05	0.4365E-02	0.2927E-02
4	0.5500E-04	-0.1633E-01	-0.1456E-01
5	-0.7340E-03	0.1177E+00	0.1167E+00
6	-0.7020E-01	0.1750E+01	0.1853E+01
7	-0.4899E+00	0.7562E+01	0.8799E+01
8	-0.1794E+01	0.1900E+02	0.2527E+02
9	-0.4423E+01	0.3193E+02	0.5190E+02
10	-0.8030E+01	0.3546E+02	0.8125E+02
11	-0.1104E+02	0.1844E+02	0.9848E+02
12	-0.1119E+02	-0.1885E+02	0.8947E+02
13	-0.7157E+01	-0.5826E+02	0.5195E+02
14	-0.1161E+00	-0.7224E+02	0.8274E+00
15	0.6299E+01	-0.4480E+02	-0.3857E+02
16	0.8184E+01	0.1124E+02	-0.4662E+02
17	0.4357E+01	0.5849E+02	-0.2328E+02
18	-0.2322E+01	0.6178E+02	0.1137E+02
19	-0.6792E+01	0.1766E+02	0.3157E+02
20	-0.5661E+01	-0.3967E+02	0.2464E+02
21	0.0000E+00	-0.6447E+02	0.0000E+00

Figure 5.6 Output for Example 2

REFERENCES

1. Cheung, Y.K. Finite strip method of elastic slabs. *Proc. A.S.C.E.*, **94**, 1365-1378, 1968.

2. Cheung, Y.K. The finite strip method in the analysis of elastic plates with two opposite simple supported ends. *Proc. Inst. Civ. Eng.*, **40**, 1-7, 1968.

3. Cheung, Y.K. Analysis of box girder bridges by the finite strip method. *A.C.I. Publication: SP 26*, 357-378, 1969.

4. Cheung, Y.K. Folded plate structure by the finite strip method. *Proc. A.S. C.E.*, **96**, 2963-2979, 1969.

5. Cheung, Y.K. *The finite strip method in structural analysis.* Pergammon Press, Oxford, 1969.

6. Loo, Y.C. and Cusens A.R. A refined finite strip method for the analysis of orthotropic plates. *Proc. Inst. Civ. Engng.*, **48**, 85-91, 1970.

7. Loo, Y.C. and Cusens A.R. *The finite strip method in bridge engineering.* Viewpoint, London, 1978

8. Timoshenko, S.P. and Woinowsky-Krieger, S. *Theory of plates and shells.* McGraw-Hill, New York, 2nd. edition, 1959

9. Hinton, E. Buckling of initially stressed Mindlin plates using a finite strip method. *Computers and Structures*, **8**, 99-105, 1978.

10. Benson, P.R. and Hinton, E. A thick finite strip for static, free vibration and stability problem. *Int. J. Num. Meth. Engng.*, **10**, 665-678, 1976.

11. Dawe, D.J. Finite strip models for vibration of Mindlin plates. *J. of Sound and Vibration*, **59**, 441-452, 1978.

12. Oñate, E. *Comparisons of finite strip methods for the analysis of box girder bridges.* M.Sc. Thesis, Dept. of Civil Engng., Univ. College of Swansea, 1976.

13. Oñate E. and Suarez, B.A Comparison of the linear, quadratic and cubic Mindlin strip elements for analysis of thick and thin plates. *Computers and Structures*, **17**, 427-439, 1983.

14. Oñate, E. and Suarez, B.A. A unified approach for the analysis of bridges, plates and axisymmetric shells using the linear Mindlin strip element. *Computers and Structures*, **17**, 407-426, 1983.

15. Bathe, K.J. and Wilson, E.L. *Numerical methods in finite element analysis* Prentice-Hall, New Jersey, 1976.

16. Roufaeil, O.L. and Dawe, D.J. Vibration analysis of rectangular Mindlin plates by the finite strip method. *Computers and Structures*, **12**, 833-842, 1980.

FINITE ELEMENT FREE VIBRATION AND BUCKLING ANALYSIS OF INITIALLY STRESSED MINDLIN PLATES

E. HINTON*, Dj. VUKSANOVIC** and H.C. HUANG***

*Department of Civil Engineering, University College of Swansea, United Kingdom.
**Faculty of Civil Engineering, University of Belgrade, Yugoslavia.
***Department of Mechanics, Tianjin University, People's Republic of China.

1. INTRODUCTION

The main objective of this chapter is to present the finite element free vibration and buckling analysis of initially stressed Mindlin plates. In recent years an increasing number of finite element models based on Mindlin plate theory have started to appear. All of these research efforts have been directed towards the development of the ideal Mindlin plate element which may be used in both thick and thin plate situations. Herein, for implementation purposes, the 9-noded Lagrangian Mindlin plate element with enhanced shear interpolation has been used. This element satisfies most of the requirements of the ideal Mindlin plate element. After a brief review of Mindlin plate theory in Section 2 the main features of the 9-noded plate element are described in Section 3. In Section 4 the element mass matrix and geometric stiffness matrix are derived. This chapter also presents a well documented program called VIBUK for free vibration, initially stressed vibration and buckling analysis of Mindlin plates, as well as a set of user instructions for VIBUK. Some examples demonstrating the use of the program and the performance of the used plate element are given in Section 7.

2. REVIEW OF MINDLIN PLATE THEORY

Although the main equations of Mindlin plate theory have already been presented in Chapter 1, for completeness, a brief resumé is now provided.

2.1 Mindlin Plate Formulation

Mindlin plate theory [1] allows for transverse shear deformation effects and thus offers an attractive alternative to classical Kirchhoff thin plate theory. The main assumptions are that:

a) displacements are small compared to the plate thickness,

b) the stress normal to the plate mid-surface is negligible and

c) normals to the mid-surface before deformation remain straight but not necessarily normal to the mid-surface after deformation.

A typical Mindlin plate is shown in Figure 2.1(a) and if the xy-plane is taken as the reference plane then the plate displacements can be expressed as

$$\begin{aligned} U(x,y,z) &= z\ \theta_x(x,y) \\ V(x,y,z) &= z\ \theta_y(x,y) \\ W(x,y,z) &= w(x,y) \end{aligned} \tag{2.1}$$

where w, θ_x and θ_y are weighted averages for the transverse deflection and rotations of the normal in the xz and yz-planes respectively.

The strain energy for an initially stressed Mindlin plate can be derived assuming that initial in-plane stresses [2,3]

$$\underline{\sigma}^o = \begin{bmatrix} \sigma_x^o \\ \sigma_y^o \\ \tau_{xy}^o \end{bmatrix} \tag{2.2}$$

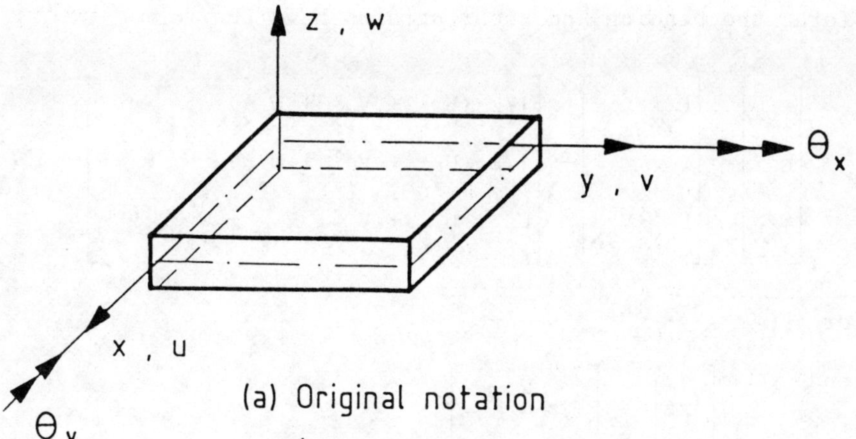

(a) Original notation

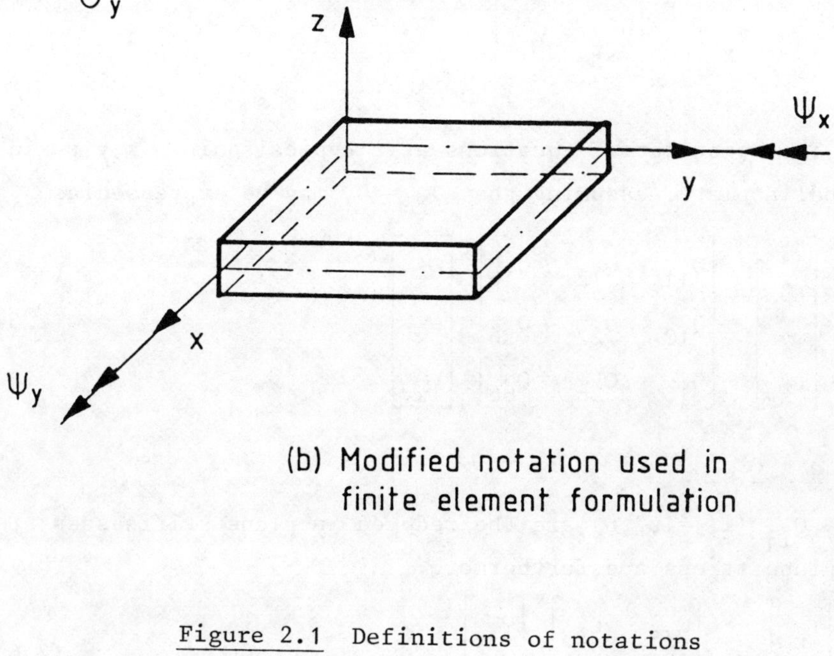

(b) Modified notation used in finite element formulation

Figure 2.1 Definitions of notations

act on the second order strains in the Mindlin plate. Therefore, the bending and shear strains have the form

$$\begin{bmatrix} \varepsilon_x \\ \varepsilon_y \\ \gamma_{xy} \end{bmatrix} = \begin{bmatrix} U_{,x} \\ V_{,y} \\ U_{,y}+V_{,x} \end{bmatrix} + \begin{bmatrix} 1/2\ (U_{,x}^{2} + V_{,x}^{2} + W_{,x}^{2}) \\ 1/2\ (U_{,y}^{2} + V_{,y}^{2} + W_{,y}^{2}) \\ U_{,x} \cdot U_{,y} + V_{,x} \cdot V_{,y} + W_{,x} \cdot W_{,y} \end{bmatrix} \tag{2.3}$$

or $\underline{\varepsilon} = \underline{\varepsilon}^{o} + \underline{\varepsilon}^{L}$

and

$$\underline{\gamma} = \begin{bmatrix} \gamma_{xz} \\ \gamma_{yz} \end{bmatrix} = \begin{bmatrix} U_{,z} + W_{,x} \\ V_{,z} + W_{,y} \end{bmatrix} \tag{2.4}$$

The constitutive equations at a typical point (x,y,z) in a Mindlin plate, assuming that $\sigma_z = 0$, may be expressed as

$$\begin{bmatrix} \sigma_x \\ \sigma_y \\ \tau_{xy} \end{bmatrix} = \begin{bmatrix} Q_{11} & Q_{12} & Q_{16} \\ Q_{12} & Q_{22} & Q_{26} \\ Q_{16} & Q_{26} & Q_{66} \end{bmatrix} \begin{bmatrix} \varepsilon_x \\ \varepsilon_y \\ \gamma_{xy} \end{bmatrix} \tag{2.5}$$

or $\underline{\sigma} = \underline{Q}\ \underline{\varepsilon}$

where Q_{ij} (i,j=1,2,6) are the reduced in-plane stiffnesses for plane stress and furthermore

$$\begin{bmatrix} \tau_{xz} \\ \tau_{yz} \end{bmatrix} = \begin{bmatrix} C_{55} & C_{45} \\ C_{45} & C_{44} \end{bmatrix} \begin{bmatrix} \gamma_{xz} \\ \gamma_{yz} \end{bmatrix} \tag{2.6}$$

or $\underline{\tau} = \underline{C}\ \underline{\gamma}$

where C_{ij} (i,j=4,5) are appropriate elastic constants.
Using (2.1) the strains (2.3) and (2.4) may be written as

$$\begin{bmatrix} \varepsilon_x \\ \varepsilon_y \\ \gamma_{xy} \end{bmatrix} = z \begin{bmatrix} \theta_{x,x} \\ \theta_{y,y} \\ \theta_{x,y} + \theta_{y,x} \end{bmatrix} + \begin{bmatrix} 1/2\ z^2(\theta_{x,x}^2 + \theta_{y,x}^2) + 1/2\ w_{,x}^2 \\ 1/2\ z^2(\theta_{x,y}^2 + \theta_{y,y}^2) + 1/2\ w_{,y}^2 \\ \theta_{x,x} . \theta_{x,y} + \theta_{y,x} . \theta_{y,y} + w_{,x} . w_{,y} \end{bmatrix} \tag{2.7}$$

with

$$\underline{\varepsilon}_b = \begin{bmatrix} \theta_{x,x} \\ \theta_{y,y} \\ \theta_{x,y} + \theta_{y,x} \end{bmatrix} \tag{2.8}$$

and

$$\begin{bmatrix} \gamma_{xz} \\ \gamma_{yz} \end{bmatrix} = \begin{bmatrix} \theta_x + w_{,x} \\ \theta_y + w_{,y} \end{bmatrix} \tag{2.9}$$

or $\underline{\gamma} = \underline{\varepsilon}_s$

The strain energy for an initially stressed Mindlin plate, after neglecting terms with third and higher powers in displacement gradients, can be written as

$$\text{S.E.} = \frac{1}{2} \iiint (\underline{\varepsilon}^o)^T \underline{Q}\ \underline{\varepsilon}^o\, dxdydz + \frac{1}{2} \iiint \underline{\gamma}^T\ \underline{C}\ \underline{\gamma}\ dxdydz$$

$$+ \iiint (\underline{\sigma}^o)^T\ \underline{\varepsilon}^L\ dxdydz \tag{2.10}$$

or, after integration over the plate thickness h, as

$$\text{S.E.} = \frac{1}{2} \iint \underline{\varepsilon}_b^T\ \underline{D}_b\ \underline{\varepsilon}_b\ dxdy + \frac{1}{2} \iint \underline{\varepsilon}_s^T\ \underline{D}_s\ \underline{\varepsilon}_s\ dxdy$$

$$+ \frac{1}{2} \iint [w_{,x},\ w_{,y}]\ \underline{\hat{\sigma}}^o \begin{bmatrix} w_{,x} \\ w_{,y} \end{bmatrix} h\ dxdy$$

$$+ \frac{1}{2} \iint [\theta_{x,x}, \theta_{x,y}] \, \underline{\hat{\sigma}}^o \begin{bmatrix} \theta_{x,x} \\ \theta_{x,y} \end{bmatrix} \frac{h^3}{12} \, dxdy$$

$$+ \frac{1}{2} \iint [\theta_{y,x}, \theta_{y,y}] \, \underline{\hat{\sigma}}^o \begin{bmatrix} \theta_{y,x} \\ \theta_{y,y} \end{bmatrix} \frac{h^3}{12} \, dxdy \qquad (2.11)$$

where

$$\underline{\hat{\sigma}}^o = \begin{bmatrix} \sigma_x^o & \tau_{xy}^o \\ \tau_{xy}^o & \sigma_y^o \end{bmatrix} \qquad (2.12)$$

The plate constitutive equations can be written as

$$\begin{bmatrix} M_x \\ M_y \\ M_{xy} \end{bmatrix} = \begin{bmatrix} D_{11} & D_{12} & D_{16} \\ D_{12} & D_{22} & D_{26} \\ D_{16} & D_{26} & D_{66} \end{bmatrix} \begin{bmatrix} \theta_{x,x} \\ \theta_{y,y} \\ \theta_{x,y} + \theta_{y,x} \end{bmatrix} \qquad (2.13)$$

or $\underline{\sigma}_b = \underline{D}_b \, \underline{\varepsilon}_b$

and

$$\begin{bmatrix} Q_x \\ Q_y \end{bmatrix} = \begin{bmatrix} D_{55} & D_{45} \\ D_{45} & D_{44} \end{bmatrix} \begin{bmatrix} \theta_x + w_{,x} \\ \theta_y + w_{,y} \end{bmatrix} \qquad (2.14)$$

or $\underline{\sigma}_s = \underline{D}_s \, \underline{\varepsilon}_s$

in which

$$D_{ij} = \int_{-h/2}^{+h/2} Q_{ij} \, z^2 \, dz \qquad (i,j=1,2,6)$$

$$= K_{ij}^2 \int_{-h/2}^{+h/2} C_{ij} \, dz \qquad (i,j=4,5) \qquad (2.15)$$

where K_{ij}^2 are shear correction factors.

2.2 Modified Notation

In the section which deals with the finite element program, a modified definition of the rotations is adopted in which

$$\begin{bmatrix} \theta_x \\ \theta_y \end{bmatrix} = \begin{bmatrix} -1 & 0 \\ 0 & -1 \end{bmatrix} \begin{bmatrix} \psi_x \\ \psi_y \end{bmatrix} \qquad (2.16)$$

see Figure 2.1(b).

3. MINDLIN PLATE ELEMENT

3.1 Finite Element Formulation

It is well known that finite elements based on Mindlin's plate theory require only C(0) continuity of the lateral displacement and independent rotations. This is an important advantage over finite elements based on classical thin plate Kirchhoff theory where C(1) continuity is required. Thus, it would appear that Mindlin plate elements are simpler to formulate and they have the added advantage of being able to model shear-weak as well as shear-stiff plates - if transverse shear effects are present in the plate they are automatically modelled with Mindlin elements. However, several difficulties can be encountered when Mindlin plate elements are used in thin plate situations. Full integration of the stiffness matrices leads to locking behaviour and while reduced or selective integration can often overcome these difficulties [4,5], overstiff solutions may still occur in problems with highly constrained boundaries. On the other hand, when such elements are used in problems with lightly constrained boundaries the solutions may fail due to the formation of mechanisms or be polluted by oscillations caused by near-mechanisms [6].

In recent years there has been much research activity directed towards the development of methods for overcoming these difficulties. Some recent contributions are those presented by MacNeal [7], Dvorkin and Bathe [8], Crisfield [9] and Huang and Hinton [10,11]. In the present work, the solution given by Huang and Hinton for 9-node Lagrangian Mindlin plate element with enhanced shear interpolation is presented.

For the general case of an n-noded Mindlin plate element the displacement variation over the element is given by the expression

$$\begin{bmatrix} w \\ \theta_x \\ \theta_y \end{bmatrix} = \sum_{i=1}^{n} \begin{bmatrix} N_i & 0 & 0 \\ 0 & N_i & 0 \\ 0 & 0 & N_i \end{bmatrix} \begin{bmatrix} w_i \\ \theta_{xi} \\ \theta_{yi} \end{bmatrix} \tag{3.1}$$

or $\underline{u} = \sum_{i=1}^{n} \underline{N}_i \, \underline{a}_i$

where w_i, θ_{xi} and θ_{yi} are the corresponding displacement and rotation values at node i and N_i is the shape function associated with node i expressed in terms of the local coordinate system (ξ,η).

Curvature-displacement relations may now be written as

$$\underline{\varepsilon}_b = \sum_{i=1}^{n} \underline{B}_{bi} \, \underline{a}_i \tag{3.2}$$

where $\underline{B}_{bi}$ is the curvature-displacement matrix associated with the node i

$$\underline{B}_{bi} = \begin{bmatrix} 0 & N_{i,x} & 0 \\ 0 & 0 & N_{i,y} \\ 0 & N_{i,y} & N_{i,x} \end{bmatrix} \tag{3.3}$$

The shear strains can be written as

$$\underline{\varepsilon}_s = \sum_{i=1}^{n} \underline{B}_{si}\, \underline{a}_i \tag{3.4}$$

where $\underline{B}_{si}$ is the shear-displacement matrix associated with the node i

$$\underline{B}_{si} = \begin{bmatrix} N_{i,x} & N_i & 0 \\ N_{i,y} & 0 & N_i \end{bmatrix} \tag{3.5}$$

In an isoparametric formulation, the same interpolation functions are used to describe the geometry and displacement variation. Thus

$$\begin{bmatrix} x \\ y \end{bmatrix} = \sum_{i=1}^{n} \begin{bmatrix} N_i & 0 \\ 0 & N_i \end{bmatrix} \begin{bmatrix} x_i \\ y_i \end{bmatrix} \tag{3.6}$$

where x_i and y_i are the coordinates of node i. The Jacobian matrix of the element can be written as

$$\underline{J} = \begin{bmatrix} x_{,\xi} & y_{,\xi} \\ x_{,\eta} & y_{,\eta} \end{bmatrix} = \begin{bmatrix} \sum_{i=1}^{n} N_{i,\xi}\, x_i & \sum_{i=1}^{n} N_{i,\xi}\, y_i \\ \sum_{i=1}^{n} N_{i,\eta}\, x_i & \sum_{i=1}^{n} N_{i,\eta}\, y_i \end{bmatrix} \tag{3.7}$$

The inverse of Jacobian matrix $\underline{J}$ may be expressed as

$$\underline{J}^{-1} = \begin{bmatrix} \xi_{,x} & \eta_{,x} \\ \xi_{,y} & \eta_{,y} \end{bmatrix} = \frac{1}{\det\underline{J}} \begin{bmatrix} y_{,\eta} & -y_{,\xi} \\ -x_{,\eta} & x_{,\xi} \end{bmatrix} \tag{3.8}$$

where $\det\underline{J}$ is the determinant of the Jacobian matrix. The Cartesian shape function derivatives $N_{i,x}$ and $N_{i,y}$ can be obtained by the chain rule of differentiation. Thus

$$N_{i,x} = N_{i,\xi} \cdot \xi_{,x} + N_{i,\eta} \cdot \eta_{,x}$$
$$N_{i,y} = N_{i,\xi} \cdot \xi_{,y} + N_{i,\eta} \cdot \eta_{,y} \qquad (3.9)$$

An element of area may be expressed as

$$dxdy = \det \underline{J} \; d\xi d\eta \qquad (3.10)$$

The contributions to the submatrix of the element stiffness matrix linking nodes i and j are defined in the usual way

$$\underline{K}^e_{bij} = \int_{-1}^{+1} \int_{-1}^{+1} \underline{B}^T_{bi} \, \underline{D}_b \, \underline{B}_{bj} \, \det \underline{J} \; d\xi d\eta$$
$$\underline{K}^e_{sij} = \int_{-1}^{+1} \int_{-1}^{+1} \underline{B}^T_{si} \, \underline{D}_s \, \underline{B}_{sj} \, \det \underline{J} \; d\xi d\eta \qquad (3.11)$$

respectively associated with the bending and shear strain energies. So, the stiffness terms linking nodes i and j may be written as

$$\underline{K}^e_{ij} = \underline{K}^e_{bij} + \underline{K}^e_{sij} \qquad (3.12)$$

For thin plate situations the transverse shear strains should tend towards zero, so that

$$\underline{\varepsilon}_s = \begin{bmatrix} \gamma_{xz} \\ \gamma_{yz} \end{bmatrix} = \begin{bmatrix} \theta_x + w_{,x} \\ \theta_y + w_{,y} \end{bmatrix} \rightarrow \underline{0} \qquad (3.13)$$

In the ξ-η coordinate system the following condition should also hold

$$\begin{bmatrix} \gamma_{\xi\zeta} \\ \gamma_{\eta\zeta} \end{bmatrix} = \begin{bmatrix} \theta_\xi + w_{,\xi} \\ \theta_\eta + w_{,\eta} \end{bmatrix} \rightarrow \underline{0} \qquad (3.14)$$

The shear strain energy terms may be interpreted as penalty functions which force the shear strains to equal zero as the plate thickness-to-span ratio is reduced. The imposition of these constraints leads to a deterioration of the stiffness matrix and overstiff results are obtained. To overcome this problem substitute shear strain fields have been used.

3.2 Substitute Shear Strain Field

Recently, it was mentioned by Huang and Hinton for developing 9-node element that in conventional Mindlin plate elements the polynomial terms for θ_ξ and $w_{,\xi}$ and for θ_η and $w_{,\eta}$ do not match since

$$\begin{aligned}
\theta_\xi &= \theta_\xi(1,\xi,\eta,\xi\eta,\xi^2,\eta^2,\xi^2\eta,\xi\eta^2,\xi^2\eta^2) \\
w_{,\xi} &= w_{,\xi}(1,\xi,\eta,\xi\eta,\eta^2,\xi\eta^2) \\
\theta_\eta &= \theta_\eta(1,\xi,\eta,\xi\eta,\xi^2,\eta^2,\xi^2\eta,\xi\eta^2,\xi^2\eta^2) \\
w_{,\eta} &= w_{,\eta}(1,\xi,\eta,\xi\eta,\xi^2,\xi^2\eta)
\end{aligned} \qquad (3.15)$$

This fact is unfortunate since for thin plate situations conditon (3.14) should hold. However, with appropriate polynomial terms it is possible to develop an element [11] which has the requisite number of zero energy modes, does not lock and passes the appropriate patch tests exactly. Because the substitute shear strain field is used for $\gamma_{\xi\zeta}$ and $\gamma_{\eta\zeta}$ a constrained functional replaces the total potential energy expression and has form

$$\bar{\pi} = \pi + \int_A \lambda_{13}(\bar{\gamma}_{\xi\zeta} - \gamma_{\xi\zeta})dA + \int_A \lambda_{23}(\bar{\gamma}_{\eta\zeta} - \gamma_{\eta\zeta})dA \qquad (3.16)$$

where λ_{13} and λ_{23} are Lagrangian multipliers and are independent functions, and the total potential energy is

$$\pi = \frac{1}{2} \int_A \underline{\varepsilon}_b^T \, \underline{D}_b \, \underline{\varepsilon}_b \, dA + \frac{1}{2} \int_A \underline{\varepsilon}_s^T \, \underline{D}_s \, \underline{\varepsilon}_s \, dA - W \tag{3.17}$$

where W is potential energy of the applied loads. The terms $\gamma_{\xi\zeta}$ and $\gamma_{\eta\zeta}$ are the transverse shear strains evaluated from the displacement and normal rotation fields. The substitute strain fields are chosen as

$$\begin{aligned} \bar{\gamma}_{\xi\zeta} &= \sum_{i=1}^{n} \sum_{j=1}^{m} R_{ij}(\xi,\eta) \, \bar{\gamma}^{ji} \\ \bar{\gamma}_{\eta\zeta} &= \sum_{i=1}^{m} \sum_{j=1}^{n} S_{ij}(\xi,\eta) \, \bar{\gamma}^{ij} \end{aligned} \tag{3.18}$$

in which $\bar{\gamma}^{ji}_{\xi\zeta}$ and $\bar{\gamma}^{ij}_{\eta\zeta}$ are the mxn unknown substitute shear strain parameters associated with two sets of mxn sampling points $(\hat{\xi}_i,\hat{\eta}_j)$ and $(\hat{\hat{\xi}}_j,\hat{\hat{\eta}}_i)$, R_{ij} and S_{ij} are appropriate interpolation functions. In order to eliminate locking behaviour the constraints should not be too strong, so λ_{13} and λ_{23} are chosen as Dirac delta functions of the following form

$$\begin{aligned} \lambda_{13} &= \sum_{i=1}^{n} \sum_{j=1}^{m} \lambda_{13}^{ji} \, \delta(\hat{\xi}_i-\xi) \, \delta(\hat{\eta}_j-\eta) \\ \lambda_{23} &= \sum_{i=1}^{m} \sum_{j=1}^{n} \lambda_{23}^{ij} \, \delta(\hat{\hat{\xi}}_i-\xi) \, \delta(\hat{\hat{\eta}}_j-\eta) \end{aligned} \tag{3.19}$$

Upon substitution of (3.19) into (3.16) and upon subsequent satisfaction of stationarity of $\bar{\pi}$, the following relationships are obtained

$$\begin{aligned} \bar{\gamma}_{\xi\zeta}(\hat{\xi}_i,\hat{\eta}_j) &= \gamma_{\xi\zeta}(\hat{\xi}_i,\hat{\eta}_j) \qquad (i=1,m,\ j=1,n) \\ \bar{\gamma}_{\eta\zeta}(\hat{\hat{\xi}}_j,\hat{\hat{\eta}}_i) &= \gamma_{\eta\zeta}(\hat{\hat{\xi}}_j,\hat{\hat{\eta}}_i) \qquad (i=1,n,\ j=1,m) \end{aligned} \tag{3.20}$$

If (3.20) can be satisfied in advance then it is possible to work with the following functional

$$\pi = \frac{1}{2} \int_A \underline{\varepsilon}_b^T \, \underline{D}_b \, \underline{\varepsilon}_b \, dA + \frac{1}{2} \int_A \underline{\bar{\varepsilon}}_s^T \, \underline{D}_s \, \underline{\bar{\varepsilon}}_s \, dA - W \tag{3.21}$$

in which

$$\underline{\bar{\varepsilon}}_s = \begin{bmatrix} \bar{\gamma}_{xz} \\ \bar{\gamma}_{yz} \end{bmatrix} \tag{3.22}$$

where $\bar{\gamma}_{xz}$ and $\bar{\gamma}_{yz}$ are obtained from $\bar{\gamma}_{\xi\zeta}$ and $\bar{\gamma}_{\eta\zeta}$ (3.18), by tensor transformation.

The transformation of the strain tensor in curvilinear coordinates is

$$e_{\alpha\beta} = \frac{\partial x^i}{\partial \xi^\alpha} \cdot \frac{\partial x^j}{\partial \xi^\beta} \varepsilon_{ij} \tag{3.23}$$

where it is assumed that $e_{\alpha\beta}$ is the strain tensor in (ξ,η) or (ξ_1,ξ_2) coordinate system and ε_{ij} is the strain tensor in the (x,y) or (x_1,x_2) system.

For the plate it is possible to write that

$$x_{,\zeta} = y_{,\zeta} = z_{,\xi} = z_{,\eta} = 0 \tag{3.24}$$

and consequently the shear can be expressed as

$$\begin{bmatrix} \bar{\gamma}_{\xi\zeta} \\ \bar{\gamma}_{\eta\zeta} \end{bmatrix} = \underline{L} \begin{bmatrix} \bar{\gamma}_{xz} \\ \bar{\gamma}_{yz} \end{bmatrix} \tag{3.25}$$

in which

$$\underline{L} = z_{,\zeta} \begin{bmatrix} x_{,\xi} & y_{,\xi} \\ x_{,\eta} & y_{,\eta} \end{bmatrix} = \frac{h}{2} \underline{J} \tag{3.26}$$

Similarly, since

$$\xi_{,z} = \eta_{,z} = \zeta_{,x} = \zeta_{,y} = 0 \tag{3.27}$$

it is possible to write

$$\begin{bmatrix} \bar{\gamma}_{xz} \\ \bar{\gamma}_{yz} \end{bmatrix} = \underline{L}^{-1} \begin{bmatrix} \bar{\gamma}_{\xi\zeta} \\ \bar{\gamma}_{\eta\zeta} \end{bmatrix} \tag{3.28}$$

where

$$\underline{L}^{-1} = \frac{2}{h} \underline{J}^{-1}$$

For implementation purposes it is simply necessary to evaluate

$$\underline{K}^{e}_{sij} = \int_{-1}^{+1} \int_{-1}^{+1} \underline{\bar{B}}^{T}_{si} \, \underline{D}_{s} \, \underline{\bar{B}}_{sj} \, \det\underline{J} \, d\xi d\eta \tag{3.29}$$

where $\underline{\bar{B}}_{si}$ is the appropriate substitute strain matrix and the full integration used to evaluate $\underline{K}^{e}_{bij}$ is again used to evaluate $\underline{K}^{e}_{sij}$.

For 9-node Lagrangian Mindlin plate element positions of sampling points for $\bar{\gamma}^{ij}_{\xi\zeta}$ and $\bar{\gamma}^{ij}_{\eta\zeta}$ are shown on Figure 3.1. According to (3.18) substitute strain fields are

$$\begin{aligned} \bar{\gamma}_{\xi\zeta} &= \sum_{i=1}^{2} \sum_{j=1}^{3} P_i(\xi) \, Q_j(\eta) \, \bar{\gamma}^{ji}_{\xi\zeta} \\ \bar{\gamma}_{\eta\zeta} &= \sum_{i=1}^{3} \sum_{j=1}^{2} Q_i(\xi) \, P_j(\eta) \, \bar{\gamma}^{ij}_{\eta\zeta} \end{aligned} \tag{3.30}$$

where substitute interpolation functions for shear strains are

$$\begin{aligned} Q_1(s) &= s(1+s)/2 \qquad & P_1(s) &= (1+s/a)/2 \\ Q_2(s) &= 1-s^2 \qquad & P_2(s) &= (1-s/a)/2 \\ Q_3(s) &= s(s-1)/2 & & \end{aligned} \tag{3.31}$$

with $a = 1/\sqrt{3}$.

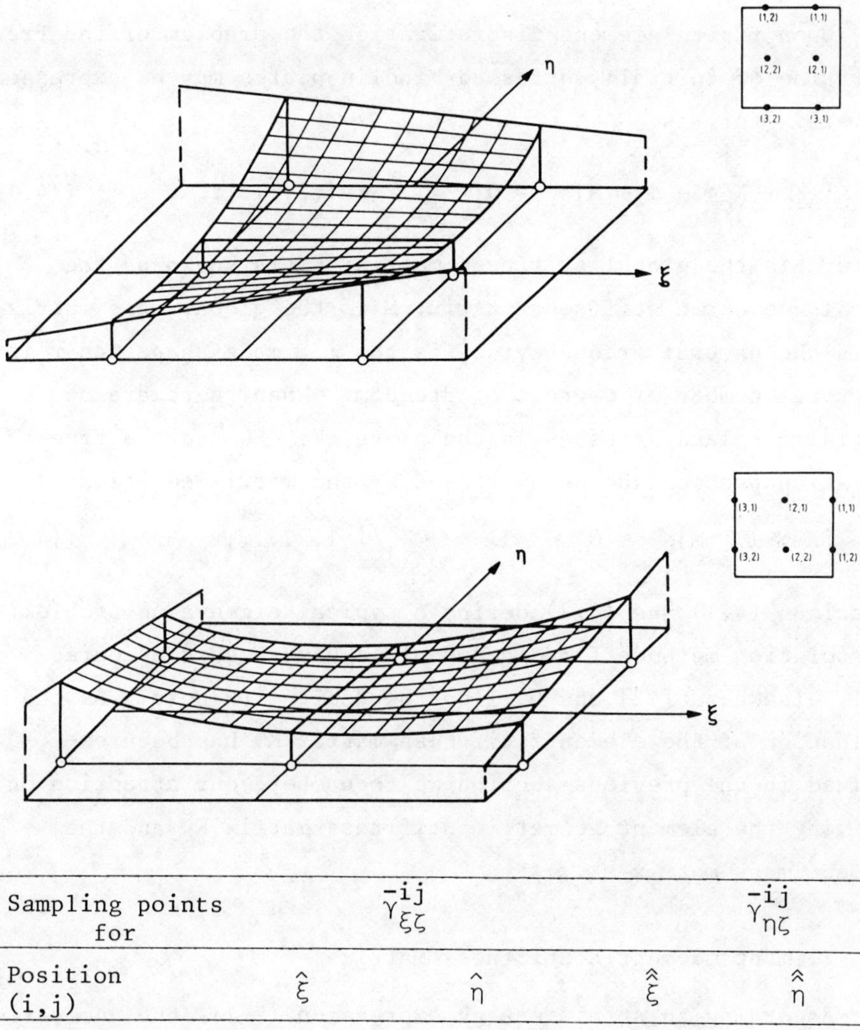

Sampling points for	$\bar{\gamma}^{ij}_{\xi\zeta}$		$\bar{\gamma}^{ij}_{\eta\zeta}$	
Position (i,j)	$\hat{\xi}$	$\hat{\eta}$	$\hat{\hat{\xi}}$	$\hat{\hat{\eta}}$
(1,1)	a	1	1	a
(1,2)	-a	1	1	-a
(2,1)	a	0	0	a
(2,2)	-a	0	0	-a
(3,1)	a	-1	-1	a
(3,2)	-a	-1	-1	-a

$a = 1/\sqrt{3}$

Figure 3.1 Sampling positions for shear interpolation in the 9-node Lagrangian Mindlin plate element

4. FREE VIBRATION AND INITIALLY STRESSED VIBRATION PROBLEMS

Upon finite element discretization the problem of the free vibration of initially stressed Mindlin plates may be expressed in matrix form as

$$[(\underline{K} + \underline{K}_G) - \omega_i^2\ \underline{M}]\underline{a}^i = \underline{0} \qquad i=1,2,\ldots,r \tag{4.1}$$

where $\underline{K}$ is the global stiffness matrix; $\underline{K}_G$ is known as the global geometric stiffness matrix; $\underline{M}$ is the global mass matrix; ω_i is the natural frequency; $\underline{a}^i$ is the ith mode shape and r is the total number of degrees of freedom. When there are no initial in-plane stresses in the plate, $\underline{K}_G = 0$ and the free vibration problem can be expressed by the matrix equation

$$[\underline{K} - \omega_i^2\ \underline{M}]\underline{a}^i = \underline{0} \qquad i=1,2,\ldots,r \tag{4.2}$$

Equations (4.1) and (4.2) define a typical eigenvalue problem. The solution methods for eigenproblems have been considered fully elsewhere [12] and will not be dealt with here. As the evaluation of the element stiffness matrix $\underline{K}^e$ has been explained in the previous section we focus here our attention on deriving the element geometric stiffness matrix $\underline{K}_G^e$ and the element mass matrix $\underline{M}^e$.

4.1 Element Geometric Stiffness Matrix

According to strain energy expression (2.11) the geometric stiffness matrix may be written as

$$\underline{K}_G^e = \underline{K}_{Gb}^e + \underline{K}_{Gs}^e \tag{4.3}$$

A typical submatrix of $\underline{K}_{Gb}^e$ linking nodes i and j can be expressed as

$$\underline{K}_{Gbij}^e = \int_{-1}^{+1}\int_{-1}^{+1} \underline{G}_{bi}^T\ \underline{\hat{\sigma}}^o\ \underline{G}_{bj}\ h \det\underline{J}\ d\xi d\eta \tag{4.4}$$

where

$$\underline{G}_{bi} = \begin{bmatrix} N_{i,x} & 0 & 0 \\ N_{i,y} & 0 & 0 \end{bmatrix} \tag{4.5}$$

and $\hat{\underline{\sigma}}^o$ is defined by (2.12).

A typical submatrix of $\underline{K}^e_{Gs}$ linking nodes i and j can be expressed as

$$\underline{K}^e_{Gsij} = \int_{-1}^{+1}\int_{-1}^{+1} \underline{G}^T_{s1i}\ \hat{\underline{\sigma}}^o\ \underline{G}_{s1j}\ \frac{h^3}{12}\ \det\underline{J}\ d\xi d\eta\ + + \int_{-1}^{+1}\int_{-1}^{+1} \underline{G}^T_{s2i}\ \hat{\underline{\sigma}}^o\ \underline{G}_{s2j}\ \frac{h^3}{12}\ \det\underline{J}\ d\xi d\eta \tag{4.6}$$

where

$$\underline{G}_{s1i} = \begin{bmatrix} 0 & N_{i,x} & 0 \\ 0 & N_{i,y} & 0 \end{bmatrix}$$

$$\underline{G}_{s2i} = \begin{bmatrix} 0 & 0 & N_{i,x} \\ 0 & 0 & N_{i,y} \end{bmatrix} \tag{4.7}$$

$\underline{K}^e_{Gs}$ is the part of geometric stiffness matrix associated with shear deformations and in the case of thin plates can be omitted. However, its effect becomes significant for thick plate situations.

4.2 Element Mass Matrix

4.2.1 Element consistent mass matrix

If the shape functions used to describe the variation of the acceleration field over the element are the same as those used to describe the displacement variation over the element then the corresponding mass matrix is known as the consistent mass matrix. A typical submatrix of the consistent mass matrix which allows for the effects of rotatory inertia and links nodes i and j can be expressed as

$$\underline{M}^e_{ij} = C_{ij} \begin{bmatrix} h & 0 & 0 \\ 0 & h^3/12 & 0 \\ 0 & 0 & h^3/12 \end{bmatrix} \tag{4.8}$$

for elements of constant thickness. The mass matrix coefficients C_{ij} are

$$C_{ij} = \int_{-1}^{+1} \int_{-1}^{+1} \rho\, N_i N_j \det\underline{J}\, d\xi d\eta \tag{4.9}$$

The total mass of the element should be preserved. However, this may not always be strictly true for elements which do not have a constant $\det\underline{J}$ at all points,(i.e. distorted elements). One possible remedy would be to evaluate the total mass of each element

$$M^e = \int_{-1}^{+1} \int_{-1}^{+1} \rho \det\underline{J}\, d\xi d\eta \tag{4.10}$$

by a high order Gauss-Legendre product rule and scale the mass matrix coefficients to sum this total mass value. As shown below $\sum_{i=1}^{n} \sum_{j=1}^{n} C_{ij}$ should give the total mass of the element, provided that $\det\underline{J}$ is constant within element

$$\begin{aligned} \sum_{i=1}^{n} \sum_{j=1}^{n} C_{ij} &= \sum_{i=1}^{n} \sum_{j=1}^{n} \int_{-1}^{+1} \int_{-1}^{+1} \rho\, N_i N_j \det\underline{J}\, d\xi d\eta = \\ &= \int_{-1}^{+1} \int_{-1}^{+1} \rho \sum_{i=1}^{n} \sum_{j=1}^{n} N_i N_j \det\underline{J}\, d\xi d\eta = \\ &= \int_{-1}^{+1} \int_{-1}^{+1} \rho \sum_{i=1}^{n} N_i \det\underline{J}\, d\xi d\eta = \\ &= \int_{-1}^{+1} \int_{-1}^{+1} \rho \det\underline{J}\, d\xi d\eta \end{aligned} \tag{4.11}$$

since $\sum_{i=1}^{n} N_i = 1$.

5. STABILITY PROBLEMS

Following a finite element spatial discretization, the stability problem of initially stressed Mindlin plates can be expressed in matrix form as

$$[\underline{K} - \lambda \underline{K}_G]\underline{a}^i = 0 \qquad i=1,2,....,r \tag{5.1}$$

where $\underline{K}$ is the global stiffness matrix, $\underline{K}_G$ is the global geometric stiffness matrix and λ is a constant by which the chosen in-plane loads must be multiplied to cause buckling. Vector $\underline{a}^i$ gives the ith buckling mode and r is the total number of degrees of freedom. From (5.1) it follows that all the in-plane stresses must be simultaneously increased by a factor λ which will increase the geometric stiffness matrix proportionally. Thus, buckling loads can be found by solving the typical eigenvalue problem.

6. PROGRAM VIBUK

6.1 Introduction

This section describes VIBUK which is a program for the free vibration, initially stressed vibration and buckling analysis of Mindlin plates. In order to make all subroutines in VIBUK modular in form we have adopted a type of dynamic dimensioning. Dimensions are fixed in the main routine and all necessary information is transmitted between routines by the use of arguments. This approach has the advantage that the maximum dimensions can be updated in a very simple manner. Only the DIMENSION statements in the main segment which sets the maximum dimension sizes need modification.

Program VIBUK consists of 5 main modules

(1) INPUT which reads in most of the input data

(2) STIFPB which evaluates stiffness matrices and geometric stiffness matrices for Mindlin plate elements

(3) CONMAS which evaluates mass matrices for Mindlin plate elements

(4) BERKEL which is an eigenvalue solver

(5) OUTPUT which outputs the results.

Program VIBUK is written in a modular form in such a way that users can easily implement their own modules for eigenvalue solution and for output. Thus, BERKEL and OUTPUT are not compulsory routines in the program. They are routines which illustrate the implementation of the eigenvalue solver, described and coded by Bathe and Wilson [12], which employs a subspace iteration method with Sturm sequence checks.

6.2 Glossary of Variable Names

Main Arrays

Array name	Description
COORD(MPOIN,NDIME)	x and y coordinates
ESTIF(27,27)	element stiffness matrix
EMASS(27,27)	element mass matrix
GSTIF(27,27)	geometric element stiffness matrix
IFPRE(MVFIX,NDOFN)	fixity code matrix 0 - free 1 - fixed
ISTRN(MELEM)	initial stress set numbers for each element
LNODS(MELEM,9)	element nodal connectivities
MATNO(MELEM)	material set numbers for each element
NOFIX(MVFIX)	nodes with at least one prescribed variable

PROPS(NMATS,8)	properties for each material set
STREM(MISTR,3)	stresses (σ_x^o, σ_y^o, τ_{xy}^o) for each initial stress set.

Main Variables

Variable	Description
ICONT	indicator which controls type of analysis to be used =1 free vibration analysis =2 initially stressed vibration analysis =3 buckling analysis
ILBTO	indicator of the type of mass matrix to be used =0, consistent mass matrix =1, lumped mass matrix
MELEM	maximum number of elements
MEVAB	=27, maximum number of element variables
MISTR	maximum number of initial stress sets
MMATS	maximum number of material sets
MPOIN	maximum number of nodal points
MVFIX	maximum number of restrained nodes
NDIME	=2, number of dimensions
NDOFN	=3, number of degrees of freedom per node
NELEM	number of elements
NEVAB	=27, number of element variables
NGAUB	= 3, Gauss-Legendre rule to evaluate the bending stiffness matrix
NGAUS	= 3, Gauss-Legendre rule to evaluate the shear stiffness matrix

NISTR	number of initial stress sets
NMATS	number of material sets
NMODE	number of eigenmodes required
NNODE	=9, number of nodes per element
NPOIN	number of nodal points
NVFIX	number of restrained nodes

6.3 Main Segment

The main segment which controls the calling of the major subroutines is now described. The Nassi-Schneiderman (NS) chart for this routine is shown in Figure 6.1.

Initialise variables in DATA statement etc. [MAIN 28-34]	1
Call INPUT to read in most of the data [MAIN 38-41]	2
Call STIFPB to evaluate element stiffness matrices and geometric stiffness matrices [MAIN 45-47]	3
If a buckling analysis is required jump to 6, otherwise continue [MAIN 48]	4
Call CONMAS to evaluate element mass matrices [MAIN 52-54]	5
Call BERKEL for subspace iteration [MAIN 58-62]	6
Call OUTPUT to print the results [MAIN 66-67]	7

Figure 6.1 NS chart for the main segment

```
C***********************************************************************MAIN   1
C*                                                                     *MAIN   2
C*    PROGRAM FOR FREE VIBRATION, INITIALLY STRESSED VIBRATION         *MAIN   3
C*      AND BUCKLING ANALYSIS OF PLATES USING MINDLIN THEORY           *MAIN   4
C*                                                                     *MAIN   5
C***********************************************************************MAIN   6
      IMPLICIT REAL*8(A-H,O-Z)                                          MAIN   7
C                                                                       MAIN   8
C*** DIMENSIONS ASSOCIATED WITH SUBROUTINES INPUT, STIFPB AND           MAIN   9
C*** CONMAS                                                             MAIN  10
C                                                                       MAIN  11
      DIMENSION COORD(121,2),ESTIF(27,27),EMASS(27,27),GSTIF(27,27),    MAIN  12
     .          IFPRE(65,3),ISTRN(25),LNODS(25,9),MATNO(25),NOFIX(65),  MAIN  13
     .          PROPS(10,8),STREM(25,3)                                 MAIN  14
```

```
C
C*** DIMENSIONS ASSOCIATED WITH SUBROUTINES BERKEL AND OUTPUT
C
      DIMENSION A(10000),AD(3,121),AR(171),B(10000),BR(171),BS(378),
     .          BUP(18),BLO(18),BUPC(18),D(18),ER(363,18),EIGV(18),
     .          ID(3,121),LM(27,25),MHT(363),MAXA(364),R(363,18),
     .          RTOLV(18),S(378),TT(363),VEC(18,18),W(363)
C*********************************************************************
C
C                 DYNAMIC  DIMENSIONING
C
C*********************************************************************
C
      DATA MPOIN/121/,MVFIX/65/,MELEM/25/,MMATS/10/,MISTR/25/,
     .     NDIME/2/,NNODE/9/,NGAUB/3/,NGAUS/3/,NDOFN/3/
C
      DATA MAHAM/378/,MAXNN/363/,MANNM/364/,MMODE/10/,MNEBS/10000/,
     .     MITEV/18/,MDISV/171/
C
      MEVAB=NDOFN*9
C
C*** CALL SUBROUTINE WHICH READS IN MOST OF THE DATA
C
      CALL  INPUT    (COORD,ICONT,IFPRE,ILBTO,ISTRN,LNODS,MATNO,
     .                MVFIX,MISTR,MMATS,MPOIN,MELEM,NPOIN,NELEM,
     .                NVFIX,NNODE,NDOFN,NMATS,NDIME,NMODE,NEVAB,
     .                NISTR,NOFIX,PROPS,STREM)
C
C*** FORM THE ELEMENT STIFFNESS MATRICES
C
      CALL  STIFPB   (COORD,ICONT,ISTRN,LNODS,MATNO,MELEM,MEVAB,
     .                MMATS,MISTR,MPOIN,NELEM,NEVAB,NGAUB,NGAUS,
     .                NNODE,PROPS,STREM)
      IF (ICONT.EQ.3) GO TO 10
C
C*** SET UP THE ELEMENT MASS MATRIX
C
      CALL  CONMAS   (COORD,ILBTO,LNODS,MATNO,MPOIN,MELEM,
     .                MMATS,NEVAB,NELEM,NNODE,NDIME,NDOFN,
     .                PROPS)
C
C*** SUBSPACE ITERATION
C
   10 CALL  BERKEL   (A,AR,B,BR,BS,BUP,BLO,BUPC,D,ER,EIGV,ICONT,
     .                ID,IFPRE,LM,LNODS,MHT,MAXA,MAHAM,MAXNN,MANNM,
     .                MITEV,MDISV,MNEBS,MPOIN,MELEM,MVFIX,NMODE,
     .                NPOIN,NEQ,NVFIX,NOFIX,NDOFN,NELEM,NEVAB,
     .                NNODE,RTOLV,S,TT,VEC,W)
C
C*** CALL SUBROUTINE WHICH OUTPUTS THE RESULTS
C
      CALL  OUTPUT   (AD,D,EIGV,ICONT,ID,MPOIN,MAXNN,MITEV,NDOFN,
     .                NMODE,NEQ,NPOIN,R)
      STOP
      END
```

6.4 INPUT MODULE

6.4.1 Subroutine INPUT

The main function of INPUT is to read in most of the input data. The NS chart for INPUT is given in Figure 6.2.

Read and write problem title [INPU 16-19]	1
Read and write control indicator [INPU 21-32]	2
Read and write control data [INPU 36-41]	3
Read and write element connections, property numbers and initial stress set numbers [INPU 45-52]	4
Initialise array COORD [INPU 56-58]	5
Read nodal coordinates [INPU 62-68]	6
Interpolate coordinates of midside nodes for straight sides by calling NODEXY [INPU 72-73]	7
Write all nodal coordinates [INPU 74-76]	8
Read and write the fixity conditions [INPU 80-87]	9
Read and write element properties [INPU 91-100]	10
If a free vibration analysis is required go to end, otherwise continue [INPU 101]	11
Read and write initial stress data sets [INPU 105-113]	12

Figure 6.2 NS chart for INPUT

```
      SUBROUTINE INPUT   (COORD,ICONT,IFPRE,ILBTO,ISTRN,LNODS,MATNO,
     .                    MVFIX,MISTR,MMATS,MPOIN,MELEM,NPOIN,NELEM,
     .                    NVFIX,NNODE,NDOFN,NMATS,NDIME,NMODE,NEVAB,
     .                    NISTR,NOFIX,PROPS,STREM)
C***********************************************************************
C
C***  INPUT MAIN DATA
C
C***********************************************************************
      IMPLICIT REAL*8(A-H,O-Z)
C
      DIMENSION COORD(MPOIN,NDIME),IFPRE(MVFIX,NDOFN),ISTRN(MELEM),
     .          LNODS(MELEM,9),MATNO(MELEM),NOFIX(MVFIX),PROPS(MMATS,8),
     .          STREM(MISTR,3),TITLE(20)
C
      READ(5,870) TITLE
      WRITE(6,875)TITLE
  870 FORMAT(20A4)
  875 FORMAT(///,1X,20A4)
C
      READ(5,880)ICONT
  880 FORMAT(I5)
      GO TO (2,4,6)ICONT
    2 WRITE(6,885)ICONT
  885 FORMAT(//34H THIS IS A FREE VIBRATION ANALYSIS,4X,6HICONT=,I3)
      GO TO 8
    4 WRITE(6,890)ICONT
  890 FORMAT(//49H THIS IS AN INITIALLY STRESSED VIBRATION ANALYSIS,
     .       4X,6HICONT=,I3)
      GO TO 8
    6 WRITE(6,895)ICONT
  895 FORMAT(//28H THIS IS A BUCKLING ANALYSIS,4X,6HICONT=,I3)
C
C*** READ THE FIRST DATA CARD, AND ECHO IT IMMEDIATELY.
C
    8 READ(5,900) NPOIN,NELEM,NVFIX,NMATS,NISTR,ILBTO,NMODE
  900 FORMAT(14I5)
      NEVAB=NDOFN*NNODE
      WRITE(6,905) NPOIN,NELEM,NVFIX,NMATS,NISTR,ILBTO,NMODE
  905 FORMAT(//8H NPOIN =,I4,4X,8H NELEM =,I4,4X,8H NVFIX =,I4,4X,
     .8H NMATS =,I4,//8H NISTR =,I4,4X,8H ILBTO =,I4,4X,8H NMODE =,I4)
C
C*** READ THE ELEMENT NODAL CONNECTIONS, AND THE PROPERTY NUMBERS.
C
      WRITE(6,910)
  910 FORMAT(//6H ELEM.,2X,7HMAT.SET,12X,12HNODE NUMBERS,20X,7HSTR.SET)
      DO 10 IELEM=1,NELEM
      READ(5,900)NUMEL,MATNO(NUMEL),(LNODS(NUMEL,INODE),INODE=1,NNODE),
     .           ISTRN(NUMEL)
   10 WRITE(6,915)NUMEL,MATNO(NUMEL),(LNODS(NUMEL,INODE),INODE=1,NNODE),
     .             ISTRN(NUMEL)
  915 FORMAT(1X,I3,5X,I3,1X,9I5,2X,I3)
C
C*** ZERO ALL THE NODAL COORDINATES, PRIOR TO READING SOME OF THEM.
C
      DO 20 IPOIN=1,NPOIN
      DO 20 IDIME=1,NDIME
   20 COORD(IPOIN,IDIME)=0.0
```

```
C
C*** READ SOME NODAL COORDINATES, FINISHING WITH THE LAST NODE OF ALL.
C
      WRITE(6,920)
  920 FORMAT(//25H  NODAL POINT COORDINATES)
      WRITE(6,925)
  925 FORMAT(6H  NODE,7X,1HX,9X,1HY)
   30 READ(5,930) IPOIN,(COORD(IPOIN,IDIME),IDIME=1,NDIME)
  930 FORMAT(I5,5F10.5)
      IF(IPOIN.NE.NPOIN) GO TO 30
C
C*** INTERPOLATE COORDINATES OF MID-SIDE NODES
C
      CALL NODEXY(COORD,LNODS,MELEM,MPOIN,NDIME,
     .            NELEM,NNODE)
      DO 50 IPOIN=1,NPOIN
   50 WRITE(6,935) IPOIN,(COORD(IPOIN,IDIME),IDIME=1,NDIME)
  935 FORMAT(1X,I5,3F10.3)
C
C*** READ THE FIXED VALUES.
C
      WRITE(6,940)
  940 FORMAT(//17H RESTRAINED NODES)
      WRITE(6,945)
  945 FORMAT(5H NODE,1X,4HCODE)
   70 DO 80 IVFIX=1,NVFIX
      READ(5,950) NOFIX(IVFIX),(IFPRE(IVFIX,IDOFN),IDOFN=1,NDOFN)
   80 WRITE(6,950) NOFIX(IVFIX),(IFPRE(IVFIX,IDOFN),IDOFN=1,NDOFN)
  950 FORMAT(1X,I4,2X,3I1)
C
C*** READ THE AVAILABLE SELECTION OF ELEMENT PROPERTIES.
C
      WRITE(6,960)
  960 FORMAT(//21H  MATERIAL PROPERTIES)
      WRITE(6,965)
  965 FORMAT(8H  NUMBER,7X,10HPROPERTIES)
      DO 100 IMATS=1,NMATS
      READ(5,900)NUMAT
      READ(5,970) (PROPS(NUMAT,IPROP),IPROP=1,8)
  970 FORMAT(8F10.5)
  100 WRITE(6,980) NUMAT,(PROPS(NUMAT,IPROP),IPROP=1,8)
  980 FORMAT(1X,I5,7X,3E14.6/13X,3E14.6/13X,2E14.6)
      IF (ICONT.EQ.1) GO TO 110
C
C*** READ THE INITIAL IN-PLANE STRESSES
C
      WRITE(6,985)
  985 FORMAT(//30H THE INITIAL IN-PLANE STRESSES)
      WRITE(6,990)
  990 FORMAT(7H NUMBER,5X,7HSIGMA-X,6X,7HSIGMA-Y,6X,8HSIGMA-XY)
      DO 120 IISTR=1,NISTR
      READ(5,995)NUSTR,(STREM(NUSTR,IPROP),IPROP=1,3)
  995 FORMAT(I5,3F10.5)
  120 WRITE(6,1000)NUSTR,(STREM(NUSTR,IPROP),IPROP=1,3)
 1000 FORMAT(I5,1X,3E14.6)
  110 RETURN
      END
```

6.4.2 Subroutine NODEXY

```
      SUBROUTINE NODEXY    (COORD,LNODS,MELEM,MPOIN,NDIME,
                            NELEM,NNODE)
C**********************************************************************
C
C***  INTERPOLATES MIDSIDE NODE COORDINATES FOR 9-NODED
C***  ELEMENTS PROVIDED THAT THE SIDES ARE STRAIGHT
C
C**********************************************************************
      IMPLICIT REAL*8(A-H,O-Z)
C
      DIMENSION COORD(MPOIN,NDIME),LNODS(MELEM,9)
C
      LNODE=NNODE-1
C
C*** LOOP OVER EACH ELEMENT
C
      DO 70 IELEM = 1,NELEM
C
C*** LOOP OVER EACH ELEMENT EDGE
C
      DO 80 INODE = 1,LNODE,2
C
C*** COMPUTE THE NODE NUMBER OF THE FIRST NODE
C
      NODST = LNODS(IELEM,INODE)
      IGASH = INODE + 2
      IF(IGASH.GT.LNODE) IGASH = 1
C
C*** COMPUTE THE NODE NUMBER OF THE LAST NODE
C
      NODFN = LNODS(IELEM,IGASH)
      MIDPT = INODE + 1
C
C*** COMPUTE THE NODE NUMBER OF THE INTERMEDIATE NODE
C
      NODMD = LNODS(IELEM,MIDPT)
      TOTAL = ABS(COORD(NODMD,1))+ ABS(COORD(NODMD,2))
C
C*** IF THE COORDINATE OF THE INTERMEDIATE NODE ARE BOTH ZERO
C    INTERPOLATE BY A STRAIGHT LINE.
C
      IF (TOTAL.GT.0.0) GO TO 80
      KOUNT = 1
   50 COORD(NODMD,KOUNT) = (COORD(NODFN,KOUNT) + COORD(NODST,KOUNT))/2
      KOUNT = KOUNT + 1
      IF(KOUNT.EQ.2) GO TO 50
   80 CONTINUE
   70 CONTINUE
C
      RETURN
      END
```

6.5 STIFFNESS MODULE

6.5.1 Subroutine STIFPB

The main function of STIFPB is to evaluate stiffness matrices and geometric stiffness matrices for elastic Mindlin plate elements. The NS chart for STIFPB is listed in Figure 6.3.

Rewind files 1 and 2 ready for writing stiffness matrices and geometric stiffness matrices [STIF 21-22] 1

Loop over each element [STIF 26] 2

Extract element material set number and nodal coordinates [STIF 27-35] 3

Initialise stiffness matrix array ESTIF and integration point counter [STIF 39-46] 4

Call GAUSSQ to extract sampling positions and weights for 3-point Gauss-Legendre rule used in the numerical integration [STIF 53] 5

Loop over each Gauss point in ξ-direction [STIF 54] 6

Extract ξ sampling point [STIF 55] 7

Loop over each Gauss point in η-direction STIF 56] 8

Extract η sampling point and increment Gauss point counter by 1 [STIF 57-58] 9

Accumulate contributions from $\underline{K}_b^e$ to the upper triangular part of $\underline{K}^e$ [STIF 62-83] 10

Re-initialise Gauss point counter KSAMP [STIF 88] 11

Call BSAMP to sample B matrix at 12 points [STIF 89] 12

A

A

Call GAUSSQ to extract sampling positions and weights for 3-point Gauss-Legendre rule used in numerical integration
[STIF 96] 13

Loop over each Gauss point in ξ-direction
[STIF 97] 14

Extract ξ sampling point
[STIF 98] 15

Loop over each Gauss point in η-direction
[STIF 99] 16

Extract η sampling point and increment Gauss point counter by 1
[STIF 100-101] 17

Accumulate contributions from $\underline{K}_s^e$ to the upper triangular part of $\underline{K}^e$
[STIF 105-122] 18

Make $\underline{K}^e$ symmetric and write to file 1 for later use
[STIF 126-132] 19

If a free vibration analysis is required with no initial stress go to end otherwise continue
[STIF 133] 20

Extract element initial stress set number
[STIF 134] 21

Initialise geometric stiffness matrix array GSTIF and integration point counter
[STIF 138-145] 22

Evaluate part of geometric stiffness matrix associated with bending deformation
<u>Repeat steps 5-10</u>
[STIF 146-164] 23-28

Loop over two parts of geometric stiffness matrix associated with shear deformation
[STIF 169] 29

Initialise integration point counter
[STIF 170] 30

Evaluate part of geometric stiffness matrix associated with shear deformation
<u>Repeat steps 5-10</u>
[STIF 171-190] 31-36

Make $\underline{K}_G^e$ symmetric and write to file 2 for later use
[STIF 191-194] 37

<u>Figure 6.3</u> NS chart for STIFPB

The expanded chart for the section dealing with the numerical integration of bending stiffness matrix $\underline{K}_b^e$ is given in Figure 6.4.

Call SFR2 to evaluate $N_i, N_{i,\xi}, N_{i,\eta}$ at Gauss points [STIF 62] 10.1

Call JACOB2 to evaluate $\underline{J}, \underline{J}^{-1}, \det\underline{J}, N_{i,x}, N_{i,y}$ and Gauss point coordinates [STIF 63-64] 10.2

Evaluate DAREA=det$\underline{J}$ * Gauss point weights [STIF 65] 10.3

Call MODPB to evaluate $\underline{D}_b$ [STIF 69-70] 10.4

Loop over inode = 1,9 [STIF 75] 10.5

Call BMATPB to evaluate $\underline{B}_b$ (inode) [STIF 76-77] 10.6

Loop over jnode=inode,9 [STIF 78] 10.7

Call BMATPB to evaluate $\underline{B}_b$ (jnode) [STIF 79-80] 10.8

Call SUBPB to evaluate contribution to bending stiffness sub-matrix $\underline{K}_b^e$ (inode,jnode) [STIF 81-82] 10.9

Figure 6.4 NS chart for numerical integration of $\underline{K}_b^e$

The expanded chart for the section dealing with the numerical integration of the shear stiffness matrix $\underline{K}_s^e$ is given in Figure 6.5.

Call SFR2 to evaluate $N_i, N_{i,\xi}, N_{i,\eta}$ at Gauss points [STIF 105]	18.1
Call JACOB2 to evaluate $\underline{J}, \underline{J}^{-1}$, det$\underline{J}$, $N_{i,x}, N_{i,y}$ and Gauss point coordinates [STIF 106-107]	18.2
Call SFRM to evaluate shear shape functions SHAP1 and SHAP2 [STIF 108]	18.3
Evaluate DAREA=det$\underline{J}$ * Gauss point weights [STIF 109]	18.4
Call MODPB to evaluate $\underline{D}_s$ [STIF 110]	18.5
Loop over inode=1,9 [STIF 111]	18.6
Set up counter IPOSN=(inode-1)*3 necessary for later matrix multiplications [STIF 112]	18.7
Call BMOTPB to evaluate $\bar{\underline{B}}_s$ (inode) [STIF 113]	18.8
Loop over jnode=inode,9 [STIF 114]	18.9
Set up counter IPOSN=(jnode-1)*3 necessary for later matrix multiplications [STIF 115]	18.10
CALL BMOTPB to evaluate $\bar{\underline{B}}_s$ (jnode) [STIF 116]	18.11
Call SUBPB to evaluate contributions to shear stiffness sub-matrix $\underline{K}_s^e$ (inode, jnode) [STIF 117-118]	18.12

Figure 6.5 NS chart for numerical integration of $\underline{K}_s^e$

The expanded chart for the section dealing with the numerical integration of the bending geometric stiffness matrix $\underline{K}^e_{Gb}$ is given in Figure 6.6. The numerical integration of $\underline{K}^e_{Gs}$ is performed in a similar manner.

Call SFR2 to evaluate N_i, $N_{i,\xi}$, $N_{i,\eta}$ at Gauss points [STIF 152] 28.1

Call JACOB2 to evaluate $\underline{J}$, $\underline{J}^{-1}$, det$\underline{J}$, $N_{i,x}$, $N_{i,y}$ and Gauss point coordinates [STIF 153-154] 28.2

Evaluate DAREA = det$\underline{J}$ $*$ Gauss point weights [STIF 155] 28.3

Call SIGMAT to evaluate $\hat{\underline{\sigma}}^o$ [STIF 156-157] 28.4

Loop over inode=1,9 [STIF 158] 28.5

- Call GMATPB to evaluate $\underline{G}_b$ (inode) [STIF 159] 28.6
- Loop over jnode=inode,9 [STIF 160] 28.7
  - Call GMATPB to evaluate $\underline{G}_b$ (jnode) [STIF 161] 28.8
  - Call SUBPB to evaluate contribution to bending geometric sub-matrix $\underline{K}^e_{Gb}$ (inode, jnode) [STIF 162-163] 28.9

Figure 6.6 NS chart for numerical integration of $\underline{K}^e_{Gb}$

```
      SUBROUTINE STIFPB (COORD,ICONT,ISTRN,LNODS,MATNO,MELEM,           STIF   1
     .                  MEVAB,MMATS,MISTR,MPOIN,NELEM,NEVAB,            STIF   2
     .                  NGAUB,NGAUS,NNODE,PROPS,STREM)                  STIF   3
C***********************************************************************STIF   4
C                                                                       STIF   5
C*** EVALUATE STIFFNESS MATRICES AND GEOMETRIC STIFFNESS MATRICES       STIF   6
C*** FOR ELASTIC MINDLIN PLATE ELEMENTS                                 STIF   7
C                                                                       STIF   8
C***********************************************************************STIF   9
      IMPLICIT REAL*8(A-H,O-Z)                                          STIF  10
```

```
      DIMENSION
     .          BSHEI(2,3),BSHEJ(2,3),BMETA(6,27),BMEXI(6,27),
     .          BFLEI(3,3),BFLEJ(3,3),CARTD(2,9),COORD(MPOIN,2),
     .          DERIV(2,9),DFLEX(3,3),DSHER(2,2),
     .          ELCOD(2,9),ESTIF(27,27),GSTIF(27,27),GPCOD(2,9),
     .          GFLEI(2,3),GFLEJ(2,3),GSHEI(2,3),GSHEJ(2,3),
     .          ISTRN(MELEM),LNODS(MELEM,9),MATNO(MELEM),POSGP(3),
     .          PROPS(MMATS,8),SHAPE(9),SHAP1(6),SHAP2(6),
     .          STREM(MISTR,3),SIGMX(2,2),WEIGP(3),XJACI(2,2),
     .          XJACM(2,2)
      REWIND 1
      REWIND 2
C
C*** LOOP OVER EACH ELEMENT
C
      DO 80 IELEM=1,NELEM
      LPROP=MATNO(IELEM)
C
C*** EVALUATE THE COORDINATES OF THE ELEMENT NODAL POINTS
C
      DO 10 INODE=1,NNODE
      LNODE=LNODS(IELEM,INODE)
      LNODE=IABS(LNODE)
      DO 10 IDIME=1,2
   10 ELCOD(IDIME,INODE)=COORD(LNODE,IDIME)
C
C*** INITIALIZE THE ELEMENT STIFFNESS MATRIX
C
      DO 20 IEVAB=1,NEVAB
      DO 20 JEVAB=1,NEVAB
   20 ESTIF(IEVAB,JEVAB)=0.0
C
C*** EVALUATE PART OF STIFFNESS MATRIX
C    ASSOCIATED WITH BENDING DEFORMATION
C
      KGASP=0
C
C*** ENTER LOOPS FOR AREA NUMERICAL INTEGRATION
C
C
C*** SET UP GAUSSIAN INTEGRATION CONSTANTS
C
      CALL      GAUSSQ    (NGAUB,POSGP,WEIGP)
      DO 40 IGAUS=1,NGAUB
      EXISP=POSGP(IGAUS)
      DO 40 JGAUS=1,NGAUB
      KGASP=KGASP+1
      ETASP=POSGP(JGAUS)
C
C*** EVALUATE THE SHAPE FUNCTIONS,ELEMENTAL AREA,ETC
C
      CALL      SFR2      (DERIV,ETASP,EXISP,NNODE,SHAPE)
      CALL      JACOB2    (CARTD,DERIV,DJACB,ELCOD,GPCOD,IELEM,
     .                     KGASP,NNODE,SHAPE,XJACI,XJACM)
      DAREA=DJACB*WEIGP(IGAUS)*WEIGP(JGAUS)
C
C*** EVALUATE THE B AND DB MATRICES
C
      CALL      MODPB     (DFLEX,DSHER,LPROP,MMATS,PROPS,
     .                         1,     0)
C
```

```
C
C*** CALCULATE THE ELEMENT STIFFNESSES
C
      DO 30 INODE=1,NNODE
      CALL      BMATPB    (BFLEI,BSHEI,CARTD,INODE,SHAPE,
     .                         1,    0)
      DO 30 JNODE=INODE,NNODE
      CALL      BMATPB    (BFLEJ,BSHEJ,CARTD,JNODE,SHAPE,
     .                         1,    0)
   30 CALL      SUBPB     (BFLEI,BFLEJ,DAREA,DFLEX,ESTIF,INODE,
     .                     JNODE,    3,    3,    3)
   40 CONTINUE
C
C*** EVALUATE PART OF STIFFNESS MATRIX
C    ASSOCIATED WITH SHEAR DEFORMATION
C
      KGASP=0
      CALL BSAMP(BMETA,BMEXI,ELCOD,IELEM,NNODE)
C
C*** ENTER LOOPS FOR AREA INTEGRATION
C
C
C*** SET UP GAUSSIAN INTEGRATION CONSTANTS
C
      CALL      GAUSSQ      (NGAUS,POSGP,WEIGP)
      DO 60 IGAUS=1,NGAUS
      EXISP=POSGP(IGAUS)
      DO 60 JGAUS=1,NGAUS
      KGASP=KGASP+1
      ETASP=POSGP(JGAUS)
C
C*** EVALUATE THE SHAPE FUNCTIONS,ELEMENTAL AREA,ETC
C
      CALL       SFR2       (DERIV,ETASP,EXISP,NNODE,SHAPE)
      CALL       JACOB2     (CARTD,DERIV,DJACB,ELCOD,GPCOD,IELEM,
     .                       KGASP,NNODE,SHAPE,XJACI,XJACM)
      CALL SFRM(ETASP,EXISP,SHAP1,SHAP2)
      DAREA=DJACB*WEIGP(IGAUS)*WEIGP(JGAUS)
      CALL MODPB(DFLEX,DSHER,LPROP,MMATS,PROPS,0,1)
      DO 50 INODE=1,NNODE
      IPOSN=(INODE-1)*3
      CALL BMOTPB(BMETA,BMEXI,BSHEI,IPOSN,SHAP1,SHAP2,XJACI)
      DO 50 JNODE=INODE,NNODE
      IPOSN=(JNODE-1)*3
      CALL BMOTPB(BMETA,BMEXI,BSHEJ,IPOSN,SHAP1,SHAP2,XJACI)
      CALL SUBPB(BSHEI,BSHEJ,DAREA,DSHER,ESTIF,INODE,
     .          JNODE,3,2,3)
   50 CONTINUE
C
C
   60 CONTINUE
C
C*** CONSTRUCT THE LOWER TRIANGLE OF THE STIFFNESS MATRIX
C
      DO 70 IEVAB=1,NEVAB
      DO 70 JEVAB=IEVAB,NEVAB
   70 ESTIF(JEVAB,IEVAB)=ESTIF(IEVAB,JEVAB)
C
C*** STORE THE STIFFNESS MATRIX ON DISC FILE
C
      WRITE(1) ESTIF
      IF (ICONT.EQ.1) GO TO 80
```

```
      NPROP=ISTRN(IELEM)
C
C*** INITIALIZE THE GEOMETRIC ELEMENT STIFFNESS MATRIX
C
      DO 90 IEVAB=1,NEVAB
      DO 90 JEVAB=1,NEVAB
   90 GSTIF(IEVAB,JEVAB)=0.0
C
C*** EVALUATE PART OF GEOMETRIC STIFFNESS MATRIX ASSOCIATED
C    WITH BENDING DEFORMATION
C
      KGASP=0
      CALL    GAUSSQ    (NGAUB,POSGP,WEIGP)
      DO 100 IGAUS=1,NGAUB
      EXISP=POSGP(IGAUS)
      DO 100 JGAUS=1,NGAUB
      KGASP=KGASP+1
      ETASP=POSGP(JGAUS)
      CALL    SFR2      (DERIV,ETASP,EXISP,NNODE,SHAPE)
      CALL    JACOB2    (CARTD,DERIV,DJACB,ELCOD,GPCOD,IELEM,
     .                   KGASP,NNODE,SHAPE,XJACI,XJACM)
      DAREA=DJACB*WEIGP(IGAUS)*WEIGP(JGAUS)
      CALL    SIGMAT    (LPROP,MISTR,MMATS,NPROP,PROPS,STREM,
     .                   SIGMX,    1,     0)
      DO 110 INODE=1,NNODE
      CALL    GMATPB    (GFLEI,GSHEI,CARTD,INODE,     1,     0)
      DO 110 JNODE=INODE,NNODE
      CALL    GMATPB    (GFLEJ,GSHEJ,CARTD,JNODE,     1,     0)
  110 CALL    SUBPB     (GFLEI,GFLEJ,DAREA,SIGMX,GSTIF,INODE,
     .                   JNODE,     3,     2,     3)
  100 CONTINUE
C
C*** EVALUATE PART OF GEOMETRIC STIFFNESS MATRIX ASSOCIATED
C    WITH SHEAR DEFORMATION
C
      DO 120 IGSHE=1,2
      KGASP=0
      CALL    GAUSSQ    (NGAUS,POSGP,WEIGP)
      DO 130 IGAUS=1,NGAUS
      EXISP=POSGP(IGAUS)
      DO 130 JGAUS=1,NGAUS
      KGASP=KGASP+1
      ETASP=POSGP(JGAUS)
      CALL    SFR2      (DERIV,ETASP,EXISP,NNODE,SHAPE)
      CALL    JACOB2    (CARTD,DERIV,DJACB,ELCOD,GPCOD,IELEM,
     .                   KGASP,NNODE,SHAPE,XJACI,XJACM)
      DAREA=DJACB*WEIGP(IGAUS)*WEIGP(JGAUS)
      CALL    SIGMAT    (LPROP,MISTR,MMATS,NPROP,PROPS,STREM,
     .                   SIGMX,    0,     1)
      DO 140 INODE=1,NNODE
      CALL    GMATPB    (GFLEI,GSHEI,CARTD,INODE,     0,IGSHE)
      DO 140 JNODE=INODE,NNODE
      CALL    GMATPB    (GFLEJ,GSHEJ,CARTD,JNODE,     0,IGSHE)
  140 CALL    SUBPB     (GSHEI,GSHEJ,DAREA,SIGMX,GSTIF,INODE,
     .                   JNODE,     3,     2,     3)
  130 CONTINUE
  120 CONTINUE
      DO 150 IEVAB=1,NEVAB
      DO 150 JEVAB=IEVAB,NEVAB
  150 GSTIF(JEVAB,IEVAB)=GSTIF(IEVAB,JEVAB)
      WRITE(2) GSTIF
   80 CONTINUE
      RETURN
      END
```

6.5.2 Subroutine GAUSSQ

```
      SUBROUTINE GAUSSQ    (NGAUS,POSGP,WEIGP)
C**********************************************************************
C
C***  SETS UP GAUSS-LEGENDRE SAMPLING POSITIONS AND WEIGHTS
C
C**********************************************************************
      IMPLICIT REAL*8(A-H,O-Z)
      DIMENSION POSGP(3),WEIGP(3)
      GO TO (1,2,3) NGAUS
    1 POSGP(1)= 0.
      WEIGP(1)= 2.
      RETURN
    2 POSGP(1)=-0.577350269189626
      POSGP(2)= 0.577350269189626
      WEIGP(1)= 1.
      WEIGP(2)= 1.
      RETURN
    3 POSGP(1)=-0.774596669241483
      POSGP(2)= 0.
      POSGP(3)= 0.774596669241483
      WEIGP(1)= 0.555555555555556
      WEIGP(2)= 0.888888888888889
      WEIGP(3)= 0.555555555555556
      RETURN
      END
```

6.5.3 Subroutine SFR2

```
      SUBROUTINE SFR2   (DERIV,ETASP,EXISP,NNODE,SHAPE)
C**********************************************************************
C
C*** EVALUATES SHAPE FUNCTIONS AND THEIR DERIVATIVES FOR
C*** 9 NODED QUADRATIC QUADRILATERAL ISOPARAMETRIC ELEMENTS
C
C**********************************************************************
      IMPLICIT REAL*8(A-H,O-Z)
C
      DIMENSION DERIV(2,9),SHAPE(9)
C
      S=EXISP
      T=ETASP
C
C*** SHAPE FUNCTIONS
C
      SHAPE(1) = 0.25*S*(S-1.)*T*(T-1.)
      SHAPE(2) = 0.5*(1.-S*S)*T*(T-1.)
      SHAPE(3) = 0.25*S*(S+1.)*T*(T-1.)
      SHAPE(4) = 0.5*S*(S+1.)*(1.-T*T)
      SHAPE(5) = 0.25*S*(S+1.)*T*(T+1.)
      SHAPE(6) = 0.5*(1.-S*S)*T*(T+1.)
      SHAPE(7) = 0.25*(S-1.)*S*T*(T+1.)
      SHAPE(8) = 0.5*S*(S-1.)*(1.-T*T)
      SHAPE(9) = (1.-S*S)*(1.-T*T)
C
C*** SHAPE FUNCTION DERIVATIVES
C
```

```
      DERIV(1,1) = 0.25*T*(T-1.)*(-1.+2.*S)
      DERIV(1,2) =-0.5*2.*S*T*(T-1.)
      DERIV(1,3) = 0.25*(1+2.*S)*T*(T-1.)
      DERIV(1,4) = 0.5*(1.+2.*S)*(1.-T*T)
      DERIV(1,5) = 0.25*(1.+2.*S)*T*(T+1.)
      DERIV(1,6) =-S*T*(T+1.)
      DERIV(1,7) = 0.25*(-1.+2.*S)*T*(T+1.)
      DERIV(1,8) = 0.5*(-1.+2.*S)*(1.-T*T)
      DERIV(1,9) =-2.*S*(1.-T*T)
C
      DERIV(2,1) = 0.25*(-1.+2.*T)*S*(S-1.)
      DERIV(2,2) = 0.5*(1.-S*S)*(-1.+2.*T)
      DERIV(2,3) = 0.25*S*(S+1.)*(-1.+2.*T)
      DERIV(2,4) =-S*T*(S+1.)
      DERIV(2,5) = 0.25*S*(S+1.)*(1.+2.*T)
      DERIV(2,6) = 0.5*(1.-S*S)*(1.+2.*T)
      DERIV(2,7) = 0.25*S*(S-1.)*(1.+2.*T)
      DERIV(2,8) =-S*T*(S-1.)
      DERIV(2,9) =-2.*T*(1.-S*S)
      RETURN
      END
```

6.5.4 Subroutine JACOB2

```
      SUBROUTINE JACOB2     (CARTD,DERIV,DJACB,ELCOD,GPCOD,IELEM,
     .                       KGASP,NNODE,SHAPE,XJACI,XJACM)
C***********************************************************************
C
C***  EVALUATE JACOBIAN MATRIX AND ITS INVERSE
C***  GAUSS POINT COORDINATES
C***  CARTESIAN SHAPE FUNCTION DERIVATIVES
C***  AT PRESENT SAMPLING POINT
C
C***********************************************************************
      IMPLICIT REAL*8(A-H,O-Z)
      DIMENSION CARTD(2,9),DERIV(2,9),ELCOD(2,9) ,GPCOD(2,9) ,SHAPE(9),
     .          XJACI(2,2),XJACM(2,2)
C
C***  CALCULATE COORDINATES OF SAMPLING POINT
C
      DO 2 IDIME=1,2
      GPCOD(IDIME,KGASP)=0.0
      DO 2 INODE=1,NNODE
      GPCOD(IDIME,KGASP)=GPCOD(IDIME,KGASP)+ELCOD(IDIME,INODE)
     .*SHAPE(INODE)
    2 CONTINUE
C
C***  CREATE JACOBIAN MATRIX XJACM
C
      DO 4 IDIME=1,2
      DO 4 JDIME=1,2
      XJACM(IDIME,JDIME)=0.0
      DO 4 INODE=1,NNODE
      XJACM(IDIME,JDIME)=XJACM(IDIME,JDIME)+DERIV(IDIME,INODE)*
     .ELCOD(JDIME,INODE)
    4 CONTINUE
C
C***  CALCULATE DETERMINANT AND INVERSE OF JACOBIAN MATRIX
C
      DJACB=XJACM(1,1)*XJACM(2,2)-XJACM(1,2)*XJACM(2,1)
```

```
      IF(DJACB) 6,6,8
    6 WRITE(6,900) IELEM
      STOP
    8 CONTINUE
      XJACI(1,1)=XJACM(2,2)/DJACB
      XJACI(2,2)=XJACM(1,1)/DJACB
      XJACI(1,2)=-XJACM(1,2)/DJACB
      XJACI(2,1)=-XJACM(2,1)/DJACB
C
C***  CALCULATE CARTESIAN DERIVATIVES
C
      DO 10 IDIME=1,2
      DO 10 INODE=1,NNODE
      CARTD(IDIME,INODE)=0.0
      DO 10 JDIME=1,2
      CARTD(IDIME,INODE)=CARTD(IDIME,INODE)+XJACI(IDIME,JDIME)*
     .DERIV(JDIME,INODE)
   10 CONTINUE
  900 FORMAT(//,36H PROGRAM HALTED IN SUBROUTINE JACOB2,/,11X,
     .22H ZERO OR NEGATIVE AREA,/,10X,16H ELEMENT NUMBER ,I5)
      RETURN
      END
```

6.5.5 Subroutine MODPB

```
      SUBROUTINE MODPB      (DFLEX,DSHER,LPROP,MMATS,PROPS,
     .                       IFFLE,IFSHE)
C**********************************************************************
C
C*** CALCULATES MATRIX OF ELASTIC RIGIDITIES
C*** FOR MINDLIN PLATE
C
C**********************************************************************
      IMPLICIT REAL*8(A-H,O-Z)
      DIMENSION DFLEX(3,3),DSHER(2,2),
     .          PROPS(MMATS,8)
      IF(PROPS(LPROP,4).NE.0.0) GO TO 30
      YOUNG=PROPS(LPROP,1)
      POISS=PROPS(LPROP,2)
      THICK=PROPS(LPROP,3)
C
C*** FORM DFLEX (ISOTROPIC)
C
   10 IF(IFFLE.EQ.0) GO TO 20
      CALL RAZERO(DFLEX,3,3)
      CONST=(YOUNG*THICK**3)/(12.*(1.-POISS*POISS))
      DFLEX(1,1)=CONST
      DFLEX(2,2)=CONST
      DFLEX(1,2)=CONST*POISS
      DFLEX(2,1)=CONST*POISS
      DFLEX(3,3)=CONST*(1.-POISS)/2.
C
C*** FORM DSHER (ISOPTROPIC)
C
   20 IF(IFSHE.EQ.0) RETURN
      CALL RAZERO(DSHER,2,2)
      DSHER(1,1)=(YOUNG*THICK)/(2.4+2.4*POISS)
      DSHER(2,2)=(YOUNG*THICK)/(2.4+2.4*POISS)
      RETURN
C
C*** FORM DFLEX (ORTHOTROPIC)
C
```

```
   30 IF(IFFLE.EQ.0) GO TO 40
      CALL RAZERO(DFLEX,3,3)
      DFLEX(1,1)=PROPS(LPROP,1)
      DFLEX(1,2)=PROPS(LPROP,2)
      DFLEX(2,1)=PROPS(LPROP,2)
      DFLEX(2,2)=PROPS(LPROP,3)
      DFLEX(3,3)=PROPS(LPROP,4)
C
C*** FORM DSHER (ORTHOTROPIC)
C
   40 IF(IFSHE.EQ.0) RETURN
      CALL RAZERO(DSHER,2,2)
      DSHER(1,1)=PROPS(LPROP,5)
      DSHER(2,2)=PROPS(LPROP,6)
      RETURN
      END
```

6.5.6 Subroutine BMATPB

```
      SUBROUTINE BMATPB    (BFLEX,BSHER,CARTD,KNODE,SHAPE,
     .                      IFFLE,IFSHE)
C**********************************************************************
C
C*** EVALUATES STRAIN-DISPLACEMENT MATRIX FOR
C*** FOR MINDLIN PLATE
C
C**********************************************************************
      IMPLICIT REAL*8(A-H,O-Z)
      DIMENSION  BFLEX(3,3),BSHER(2,3),
     .           CARTD(2,9),SHAPE(9)
      DNKDX=CARTD(1,KNODE)
      DNKDY=CARTD(2,KNODE)
C*** FORM BFLEX
   10 IF(IFFLE.EQ.0) GO TO 20
      CALL RAZERO(BFLEX,3,3)
      BFLEX(1,2)=-DNKDX
      BFLEX(2,3)=-DNKDY
      BFLEX(3,2)=-DNKDY
      BFLEX(3,3)=-DNKDX
C*** FORM BSHER
   20 IF(IFSHE.EQ.0) RETURN
      CALL RAZERO(BSHER,2,3)
      BSHER(1,1)=DNKDX
      BSHER(1,2)=-SHAPE(KNODE)
      BSHER(2,1)=DNKDY
      BSHER(2,3)=-SHAPE(KNODE)
      RETURN
      END
```

6.5.7 Subroutine SUBPB

```
      SUBROUTINE SUBPB     (BIMAT,BJMAT,DAREA,DMATX,ESTIF,INODE,
     .                      JNODE,NCOLI,NROIJ,NCOLJ)
C**********************************************************************
C
C*** CARRY OUT MATRIX MULTIPLICATION
C
C**********************************************************************
      IMPLICIT REAL*8(A-H.O-Z)
```

```
      DIMENSION BIMAT(NROIJ,NCOLI),BJMAT(NROIJ,NCOLJ),
     .          DMATX(NROIJ,NROIJ),DBMAT(3,3),
     .          ESTIF(27,27),SBSTF(3,3)
C
C*** EVALUATE  D*BJ
C
      DO 10 J=1,NCOLJ
      DO 10 I=1,NROIJ
      DBMAT(I,J)=0.0
      DO 10 K=1,NROIJ
   10 DBMAT(I,J)=DBMAT(I,J)+DMATX(I,K)*BJMAT(K,J)
C
C*** EVALUATE  BIT*(D*BJ)
C
      DO 20 J=1,NCOLJ
      DO 20 I=1,NCOLI
      SBSTF(I,J)=0.0
      DO 20 K=1,NROIJ
   20 SBSTF(I,J)=SBSTF(I,J)+BIMAT(K,I)*DBMAT(K,J)
C
C*** ASSEMBLE SBSTF INTO ELEMENT STIFFNESS MATRIX
C
      IFROW=0
      JFCOL=0
      IFROW=(INODE-1)*3+IFROW
      JFCOL=(JNODE-1)*3+JFCOL
      DO 30 I=1,NCOLI
      IRSUB=IFROW+I
      DO 30 J=1,NCOLJ
      JCSUB=JFCOL+J
   30 ESTIF(IRSUB,JCSUB)=ESTIF(IRSUB,JCSUB)+SBSTF(I,J)*DAREA
      RETURN
      END
```

6.5.8 Subroutine BSAMP

```
      SUBROUTINE BSAMP(BMETA,BMEXI,ELCOD,IELEM,NNODE)
C**********************************************************************
C
C*** SAMPLES B-MATRIX AT 12 POINTS
C
C**********************************************************************
      IMPLICIT REAL*8(A-H,O-Z)
      DIMENSION
     .         BFLEI(3,3),BMETA(6,27),BMEXI(6,27),BSHEI(2,3),
     .         BSHEX(3),CARTD(2,9),DERIV(2,9),ELCOD(2,9),
     .         GPCOD(2,9),PASGP(3),POSGP(3),SHAPE(9),WEIGP(3),
     .         XJACI(2,2),XJACM(2,2)
      DATA  PASGP/1.0,0.0,-1.0/
      CALL GAUSSQ(2,POSGP,WEIGP)
      KGISP=0
      DO 40 ISAMP=1,2
      EXISP=POSGP(ISAMP)
      DO 30 JSAMP=1,3
      KGISP=KGISP+1
      ETASP=PASGP(JSAMP)
      CALL SFR2(DERIV,ETASP,EXISP,NNODE,SHAPE)
      CALL JACOB2(CARTD,DERIV,DJACB,ELCOD,GPCOD,IELEM,KGISP,
     .            NNODE,SHAPE,XJACI,XJACM)
      IPOSN=0
      DO 20 INODE=1,NNODE
```

```
      CALL BMATPB(BFLEI,BSHEI,CARTD,INODE,SHAPE,0,1)
      DO 10 IDOFN=1,3
      IPOSN=IPOSN+1
      BSHEX(IDOFN)=XJACM(1,1)*BSHEI(1,IDOFN)
     .            +XJACM(1,2)*BSHEI(2,IDOFN)
      BMEXI(KGISP,IPOSN)=BSHEX(IDOFN)
   10 CONTINUE
   20 CONTINUE
   30 CONTINUE
   40 CONTINUE
C
      KGISP=0
      DO 80 ISAMP=1,2
      ETASP=POSGP(ISAMP)
      DO 70 JSAMP=1,3
      EXISP=PASGP(JSAMP)
      KGISP=KGISP+1
      CALL SFR2(DERIV,ETASP,EXISP,NNODE,SHAPE)
      CALL JACOB2(CARTD,DERIV,DJACB,ELCOD,GPCOD,
     .            IELEM,KGISP,NNODE,SHAPE,XJACI,XJACM)
      IPOSN=0
      DO 60 INODE=1,NNODE
      CALL BMATPB(BFLEI,BSHEI,CARTD,INODE,SHAPE,0,1)
      DO 50 IDOFN=1,3
      IPOSN=IPOSN+1
      BSHEX(IDOFN)=XJACM(2,1)*BSHEI(1,IDOFN)+
     .             XJACM(2,2)*BSHEI(2,IDOFN)
      BMETA(KGISP,IPOSN)=BSHEX(IDOFN)
   50 CONTINUE
   60 CONTINUE
   70 CONTINUE
   80 CONTINUE
      RETURN
      END
```

6.5.9 Subroutine SFRM

```
      SUBROUTINE SFRM(ETASP,EXISP,SHAP1,SHAP2)
C**********************************************************************
C
C*** SHEAR SHAPE FUNCTIONS
C
C**********************************************************************
      IMPLICIT REAL*8(A-H,O-Z)
      DIMENSION SHAP1(6),SHAP2(6)
      S=EXISP
      T=ETASP
      A=1./SQRT(3.0)
      SHAP1(1)=0.25*(1.-S/A)*T*(1.+T)
      SHAP1(4)=0.25*(1.+S/A)*T*(1.+T)
      SHAP1(2)=0.50*(1.-S/A)*(1.-T*T)
      SHAP1(5)=0.50*(1.+S/A)*(1.-T*T)
      SHAP1(3)=0.25*(1.-S/A)*T*(T-1.)
      SHAP1(6)=0.25*(1.+S/A)*T*(T-1.)
C
      SHAP2(1)=0.25*(1.-T/A)*S*(1.+S)
      SHAP2(4)=0.25*(1.+T/A)*S*(1.+S)
      SHAP2(2)=0.50*(1.-T/A)*(1.-S*S)
      SHAP2(5)=0.50*(1.+T/A)*(1.-S*S)
      SHAP2(3)=0.25*(1.-T/A)*S*(S-1.)
      SHAP2(6)=0.25*(1.+T/A)*S*(S-1.)
      RETURN
      END
```

6.5.10 Subroutine BMOTPB

```
      SUBROUTINE BMOTPB(BMETA,BMEXI,BSHEI,IPOSN,SHAP1,SHAP2,
     .                  XJACI)
C***********************************************************************
C
C*** EVALUATES SUBSTITUTE B-MATRIX
C
C***********************************************************************
      IMPLICIT REAL*8(A-H,O-Z)
      DIMENSION BMETA(6,27),BMEXI(6,27),BSHER(2,3),SHAP1(6),
     .          SHAP2(6),XJACI(2,2),BSHEI(2,3)
      DO 20 IDOFN=1,3
      BSHER(1,IDOFN)=0.0
      BSHER(2,IDOFN)=0.0
      IPOSN=IPOSN+1
      DO 10 IGOSP=1,6
      BSHER(1,IDOFN)=BSHER(1,IDOFN)+
     .               BMEXI(IGOSP,IPOSN)*SHAP1(IGOSP)
      BSHER(2,IDOFN)=BSHER(2,IDOFN)+
     .               BMETA(IGOSP,IPOSN)*SHAP2(IGOSP)
   10 CONTINUE
   20 CONTINUE
      DO 50 ISTRE=1,2
      BSHEI(ISTRE,1)=0.0
      BSHEI(ISTRE,2)=0.0
      BSHEI(ISTRE,3)=0.0
      DO 40 JSTRE=1,2
      DO 30 IDOFN=1,3
      BSHEI(ISTRE,IDOFN)=BSHEI(ISTRE,IDOFN)+
     .XJACI(ISTRE,JSTRE)*BSHER(JSTRE,IDOFN)
   30 CONTINUE
   40 CONTINUE
   50 CONTINUE
      RETURN
      END
```

6.5.11 Subroutine SIGMAT

```
      SUBROUTINE SIGMAT  (LPROP,MISTR,MMATS,NPROP,PROPS,STREM,
     .                   SIGMX,IFFLE,IFSHE)
C***********************************************************************
C
C*** FORMS SIGMA-MATRIX OF INPLANE STRESSES
C
C***********************************************************************
      IMPLICIT REAL*8(A-H,O-Z)
C
      DIMENSION PROPS(MMATS,8),STREM(MISTR,3),SIGMX(2,2)
C
      IF(PROPS(LPROP,4).NE.0.0)GO TO 5
      THICK=PROPS(LPROP,3)
      GO TO 6
    5 THICK=PROPS(LPROP,7)
    6 IF(IFFLE.EQ.0) GO TO 10
```

```
      CONST=THICK
   10 IF(IFSHE.EQ.0) GO TO 20
      CONST=THICK*THICK*THICK/12.
   20 SIGMX(1,1)=CONST*STREM(NPROP,1)
      SIGMX(2,2)=CONST*STREM(NPROP,2)
      SIGMX(1,2)=CONST*STREM(NPROP,3)
      SIGMX(2,1)=CONST*STREM(NPROP,3)
      RETURN
      END
```

6.5.12 Subroutine GMATPB

```
      SUBROUTINE  GMATPB  (GFLEX,GSHER,CARTD,KNODE,IFFLE,IGSHE)
C***********************************************************************
C
C*** CALCULATES G-MATRIX
C
C***********************************************************************
      IMPLICIT REAL*8(A-H,O-Z)
C
      DIMENSION GFLEX(2,3),GSHER(2,3),CARTD(2,9)
C
C*** FORM GFLEX
      IF(IFFLE.EQ.0) GO TO 10
      CALL RAZERO (GFLEX,2,3)
      GFLEX(1,1)=-CARTD(1,KNODE)
      GFLEX(2,1)=-CARTD(2,KNODE)
      RETURN
C*** FORM GSHER1
   10 IF(IGSHE.EQ.2) GO TO 20
      CALL RAZERO (GSHER,2,3)
      GSHER(1,2)=-CARTD(1,KNODE)
      GSHER(2,2)=-CARTD(2,KNODE)
      RETURN
C*** FORM GSHER2
   20 CALL RAZERO (GSHER,2,3)
      GSHER(1,3)=-CARTD(1,KNODE)
      GSHER(2,3)=-CARTD(2,KNODE)
      RETURN
      END
```

6.6 LUMPED MASS MODULE

6.6.1 Subroutine CONMAS

The main function of CONMAS is to evaluate consistent or lumped mass matrices for Mindlin plate elements. The NS chart for CONMAS is listed in Figure 6.7.

Rewind file 7 for writing mass matrices [CONM 16]	1
Initialise mass matrix array EMASS and set point counter to 1 [CONM 17-20]	2
Set LGAUS to 3 and call GAUSSQ to extract sampling positions and weights for 3-point Gauss-Legendre rule used in the numerical integration [CONM 24-25]	3
If ILBTO=1 call SLOBAT to extract sampling positions and weights for 3-point Lobatto integration rule otherwise continue [CONM 26]	4
Loop over each element [CONM 30]	5
Initialise TAREA, extract material set number, h, ρ and nodal coordinates [CONM 31-42]	6
Initialise array CMMAT of mass matrix coefficients [CONM 43-45]	7
Calculate the mass matrix coefficients and the whole area of the element TAREA [CONM 49-63]	8
Initialise ELMAS - total mass of the element [CONM 64]	9
Find the total mass of the element as TAREA = TAREA $*$ h $*$ ρ and as ELMAS = $\sum_{i=1}^{n} \sum_{j=1}^{n} C_{ij}$ [CONM 65-68]	10
Calculate elements of the consistent mass matrix and find their locations in $\underline{M}^e$ [CONM 73-85]	11
Write element mass matrix $\underline{M}^e$ to file 7 for later use [CONM 86]	12

Figure 6.7 NS chart for CONMAS

```
      SUBROUTINE CONMAS(COORD,ILBTO,LNODS,MATNO,MPOIN,
     .                 MELEM,MMATS,NEVAB,NELEM,NNODE,NDIME,
     .                 NDOFN,PROPS)
C**********************************************************************
C
C*** CALCULATES THE MASS/ROTARY INERTIA MATRIX FOR EACH ELEMENT.
C
C**********************************************************************
      IMPLICIT REAL*8(A-H,O-Z)
C
      DIMENSION CARTD(2,9),COORD(MPOIN,NDIME),CMMAT(9,9),
     .          DERIV(2,9),EMASS(27,27),ELCOD(2,9),GPCOD(2,9),
     .          LNODS(MELEM,9),MATNO(MELEM),PROPS(MMATS,8),
     .          POSGP(3),SHAPE(9),WEIGP(3),XJACI(2,2),XJACM(2,2)
C
      REWIND 7
      KGASP=1
      DO 10 IEVAB = 1,NEVAB
      DO 10 JEVAB = 1,NEVAB
   10 EMASS(IEVAB,JEVAB) = 0.0
C
C*** MASS TERMS WILL ALWAYS BE INTEGRATED EXACTLY.
C
      LGAUS=3
      CALL GAUSSQ(LGAUS,POSGP,WEIGP)
      IF(ILBTO.EQ.1)CALL SLOBAT(POSGP,WEIGP)
C
C*** CALCULATE THE ELEMENT NODAL MASSES USING NUMERICAL INTEGRATION
C
      DO 100 IELEM=1,NELEM
      TAREA=0.0
      LPROP=MATNO(IELEM)
      IF(PROPS(LPROP,4).NE.0.0)GO TO 20
      THICK=PROPS(LPROP,3)
      GO TO 30
   20 THICK=PROPS(LPROP,7)
   30 RHOEL=PROPS(LPROP,8)
      DO 40 INODE=1,NNODE
      LNODE=LNODS(IELEM,INODE)
      DO 40 IDIME=1,NDIME
      ELCOD(IDIME,INODE)=COORD(LNODE,IDIME)
   40 CONTINUE
      DO 50 INODE = 1,NNODE
      DO 50 JNODE = 1,NNODE
   50 CMMAT(INODE,JNODE) = 0.0
C
C*** CALCULATE THE CONSISTENT MASS MATRIX USING NUMERICAL INTEGRATION
C
      DO 60 IGAUS = 1,LGAUS
      EXISP = POSGP(IGAUS)
      DO 60 JGAUS = 1,LGAUS
      ETASP = POSGP(JGAUS)
      CALL SFR2(DERIV,ETASP,EXISP,NNODE,SHAPE)
      CALL JACOB2(CARTD,DERIV,DJACB,ELCOD,GPCOD,IELEM,
     .            KGASP,NNODE,SHAPE,XJACI,XJACM)
      DVOLU = DJACB*WEIGP(IGAUS)*WEIGP(JGAUS)
      DO 70 INODE = 1,NNODE
      DO 70 JNODE = 1,NNODE
      CMMAT(INODE,JNODE) = CMMAT(INODE,JNODE) + SHAPE(INODE)*
     .SHAPE(JNODE)*DVOLU
   70 CONTINUE
      TAREA = TAREA + DVOLU
```

```
   60 CONTINUE
      ELMAS = 0.0
      TAREA = TAREA*RHOEL*THICK
      DO 80 INODE = 1,NNODE
      DO 80 JNODE = 1,NNODE
   80 ELMAS = ELMAS + CMMAT(INODE,JNODE)
C
C*** SET UP THE ELEMENT CONSISTENT MASS MATRIX INCLUDING ROTARY INERTIA
C    TERMS
C
      DO 90 INODE = 1,NNODE
      IEVAB = (INODE - 1)*NDOFN
      DO 90 JNODE = 1,NNODE
      JEVAB = IEVAB + 1
      KEVAB = (JNODE - 1)*NDOFN
      LEVAB = KEVAB + 1
      EMASS(JEVAB,LEVAB) = TAREA*CMMAT(INODE,JNODE)/ELMAS
      DO 90 IDOFN = 2,NDOFN
      JEVAB = IEVAB + IDOFN
      LEVAB = KEVAB + IDOFN
      EMASS(JEVAB,LEVAB) = TAREA*CMMAT(INODE,JNODE)*THICK*THICK
     ./(12.0*ELMAS)
   90 CONTINUE
      WRITE(7) EMASS
  100 CONTINUE
      RETURN
      END
```

6.6.2 Subroutine SLOBAT

```
      SUBROUTINE SLOBAT(POSGP,WEIGP)
      IMPLICIT REAL*8(A-H,O-Z)
      DIMENSION POSGP(3),WEIGP(3)
C
C*** LOBATTO INTEGRATION
C
      POSGP(1) = 0.0
      POSGP(2) = 1.0
      POSGP(3) =-1.0
C
      WEIGP(1) = 1.3333333333
      WEIGP(2) = 0.3333333333
      WEIGP(3) = 0.3333333333
      RETURN
      END
```

6.7 EIGENVALUE EVALUATION MODULE

6.7.1 Subroutine BERKEL

Subroutine BERKEL is the interface routine for the eigenvalue solver. It prepares all necessary data for subspace iteration coded in subroutine SSPACE*.

BERKEL calls subroutine COLHT* to calculate column heights and subroutine ADDRES* to calculate addresses of diagonal elements in a banded matrix whose column heights are known. From files 1, 2 and 7 BERKEL reads and rewrites in vector form element stiffness matrices, element mass matrices and geometric stiffness matrices, then calls ADDBAN* to assemble the upper triangular part of those element matrices into the compacted global matrices.

BERKEL reads two indicators for subspace iteration as input data:

IFSS - indicator for Sturm sequence check and

IFPR - indicator for printing during iteration.

---

*The following subroutines are fully described and listed in "Numerical Methods in Finite Element Analysis" by K.J. Bathe and E.L. Wilson, Prentice-Hall, New Jersey, 1976.

COLHT, ADDRES and ADDBAN	pages 227 - 229
SSPACE	pages 509 - 517

To match subroutine BERKEL with subroutine OUTPUT it is necessary to do some modifications in SSPACE and they are

1. Input DATA statement - DATA IOUT1/4/
2. Substitute IOUT with IOUT1 in the following lines:

   SPCE0266 and SPCE 0269 page 511

   SPCE0292 page 512

```
      SUBROUTINE BERKEL (A,AR,B,BR,BS,BUP,BLO,BUPC,D,ER,EIGV,ICONT,
     .                   ID,IFPRE,LM,LNODS,MHT,MAXA,MAHAM,MAXNN,MANNM,
     .                   MITEV,MDISV,MNEBS,MPOIN,MELEM,MVFIX,NMODE,
     .                   NPOIN,NEQ,NVFIX,NOFIX,NDOFN,NELEM,NEVAB,
     .                   NNODE,RTOLV,S,TT,VEC,W)
C**********************************************************************
C
C*** INTERFACE ROUTINE FOR BERKELEY SOLVER AND SUBSPACE ITERATION
C
C**********************************************************************
      IMPLICIT REAL*8(A-H,O-Z)
C
      DIMENSION ESTIF(27,27),EMASS(27,27),GSTIF(27,27),
     .          IFPRE(MVFIX,NDOFN),LNODS(MELEM,9),NOFIX(MVFIX)
      DIMENSION A(MNEBS),AR(MDISV),B(MNEBS),BR(MDISV),BS(MAHAM),
     .          BUP(MITEV),BLO(MITEV),BUPC(MITEV),D(MITEV),
     .          ER(MAXNN,MITEV),EIGV(MITEV),ID(NDOFN,MPOIN),
     .          LM(27,MELEM),MHT(MAXNN),MAXA(MANNM),RTOLV(MITEV),
     .          S(MAHAM),TT(MAXNN),VEC(MITEV,MITEV),W(MAXNN)
      DATA IOUT/3/,NSTIF/8/,NITEM/16/,RTOL/0.000001/
      REWIND 1
      REWIND 2
      REWIND 7
      NROOT=NMODE
C
C***  CREATION OF ID ARRAY
C
      DO 10 IPOIN=1,NPOIN
      DO 20 IVFIX=1,NVFIX
      IF(IPOIN.NE.NOFIX(IVFIX)) GO TO 20
      DO 30 IDOFN=1,NDOFN
30    ID(IDOFN,IPOIN)=IFPRE(IVFIX,IDOFN)
      GO TO 11
20    CONTINUE
      DO 40 IDOFN=1,NDOFN
40    ID(IDOFN,IPOIN)=0
11    CONTINUE
10    CONTINUE
C
C***  NUMBER OF UNKNOWNS
C
      NEQ=0
      DO 100 IPOIN=1,NPOIN
      DO 60 IDOFN=1,NDOFN
      IF(ID(IDOFN,IPOIN)) 110,120,110
120   NEQ=NEQ+1
      ID(IDOFN,IPOIN)=NEQ
      GO TO 60
110   ID(IDOFN,IPOIN)=0
 60   CONTINUE
100   CONTINUE
C
C***  CONNECTIVITY ARRAY LM
C
      DO 50 IELEM=1,NELEM
      DO 70 IEVAB=1,NEVAB
70    LM(IEVAB,IELEM)=0
      IEVAB=1
      DO 80 INODE=1,NNODE
      IDENT=LNODS(IELEM,INODE)
      DO 80 IDOFN=1,NDOFN
      LM(IEVAB,IELEM)=ID(IDOFN,IDENT)
```

```
80    IEVAB=IEVAB+1
50    CONTINUE
C
C***  LOOP OVER ALL ELEMENTS
C
      DO 90 IELEM=1,NELEM
      CALL COLHT(MHT,NEVAB,LM(1,IELEM))
90    CONTINUE
C
C***  ADDRESES OF DIAGONAL ELEMENTS - MAXA ARRAY
C
      CALL ADDRES(MAXA,MHT,NEQ,NWK,MK)
C
C*** REWRITING OF ELEMENT STIFFNESS, ELEMENT MASS MATRIX AND
C*** GEOMETRIC STIFFNESS MATRIX IN VECTOR FORM
C
      DO 200 IELEM=1,NELEM
      READ(1) ESTIF
      IF(ICONT.EQ.3) GO TO 130
      READ(7) EMASS
      IF(ICONT.EQ.1) GO TO 140
 130  READ(2) GSTIF
      GO TO 150
 140  KOUNT=1
      DO 145 IEVAB=1,NEVAB
      DO 145 JEVAB=IEVAB,NEVAB
      S(KOUNT)=ESTIF(IEVAB,JEVAB)
      BS(KOUNT)=EMASS(IEVAB,JEVAB)
 145  KOUNT=KOUNT+1
      GO TO 170
 150  IF(ICONT.EQ.3) GO TO 160
      KOUNT=1
      DO 155 IEVAB=1,NEVAB
      DO 155 JEVAB=IEVAB,NEVAB
      S(KOUNT)=ESTIF(IEVAB,JEVAB)+GSTIF(IEVAB,JEVAB)
      BS(KOUNT)=EMASS(IEVAB,JEVAB)
 155  KOUNT=KOUNT+1
      GO TO 170
 160  KOUNT=1
      DO 165 IEVAB=1,NEVAB
      DO 165 JEVAB=IEVAB,NEVAB
      S(KOUNT)=ESTIF(IEVAB,JEVAB)
      BS(KOUNT)=GSTIF(IEVAB,JEVAB)
165   KOUNT=KOUNT+1
C
C***  COMPACTED GLOBAL STIFFNESS MATRIX
C
170   CALL ADDBAN(A,MAXA,S,LM(1,IELEM),NEVAB)
C
C***  COMPACTED GLOBAL MASS MATRIX
C
      CALL ADDBAN(B,MAXA,BS,LM(1,IELEM),NEVAB)
200   CONTINUE
C
C***  PARAMETERS FOR SUBSPACE ITERATION
C
      NNM=1+NEQ
      NWM=NWK
      NN=NEQ
      READ(5,9)  IFSS,IFPR
9     FORMAT(16I5)
```

```
      WRITE(6,3) IFSS,IFPR
3     FORMAT(//,1X,20H*STURM SEQUENCE FLAG,I5,21H*ITERATION PRINT FLAG,
     .       I5)
      NC=2*NROOT
      NC2=NROOT+8
      IF(NC.GT.NC2) NC=NC2
      NNC=NC*(NC+1)/2
C
C***  SUBSPACE ITERATION
C
      CALL SSPACE (A,B,MAXA,ER,EIGV,TT,W,AR,BR,VEC,D,RTOLV,BUP,
     .BLO,BUPC,NN,NNM,NWK,NWM,NROOT,RTOL,NC,NNC,NITEM,IFSS,
     .IFPR,NSTIF,IOUT)
C
C***  EXIT OF SUBSPACE
C
      RETURN
      END
```

6.8 OUTPUT MODULE

6.8.1 Subroutine OUTPUT

Subroutine OUTPUT simply prints out eigenvalues, modes and error norms after reading them from file 4. If printing during iteration is required (IFPR=1) corresponding results are stored in file 3.

```
      SUBROUTINE OUTPUT (AD,D,EIGV,ICONT,ID,MPOIN,MAXNN,MITEV,NDOFN,
     .                   NMODE,NEQ,NPOIN,R)
C*********************************************************************
C
C*** OUTPUTS THE RESULTS
C
C*********************************************************************
      IMPLICIT REAL*8(A-H,O-Z)
C
      DIMENSION AD(NDOFN,MPOIN),D(MITEV),EIGV(MITEV),ID(NDOFN,MPOIN),
     .          R(MAXNN,MITEV)
C
      REWIND 4
C
      READ(4,100)(EIGV(I),I=1,NMODE)
  100 FORMAT(1H0,6E22.14)
      DO 10 J=1,NMODE
   10 READ(4,110)(R(K,J),K=1,NEQ)
  110 FORMAT(1H ,12E11.4)
      READ(4,100)(D(I),I=1,NMODE)
      WRITE(6,120)
  120 FORMAT(///,1X,'THE CALCULATED VALUES ARE')
      IF (ICONT.EQ.3) GO TO 20
      WRITE(6,125)
  125 FORMAT(/,4X,'EIGENVALUES',5X,'FREQUENCIES',6X,'ERROR NORMS',/)
      DO 15 I=1,NMODE
      FREQ=SQRT(EIGV(I))
```

```
   15 WRITE(6,130)EIGV(I),FREQ,D(I)
  130 FORMAT(1X,3E16.7)
      GO TO 26
   20 WRITE(6,135)
  135 FORMAT(/,1X,'CRIT. LOAD PARAM.',3X,'ERROR NORMS',/)
      DO 25 I=1,NMODE
   25 WRITE(6,130)EIGV(I),D(I)
   26 WRITE(6,140)
  140 FORMAT(//,1X,'THE CALCULATED MODES ARE')
C
      DO 30 IMODE=1,NMODE
      DO 40 IPOIN=1,NPOIN
      DO 50 IDOFN=1,NDOFN
      IF(ID(IDOFN,IPOIN)) 60,70,60
   70 AD(IDOFN,IPOIN)=0.0
      GO TO 80
   60 M=ID(IDOFN,IPOIN)
      AD(IDOFN,IPOIN)=R(M,IMODE)
   80 CONTINUE
   50 CONTINUE
   40 CONTINUE
C
      WRITE(6,150)IMODE
  150 FORMAT(/,6H MODE=I3)
      WRITE(6,170)
  170 FORMAT(/,12X,'W',8X,'THETA-X',5X,'THETA-Y',/)
      DO 90 IPOIN=1,NPOIN
   90 WRITE(6,160)IPOIN,(AD(IDOFN,IPOIN),IDOFN=1,NDOFN)
  160 FORMAT(1X,I5,3E12.4)
   30 CONTINUE
      RETURN
      END
```

6.9 USER INSTRUCTIONS FOR PROGRAM VIBUK

DATA SET 1	PROBLEM TITLE	(20A4) one record
Cols. 1 - 80	TITLE	Title of the problem
DATA SET 2	CONTROL PARAMETER	(I5) one record
Cols. 1 - 5	ICONT	=1 free vibration analysis =2 initially stressed vibration analysis =3 buckling analysis
DATA SET 3	CONTROL DATA	(7I5) one record
Cols. 1 - 5	NPOIN	number of nodal points
6 - 10	NELEM	number of elements
11 - 15	NVFIX	number of restrained nodes
16 - 20	NMATS	number of material sets
21 - 25	NISTR	number of initial stress sets
26 - 30	ILBTO	indicator of the type of mass matrix to be used =0 consistent mass matrix (Gauss integration) =1 lumped mass matrix (Lobatto integration)
31 - 35	NMODE	number of eigenmodes required
DATA SET 4	ELEMENT CONNECTIONS	(12I5) NELEM records
Cols. 1 - 5	NUMEL	element number
6 - 10	MATNO(NUMEL)	material set number
11 - 15	LNODS(NUMEL,1)	1st nodal connection number
16 - 20	LNODS(NUMEL,2)	2nd nodal connection number
⋮	⋮	⋮
51 - 55	LNODS(NUMEL,9)	9th nodal connection number
56 - 60	ISTRN(NUMEL)	initial stress set number

DATA SET 5 NODAL COORDINATES (I5,2F10.5) NPOIN records

Cols.	1 - 5	IPOIN	nodal point number
	6 - 15	COORD(IPOIN,1)	x-coordinate
	16 - 25	COORD(IPOIN,2)	y-coordinate

[N.B. Note that coordinates for midside nodes on straight edges may be omitted.]

DATA SET 6 RESTRAINED NODES (I5,2X,3I1) NVFIX records

Cols.	1 - 5	NOFIX(IVFIX)	restrained node number
	8	IFPRE(IVFIX,1)	condition of restraint on nodal displacement w
	9	IFPRE(IVFIX,2)	condition of restraint on nodal rotation θ_x
	10	IFPRE(IVFIX,3)	condition of restraint on nodal rotation θ_y
			0 - free
			1 - fixed

DATA SET 7 MATERIAL SET DATA 1 (I5) one record

Cols.	1 - 5	NUMAT	material set number

DATA SET 8 MATERIAL SET DATA 2 (8F10.5) one record

Cols.	1 - 10	PROPS(NUMAT,1)	1st material property E or D_{11}
	11 - 20	PROPS(NUMAT,2)	2nd material property ν or D_{12}
	21 - 30	PROPS(NUMAT,3)	3rd material property h or D_{22}
	31 - 40	PROPS(NUMAT,4)	4th material property 0 or D_{66}
	41 - 50	PROPS(NUMAT,5)	5th material property 0 or D_{55}
	51 - 60	PROPS(NUMAT,6)	6th material property 0 or D_{44}
	61 - 70	PROPS(NUMAT,7)	7th material property 0 or h
	71 - 80	PROPS(NUMAT,8)	8th material property ρ-density per unit of volume

[N.B. Repeat DATA SETS 7 and 8 NMATS times.]

DATA SET 9 INITIAL STRESS SET DATA (I5,3F10.5) NISTR records

Cols.	1 - 5	NUSTR	initial stress set number
	6 - 15	STREM(NUSTR,1)	initial stress σ_x^o
	16 - 25	STREM(NUSTR,2)	initial stress σ_y^o
	26 - 35	STREM(NUSTR,3)	initial stress τ_{xy}^o

[N.B. omit this data set if ICONT = 1.]

DATA SET 10 STURM SEQUENCE INDICATORS (2I5) one record

Cols.	1 - 5	IFSS	indicator for Sturm sequence check = 0 no check is applied = 1 check is applied
	5 - 10	IFPR	indicator for printing during iteration = 0 no printing = 1 print

7. SAMPLE SOLUTIONS

7.1 Introduction

This section contains the following examples analysed using program VIBUK:

(a) free vibrations of a simply supported thin square plate $h/a = 0.01$,

(b) free vibrations of a simply supported thick square plate $h/a = 0.1$,

(c) initially stressed vibrations of a simply supported thick square plate $h/a = 0.1$,

(d) buckling analysis of a simply supported square plate of various thicknesses under uniaxial initial stress, and

(e) free vibrations of a clamped circular plate.

The first four examples are analysed using the same finite element mesh, illustrated in Figure 7.1. Results obtained using program VIBUK are compared with results obtained from closed form solution in Chapter 1.

7.2 Test Example No. 1 - Free Vibrations of a Simply Supported Thin Square Plate

Table 7.1 summarises the results for a thin square plate $h/a = 0.01$, where the values in brackets are the percentage errors with respect to the closed form solution. As a half of a plate is analysed (see Figure 7.1) symmetry and anti-symmetry conditions are considered along the central line.

TABLE 7.1 The natural frequencies ω_{mn} for a thin square plate h/a = 0.01

m	n	Closed form solution	Present finite element solution with consistent mass matrix	Present finite element solution with lumped mass matrix
1	1	19.73	19.75 (+ 0.10)	19.73 (0.00)
1	2	49.32	49.75 (+ 0.87)	49.46 (+ 0.28)
2	2	78.88	79.67 (+ 1.00)	78.80 (- 0.10)
1	3	98.58	103.13 (+ 4.62)	100.56 (+ 2.01)
2	3	128.11	132.79 (+ 3.65)	128.71 (+ 0.47)

(ω_{mn} in radian per second)

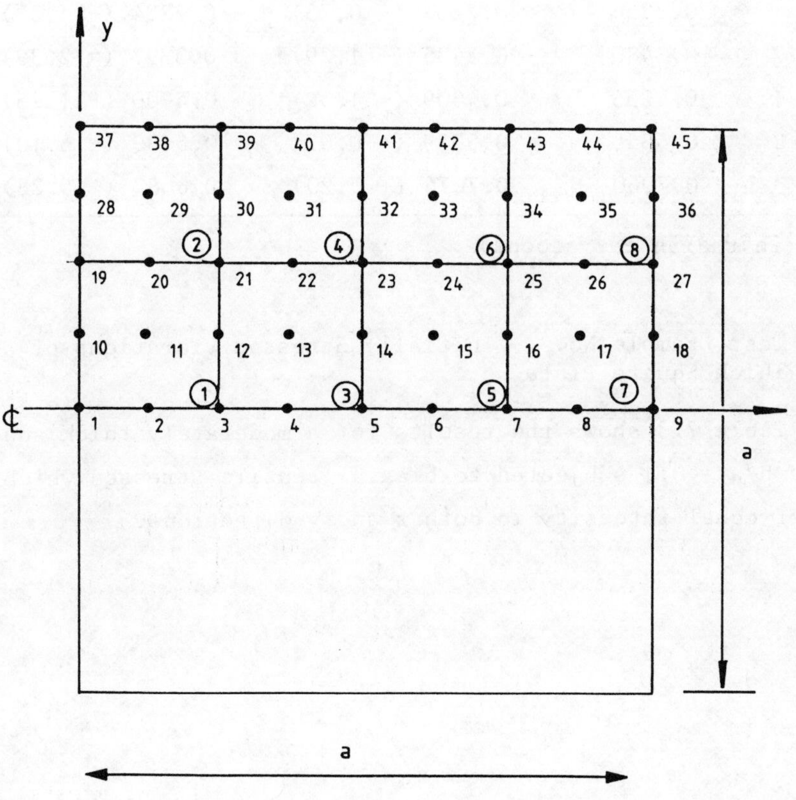

Figure 7.1 Element mesh for simply supported square plate

7.3 Test Example No. 2 - Free Vibrations of a Simply Supported Thick Square Plate

Table 7.2 shows the non-dimensionalised frequencies for a moderately thick square plate h/a = 0.1. Results are presented for the cases when both consistent and lumped mass matrices are adopted.

TABLE 7.2 The non-dimensional frequencies $\lambda = \omega_{mn}/\sqrt{\rho h^2 G}$ for a thick square plate h/a = 0.1

m	n	Closed form solution	Present finite element solution with consistent mass matrix	Present finite element solution with lumped mass matrix
1	1	0.0937	0.0931 (- 0.64)	0.0930 (- 0.75)
2	1	0.2254	0.2237 (- 0.75)	0.2224 (- 1.33)
2	2	0.3480	0.3435 (- 1.29)	0.3397 (- 2.39)
3	1	0.4253	0.4309 (+ 1.32)	0.4200 (- 1.25)
3	2	0.5355	0.5359 (+ 0.07)	0.5189 (- 3.10)
3	3	0.7060	0.7074 (+ 0.20)	0.6687 (- 5.28)

(ω_{mn} in radian per second)

7.4 Test Example No.3 - Initially Stressed Vibrations of a Thick Square Plate

Table 7.3 shows the results for a moderately thick square plate h/a = 0.1 subjected to biaxial tensile stresses which are of equal intensity in both x and y directions.

TABLE 7.3 The frequencies ω_{mn} for a thick square plate h/a = 0.1 under uniform tension F in both x and y directions

$Fa^2/\pi^2 D_{11}$	Closed form solution	Present finite element solution with consistent mass matrix	Present finite element solution with lumped mass matrix
5	36.646	36.586 (- 0.16)	36.558 (- 0.24)
10	48.135	48.095 (- 0.08)	48.058 (- 0.16)
15	57.368	57.339 (- 0.05)	57.295 (- 0.13)
20	65.308	65.286 (- 0.03)	65.236 (- 0.11)
30	78.825	78.813 (- 0.02)	78.752 (- 0.09)
50	100.547	100.548 (0.00)	100.470 (- 0.08)
100	140.892	140.911 (+ 0.01)	140.800 (- 0.06)
200	198.324	198.362 (+ 0.02)	198.206 (- 0.06)

(ω_{mn} in radian per second)

7.5 Test Example No.4 - Buckling Analysis of a Simply Suppo rted Square Plate

Table 7.4 summarises the results for simply supported square plates of various thicknesses under uniaxial initial stress. Typical input and output data for this example are given in Figures 7.2 and 7.3 respectively.

TABLE 7.4 The buckling factors $K_b = a^2 F_{CR}/\pi^2 D_{11}$ for a simply supported square plate under uniaxial initial stress ($\nu = 0.3$)

h/a	Closed form solution	Present finite element solution
0.001	4.000	4.000 (0.00)
0.05	3.944	3.932 (- 0.30)
0.10	3.786	3.734 (- 1.37)
0.20	3.264	3.128 (- 4.16)

```
  ** SQUARE PLATE H/A=0.1 UNDER UNIAXIAL INITIAL STRESS **
   3
  45    8   24    1    1    0    3
   1    1    1    2    3   12   21   20   19   10   11    1
   2    1   19   20   21   30   39   38   37   28   29    1
   3    1    3    4    5   14   23   22   21   12   13    1
   4    1   21   22   23   32   41   40   39   30   31    1
   5    1    5    6    7   16   25   24   23   14   15    1
   6    1   23   24   25   34   43   42   41   32   33    1
   7    1    7    8    9   18   27   26   25   16   17    1
   8    1   25   26   27   36   45   44   43   34   35    1
   1   0.00000   0.00000
   3   0.25000   0.00000
   5   0.50000   0.00000
   7   0.75000   0.00000
   9   1.00000   0.00000
  11   0.12500   0.12500
  13   0.37500   0.12500
  15   0.62500   0.12500
  17   0.87500   0.12500
  19   0.00000   0.25000
  21   0.25000   0.25000
  23   0.50000   0.25000
  25   0.75000   0.25000
  27   1.00000   0.25000
  29   0.12500   0.37500
  31   0.37500   0.37500
  33   0.62500   0.37500
  35   0.87500   0.37500
  37   0.00000   0.50000
  39   0.25000   0.50000
  41   0.50000   0.50000
  43   0.75000   0.50000
  45   1.00000   0.50000
   1  101
   2  001
   3  001
   4  001
   5  001
   6  001
   7  001
   8  001
   9  101
  10  101
  18  101
  19  101
  27  101
  28  101
  36  101
  37  111
  38  110
  39  110
  40  110
  41  110
  42  110
  43  110
  44  110
  45  111
   1
10920.     0.3         0.1
   1 1.
   0    1
```

Figure 7.2 Typical input data for buckling analysis

** SQUARE PLATE H/A=0.1 UNDER UNIAXIAL INITIAL STRESS **

THIS IS A BUCKLING ANALYSIS ICONT= 3

NPOIN = 45 NELEM = 8 NVFIX = 24 NMATS = 1

NISTR = 1 ILBTO = 0 NMODE = 3

ELEM.	MAT.SET	NODE NUMBERS									STR.SET
1	1	1	2	3	12	21	20	19	10	11	1
2	1	19	20	21	30	39	38	37	28	29	1
3	1	3	4	5	14	23	22	21	12	13	1
4	1	21	22	23	32	41	40	39	30	31	1
5	1	5	6	7	16	25	24	23	14	15	1
6	1	23	24	25	34	43	42	41	32	33	1
7	1	7	8	9	18	27	26	25	16	17	1
8	1	25	26	27	36	45	44	43	34	35	1

NODAL POINT COORDINATES

NODE	X	Y
1	0.000	0.000
2	0.125	0.000
3	0.250	0.000
4	0.375	0.000
5	0.500	0.000
6	0.625	0.000
7	0.750	0.000
8	0.875	0.000
9	1.000	0.000
10	0.000	0.125
11	0.125	0.125
12	0.250	0.125
13	0.375	0.125
14	0.500	0.125
15	0.625	0.125
16	0.750	0.125
17	0.875	0.125
18	1.000	0.125
19	0.000	0.250
20	0.125	0.250
21	0.250	0.250
22	0.375	0.250
23	0.500	0.250
24	0.625	0.250
25	0.750	0.250
26	0.875	0.250
27	1.000	0.250
28	0.000	0.375
29	0.125	0.375
30	0.250	0.375

Figure 7.3 Typical output data for buckling analysis

31	0.375	0.375
32	0.500	0.375
33	0.625	0.375
34	0.750	0.375
35	0.875	0.375
36	1.000	0.375
37	0.000	0.500
38	0.125	0.500
39	0.250	0.500
40	0.375	0.500
41	0.500	0.500
42	0.625	0.500
43	0.750	0.500
44	0.875	0.500
45	1.000	0.500

RESTRAINED NODES

NODE	CODE
1	101
2	001
3	001
4	001
5	001
6	001
7	001
8	001
9	101
10	101
18	101
19	101
27	101
28	101
36	101
37	111
38	110
39	110
40	110
41	110
42	110
43	110
44	110
45	111

MATERIAL PROPERTIES

NUMBER	PROPERTIES		
1	0.109200E+05	0.300000E+00	0.100000E+00
	0.000000E+00	0.000000E+00	0.000000E+00
	0.000000E+00	0.000000E+00	

THE INITIAL IN-PLANE STRESSES

NUMBER	SIGMA-X	SIGMA-Y	SIGMA-XY
1	0.100000E+01	0.000000E+00	0.000000E+00

Figure 7.3 continued

```
*STURM SEQUENCE FLAG     0*ITERATION PRINT FLAG     1


THE CALCULATED VALUES ARE

CRIT. LOAD PARAM.   ERROR NORMS

   0.3685677E+03   0.4072498E-07
   0.5283138E+03   0.4609855E-05
   0.8480634E+03   0.7617418E-04


THE CALCULATED MODES ARE

MODE=   1

             W          THETA-X      THETA-Y

      1  0.0000E+00  0.8426E+01  0.0000E+00
      2  0.1082E+01  0.7776E+01  0.0000E+00
      3  0.2002E+01  0.5958E+01  0.0000E+00
      4  0.2613E+01  0.3221E+01  0.0000E+00
      5  0.2831E+01  0.5795E-10  0.0000E+00
      6  0.2613E+01 -0.3221E+01  0.0000E+00
      7  0.2002E+01 -0.5958E+01  0.0000E+00
      8  0.1082E+01 -0.7776E+01  0.0000E+00
      9  0.0000E+00 -0.8426E+01  0.0000E+00
     10  0.0000E+00  0.7785E+01  0.0000E+00
     11  0.9991E+00  0.7184E+01 -0.1233E+01
     12  0.1848E+01  0.5505E+01 -0.2277E+01
     13  0.2412E+01  0.2976E+01 -0.2976E+01
     14  0.2613E+01  0.1503E-10 -0.3221E+01
     15  0.2412E+01 -0.2976E+01 -0.2976E+01
     16  0.1848E+01 -0.5505E+01 -0.2277E+01
     17  0.9991E+00 -0.7184E+01 -0.1233E+01
     18  0.0000E+00 -0.7785E+01  0.0000E+00
     19  0.0000E+00  0.5958E+01  0.0000E+00
     20  0.7654E+00  0.5498E+01 -0.2280E+01
     21  0.1416E+01  0.4213E+01 -0.4213E+01
     22  0.1848E+01  0.2277E+01 -0.5505E+01
     23  0.2002E+01 -0.4237E-10 -0.5959E+01
     24  0.1848E+01 -0.2277E+01 -0.5505E+01
     25  0.1416E+01 -0.4213E+01 -0.4213E+01
     26  0.7654E+00 -0.5498E+01 -0.2280E+01
     27  0.0000E+00 -0.5958E+01  0.0000E+00
     28  0.0000E+00  0.3225E+01  0.0000E+00
     29  0.4138E+00  0.2976E+01 -0.2976E+01
     30  0.7654E+00  0.2280E+01 -0.5498E+01
     31  0.9991E+00  0.1233E+01 -0.7184E+01
     32  0.1082E+01 -0.3886E-10 -0.7776E+01
     33  0.9991E+00 -0.1233E+01 -0.7184E+01
     34  0.7654E+00 -0.2280E+01 -0.5498E+01
     35  0.4138E+00 -0.2976E+01 -0.2976E+01
     36  0.0000E+00 -0.3225E+01  0.0000E+00
     37  0.0000E+00  0.0000E+00  0.0000E+00
     38  0.0000E+00  0.0000E+00 -0.3225E+01
```

Figure 7.3 continued

39	0.0000E+00	0.0000E+00	-0.5959E+01
40	0.0000E+00	0.0000E+00	-0.7786E+01
41	0.0000E+00	0.0000E+00	-0.8427E+01
42	0.0000E+00	0.0000E+00	-0.7786E+01
43	0.0000E+00	0.0000E+00	-0.5959E+01
44	0.0000E+00	0.0000E+00	-0.3225E+01
45	0.0000E+00	0.0000E+00	0.0000E+00

MODE= 2

	W	THETA-X	THETA-Y
1	0.0000E+00	0.7880E+01	0.0000E+00
2	0.9887E+00	0.5498E+01	0.0000E+00
3	0.1417E+01	0.3916E-07	0.0000E+00
4	0.9887E+00	-0.5498E+01	0.0000E+00
5	-0.8115E-08	-0.7880E+01	0.0000E+00
6	-0.9887E+00	-0.5498E+01	0.0000E+00
7	-0.1417E+01	-0.3916E-07	0.0000E+00
8	-0.9887E+00	0.5498E+01	0.0000E+00
9	0.0000E+00	0.7880E+01	0.0000E+00
10	0.0000E+00	0.7281E+01	0.0000E+00
11	0.9127E+00	0.5079E+01	-0.1049E+01
12	0.1308E+01	0.2121E-07	-0.1487E+01
13	0.9127E+00	-0.5079E+01	-0.1049E+01
14	-0.4765E-08	-0.7281E+01	0.3849E-07
15	-0.9127E+00	-0.5079E+01	0.1049E+01
16	-0.1308E+01	-0.2121E-07	0.1487E+01
17	-0.9127E+00	0.5079E+01	0.1049E+01
18	0.0000E+00	0.7281E+01	0.0000E+00
19	0.0000E+00	0.5572E+01	0.0000E+00
20	0.6991E+00	0.3887E+01	-0.1942E+01
21	0.1002E+01	-0.2615E-07	-0.2753E+01
22	0.6991E+00	-0.3887E+01	-0.1942E+01
23	0.5520E-08	-0.5572E+01	0.5901E-07
24	-0.6991E+00	-0.3887E+01	0.1942E+01
25	-0.1002E+01	0.2615E-07	0.2753E+01
26	-0.6991E+00	0.3887E+01	0.1942E+01
27	0.0000E+00	0.5572E+01	0.0000E+00
28	0.0000E+00	0.3016E+01	0.0000E+00
29	0.3781E+00	0.2104E+01	-0.2533E+01
30	0.5418E+00	-0.4836E-07	-0.3590E+01
31	0.3781E+00	-0.2104E+01	-0.2533E+01
32	0.1110E-07	-0.3016E+01	-0.1565E-07
33	-0.3781E+00	-0.2104E+01	0.2533E+01
34	-0.5418E+00	0.4836E-07	0.3590E+01
35	-0.3781E+00	0.2104E+01	0.2533E+01
36	0.0000E+00	0.3016E+01	0.0000E+00
37	0.0000E+00	0.0000E+00	0.0000E+00
38	0.0000E+00	0.0000E+00	-0.2747E+01
39	0.0000E+00	0.0000E+00	-0.3893E+01
40	0.0000E+00	0.0000E+00	-0.2747E+01
41	0.0000E+00	0.0000E+00	-0.8290E-07
42	0.0000E+00	0.0000E+00	0.2747E+01
43	0.0000E+00	0.0000E+00	0.3893E+01
44	0.0000E+00	0.0000E+00	0.2747E+01
45	0.0000E+00	0.0000E+00	0.0000E+00

Figure 7.3 continued

MODE= 3

	W	THETA-X	THETA-Y
1	0.0000E+00	-0.7340E+01	0.0000E+00
2	-0.8429E+00	-0.2657E+01	0.0000E+00
3	-0.6827E+00	0.5190E+01	0.0000E+00
4	0.3491E+00	0.6416E+01	0.0000E+00
5	0.9654E+00	0.9965E-06	0.0000E+00
6	0.3491E+00	-0.6416E+01	0.0000E+00
7	-0.6827E+00	-0.5190E+01	0.0000E+00
8	-0.8429E+00	0.2657E+01	0.0000E+00
9	0.0000E+00	0.7340E+01	0.0000E+00
10	0.0000E+00	-0.6782E+01	0.0000E+00
11	-0.7783E+00	-0.2455E+01	0.8082E+00
12	-0.6303E+00	0.4795E+01	0.6310E+00
13	0.3224E+00	0.5928E+01	-0.3347E+00
14	0.8914E+00	0.2695E-06	-0.8924E+00
15	0.3224E+00	-0.5928E+01	-0.3347E+00
16	-0.6303E+00	-0.4795E+01	0.6310E+00
17	-0.7783E+00	0.2455E+01	0.8082E+00
18	0.0000E+00	0.6782E+01	0.0000E+00
19	0.0000E+00	-0.5191E+01	0.0000E+00
20	-0.5961E+00	-0.1879E+01	0.1498E+01
21	-0.4827E+00	0.3670E+01	0.1170E+01
22	0.2469E+00	0.4537E+01	-0.6204E+00
23	0.6827E+00	-0.7046E-06	-0.1654E+01
24	0.2469E+00	-0.4537E+01	-0.6204E+00
25	-0.4827E+00	-0.3670E+01	0.1170E+01
26	-0.5961E+00	0.1879E+01	0.1498E+01
27	0.0000E+00	0.5191E+01	0.0000E+00
28	0.0000E+00	-0.2809E+01	0.0000E+00
29	-0.3224E+00	-0.1017E+01	0.1951E+01
30	-0.2611E+00	0.1986E+01	0.1523E+01
31	0.1335E+00	0.2455E+01	-0.8082E+00
32	0.3692E+00	-0.6507E-06	-0.2154E+01
33	0.1335E+00	-0.2455E+01	-0.8082E+00
34	-0.2611E+00	-0.1986E+01	0.1523E+01
35	-0.3224E+00	0.1017E+01	0.1951E+01
36	0.0000E+00	0.2809E+01	0.0000E+00
37	0.0000E+00	0.0000E+00	0.0000E+00
38	0.0000E+00	0.0000E+00	0.2118E+01
39	0.0000E+00	0.0000E+00	0.1654E+01
40	0.0000E+00	0.0000E+00	-0.8775E+00
41	0.0000E+00	0.0000E+00	-0.2339E+01
42	0.0000E+00	0.0000E+00	-0.8775E+00
43	0.0000E+00	0.0000E+00	0.1654E+01
44	0.0000E+00	0.0000E+00	0.2119E+01
45	0.0000E+00	0.0000E+00	0.0000E+00

Figure 7.3 continued

7.6 Test Example No. 5 - Free Vibrations of a Clamped Circular Plate

In this example, free vibrations of a clamped circular plate are studied using a 12 element mesh shown in Figure 7.4. As a quarter of a circular plate is analysed, three different types of boundary conditions along the axes of symmetry are considered,

(a) symmetry conditions on both edges (SS),

(b) symmetry and anti-symmetry conditions on each edge respectively (SA), and

(c) anti-symmetry conditions on both edges (AA).

Table 7.5 compares results obtained using finite elements with analytical ones given by Leissa [13]. Typical input data and results for this example (AA) are given on Figures 7.5 and 7.6.

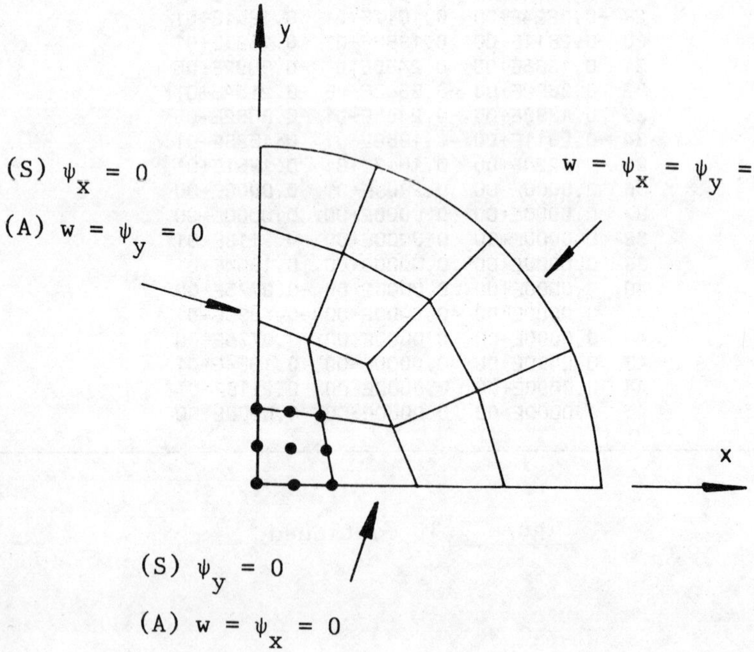

Figure 7.4 Mesh for symmetric quadrant of clamped circular plate

TABLE 7.5 Values of $\lambda^2 = \omega a^2 \sqrt{\rho/D_{11}}$ for a clamped circular plate of thickness-to-radius $h/a = 0.01$

No. of Nodal Circles S	Type of Analysis	Number of modes n				
		0	1	2	3	4
	A.S.	10.2158	21.26	34.88	51.04	69.6659
0	C.M.M.	10.2185(+0.03)	21.29(+0.14)	34.99(+0.32)	51.49(+0.88)	70.4071(+1.06)
	L.M.M.	10.2184(+0.03)	21.27(+0.05)	34.92(+0.12)	51.29(+0.49)	69.6513(-0.02)
	A.S.	39.771	60.82	84.58	111.01	140.1079
1	C.M.M.	40.099(+0.82)	61.99(+1.92)	86.98(+2.84)	116.28(+4.75)	147.4777(+5.26)
	L.M.M.	40.022(+0.63)	61.69(+1.43)	86.44(+2.20)	114.50(+3.14)	142.9976(+2.06)

A.S. -analytical solution

C.M.M. -finite element solution with consistent mass matrix

L.M.M. -finite element solution with lumped mass matrix

```
CLAMPED CIRCULAR PLATE
  1
 61   12   24    1    1    1    8
  1    1    1    2    3   12   21   20   19   10   11
  2    1    3    4    5   14   23   22   21   12   13
  3    1   19   20   21   30   39   38   37   28   29
  4    1   21   22   23   32   41   40   39   30   31
  5    1    5    6    7   16   25   24   23   14   15
  6    1   23   24   25   34   43   42   41   32   33
  7    1   39   40   41   42   43   50   55   48   49
  8    1   37   38   39   48   55   54   53   46   47
  9    1    7    8    9   18   27   26   25   16   17
 10    1   25   26   27   36   45   44   43   34   35
 11    1   55   50   43   44   45   52   57   56   51
 12    1   53   54   55   56   57   60   61   58   59
  1        0.0        0.0
  3       0.25        0.0
  5        0.5        0.0
  7       0.75        0.0
  9        1.0        0.0
 11     0.1067     0.1067
 13     0.3384     0.0884
 15    0.57925     0.1105
 17    0.82852    0.16198
 18     0.9808     0.1951
 19        0.0       0.25
 21     0.1768     0.1768
 23     0.4268     0.1768
 25     0.6402     0.2652
 27     0.9239     0.3827
 29     0.0884     0.3384
 31    0.28348    0.28348
 33     0.4877    0.33145
 35    0.70038    0.47132
 36     0.8315     0.5556
 37        0.0        0.5
 39     0.1768     0.4268
 41     0.3535     0.3535
 43     0.5303     0.5303
 45     0.7071     0.7071
 47     0.1105    0.57925
 49    0.33145     0.4877
 51    0.47132    0.70038
 52     0.5556     0.8315
 53        0.0       0.75
 55     0.2652     0.6402
 57     0.3827     0.9239
 59    0.16198    0.82852
 60     0.1951     0.9808
 61        0.0        1.0
  1  111
  2  110
  3  110
  4  110
  5  110
  6  110
  7  110
```

Figure 7.5 Input data for free vibration analysis of clamped circular plate (AA)

```
    8  110
    9  111
   10  101
   18  111
   19  101
   27  111
   28  101
   36  111
   37  101
   45  111
   46  101
   52  111
   53  101
   57  111
   58  101
   60  111
   61  111
    1
11669328. 0.166     0.01       0.         0.         0.         0.        100.
    0   1
```

Figure 7.5 (continued)

```
  CLAMPED CIRCULAR PLATE

THIS IS A FREE VIBRATION ANALYSIS    ICONT=  1

NPOIN =  61     NELEM =  12     NVFIX =  24     NMATS =   1

NISTR =   1     ILBTO =   1     NMODE =   8

ELEM.  MAT.SET               NODE NUMBERS                        STR.SET
  1        1      1     2     3    12    21    20    19    10    11     0
  2        1      3     4     5    14    23    22    21    12    13     0
  3        1     19    20    21    30    39    38    37    28    29     0
  4        1     21    22    23    32    41    40    39    30    31     0
  5        1      5     6     7    16    25    24    23    14    15     0
  6        1     23    24    25    34    43    42    41    32    33     0
  7        1     39    40    41    42    43    50    55    48    49     0
  8        1     37    38    39    48    55    54    53    46    47     0
  9        1      7     8     9    18    27    26    25    16    17     0
 10        1     25    26    27    36    45    44    43    34    35     0
 11        1     55    50    43    44    45    52    57    56    51     0
 12        1     53    54    55    56    57    60    61    58    59     0
```

Figure 7.6 Output data for free vibration analysis of clamped circular plate

NODAL POINT COORDINATES

NODE	X	Y
1	0.000	0.000
2	0.125	0.000
3	0.250	0.000
4	0.375	0.000
5	0.500	0.000
6	0.625	0.000
7	0.750	0.000
8	0.875	0.000
9	1.000	0.000
10	0.000	0.125
11	0.107	0.107
12	0.213	0.088
13	0.338	0.088
14	0.463	0.088
15	0.579	0.110
16	0.695	0.133
17	0.829	0.162
18	0.981	0.195
19	0.000	0.250
20	0.088	0.213
21	0.177	0.177
22	0.302	0.177
23	0.427	0.177
24	0.534	0.221
25	0.640	0.265
26	0.782	0.324
27	0.924	0.383
28	0.000	0.375
29	0.088	0.338
30	0.177	0.302
31	0.283	0.283
32	0.390	0.265
33	0.488	0.331
34	0.585	0.398
35	0.700	0.471
36	0.832	0.556
37	0.000	0.500
38	0.088	0.463
39	0.177	0.427
40	0.265	0.390
41	0.354	0.354
42	0.442	0.442
43	0.530	0.530
44	0.619	0.619
45	0.707	0.707
46	0.000	0.625
47	0.110	0.579
48	0.221	0.534
49	0.331	0.488
50	0.398	0.585
51	0.471	0.700
52	0.556	0.832
53	0.000	0.750
54	0.133	0.695
55	0.265	0.640
56	0.324	0.782

Figure 7.6 continued

57	0.383	0.924
58	0.000	0.875
59	0.162	0.829
60	0.195	0.981
61	0.000	1.000

RESTRAINED NODES

NODE	CODE
1	111
2	110
3	110
4	110
5	110
6	110
7	110
8	110
9	111
10	101
18	111
19	101
27	111
28	101
36	111
37	101
45	111
46	101
52	111
53	101
57	111
58	101
60	111
61	111

MATERIAL PROPERTIES

NUMBER	PROPERTIES		
1	0.116693E+08	0.166000E+00	0.100000E-01
	0.000000E+00	0.000000E+00	0.000000E+00
	0.000000E+00	0.100000E+03	

*STURM SEQUENCE FLAG 0*ITERATION PRINT FLAG 1

THE CALCULATED VALUES ARE

EIGENVALUES	FREQUENCIES	ERROR NORMS
0.1219164E+04	0.3491653E+02	0.2884476E-12
0.5056460E+04	0.7110879E+02	0.1647305E-09
0.7471793E+04	0.8643953E+02	0.1288822E-09
0.1370342E+05	0.1170616E+03	0.4081479E-07
0.2152921E+05	0.1467283E+03	0.2162705E-05
0.2561809E+05	0.1600565E+03	0.2257800E-05
0.2689752E+05	0.1640046E+03	0.6341548E-07
0.4308844E+05	0.2075776E+03	0.2794993E-04

Figure 7.6 continued

THE CALCULATED MODES ARE

MODE= 1

	W	THETA-X	THETA-Y
1	0.0000E+00	0.0000E+00	0.0000E+00
2	0.0000E+00	0.0000E+00	0.5301E+01
3	0.0000E+00	0.0000E+00	0.9324E+01
4	0.0000E+00	0.0000E+00	0.1091E+02
5	0.0000E+00	0.0000E+00	0.1010E+02
6	0.0000E+00	0.0000E+00	0.7304E+01
7	0.0000E+00	0.0000E+00	0.3805E+01
8	0.0000E+00	0.0000E+00	0.1018E+01
9	0.0000E+00	0.0000E+00	0.0000E+00
10	0.0000E+00	0.5301E+01	0.0000E+00
11	0.4725E+00	0.4177E+01	0.4177E+01
12	0.7202E+00	0.2424E+01	0.7774E+01
13	0.9198E+00	0.7629E+00	0.9909E+01
14	0.9100E+00	-0.9220E+00	0.9747E+01
15	0.8923E+00	-0.2551E+01	0.7303E+01
16	0.6613E+00	-0.3534E+01	0.4164E+01
17	0.2597E+00	-0.3109E+01	0.9570E+00
18	0.0000E+00	0.0000E+00	0.0000E+00
19	0.0000E+00	0.9324E+01	0.0000E+00
20	0.7202E+00	0.7774E+01	0.2424E+01
21	0.1166E+01	0.5314E+01	0.5314E+01
22	0.1646E+01	0.2314E+01	0.7489E+01
23	0.1732E+01	-0.9891E+00	0.7697E+01
24	0.1743E+01	-0.3923E+01	0.4924E+01
25	0.1353E+01	-0.6048E+01	0.1754E+01
26	0.4876E+00	-0.5423E+01	-0.9300E+00
27	0.0000E+00	0.0000E+00	0.0000E+00
28	0.0000E+00	0.1091E+02	0.0000E+00
29	0.9198E+00	0.9909E+01	0.7629E+00
30	0.1646E+01	0.7489E+01	0.2314E+01
31	0.2189E+01	0.3713E+01	0.3713E+01
32	0.2300E+01	-0.2471E+00	0.4522E+01
33	0.2256E+01	-0.4091E+01	0.9418E+00
34	0.1678E+01	-0.6653E+01	-0.2169E+01
35	0.6478E+00	-0.6267E+01	-0.3412E+01
36	0.0000E+00	0.0000E+00	0.0000E+00
37	0.0000E+00	0.1010E+02	0.0000E+00
38	0.9100E+00	0.9747E+01	-0.9220E+00
39	0.1732E+01	0.7697E+01	-0.9891E+00
40	0.2300E+01	0.4522E+01	-0.2471E+00
41	0.2531E+01	0.8403E+00	0.8403E+00
42	0.2305E+01	-0.3155E+01	-0.3155E+01
43	0.1496E+01	-0.5754E+01	-0.5754E+01
44	0.4938E+00	-0.4896E+01	-0.4896E+01
45	0.0000E+00	0.0000E+00	0.0000E+00
46	0.0000E+00	0.7304E+01	0.0000E+00
47	0.8923E+00	0.7303E+01	-0.2551E+01
48	0.1743E+01	0.4924E+01	-0.3923E+01
49	0.2256E+01	0.9418E+00	-0.4091E+01
50	0.1678E+01	-0.2169E+01	-0.6653E+01

Figure 7.6 continued

51	0.6478E+00	-0.3412E+01	-0.6267E+01
52	0.0000E+00	0.0000E+00	0.0000E+00
53	0.0000E+00	0.3805E+01	0.0000E+00
54	0.6613E+00	0.4164E+01	-0.3534E+01
55	0.1353E+01	0.1754E+01	-0.6048E+01
56	0.4876E+00	-0.9300E+00	-0.5423E+01
57	0.0000E+00	0.0000E+00	0.0000E+00
58	0.0000E+00	0.1018E+01	0.0000E+00
59	0.2597E+00	0.9570E+00	-0.3109E+01
60	0.0000E+00	0.0000E+00	0.0000E+00
61	0.0000E+00	0.0000E+00	0.0000E+00

Figure 7.6 continued

REFERENCES

1. MINDLIN, R.D.
"Influence of rotatory inertia and shear on flexural motions of isotropic elastic plates",
J. Appl. Mech., 37, 1031-1036, 1951.

2. BENSON, P.R. and HINTON, E.
"A thick finite strip solution for static, free vibration and stability problems",
Int. J. Num. Meth. Engng., 10, 665-678, 1976.

3. BRUNELLE, E.J. and ROBERTSON, S.R.
"Initially stressed Mindlin plates",
AIAA J., 12(8), 1036-1045, 1974.

4. ZIENKIEWICZ, O.C., TAYLOR, R.L. and TOO, J.M.
"Reduced integration in general analysis of plates and shells",
Int. J. Num. Meth. Engng., 3, 275-290, 1971.

5. HUGHES, T.J.R., COHEN, M. and HAROUN, M.
"Reduced and selective integration techniques in the finite element analysis of plates",
Nucl. Engng. and Design, 46, 203-222, 1978.

6. ONATE, E., HINTON,E. and GLOVER, N.
"Techniques for improving the performance of Ahmad shell elements"
Proc. Int. Conf. Appl. Num. Modelling, Madrid,
Pentech Press, 1978.

7. MacNEAL, R.H.
"A simple quadrilateral shell element",
Comput. and Structures, 8, 175-183, 1978.

8. DVORKIN, E.N. and BATHE, K.J.
"A continuum mechanics based four-node shell element for general non-linear analysis",
Eng. Comput., 1, 77-88, 1984.

9. CRISFIELD, M.A.
"A quadratic Mindlin element using shear constraints",
Comput. and Structures, 18, 833-852, 1984.

10. HUANG, H.C. and HINTON, E.
"An improved Lagrangian 9-node Mindlin plate element",
Proc. NUMETA85 Swansea, Volume2, 707-713, Balkema, Amsterdam, 1985.

11. HUANG, H.C. and HINTON, E.
"A nine node Lagrangian Mindlin plate element with enhanced shear interpolation",
Eng. Comput., 1, 369-379, 1984.

12. BATHE,K.J. and WILSON, E.L.
"Numerical Methods in Finite Element Analysis",
Prentice-Hall, New Jersey, 1976.

13. LEISSA, A.W.
"Vibration of Plates",
NASA SP-160, Washington, D.C., 1969.

A STUDY OF THE FREE VIBRATIONS OF SQUARE PLATES WITH VARIOUS EDGE CONDITIONS

BAHAA S. AL JANABI* and E. HINTON**

*** MTC, Baghdad, Iraq**

**** University College of Swansea, U.K.**

1. INTRODUCTION

In a previous chapter in this book, a finite element program for the free vibration and buckling analysis of Mindlin plates, called VIBUK, was presented. The 9-noded Mindlin plate element of Huang and Hinton [1] with assumed shear strain interpolation was incorporated in VIBUK. In this chapter, a parametric study is undertaken using VIBUK and featuring a series of square plates with various boundary conditions and thickness-to-span ratios.

The purposes of the study are threefold:

(1) to study the behaviour of square plates with various boundary conditions,

(2) to check the behaviour of the Huang/Hinton plate element (and, in particular the use of lumped versus consistent mass representation), and

(3) to provide benchmark tests for other finite element workers.

Before proceeding to the parametric study, the overall organisation and layout of the study is described in the next section.

2. ORGANISATION OF STUDY

2.1 Plate geometry

Square plates of side length a are adopted in the study . Two thickness-to-span (h/a) ratios of 0.1 and 0.01 are considered; the importance of shear deformation effects for the thicker plate are highlighted.

2.2 Boundary conditions

Three different types of boundary conditions are considered:

(a) *simply supported edge* (S) in which the lateral displacement w, the bending moment M_n (normal to boundary edge) and the rotation of the midplane normal θ_t (in the plane which is tangential to the boundary edge) all vanish, so that

$$w = M_n = \theta_t = 0$$

(b) *clamped edge* (C) in which the lateral displacement w, the rotations θ_n (in the plane normal to the boundary edge) and θ_t all vanish, so that

$$w = \theta_n = \theta_t = 0$$

(c) *free edge* (F) in which the shear force normal to the edge Q_n, the bending moment normal to the edge M_n and the twisting moment M_{nt} on the plane tangential to the edge all vanish, so that

$$Q_n = M_n = M_{nt} = 0$$

Various combinations of these boundary conditions are included in the study. A simple convention is adopted to define the boundary conditions in a particular study. For example, S-C-S-F implies two opposite edges are simply supported with clamped and free boundary conditions on the other edges.

2.3 Non-dimensional frequency parameters

The frequencies are presented in non-dimensional form using the parameter

$$\Omega_{mn} = \omega_{mn} a(\rho/G)^{1/2}$$

where ω_{mn} is the frequency, a is the plate side length, ρ is the mass density per unit volume and G is the shear modulus. Note that $G = E/2(1+\nu)$ in which E is the elastic modulus and ν is the Poisson's ratio. Unless otherwise stated, the subscipts m and n are the number of half-waves occurring in the modes shapes in the x and y directions respectively.

2.4 Mass representations

In the finite element analysis two different mass representations are adopted:

(a) *consistent mass* – in which a 3×3 Gauss-legendre is used to evaluate the consistent mass matrix.

(b) *lumped mass* – in which a 3×3 Lobatto rule is used to evalute the mass matrix and since the sampling points coincide with the nodes a diagonal matrix is obtained. This mass representation is particularly important fo use with the explicit central difference, time stepping scheme for solving transient dynamic equations.

Rotatory inertia effects are included.

2.5 Symmetry of modes

Square plates with symmetric boundary conditions (e.g S-S-S-S and C-C-C-C) have symmetric modes with identical frequencies (e.g. the m, n and n, m modes have identical frequencies). Thus, the pairs of modes may appear in various forms – i.e. linear combinations. As the closed-form solutions used for comparisons usually involve Fourier series, the geometry of the mesh used in the finite element representation is lightly perturbed in order to present the modes in a form of the type used in the closed form solution. This usually works, but there are some instances where a non-standard form of a particular mode is obtained.

2.6 Reference solutions

To check the finite element solutions, reference is made to closed form and finite strip solutions based on 3D, classical thin plate and Mindlin plate theories.

2.7 Finite element idealisation

In all of the studies, program VIBUK (described in an earlier chapter of this book)is adopted using a 10×10 mesh of 9-noded, Huang/Hinton, Mindlin plate bending elements.

2.8 Typical presentation of results

Each problem considered is briefly described and tables of non-dimensional frequency parameters are presented together with the mode shapes. The mode shapes are illustrated with figures of:

(a) *nodal lines* which are contours of zero lateral displacement w, and

(b) *3D views* of the mode shapes with hidden-line removal.

3. PARAMETRIC STUDY

3.1 S-S-S-S plate

The first fifteen modes of vibration for both a thick and a thin plate are obtained using program VIBUK with a 10×10 mesh of Mindlin plate bending elements. Simple support (S) conditions are assumed on each boundary. For the thick plate a span-to-thickness ratio (h/a) equal to 0.1 is adopted, whereas for the thin plate a value of $h/a = 0.01$ is used. Both lumped and consistent mass representations are employed in this study. The shear modification factor k^2 is taken as 0.833.

For comparisons with the finite element solutions, use is made of closed form, Mindlin plate solutions (including rotatory inertia effects as described and coded in Chapter 1 * of this book [2]) and also closed form, 3-D solution [3]. Also, a closed form thin plate solution [4] is shown for comparison.

Tables 3.1 and 3.2 list the frequency parameters for the two plates. The values in parentheses are the percentage errors in the freqencies when compared with the closed form, Mindlin solution. For the thick plate with $h/a = 0.1$, discepancies occur in the values of the frequencies obtained for the higher modes by the thin plate solution which ignores the effects of shear deformation. The finite element solutions have errors of less than 0.4% compared with the closed form, Mindlin solution. The lumped mass representation is slightly superior to the consistent mass idealisation with maximum errors of 0.15%. Figure 3.1 shows the nodal lines (i.e. contours of zero lateral displacement amplitude) for the 14 modes. Figure 3.2 provides a three-dimensional view of the modes for extra clarity.

3.2 C-C-C-C plate

The first fifteen modes of vibration for both a thick and a thin plate are obtained using program VIBUK with a 10×10 mesh of Mindlin plate bending elements. Clamped support (C) conditions are assumed on each boundary. Ashear modification factor of $k^2 = 0.8601$ is employed.

For comparisons with the finite element solutions, use is made of closed form, Mindlin plate solutions (including rotatory inertia) presented by Dawe and Roufaeil [5] and also, closed form thin plate solutions [4].

Tables 3.3 and 3.4 list the frequency parameters for the two plates. Figure 3.3 shows the nodal lines for the 14 modes. Figure 3.4 provides a three-dimensional view of the modes for extra clarity.

---

* See also the Additional Notes at the end of the book.

Table 3.1 Frequency parameters Ω_{mn} for a S-S-S-S plate:
$h/a = 0.1,\ k^2 = 0.833,\ \nu = 0.3$

		Ω_{mn}				
m	n	3D closed form	Mindlin closed form.	f.e. lumped mass	f.e. consist. mass	thin plate c. form
1	1	0.932	0.930	0.930 (+0.0)	0.930 (+0.0)	0.963 (+3.55)
2 1	1 2	2.226	2.219	2.219 (+0.0)	2.219 (+0.0)	2.408 (+8.52)
2	2	3.421	3.406	3.405 (+0.0)	3.406 (+0.03)	3.853 (+13.16)
3 1	1 3	4.171	4.149	4.151 (+0.05)	4.154 (+0.12)	4.816 (+16.07)
3 2	2 3	5.239	5.206	5.205 (+0.0)	5.210 (+0.10)	6.261 (+20.29)
4 1	1 4	—	6.520	6.526 (+0.09)	6.542 (+0.34)	—
3	3	6.889	6.834	6.830 (-0.06)	6.841 (+0.10)	8.668 (+26.84)
4 2	2 4	7.511	7.446	7.448 (+0.03)	7.467 (+0.28)	9.632 (+29.36)
4 3	3 4	9.268	8.896	8.889 (-0.08)	8.918 (+0.25)	12.521 (+40.75)

Table 3.2 Frequency parameters Ω_{mn} for a S-S-S-S plate: $h/a = 0.01$, $k^2 = 0.833$, $\nu = 0.3$

		Ω_{mn}			
m	n	Mindlin closed form	f.e. lumped mass	f.e. consis. mass	thin plate c. form
1	1	0.09629	0.09628 (-0.01)	0.09628 (-0.01)	0.09632 (+0.03)
2 1	1 2	0.2406	0.2406 (+0.0)	0.2406 (+0.0)	0.2408 (+0.08)
2	2	0.3848	0.3847 (-0.03)	0.3848 (+0.0)	0.3853 (+0.13)
3 1	1 3	0.4809	0.4810 (+0.02)	0.4814 (+0.10)	0.4816 (+0.15)
3 2	2 3	0.6249	0.6247 (-0.03)	0.6253 (+0.06)	0.6261 (+0.19)
4 1	1 4	0.8167	0.8179 (+0.15)	0.8198 (+0.38)	0.8187 (+0.24)
3	3	0.8647	0.8639 (-0.09)	0.8652 (+0.06)	—
4 2	2 4	0.9605	0.9609 (+0.04)	0.9633 (+0.29)	—
4 3	3 4	1.1997	1.199 (-0.06)	1.203 (+0.28)	—

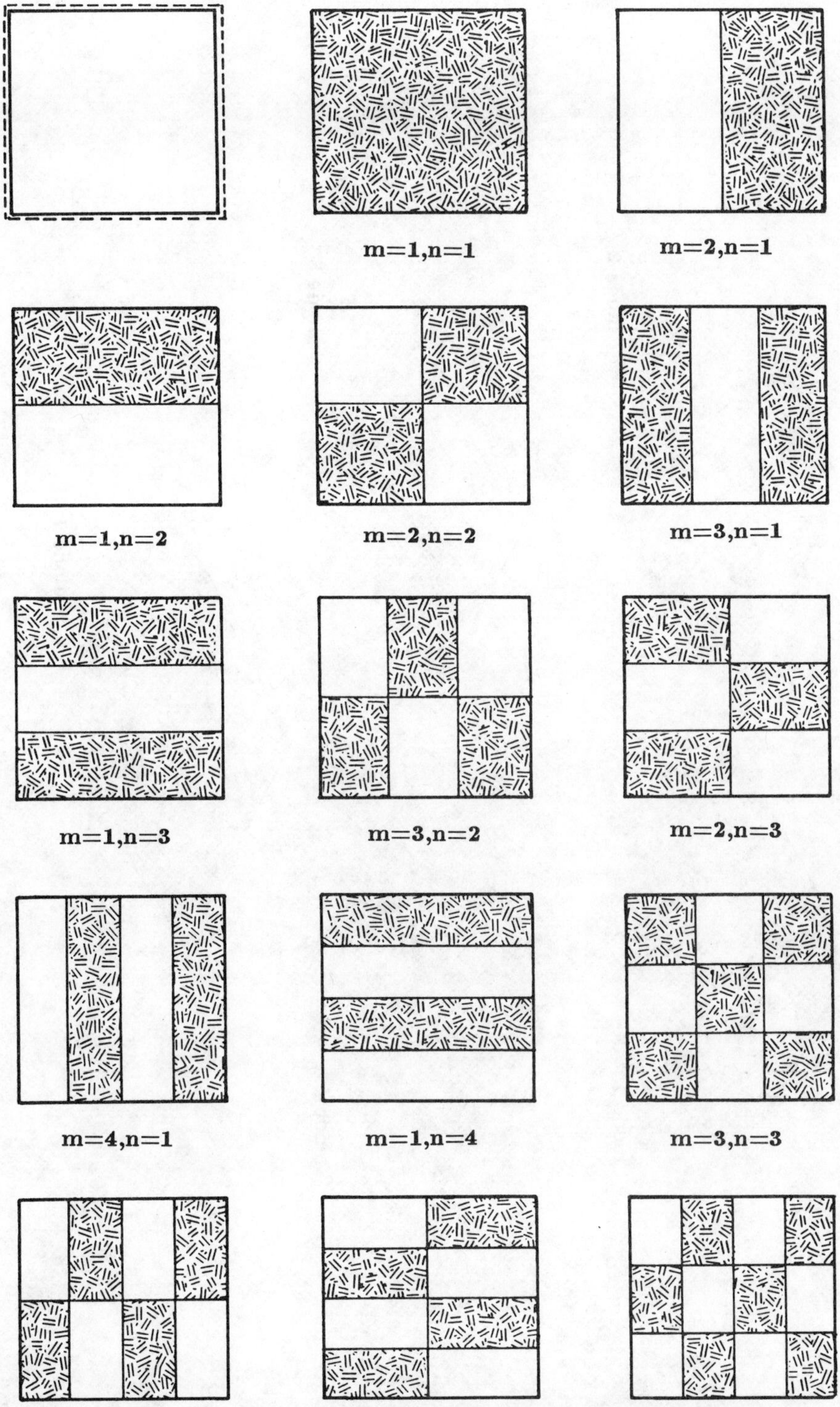

Figure 3.1 Nodal lines for S-S-S-S square plate

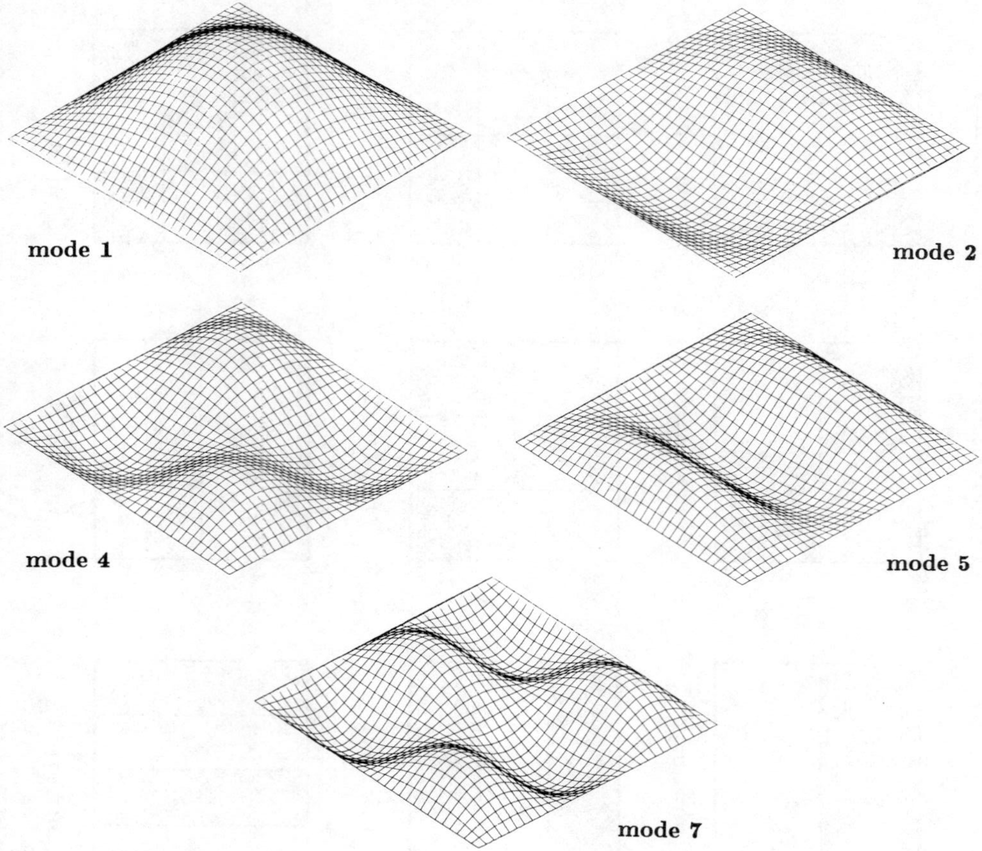

Figure 3.2 Mode shapes for S-S-S-S square plate

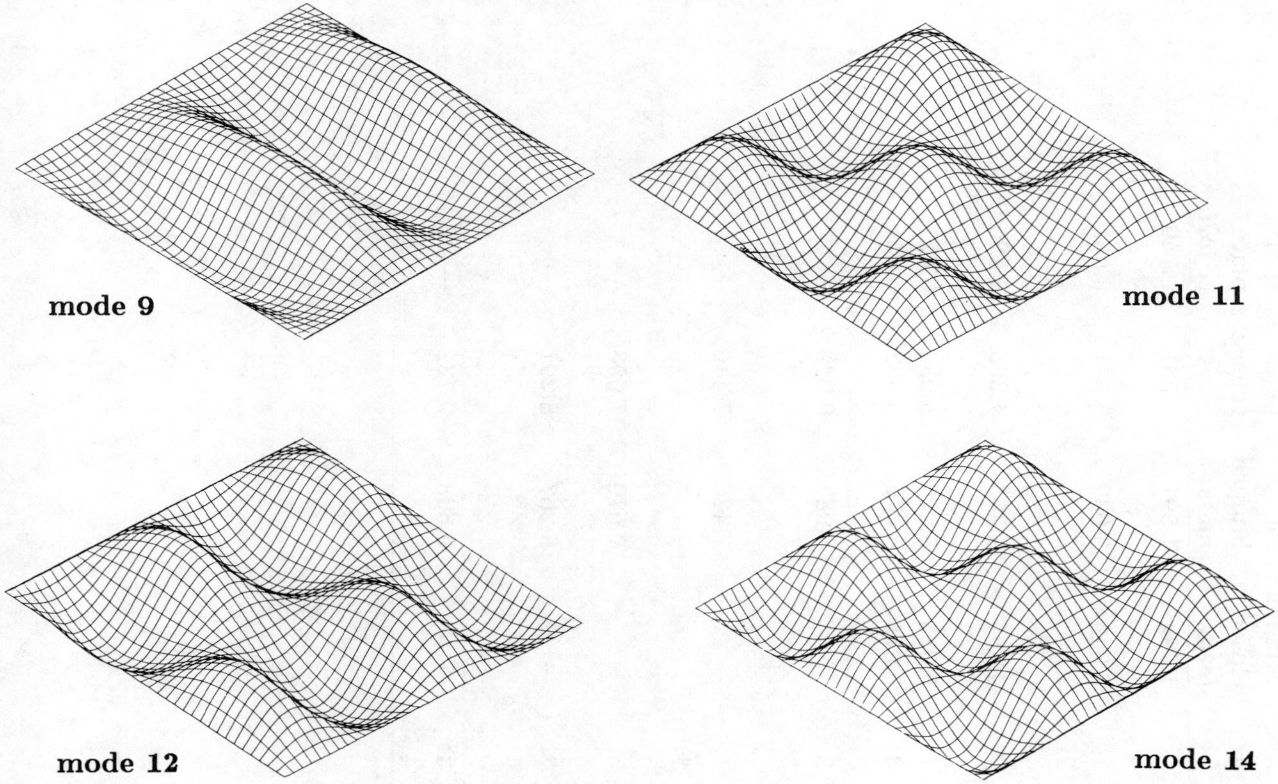

Figure 3.2 Mode shapes for S-S-S-S square plate contd ...

Table 3.3 Frequency parameters Ω_{mn} for a C-C-C-C plate: $h/a = 0.1$, $k^2 = 0.8601$, $\nu = 0.3$

		Ω_{mn}			
m	n	Mindlin closed form.	f.e. lumped mass	f.e. consist. mass	thin plate c. form
1	1	1.594	1.591	1.591	1.756
2 1	1 2	3.046	3.039	3.041	3.581
2	2	4.285	4.263	4.265	5.280
3	1	5.035	5.029	5.034	6.421
1	3	5.078	5.076	5.082	6.451
3 2	2 3	—	6.082	6.089	—
4 1	1 4	—	7.426	7.446	—
3	3	—	7.679	7.693	—
4 2	2 4	—	8.267	8.291	—
4 3	3 4	—	9.698	9.732	—

Table 3.4 Frequency parameters Ω_{mn} for a C-C-C-C plate: $h/a = 0.01$, $k^2 = 0.8601$, $\nu = 0.3$

		Ω_{mn}			
m	n	Mindlin closed form	f.e. lumped mass	f.e. consis. mass	thin plate c. form
1	1	0.1754	0.1754	0.1754	0.1756
2	1	0.3576	0.3574	0.3576	0.3581
1	2				
2	2	0.5274	0.5264	0.5268	0.5280
3	1	0.6402	0.6406	0.6415	0.6421
1	3	0.6432	0.6437	0.6446	0.6432
3	2	—	0.8021	0.8021	—
2	3				
4	1	—	1.0261	1.0295	—
1	4				
3	3	—	1.0678	1.0705	—
4	2	—	1.1776	1.1818	—
2	4				
4	3	—	1.4373	1.4436	—
3	4				

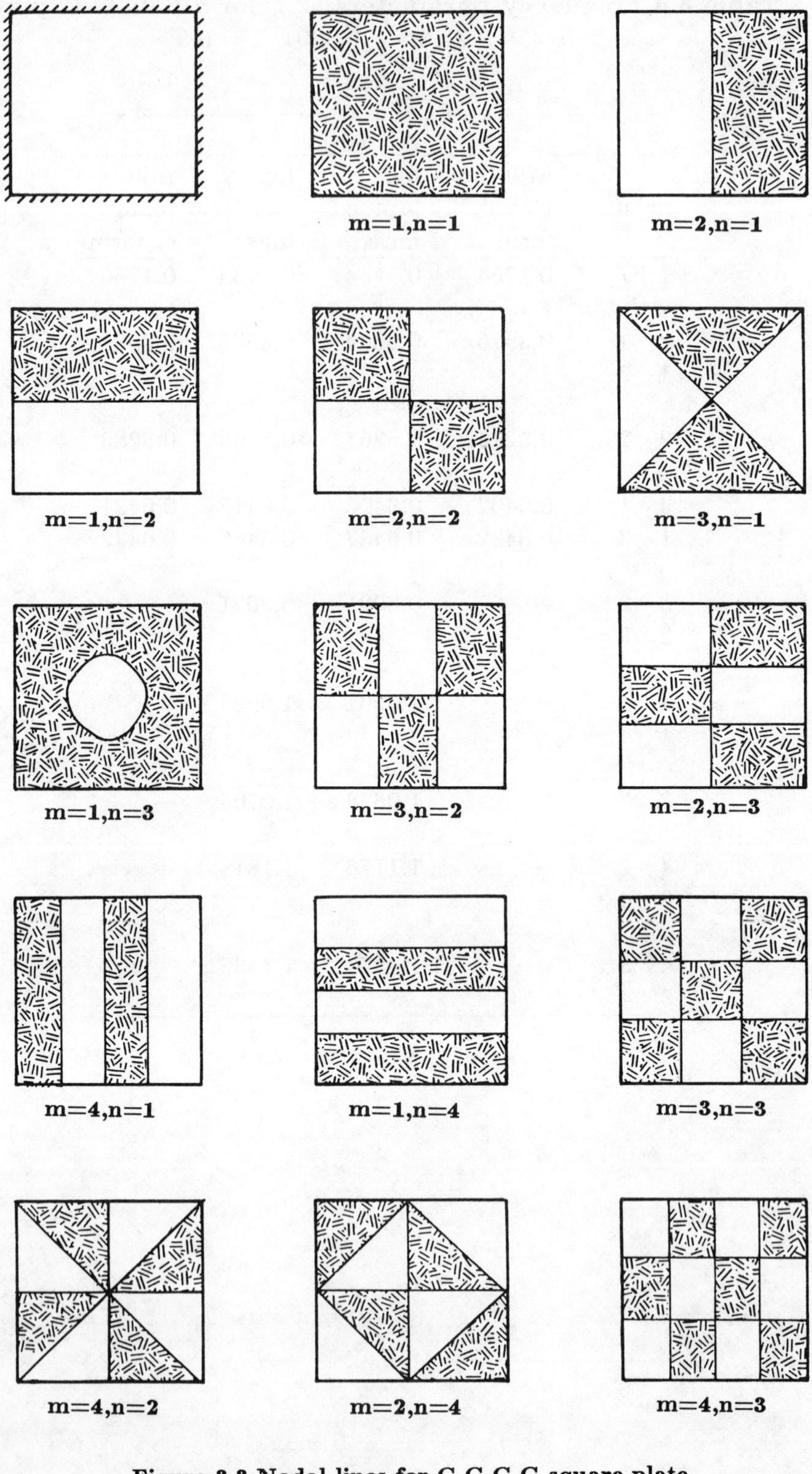

Figure 3.3 Nodal lines for C-C-C-C square plate

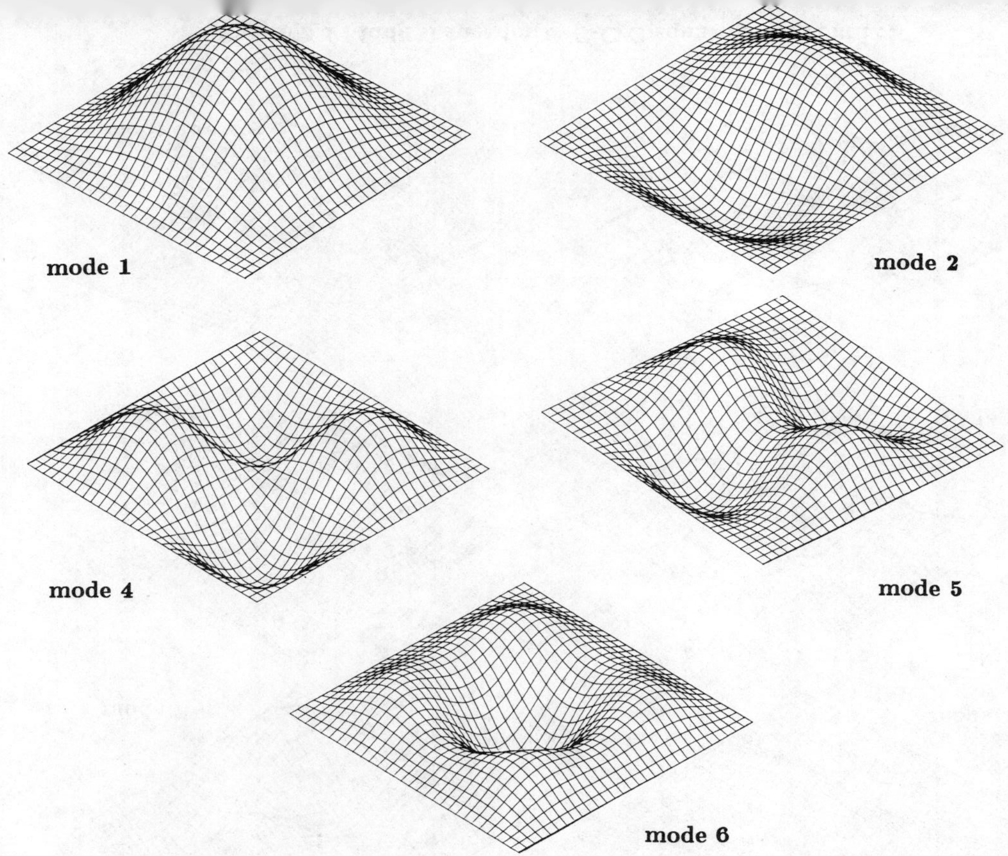

Figure 3.4 Mode shapes for C-C-C-C square plate

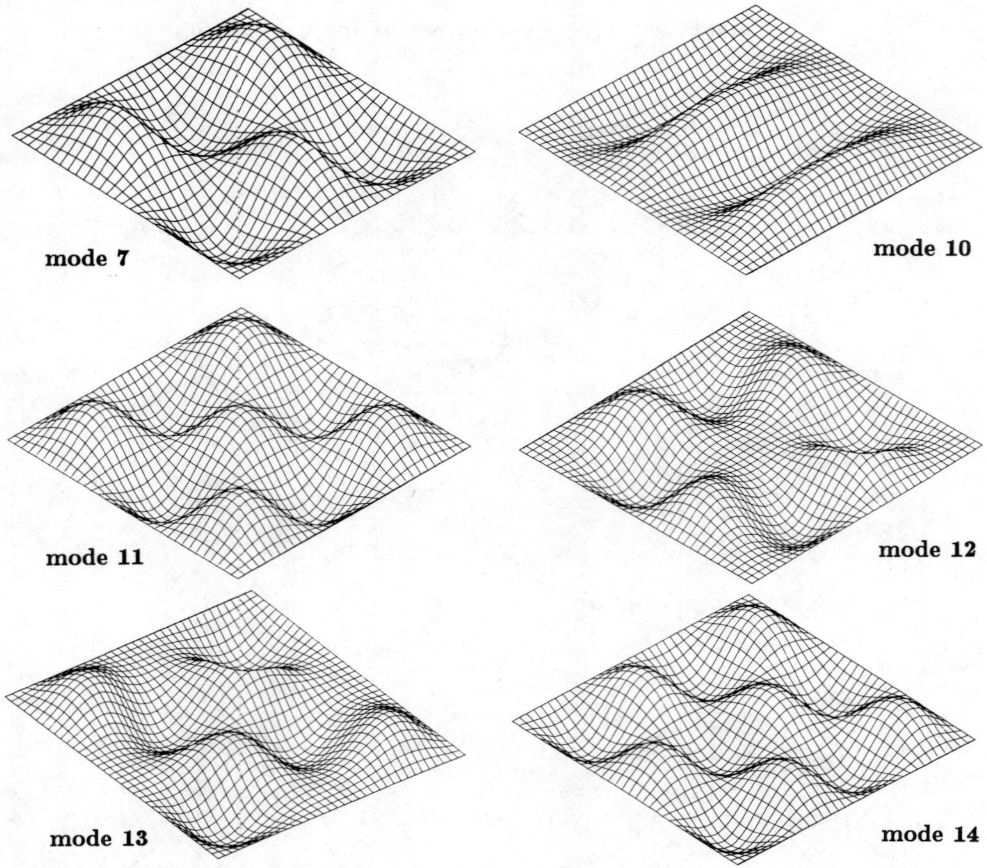

Figure 3.4 Mode shapes for C-C-C-C square plate contd ...

3.3 Plates with other boundary conditions

The first fourteen modes of vibration of plates with the following boundary conditions are obtained using program VIBUK:

(a) S-C-S-C

(b) S-C-S-S

(c) C-C-C-F

(d) S-C-S-F

For comparisons with the finite element solutions, use is made of closed form Mindlin plate solutions (including rotatory inertia) presented by Dawe and Roufaeil [5], Mindlin finite strip solutions [6] and also, closed form thin plate solutions [4].

Both thick and thin plates are considered and Tables 3.5-3.12 list the frequency parameters. Figures 3.5-3.12 show the nodal lines (i.e. contours of zero lateral displacement amplitude) for the 14 modes and also provide three-dimensional views of the modes for extra clarity.

A value of the shear modification factor of $k^2 = 0.822$ is adopted for all cases except the C-C-C-F plate where a value of $k^2 = 0.8601$ is used to conform to the solutions presented by Dawe and Roufaeil [5] which are used for comparison.

3.4 Discussion

In all cases there is good agreement between the Mindlin plate solutions based on closed form, finite strip and finite element formulations.

The limitations of the use of thin plate theory are highlighted — particularly for thick plate analysis and for the prediction of the frequencies for the higher modes.

Lumped mass representation (based on Lobatto integration) provides greater accuracy than consistent mass idealisation.

Table 3.5 Frequency parameters Ω_{mn} for a S-C-S-C plate: $h/a = 0.1$, $k^2 = 0.822$, $\nu = 0.3$

		Ω_{mn}				
m	n	Mindlin closed form	Mindlin finite strip	f.e. lumped mass	f.e. consist. mass	thin plate c. form
1	1	1.302	1.300	1.300	1.300	1.413
2	1	2.398	2.394	2.394	2.394	2.671
1	2	2.888	2.885	2.885	2.886	3.383
2	2	3.852	3.839	3.839	3.841	4.615
3	1	4.237	4.232	4.232	4.236	4.988
1	3	4.939	4.936	4.939	4.944	6.299
3	2	—	—	5.457	5.462	—
2	3	—	—	5.791	5.797	—
4	1	—	—	6.561	6.576	—
3	3	—	—	7.217	7.229	—
4	2	—	—	7.312	7.331	—
1	4	—	—	7.585	7.605	—
2	4	—	—	8.074	8.097	—
5	1	—	—	9.125	9.156	—

Table 3.6 Frequency parameters Ω_{mn} for a S-C-S-C plate: $h/a = 0.01,\ k^2 = 0.822,\ \nu = 0.3$

		Ω_{mn}				
m	n	Mindlin closed form	Mindlin finite strip	f.e. lumped mass	f.e. consis. mass	thin plate c. form
1	1	0.1411	0.1411	0.1411	0.1411	0.1413
2	1	0.2668	0.2668	0.2668	0.2668	0.2671
1	2	0.3377	0.3376	0.3377	0.3378	0.3383
2	2	0.4608	0.4604	0.4604	0.4606	0.4615
3	1	0.4979	0.4977	0.4979	0.4983	0.4988
1	3	0.6279	0.6279	0.6287	0.6295	0.6299
3	2	—	—	0.6819	0.6827	—
2	3	—	—	0.7528	0.7539	—
4	1	—	—	0.8301	0.8321	—
3	3	—	—	0.9705	0.9725	—
4	2	—	—	1.0052	1.0078	—
1	4	—	—	1.0158	1.0192	—
2	4	—	—	1.1415	1.1454	—
5	1	—	—	1.2623	1.2692	—

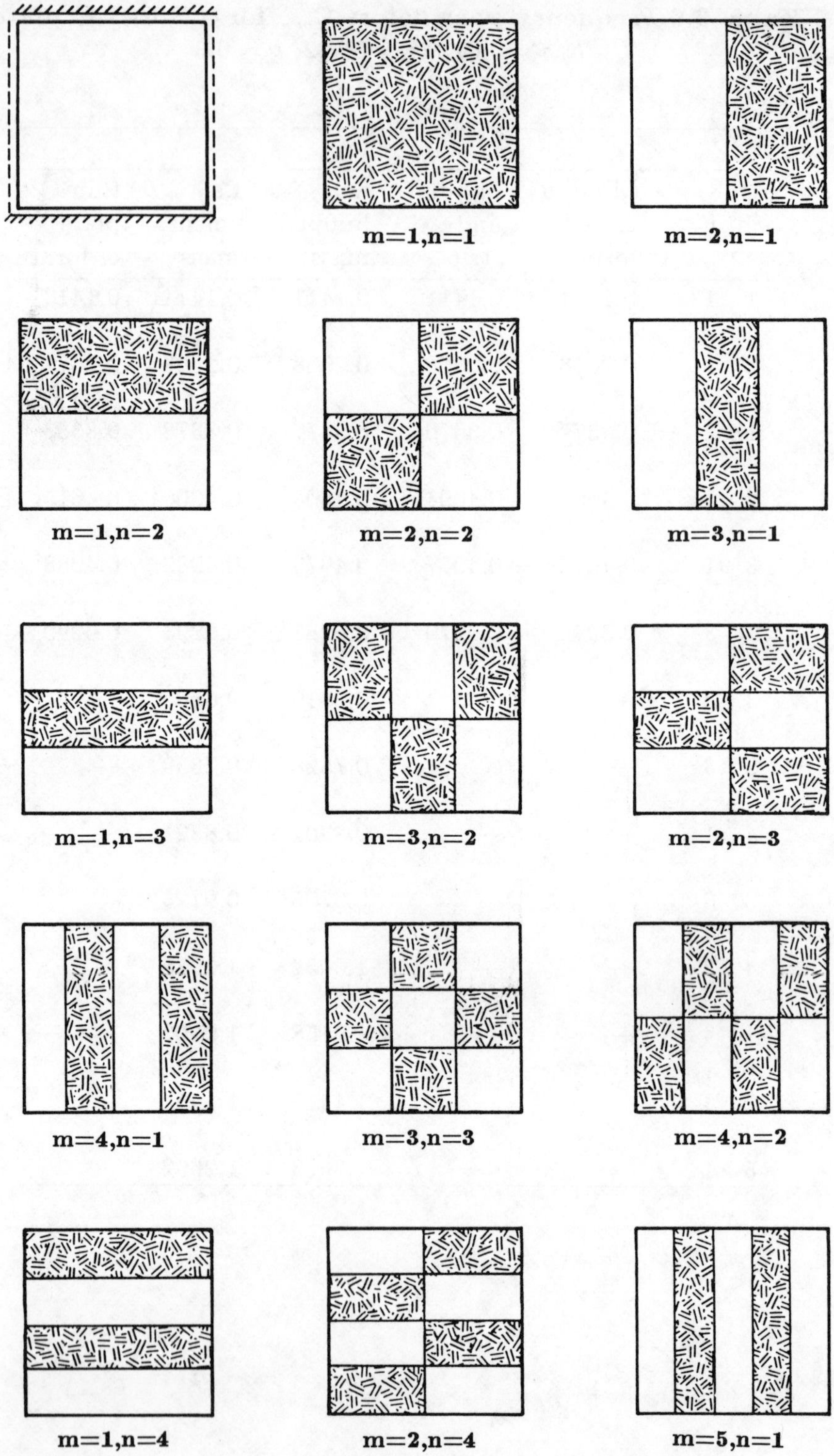

Figure 3.5 Nodal lines for S-C-S-C square plate

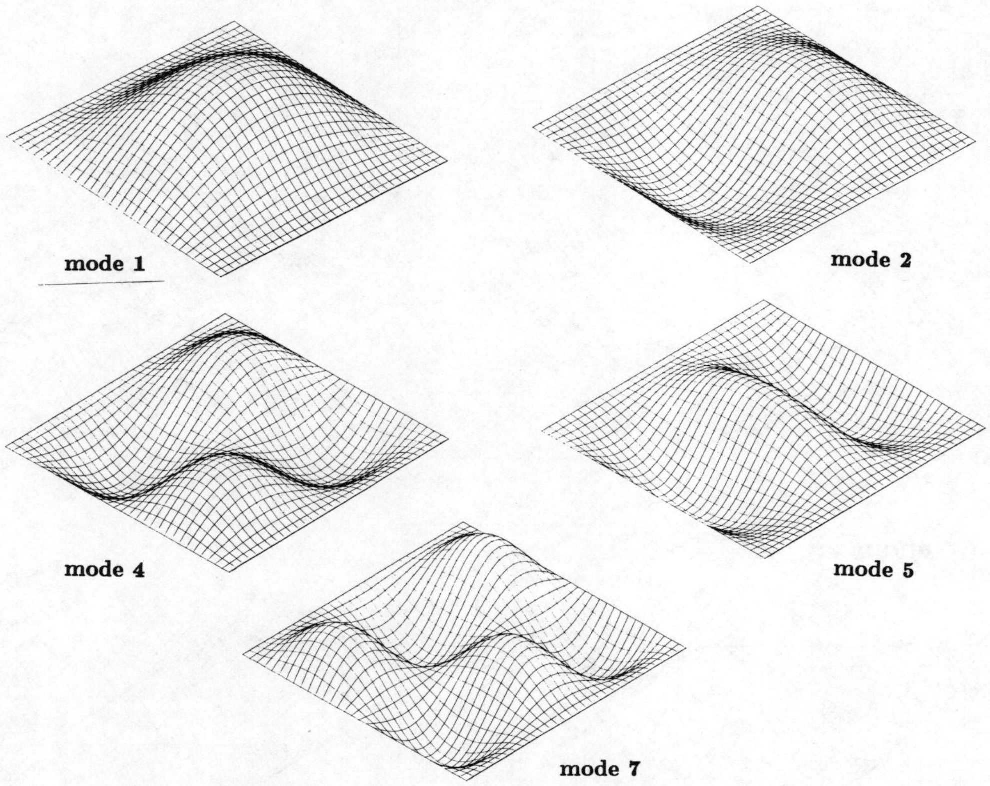

Figure 3.6 Mode shapes for S-C-S-C square plate

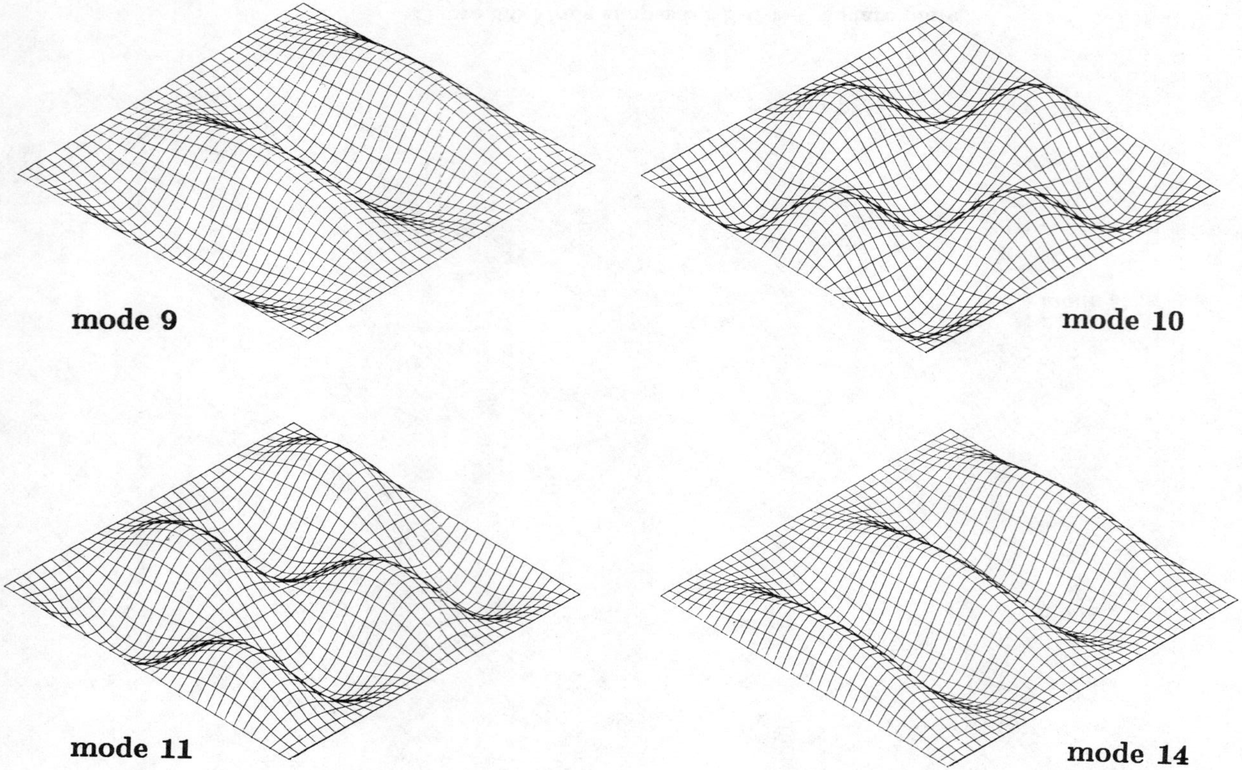

Figure 3.6 Mode shapes for S-C-S-C square plate contd ...

Table 3.7 Frequency parameters Ω_{mn} for a S-C-S-S plate: $h/a = 0.1$, $k^2 = 0.822$, $\nu = 0.3$

		Ω_{mn}				
m	n	Mindlin closed form	Mindlin finite strip	f.e. lumped mass	f.e. consist. mass	thin plate c. form
1	1	1.092	1.092	1.092	1.092	1.154
2	1	2.298	2.296	2.296	2.296	2.521
1	2	2.543	2.542	2.542	2.542	2.862
2	2	3.616	3.611	3.611	3.612	4.203
3	1	4.187	4.184	4.185	4.189	4.893
1	3	4.543	4.541	4.543	4.547	5.525
3	2	—	—	5.321	5.326	—
2	3	—	—	5.491	5.496	—
4	1	—	—	6.536	6.552	—
3	3	—	—	6.919	6.936	—
1	4	—	—	7.014	7.025	—
4	2	—	—	7.506	7.525	—
2	4	—	—	7.755	7.776	—
4	3	—	—	8.994	9.023	—

Table 3.8 Frequency parameters Ω_{mn} for a S-C-S-S plate: $h/a = 0.01,\ k^2 = 0.822,\ \nu = 0.3$

		Ω_{mn}				
m	n	Mindlin closed form	Mindlin finite strip	f.e. lumped mass	f.e. consis. mass	thin plate c. form
1	1	0.1153	0.1153	0.1153	0.1153	0.1154
2	1	0.2521	0.2519	0.2519	0.2519	0.2521
1	2	0.2858	0.2858	0.2858	0.2858	0.2862
2	2	0.4199	0.4195	0.4195	0.4196	0.4203
3	1	0.4889	0.4883	0.4885	0.4889	0.4893
1	3	0.5533	0.5513	0.5516	0.5521	0.5525
3	2	—	—	0.6511	0.6518	—
2	3	—	—	0.6854	0.6862	—
4	1	—	—	0.8235	0.8254	—
3	3	—	—	0.9136	0.9158	—
1	4	—	—	0.9142	0.9162	—
4	2	—	—	0.9815	0.9840	—
2	4	—	—	1.0478	1.0508	—
4	3	—	—	1.2403	1.2444	—

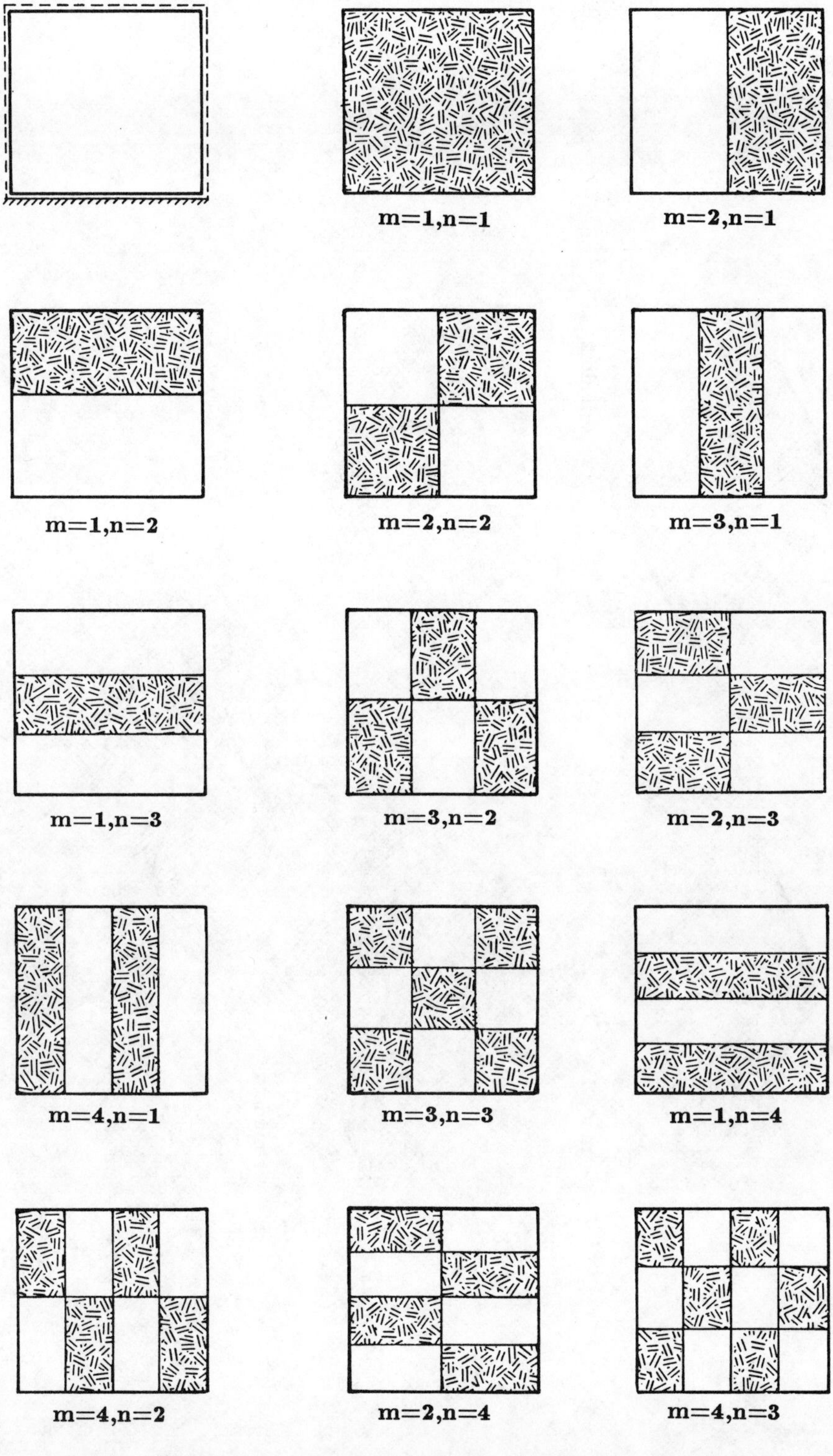

Figure 3.7 Nodal lines for S-C-S-S square plate

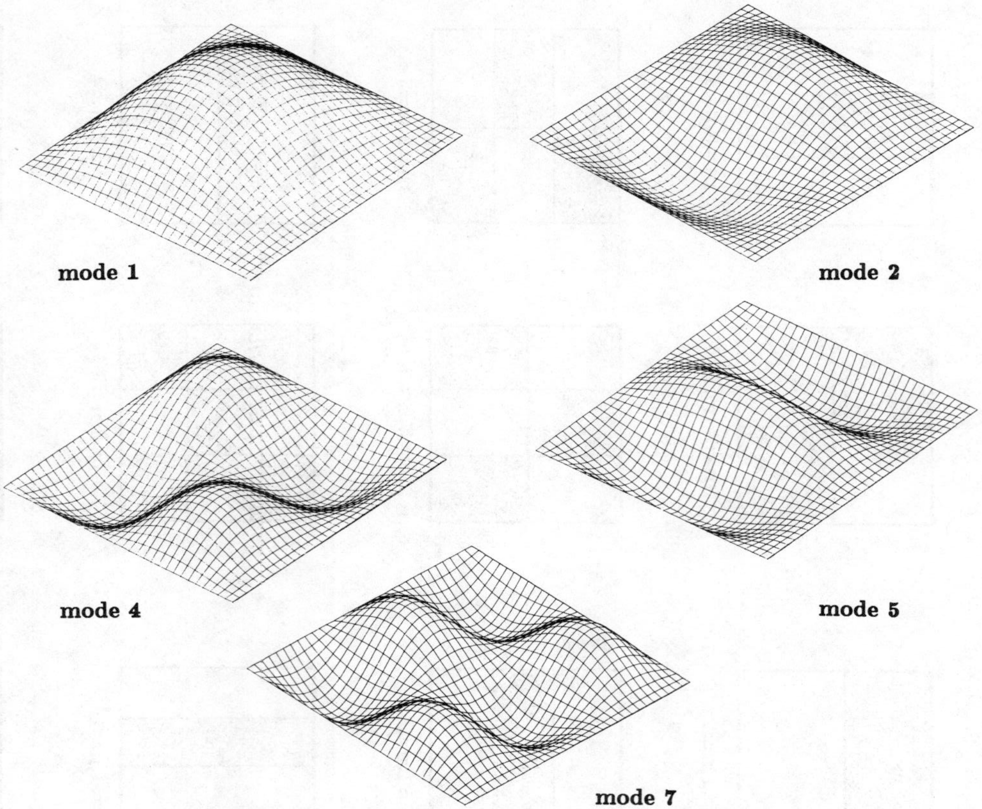

Figure 3.8 Mode shapes for S-C-S-S square plate

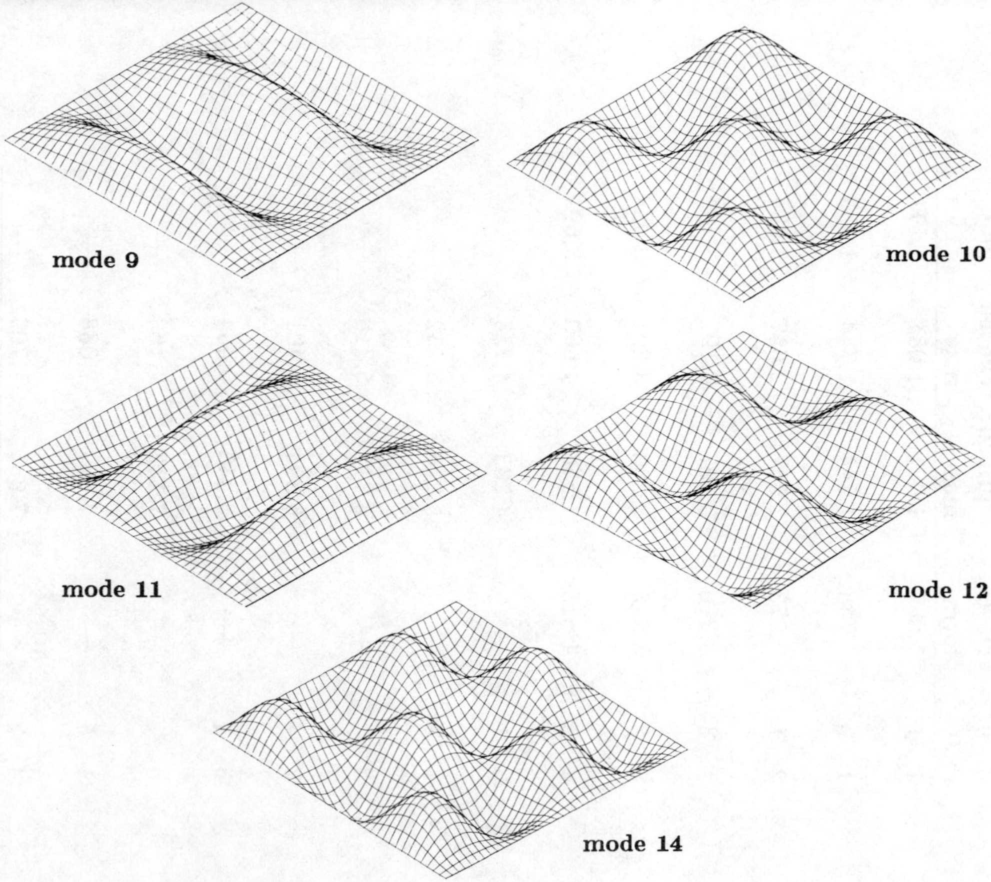

Figure 3.8 Mode shapes for S-C-S-S square plate contd ...

Table 3.9 Frequency parameters Ω_{mn} for a C-C-C-F plate: $h/a = 0.1,\ k^2 = 0.8601,\ \nu = 0.3$

		Ω_{mn}			
m	n	Mindlin closed form	f.e. lumped mass	f.e. consist. mass	thin plate c. form
1	1	1.089	1.081	1.081	1.171
1	2	1.758	1.744	1.744	1.953
2	1	2.673	2.657	2.657	3.094
1	3	3.216	3.197	3.197	3.744
2	2	3.318	3.290	3.291	3.938
2	3	4.615	4.558	4.560	5.699
3	1	—	4.733	4.738	—
1	4	—	5.246	5.252	—
3	2	—	5.313	5.318	—
2	4	—	6.393	6.401	—
3	3	—	6.446	6.454	—
4	1	—	7.143	7.163	—
1	5	—	7.667	7.688	—
4	2	—	7.685	7.709	—

Table 3.10 Frequency parameters Ω_{mn} for a C-C-C-F plate: $h/a = 0.01,\ k^2 = 0.8601,\ \nu = 0.3$

		Ω_{mn}			
m	n	Mindlin closed form	f.e. lumped mass	f.e. consis. mass	thin plate c. form
1	1	0.1171	0.1166	0.1166	0.1171
1	2	0.1951	0.1949	0.1949	0.1953
2	1	0.3093	0.3080	0.3082	0.3094
1	3	0.3740	0.3736	0.3737	0.3744
2	2	0.3931	0.3922	0.3924	0.3938
2	3	0.5695	0.5674	0.5678	0.5699
3	1	—	0.5955	0.5963	—
1	4	—	0.6547	0.6556	—
3	2	—	0.6825	0.6835	—
2	4	—	0.8402	0.8416	—
3	3	—	0.8591	0.8605	—
4	1	—	0.9800	0.9833	—
1	5	—	1.0360	1.0397	—
4	2	—	1.0684	1.0720	—

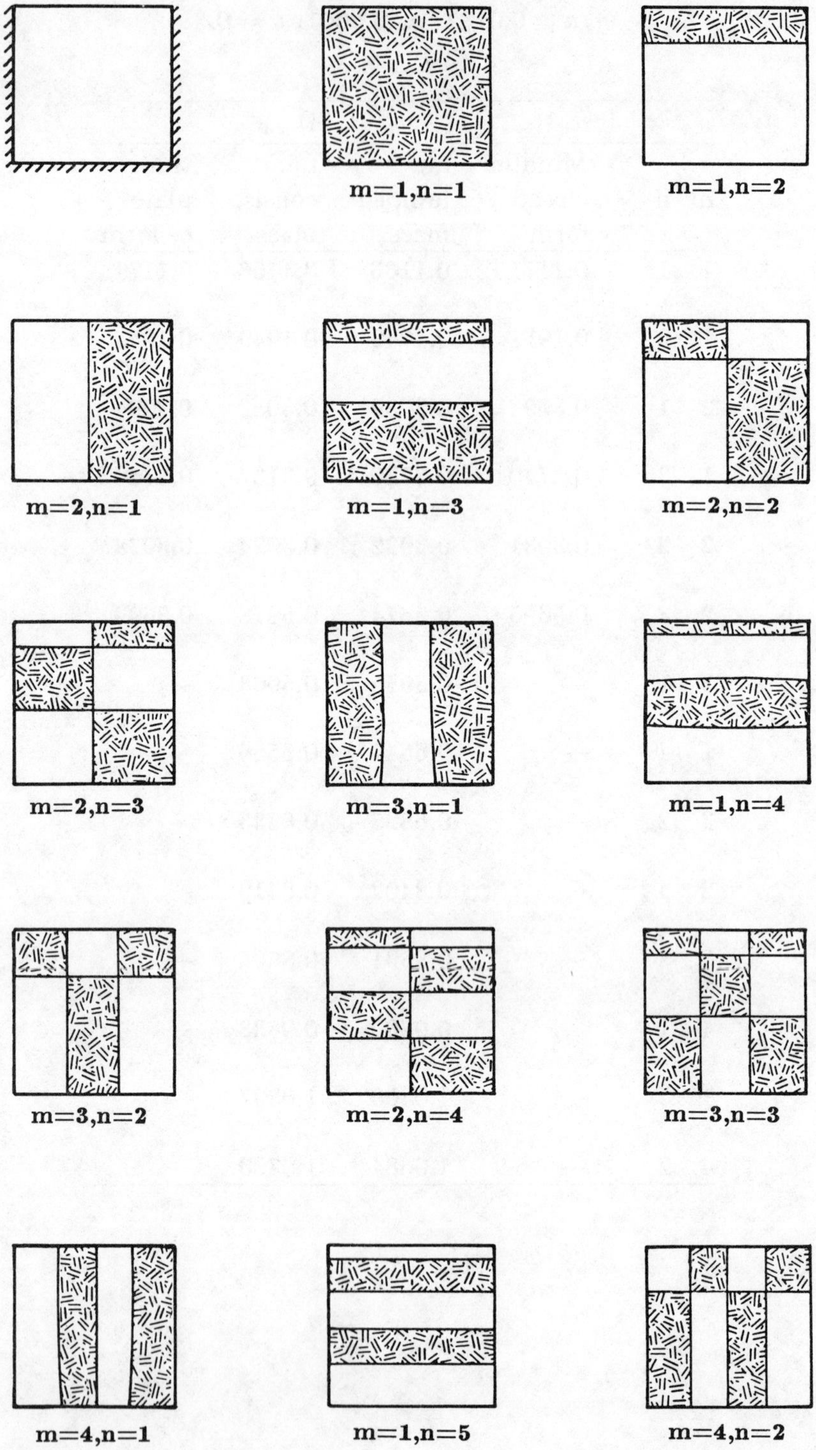

Figure 3.9 Nodal lines for C-C-C-F square plate

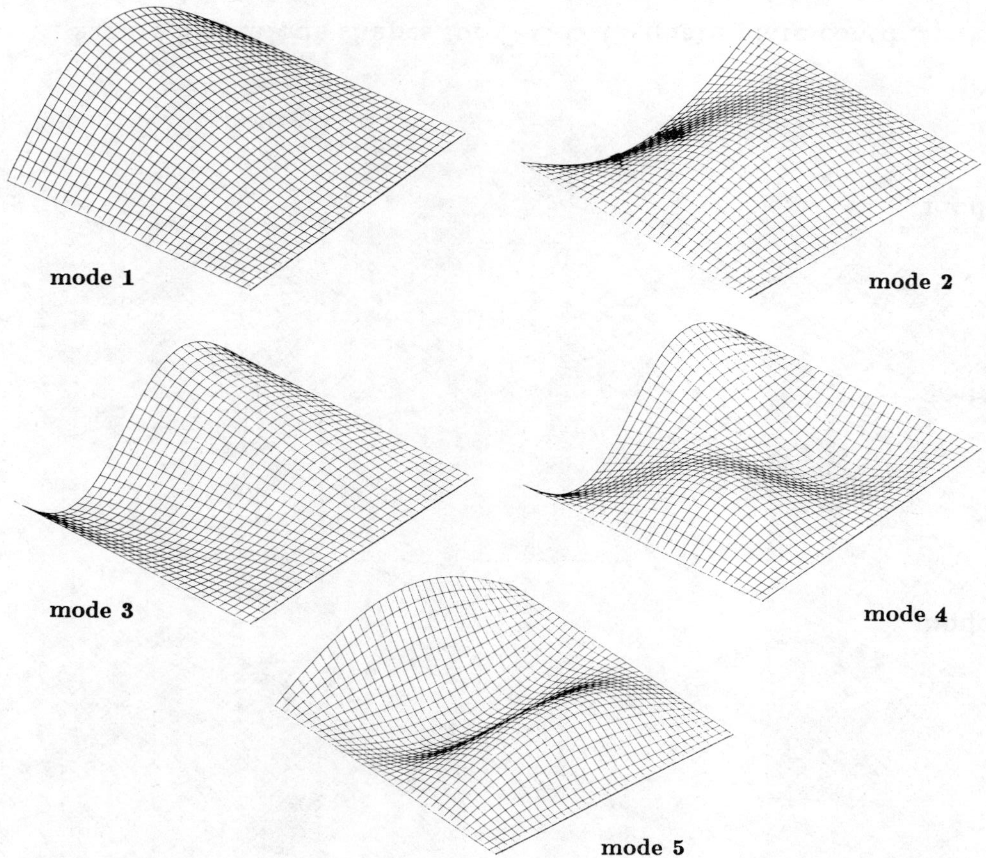

Figure 3.10 Mode shapes for C-C-C-F square plate

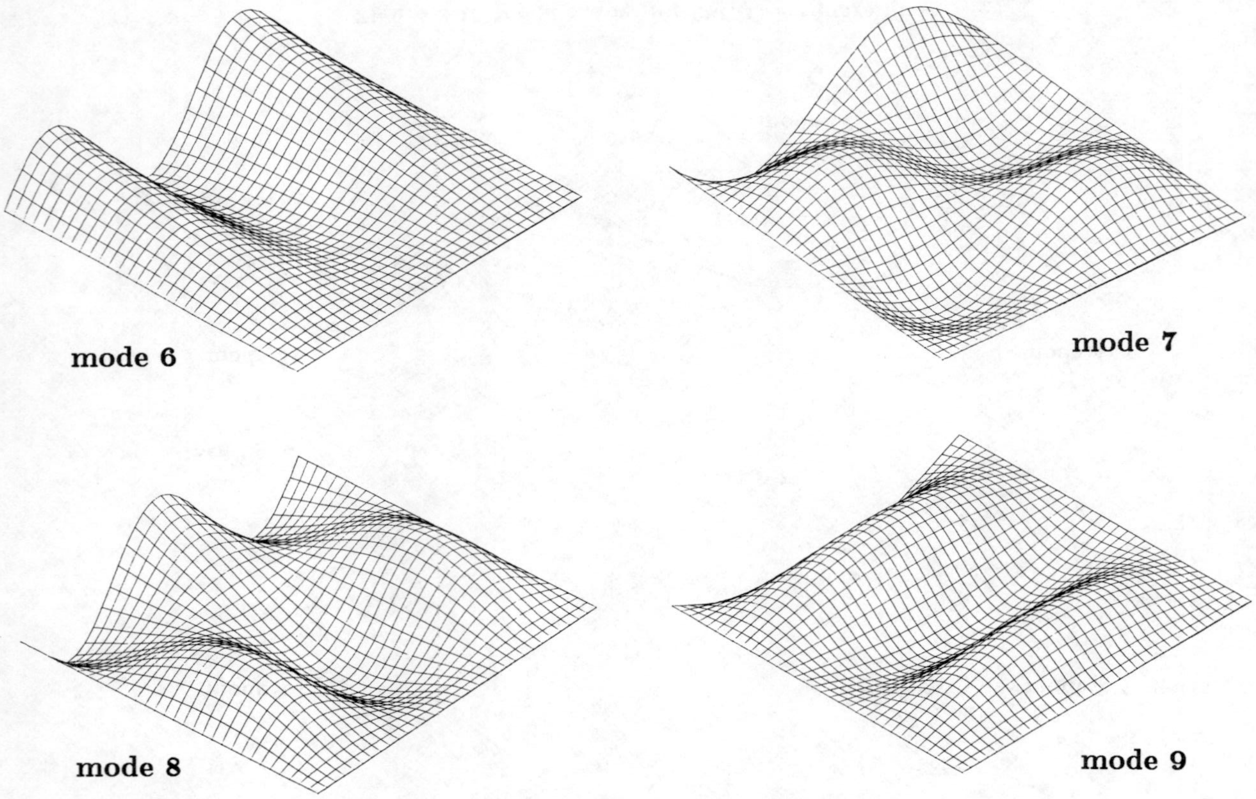

Figure 3.10 Mode shapes for C-C-C-F square plate contd ...

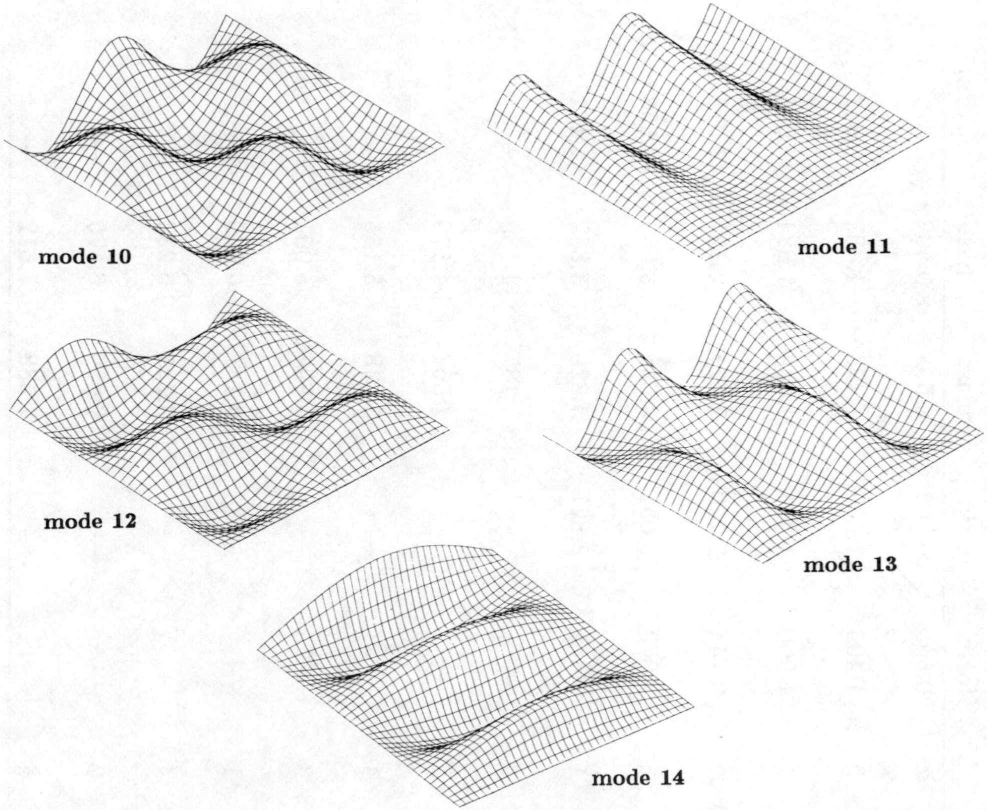

Figure 3.10 Mode shapes for C-C-C-F square plate contd ...

Table 3.11 Frequency parameters Ω_{mn} for a S-C-S-F plate:
$h/a = 0.1$, $k^2 = 0.822$, $\nu = 0.3$

		Ω_{mn}				
m	n	Mindlin closed form	Mindlin finite strip	f.e. lumped mass	f.e. consist. mass	thin plate c. form
1	1	0.603	0.598	0.598	0.598	0.619
1	2	1.495	1.483	1.483	1.483	1.613
2	1	1.900	1.884	1.884	1.884	2.035
2	2	2.744	2.720	2.721	2.721	3.075
1	3	3.073	3.057	3.058	3.059	3.533
3	1	3.855	3.827	3.829	3.832	4.421
2	3	—	—	4.187	4.189	—
3	2	—	—	4.567	4.570	—
1	4	—	—	5.148	5.155	—
3	3	—	—	5.894	5.901	—
4	1	—	—	6.141	6.149	—
2	4	—	—	6.221	6.236	—
4	2	—	—	6.859	6.876	—
1	5	—	—	7.588	7.612	—

Table 3.12 Frequency parameters Ω_{mn} for a S-C-S-F plate: $h/a = 0.01$, $k^2 = 0.822$, $\nu = 0.3$

		Ω_{mn}				
m	n	Mindlin closed form	Mindlin finite strip	f.e. lumped mass	f.e. consis. mass	thin plate c. form
1	1	0.0622	0.0619	0.0619	0.0619	0.0619
1	2	0.1612	0.1611	0.1611	0.1611	0.1613
2	1	0.2045	0.2033	0.2033	0.2033	0.2035
2	2	0.3075	0.3070	0.3070	0.3070	0.3075
1	3	0.3528	0.3526	0.3527	0.3528	0.3533
3	1	0.4438	0.4413	0.4416	0.4420	0.4421
2	3	—	—	0.5021	0.5023	—
3	2	—	—	0.5449	0.5453	—
1	4	—	—	0.6402	0.6410	—
3	3	—	—	0.7429	0.7438	—
4	1	—	—	0.7768	0.7786	—
2	4	—	—	0.7899	0.7911	—
4	2	—	—	0.8787	0.8808	—
1	5	—	—	1.0251	1.0287	—

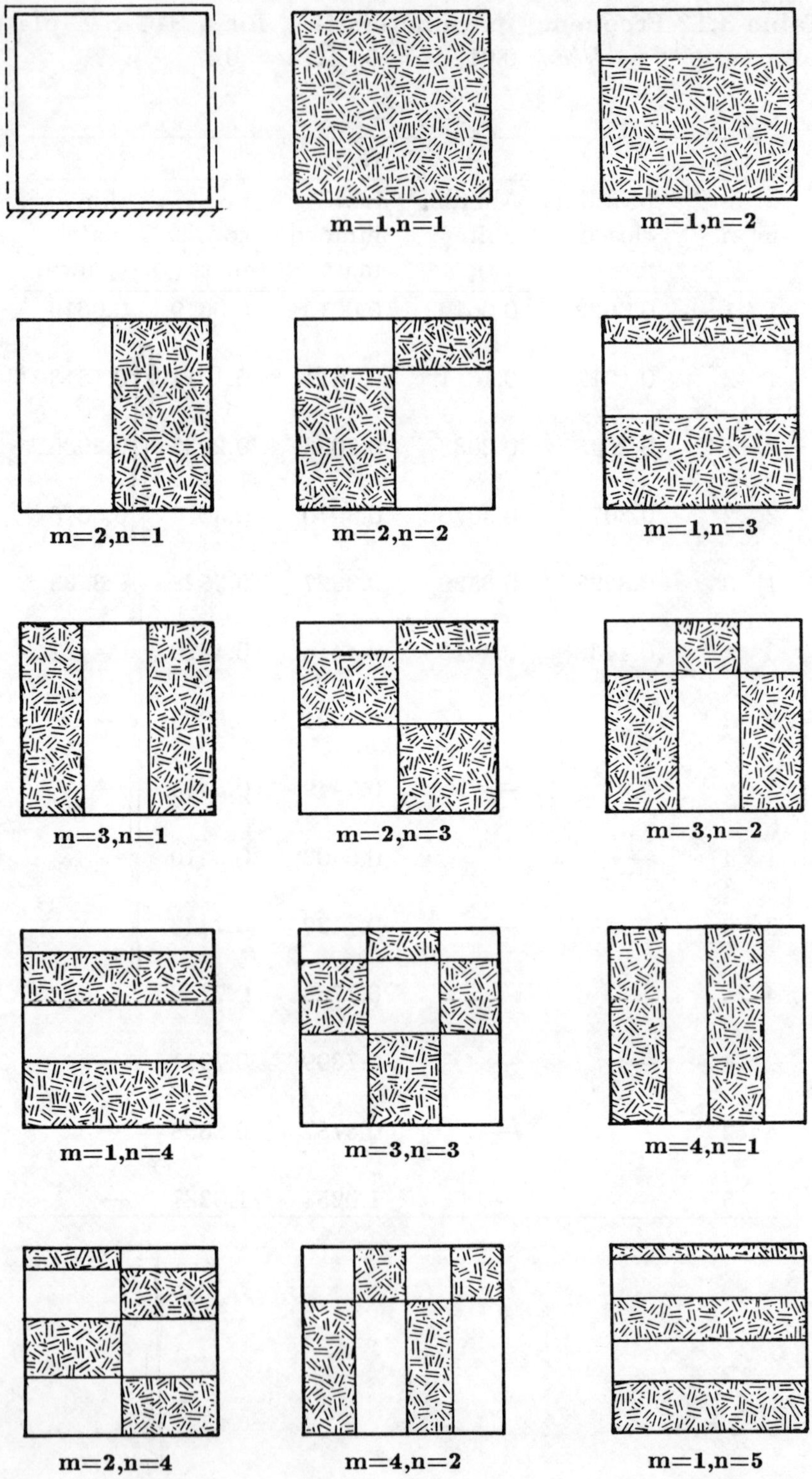

Figure 3.11 Nodal lines for S-C-S-F square plate

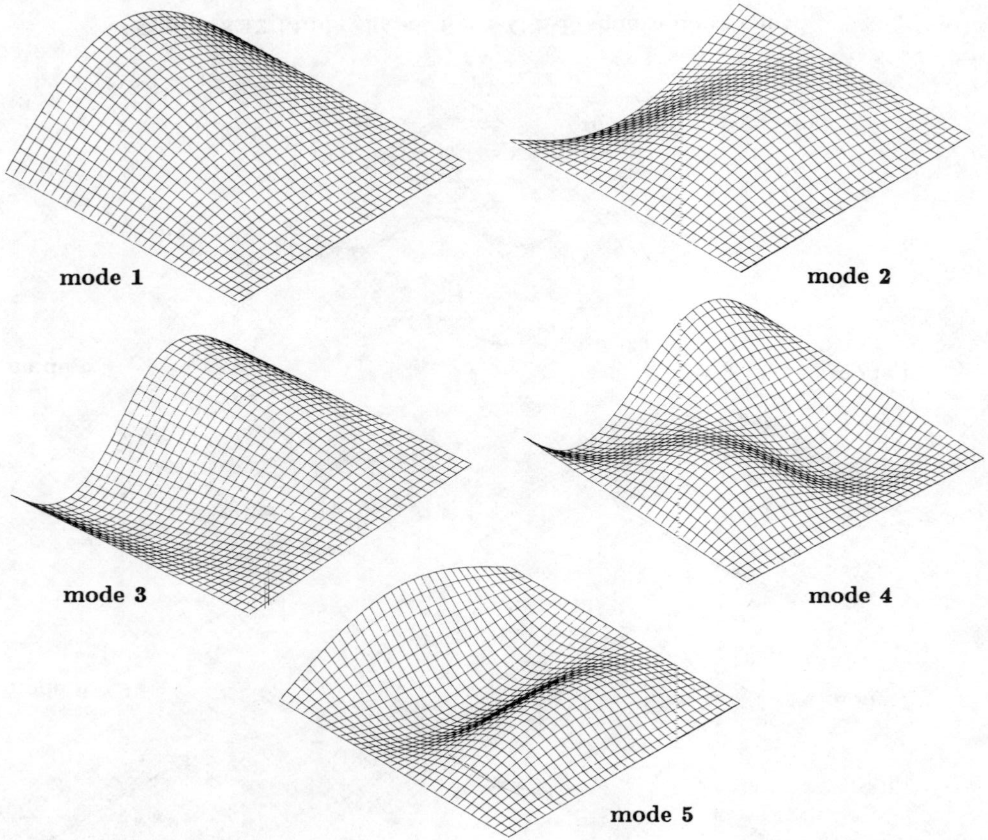

Figure 3.12 Mode shapes for S-C-S-F square plate

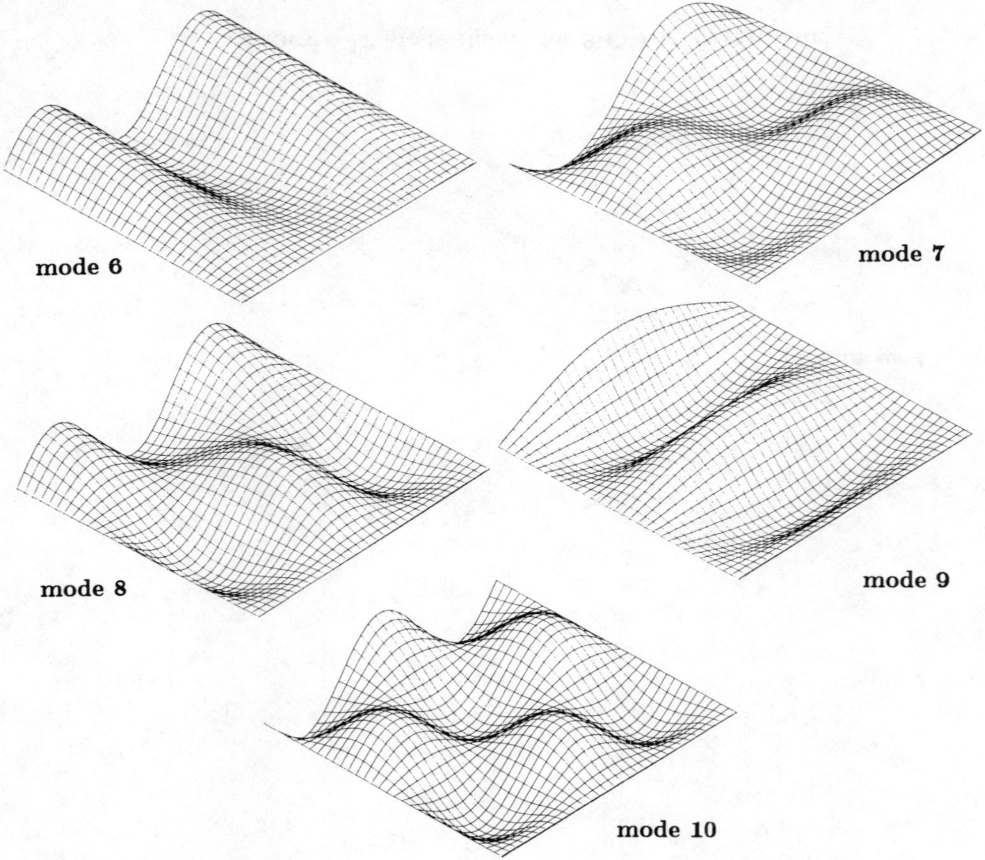

Figure 3.12 Mode shapes for S-C-S-F square plate contd ...

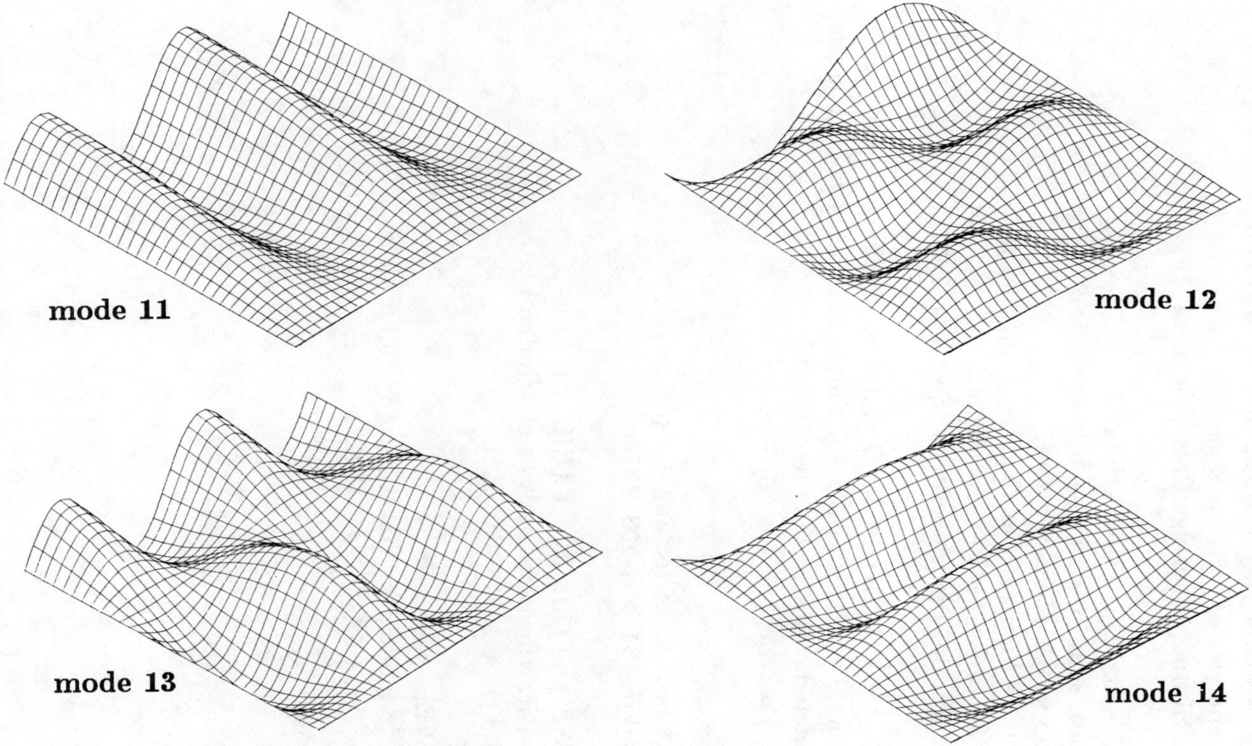

Figure 3.12 Mode shapes for S-C-S-F square plate contd ...

REFERENCES

1. E. HINTON, Dj. VUKSANOVIC and H.C. HUANG, Finite element free vibration and buckling analysis of initially stressed Mindlin plates, Chapter 3 of *'Numerical methods and software for dynamic analysis of plates and shells'*, ed. by E. Hinton, Pineridge Press, Swansea, 1987.

2. E.HINTON and Dj. VUKSANOVIC, Closed form solutions for dynamic analysis of simply supported Mindlin plates, Chapter 1 of *'Numerical methods and software for dynamic analysis of plates and shells'*, ed. by E. Hinton, Pineridge Press, Swansea, 1987.

3. S. SRINIVAS, C.V. JOGA RAO and A.K. RAO, An exact analysis for vibration of simply supported homogeneous and laminated, thick rectangular plates, *J. Sound Vib.*, **12**, 187-199, 1970.

4. A.W. LEISSA, The free vibration of rectangular plates, *J. Sound Vib.*, **31**, 257-293, 1973.

5. D.J. DAWE and O.L. ROUFAEIL, Rayleigh-Ritz vibration analysis of Mindlin plates, *J. Sound Vib.*, **69**, 345-359, 1980.

6. D.J. DAWE, Finite strip models for vibration of Mindlin plates, *J. Sound. Vib.*, **59**, 441-452, 1978.

EXPLICIT TRANSIENT DYNAMIC FINITE ELEMENT ANALYSIS OF INITIALLY STRESSED MINDLIN PLATES

E. HINTON* and Dj. VUKSANOVIC**

*Dept. of Civil Engng., Univ. Coll. of Swansea, U.K.
**Faculty of Civil Engng., Univ. of Belgrade, Yugoslavia

1. INTRODUCTION

This chapter is concerned with the transient dynamic analysis of initially stressed plates using nine-noded Mindlin plate elements. The time integration is carried out using the explicit central difference scheme and since a diagonal mass matrix is incorporated no matrix factorisation is required.

Since the mass and stiffness matrices for the 9-node element QUAD9* have already been described in detail in Chapter 3 they will not be repeated here. Section 2 deals with the time stepping algorithm and includes details of the starting algorithm and an estimate for the critical time step required to prevent instability of the solution. Section 3 describes in detail the finite element program DYNAM and includes a glossary of variable names, listings and brief descriptions of the subroutines and a set of user instructions. In the final section some sample solutions are presented with typical input and output data associated with program DYNAM. Comparisons are provided with the closed form solution provided in Chapter 1.

2. EXPLICIT TIME INTEGRATION SCHEME

2.1 Central Difference Approximation

Upon finite element discretization the dynamic equilibrium equations of an initially stressed system in motion can be written in matrix form as

$$\underline{M}\,\ddot{\underline{d}} + \underline{C}\,\dot{\underline{d}} + (\underline{K} + \underline{K}_G)\underline{d} = \underline{f} \tag{2.1}$$

where $\underline{M}$, $\underline{C}$, $\underline{K}$ and $\underline{K}_G$ are the global mass, damping, stiffness and geometric stiffness matrices respectively; $\underline{f}$ is the external load vector; and $\ddot{\underline{d}}$, $\dot{\underline{d}}$ and $\underline{d}$ are the acceleration, velocity and displacement vectors of the finite element assemblage. Instead of satisfying (2.1) at any time t, in the central difference scheme (2.1) is satisfied only at discrete time intervals Δt apart. This means that at time t_n we have

$$\underline{M}\,\ddot{\underline{d}}_n + \underline{C}\,\dot{\underline{d}}_n + \underline{p}_n = \underline{f}_n \tag{2.2}$$

where $\underline{p}_n$ is the global vector of internal resisting nodal forces. We now employ a temporal discretization of the dynamic equilibrium equations by approximating the accelerations and velocities using finite difference expressions. In particular we adopt a central difference approximation [1] so that the accelerations can be written as

$$\ddot{\underline{d}}_n = \frac{1}{(\Delta t)^2}\,(\underline{d}_{n+1} - 2\underline{d}_n + \underline{d}_{n-1}) \tag{2.3}$$

and the velocities are written as

$$\dot{\underline{d}}_n = \frac{1}{2\Delta t}\,(\underline{d}_{n+1} - \underline{d}_{n-1}) \tag{2.4}$$

in which Δt is the time step or interval so that we are sampling the displacements at time stations $t_n - \Delta t$, t_n and $t_n + \Delta t$.

Substituting the relations for $\ddot{\underline{d}}_n$ and $\dot{\underline{d}}_n$ in (2.3) and (2.4), respectively, into (2.2), we obtain

$$\underline{M}\left(\frac{\underline{d}_{n+1} - 2\underline{d}_n + \underline{d}_{n-1}}{(\Delta t)^2}\right) + \underline{C}\left(\frac{\underline{d}_{n+1} - \underline{d}_{n-1}}{2\Delta t}\right) + \underline{p}_n = \underline{f}_n \tag{2.5}$$

which can be rearranged to give

$$\underline{d}_{n+1} = (\underline{M} + \frac{\Delta t}{2}\underline{C})^{-1} [(\Delta t)^2 (-\underline{p}_n + \underline{f}_n) + 2\underline{M}\,\underline{d}_n - - (\underline{M} - \frac{\Delta t}{2}\underline{C})\underline{d}_{n-1}] \qquad (2.6)$$

It should be noted that the displacements at time station $t_n+\Delta t$ are given explicitly in terms of the displacements at time stations t_n and $t_n-\Delta t$.

If the mass matrix $\underline{M}$ and the damping matrix $\underline{C}$ are diagonal then the solution of (2.6) becomes trivial and we have

$$d_{n+1}^{(i)} = (m_{ii} + \frac{\Delta t}{2} c_{ii})^{-1} [(\Delta t)^2 (- p_n^{(i)} + f_n^{(i)}) + 2m_{ii}\, d_n^{(i)} - (m_{ii} - \frac{\Delta t}{2} c_{ii})\, d_{n-1}^{(i)}] \qquad (2.7)$$

where superscript (i) denotes i^{th} component of the corresponding vectors and m_{ii} and c_{ii} are the diagonal terms of the mass and damping matrices. From (2.7) it is obvious that for each displacement degree of freedom at time $t_n+\Delta t$ we have a separate equation involving information regarding the degree of freedom at times t_n and $t_n-\Delta t$. No matrix factorisation or sophisticated equation solving is therefore necessary.

2.2 Starting Algorithm

The governing equilibrium equation at time station $t_n+\Delta t$ in the central difference method involves information at the two previous time stations t_n and $t_n-\Delta t$. A starting algorithm is therefore necessary and from initial conditions the values $\underline{d}(0-\Delta t)$ may be obtained. From (2.4) we have

$$\dot{\underline{d}}(0) = \frac{\underline{d}(0+\Delta t) - \underline{d}(0-\Delta t)}{2\Delta t} \qquad (2.8)$$

or $\quad \underline{d}(0-\Delta t) = - 2\Delta t\, \dot{\underline{d}}(0) + \underline{d}(0+\Delta t) \qquad (2.9)$

Upon substitution (2.9) into (2.7) we can write

$$d_1^{(i)} = \frac{(\Delta t)^2}{2m_{ii}} (-p_o^{(i)} + f_o^{(i)}) + d_o^{(i)} + \Delta t \left(1 - \frac{c_{ii}\Delta t}{2m_{ii}}\right) \dot{d}_o^{(i)} \tag{2.10}$$

Assuming that the system has no physical damping, $c_{ii}=0$, expressions (2.7) and (2.10) become simpler; for some more detail about damping see reference [2].

2.3 Critical Time Step

A very important factor in the use of the central difference scheme is the selection of an appropriate time step. Small time steps are required for accurate and stable solutions whereas for reasons of economy we would prefer large time steps. From stability considerations, the time step length is limited by the expression [2]

$$\Delta t \leqq \frac{2}{\omega_{max}} \tag{2.11}$$

where ω_{max} is the highest circular frequency of the finite element mesh. To avoid the exact evaluation of the highest finite element mesh frequency approximate expressions are usually employed. The estimate of the critical time step length of the transient solution of Mindlin plates given by Tsui and Tong [3] has been extensively tested [4,5,6] giving excellent results. The critical time step length is thus given as

$$\Delta t = \gamma L_s \left\{ \frac{\rho(1-\nu^2)/E}{2+0.83(1-\nu)[1+1.5(L_s/h)^2]} \right\}^{\frac{1}{2}} \tag{2.12}$$

where L_s is the smallest distance between adjacent nodes in any element used and γ is a correction factor which is some number less than unity. Hinton et al. [4] found that $\gamma = 0.70$ is a safe value to use in a similar context for an 8-noded quadrilateral isoparametric plate bending element.

3. PROGRAM DYNAM

3.1 Introduction

This section describes DYNAM which is a program for the transient dynamic analysis of initially stressed plates using Mindlin plate theory. As we have adopted dynamic dimensioning in DYNAM all the subroutines presented here are modular in form.

Program DYNAM consists of 10 main modules:

(a) INPUT which reads in most of the input data,

(b) LUMASS which forms the lumped mass matrix,

(c) STIFPB which evaluates stiffness matrices and geometric stiffness matrices,

(d) FIXITY which inserts the boundary conditions,

(e) LOADPB which calculates the element nodal forces,

(f) FUNCT which sets the value of the time varying function for a particular time step,

(g) STEP1 which is starting algorithm of the time stepping scheme,

(h) STEPN which is time stepping routine,

(i) RESIDU which calculates internal forces, and

(j) OUTPUT which prints out the results.

The main variables used in DYNAM will be now described in a glossary.

3.2 Glossary of Variable Names

Main Arrays

Array name	Description
ASDIS(MTOTV)	nodal unknowns written in the sequence w, θ_x, θ_y
COORD(MPOIN,NDIME)	x and y coordinates
DLAST(MTOTV)	vector containing nodal displacements at time t_{n-1}
ESTIF(27,27)	element stiffness matrix
FORCE(MTOTV)	applied load vector

Array name	Description
GSTIF(27,27)	geometric element stiffness matrix
IFPRE(MVFIX,NDOFN)	fixity code for restrained nodes 0 - free 1 - restrained
ISTRN(MELEM)	initial stress set numbers for each element
KOUNT(MPOIN)	number of elements attached to a node
LNODS(MELEM,9)	element nodal connectivities
LSELN(MSELN)	node numbers for selective output
MATNO(MELEM)	material set numbers for each element
NOFIX(MVFIX)	nodes with at least one restrained variable
NOUTP(2)	step numbers at which output for displacements and stresses is required
PROPS(MMATS,9)	properties for each material set
RESID(MTOTV)	internal resisting nodal forces vector
RLOAD(MELEM,27)	internal forces at element level
STREM(MISTR,3)	initial stresses σ_x^o, σ_y^o, τ_{xy}^o for each initial stress set
STRND(MPOIN,5)	averaged nodal stress resultants
TDISP(MTOTV)	vector containing nodal displacements at time t_n (t_{n+1})
VELOC(MTOTV)	initial velocity vector
XMASS(MTOTV)	lumped mass vector

Main Variables

Variable	Description
MELEM	maximum number of elements
MEVAB	=27, maximum number of element variables
MISTR	maximum number of initial stress sets
MMATS	maximum number of material sets
MPOIN	maximum number of nodal points
MSELN	maximum number of nodes for selective output
MTOTV	maximum total number of variables

Variable	Description
MVFIX	maximum number of restrained nodes
NDIME	=2, number of dimensions
NDOFN	=3, number of degrees of freedom per node
NELEM	number of elements
NEVAB	=27, number of element variables
NGAUB	=3, Gauss-Legendre rule to evaluate the bending stiffness matrix
NGAUS	=3, Gauss-Legendre rule to evaluate the shear stiffness matrix
NISTR	number of initial stress sets
NMATS	number of material sets
NNODE	=9, number of nodes per element
NPOIN	number of nodal points
NSELN	number of nodes for selective output
NSTEP	number of time steps
NTOTV	total number of variables
NVFIX	number of restrained nodes

3.3 Main Segment

The Nassi-Schneiderman (NS) chart for the main segment of the DYNAM is shown in Figure 3.1.

Initialise variables in DATA statement etc.	[MAIN 21-25]	1
Call INPUT module to read in most of the data	[MAIN 29-33]	2
Call LUMASS to form lumped mass vector	[MAIN 37-39]	3
Call STIFPB to evaluate element stiffness matrices and geometric stiffness matrices	[MAIN 43-45]	4
Call FIXITY to insert the boundary conditions	[MAIN 49]	5
Call LOADPB to form applied load vector	[MAIN 53-55]	6
Initialise step counter and set the value of the time varying function for the initial time step	[MAIN 59-60]	7
Call STEP1 which is initial part of time stepping	[MAIN 61-62]	8
Call RESIDU to calculate internal forces vector	[MAIN 63-64]	9
Call OUTPUT to print out the results	[MAIN 65-68]	10
Loop over each time step	[MAIN 73]	11
Set the value of the time varying function for each time step	[MAIN 74]	12
Call STEPN which is time stepping algorithm	[MAIN 75-76]	13
Call RESIDU to calculate internal forces vector	[MAIN 77-78]	14
Call OUTPUT to print out the results	[MAIN 79-82]	15

Figure 3.1 NS chart for master routine of DYNAM

```
C***********************************************************************
C*                                                                     *
C*   PROGRAM FOR INITIALLY STRESSED TRANSIENT DYNAMIC ANALYSIS         *
C*            OF PLATES USING MINDLIN THEORY                           *
C*                                                                     *
C***********************************************************************
      IMPLICIT REAL*8(A-H,O-Z)
C
      DIMENSION ASDIS(600),COORD(200,2),DLAST(600),ESTIF(27,27),
     .          FORCE(600),GSTIF(27,27),IFPRE(60,3),ISTRN(140),
     .          KOUNT(200),LNODS(140,9),LSELN(50),MATNO(140),NOFIX(60),
     .          NOUTP(2),PROPS(10,9),RESID(600),RLOAD(140,27),
     .          STREM(140,3),STRND(200,5),TDISP(600),VELOC(600),
     .          XMASS(600)
C***********************************************************************
C
C        DYNAMIC  DIMENSIONING
C
C***********************************************************************
C
      DATA MPOIN/200/,MVFIX/60/,MELEM/140/,MMATS/10/,MISTR/140/,
     .     MSELN/50/,NDIME/2/,NNODE/9/,NGAUB/3/,NGAUS/3/,NDOFN/3/
C
      MTOTV=MPOIN*NDOFN
      MEVAB=NDOFN*9
C
C** CALL THE SUBROUTINE WHICH READS IN MOST OF THE DATA
C
      CALL   INPUT   (COORD,DTIME,DTEND,ICONT,IFPRE,ISTRN,LNODS,
     .                LSELN,MATNO,MVFIX,MISTR,MMATS,MPOIN,MELEM,
     .                MTOTV,MSELN,NPOIN,NELEM,NVFIX,NNODE,NDOFN,
     .                NMATS,NDIME,NSELN,NEVAB,NISTR,NOFIX,NSTEP,
     .                NOUTP,NTOTV,PROPS,STREM,TDISP,VELOC)
C
C** CALL THE SUBROUTINE WHICH FORMS THE LUMPED MASS MATRIX
C
      CALL   LUMASS  (COORD,LNODS,MATNO,MELEM,MMATS,MPOIN,MTOTV,
     .                NDIME,NDOFN,NGAUB,NELEM,NNODE,NTOTV,PROPS,
     .                XMASS)
C
C** CALL THE SUBROUTINE WHICH FORMS THE STIFNESS MATRIX
C
      CALL   STIFPB  (COORD,ICONT,ISTRN,LNODS,MATNO,MELEM,MEVAB,
     .                MMATS,MISTR,MPOIN,NELEM,NEVAB,NGAUB,NGAUS,
     .                NNODE,PROPS,STREM)
C
C** CALL THE SUBROUTINE WHICH INSERTS THE BOUNDARY CONDITIONS
C
      CALL   FIXITY  (IFPRE,MTOTV,MVFIX,NDOFN,NOFIX,NVFIX,XMASS)
C
C** CALL THE SUBROUTINE WHICH CALCULATES THE ELEMENT NODAL FORCES
C
      CALL   LOADPB  (COORD,FORCE,LNODS,MATNO,MELEM,MMATS,MPOIN,
     .                MTOTV,NDIME,NDOFN,NGAUB,NELEM,NEVAB,NNODE,
     .                PROPS,RLOAD,NPOIN)
C
C** INITIAL TIME STEP
```

```
C
      ISTEP = 0
      FACTO = FUNCT(ISTEP,DTIME,DTEND)
      CALL   STEP1    (DLAST,DTIME,FACTO,FORCE,MTOTV,NDOFN,NPOIN,
     .                 RESID,TDISP,VELOC,XMASS)
      CALL   RESIDU   (ICONT,LNODS,MATNO,MELEM,MTOTV,NDOFN,NELEM,
     .                 NEVAB,NNODE,TDISP,RESID,RLOAD)
      CALL   OUTPUT   (COORD,DTIME,ISTEP,KOUNT,LNODS,LSELN,MATNO,
     .                 MELEM,MMATS,MSELN,MPOIN,MTOTV,NDOFN,NELEM,
     .                 NGAUB,NGAUS,NPOIN,NSELN,NOUTP,PROPS,STRND,
     .                 TDISP)
C
C** THE FOLLOWING SECTION CALCULATES THE STRESSES AND
C** DISPLACEMENTS AT EACH TIME STEP
C
      DO 10 ISTEP=1,NSTEP
      FACTO = FUNCT(ISTEP,DTIME,DTEND)
      CALL   STEPN    (DLAST,DTIME,FACTO,FORCE,MTOTV,NDOFN,NPOIN,
     .                 RESID,TDISP,XMASS)
      CALL   RESIDU   (ICONT,LNODS,MATNO,MELEM,MTOTV,NDOFN,NELEM,
     .                 NEVAB,NNODE,TDISP,RESID,RLOAD)
      CALL   OUTPUT   (COORD,DTIME,ISTEP,KOUNT,LNODS,LSELN,MATNO,
     .                 MELEM,MMATS,MSELN,MPOIN,MTOTV,NDOFN,NELEM,
     .                 NGAUB,NGAUS,NPOIN,NSELN,NOUTP,PROPS,STRND,
     .                 TDISP)
   10 CONTINUE
      STOP
      END
```

3.4 Subroutine INPUT

The main function of INPUT is to read in most of the input data. The NS chart for subroutine INPUT is given in Figure 3.2 and then INPUT as listed.

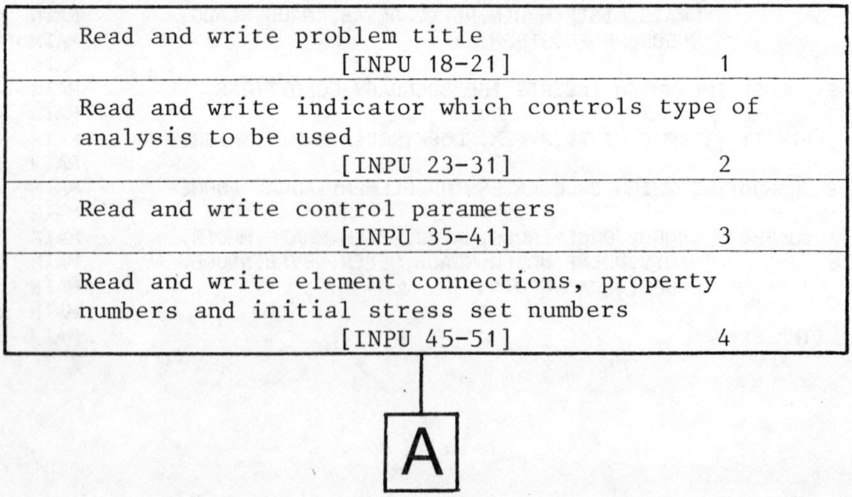

A

Initialise array COORD [INPU 56-58]	5
Read nodal coordinates [INPU 62-68]	6
Interpolate coordinates of midside nodes for straight sides by calling NODEXY [INPU 72-73]	7
Write all nodal coordinates [INPU 74-76]	8
Read and write fixity conditions [INPU 80-87]	9
Read and write element properties [INPU 91-100]	10
If it is initially stressed dynamic analysis continue otherwise jump to 13 [INPU 101]	11
Read and write initial in-plane stresses [INPU 105-113]	12
Read and write time stepping parameters [INPU 117-121]	13
Initialise initial displacement and velocity vector TDISP and VELOC [INPU 125-130]	14
Read and write initial displacements [INPU 131-144]	15
Read and write initial velocities [INPU 148-159]	16
Read and write number of nodes for selective output NSELN [INPU 163-165]	17
If NSELN = 0 go to the end otherwise continue [INPU 166]	18
Read and write node numbers for selective output [INPU 167-171]	19

Figure 3.2 NS chart for INPUT

```
      SUBROUTINE INPUT (COORD,DTIME,DTEND,ICONT,IFPRE,ISTRN,LNODS,
     .                  LSELN,MATNO,MVFIX,MISTR,MMATS,MPOIN,MELEM,
     .                  MTOTV,MSELN,NPOIN,NELEM,NVFIX,NNODE,NDOFN,
     .                  NMATS,NDIME,NSELN,NEVAB,NISTR,NOFIX,NSTEP,
     .                  NOUTP,NTOTV,PROPS,STREM,TDISP,VELOC)
C***********************************************************************
C
C*** INPUT MAIN DATA
C
C***********************************************************************
      IMPLICIT REAL*8(A-H,O-Z)
C
      DIMENSION COORD(MPOIN,NDIME),IFPRE(MVFIX,NDOFN),ISTRN(MELEM),
     .          LNODS(MELEM,9),LSELN(MSELN),MATNO(MELEM),NOFIX(MVFIX),
     .          NOUTP(2),PROPS(MMATS,9),STREM(MISTR,3),TITLE(20),
     .          TDISP(MTOTV),VELOC(MTOTV)
C
      READ(5,870) TITLE
      WRITE(6,875)TITLE
  870 FORMAT(20A4)
  875 FORMAT(///,1X,20A4)
C
      READ(5,880)ICONT
  880 FORMAT(I5)
      GO TO (2,4) ICONT
    2 WRITE(6,885)ICONT
  885 FORMAT(//37H THIS IS A TRANSIENT DYNAMIC ANALYSIS,4X,6HICONT=,I3)
      GO TO 8
    4 WRITE(6,890)ICONT
  890 FORMAT(//57H THIS IS AN INITIALLY STRESSED TRANSIENT DYNAMIC ANALY
     .SIS,4X,6HICONT=,I3)
C
C*** READ THE FIRST DATA CARD, AND ECHO IT IMMEDIATELY.
C
    8 READ(5,900) NPOIN,NELEM,NVFIX,NMATS,NISTR
  900 FORMAT(14I5)
      NEVAB=NDOFN*NNODE
      NTOTV=NPOIN*NDOFN
      WRITE(6,905) NPOIN,NELEM,NVFIX,NMATS,NISTR
  905 FORMAT(//8H NPOIN =,I4,4X,8H NELEM =,I4,4X,8H NVFIX =,I4,4X,
     .8H NMATS =,I4,//8H NISTR =,I4)
C
C*** READ THE ELEMENT NODAL CONNECTIONS, AND THE PROPERTY NUMBERS.
C
      WRITE(6,910)
  910 FORMAT(//6H ELEM.,2X,7HMAT.SET,12X,12HNODE NUMBERS,20X,7HSTR.SET)
      DO 10 IELEM=1,NELEM
      READ(5,900)NUMEL,MATNO(NUMEL),(LNODS(NUMEL,INODE),INODE=1,NNODE),
     .             ISTRN(NUMEL)
   10 WRITE(6,915)NUMEL,MATNO(NUMEL),(LNODS(NUMEL,INODE),INODE=1,NNODE),
     .               ISTRN(NUMEL)
  915 FORMAT(1X,I3,5X,I3,1X,9I5,2X,I3)
C
C*** ZERO ALL THE NODAL COORDINATES, PRIOR TO READING SOME OF THEM.
C
      DO 20 IPOIN=1,NPOIN
      DO 20 IDIME=1,NDIME
   20 COORD(IPOIN,IDIME)=0.0
C
C*** READ SOME NODAL COORDINATES, FINISHING WITH THE LAST NODE OF ALL.
C
```

```
      WRITE(6,920)
  920 FORMAT(//25H  NODAL POINT COORDINATES)
      WRITE(6,925)
  925 FORMAT(6H  NODE,7X,1HX,9X,1HY)
   30 READ(5,930) IPOIN,(COORD(IPOIN,IDIME),IDIME=1,NDIME)
  930 FORMAT(I5,5F10.5)
      IF(IPOIN.NE.NPOIN) GO TO 30
C
C*** INTERPOLATE COORDINATES OF MID-SIDE NODES
C
      CALL NODEXY(COORD,LNODS,MELEM,MPOIN,NDIME,
     .            NELEM,NNODE)
      DO 50 IPOIN=1,NPOIN
   50 WRITE(6,935) IPOIN,(COORD(IPOIN,IDIME),IDIME=1,NDIME)
  935 FORMAT(1X,I5,3F10.3)
C
C*** READ THE FIXED VALUES.
C
      WRITE(6,940)
  940 FORMAT(//17H RESTRAINED NODES)
      WRITE(6,945)
  945 FORMAT(5H NODE,1X,4HCODE)
      DO 80 IVFIX=1,NVFIX
      READ(5,950) NOFIX(IVFIX),(IFPRE(IVFIX,IDOFN),IDOFN=1,NDOFN)
   80 WRITE(6,950) NOFIX(IVFIX),(IFPRE(IVFIX,IDOFN),IDOFN=1,NDOFN)
  950 FORMAT(1X,I4,2X,3I1)
C
C*** READ THE AVAILABLE SELECTION OF ELEMENT PROPERTIES.
C
      WRITE(6,960)
  960 FORMAT(//21H  MATERIAL PROPERTIES)
      WRITE(6,965)
  965 FORMAT(8H  NUMBER,7X,10HPROPERTIES)
      DO 100 IMATS=1,NMATS
      READ(5,900)NUMAT
      READ(5,970) (PROPS(NUMAT,IPROP),IPROP=1,9)
  970 FORMAT(8F10.5)
  100 WRITE(6,980) NUMAT,(PROPS(NUMAT,IPROP),IPROP=1,9)
  980 FORMAT(1X,I5,7X,3E14.6/13X,3E14.6/13X,3E14.6)
      IF (ICONT.EQ.1) GO TO 110
C
C*** READ THE INITIAL IN-PLANE STRESSES
C
      WRITE(6,985)
  985 FORMAT(//30H THE INITIAL IN-PLANE STRESSES)
      WRITE(6,990)
  990 FORMAT(7H NUMBER,5X,7HSIGMA-X,6X,7HSIGMA-Y,6X,8HSIGMA-XY)
      DO 120 IISTR=1,NISTR
      READ(5,995)NUSTR,(STREM(NUSTR,IPROP),IPROP=1,3)
  995 FORMAT(I5,3F10.5)
  120 WRITE(6,1000)NUSTR,(STREM(NUSTR,IPROP),IPROP=1,3)
 1000 FORMAT(I5,1X,3E14.6)
C
C*** READ TIME STEPPING INFORMATION
C
  110 READ(5,1010) NSTEP,NOUTP(1),NOUTP(2),DTIME,DTEND
 1010 FORMAT(3I5,2F10.3)
      WRITE(6,1020)NSTEP,NOUTP(1),NOUTP(2),DTIME,DTEND
 1020 FORMAT(//8H NSTEP =,I4,4X,10HNOUTP(1) =,I4,4X,10HNOUTP(2) =,I4,
     .       /8H DTIME =,E12.4,4X,8H DTEND =,E12.4)
```

```
C
C*** INITIAL DISPLACEMENTS
C
      JPOIN=0
      DO 115 IPOIN=1,NPOIN
      DO 115 IDOFN=1,NDOFN
      JPOIN=JPOIN+1
      TDISP(JPOIN)=0.0
  115 VELOC(JPOIN)=0.0
      WRITE(6,1030)
 1030 FORMAT(//4X,5H NODE,2X,16H INITIAL W-DISP.,2X,
     .       16H INITIAL XZ-ROT.,2X,16H INITIAL YZ-ROT.,/)
  125 READ(5,1040) NGASH,ZGASH,XGASH,YGASH
 1040 FORMAT(I10,3F10.5)
      NPOSN= (NGASH-1)*NDOFN+1
      TDISP(NPOSN)=ZGASH
      NPOSN= NPOSN+1
      TDISP(NPOSN)=XGASH
      NPOSN= NPOSN+1
      TDISP(NPOSN)=YGASH
      WRITE(6,1050) NGASH,ZGASH,XGASH,YGASH
 1050 FORMAT(I10,3E16.5)
      IF(NGASH.NE.NPOIN) GO TO 125
C
C*** INITIAL VELOCITIES
C
      WRITE(6,1060)
 1060 FORMAT(//4X,5H NODE,2X,16H INITIAL W-VELO.,2X,
     .       19H INITIAL XZ-ROT.VEL,2X,19H INITIAL YZ-ROT.VEL,/)
  130 READ(5,1040) NGASH,ZGASH,XGASH,YGASH
      NPOSN= (NGASH-1)*NDOFN+1
      VELOC(NPOSN)=ZGASH
      NPOSN= NPOSN+1
      VELOC(NPOSN)=XGASH
      NPOSN= NPOSN+1
      VELOC(NPOSN)=YGASH
      WRITE(6,1050) NGASH,ZGASH,XGASH,YGASH
      IF(NGASH.NE.NPOIN) GO TO 130
C
C*** READ NODE NUMBERS FOR SELECTIVE OUTPUT
C
      READ(5,880) NSELN
      WRITE(6,1070) NSELN
 1070 FORMAT(/,1X,6HNSELN=,I4)
      IF(NSELN.EQ.0) GO TO 140
      READ(5,900)  (LSELN(ISELN),ISELN=1,NSELN)
      WRITE(6,1080)(LSELN(ISELN),ISELN=1,NSELN)
 1080 FORMAT(/,1X,33HNODE NUMBERS FOR SELECTIVE OUTPUT,//,(14I5))
  140 RETURN
      END
```

3.5 Subroutine LUMASS

This subroutine evaluates the lumped mass vector for the finite element mesh. The NS chart for LUMASS is given in Figure 3.3.

1. Initialise lumped mass vector array XMASS and set point counter to 1 [LUMA 16-19]
2. Call SLOBAT to extract sampling positions and weights for 3-point Lobatto integration rule [LUMA 20]
3. Loop over each element [LUMA 21]
   4. Initialise TAREA, extract material set number, h and ρ [LUMA 22-28]
   5. Initialise vector array DIAGM of diagonal mass matrix elements and extract nodal coordinates [LUMA 29-34]
   6. Calculate the mass matrix elements and the whole area of the element TAREA [LUMA 35-47]
   7. Initialise ELMAS - total mass of the element [LUMA 48]
   8. Find the total mass of the element as TAREA = TAREA * ρ * h and as $$\text{ELMAS} = \sum_{i=1}^{n} C_{ii}$$ [LUMA 49-52]
   9. Calculate elements of the lumped mass vector and find their locations in $\underline{M}$ [LUMA 53-63]

Figure 3.3 NS chart for subroutine LUMASS

```
      SUBROUTINE LUMASS (COORD,LNODS,MATNO,MELEM,MMATS,MPOIN,MTOTV,
     .                   NDIME,NDOFN,NGAUB,NELEM,NNODE,NTOTV,PROPS,
     .                   XMASS)
C***********************************************************************
C
C*** EVALUATES LUMPED MASS MATRIX
C
C***********************************************************************
      IMPLICIT REAL*8(A-H,O-Z)
C
      DIMENSION CARTD(2,9),COORD(MPOIN,NDIME),DERIV(2,9),DIAGM(9),
     .          ELCOD(2,9),GPCOD(2,9),LNODS(MELEM,9),MATNO(MELEM),
     .          PROPS(MMATS,9),POSGP(3),SHAPE(9),WEIGP(3),XJACI(2,2),
     .          XJACM(2,2),XMASS(MTOTV)
C
      KGASP=1
      DO 5 ITOTV=1,NTOTV
      XMASS(ITOTV)=0.0
    5 CONTINUE
      CALL SLOBAT(POSGP,WEIGP)
      DO 100 IELEM=1,NELEM
      TAREA=0.0
      LPROP=MATNO(IELEM)
      IF(PROPS(LPROP,4).NE.0.0)GO TO 6
      THICK=PROPS(LPROP,3)
      GO TO 7
    6 THICK=PROPS(LPROP,7)
    7 RHOEL=PROPS(LPROP,8)
      DO 10 INODE=1,NNODE
      DIAGM(INODE)=0.0
      LNODE=LNODS(IELEM,INODE)
      DO 10 IDIME=1,NDIME
      ELCOD(IDIME,INODE)=COORD(LNODE,IDIME)
   10 CONTINUE
      DO 30 IGAUS = 1,NGAUB
      EXISP=POSGP(IGAUS)
      DO 30 JGAUS = 1,NGAUB
      ETASP=POSGP(JGAUS)
      CALL SFR2 (DERIV,ETASP,EXISP,NNODE,SHAPE)
      CALL JACOB2 (CARTD,DERIV,DJACB,ELCOD,GPCOD,IELEM,
     .             KGASP,NNODE,SHAPE,XJACI,XJACM)
      DVOLU=DJACB*WEIGP(IGAUS)*WEIGP(JGAUS)
      DO 20 INODE=1,NNODE
      DIAGM(INODE)=DIAGM(INODE)+SHAPE(INODE)*SHAPE(INODE)*DVOLU
   20 CONTINUE
      TAREA=TAREA+DVOLU
   30 CONTINUE
      ELMAS=0.0
      DO 40 INODE=1,NNODE
      ELMAS=ELMAS+DIAGM(INODE)
   40 CONTINUE
      TAREA=TAREA*RHOEL*THICK
      DO 50 INODE=1,NNODE
      LNODE=LNODS(IELEM,INODE)
      IPOSN=(LNODE-1)*NDOFN
      IPOSN=IPOSN+1
      XMASS(IPOSN)=XMASS(IPOSN)+DIAGM(INODE)*TAREA/ELMAS
      DO 50 IDOFN=2,3
      IPOSN=IPOSN+1
      XMASS(IPOSN)=XMASS(IPOSN)+DIAGM(INODE)*TAREA*THICK*THICK
     ./(12.*ELMAS)
```

```
   50 CONTINUE
  100 CONTINUE
      RETURN
      END
```

3.6 Subroutine STIFPB

The main function of STIFPB is to evaluate stiffness matrices and geometric stiffness matrices for Mindlin plate elements and to store them on disc files 1 and 2 for later use. The same stiffness module was described in detail and listed in section 6.5 of Chapter 3 and is therefore not repeated here.

3.7 Subroutine FIXITY

Subroutine FIXITY deals with the restrained degress of freedom of boundary nodes. The diagonal mass vector, XMASS, is modified for restrained degrees of freedom. The component of the XMASS vector is set to a large value such as 1E30, which artificially makes the displacement zero.

```
      SUBROUTINE FIXITY (IFPRE,MTOTV,MVFIX,NDOFN,NOFIX,NVFIX,XMASS)
C***********************************************************************
C
C*** DEALS WITH FIXED BOUNDARY NODES
C
C***********************************************************************
      IMPLICIT REAL*8(A-H,O-Z)
C
      DIMENSION IFPRE(MVFIX,NDOFN),NOFIX(MVFIX),XMASS(MTOTV)
C
      DO 10 IVFIX=1,NVFIX
      LNODE=NOFIX(IVFIX)
      DO 10 IDOFN=1,NDOFN
      IPOSN=(LNODE-1)*NDOFN+IDOFN
      IF(IFPRE(IVFIX,IDOFN).EQ.1) XMASS(IPOSN)=1.E30
   10 CONTINUE
      RETURN
      END
```

3.8 Subroutine LOADPB

Subroutine LOADPB evaluates the element nodal forces for

(a) uniformly distributed lateral loading, and

(b) point loads.

The NS chart for LOADPB is given in Figure 3.4 and the expanded chart for the section dealing with consistent nodal force evaluation is given in Figure 3.5.

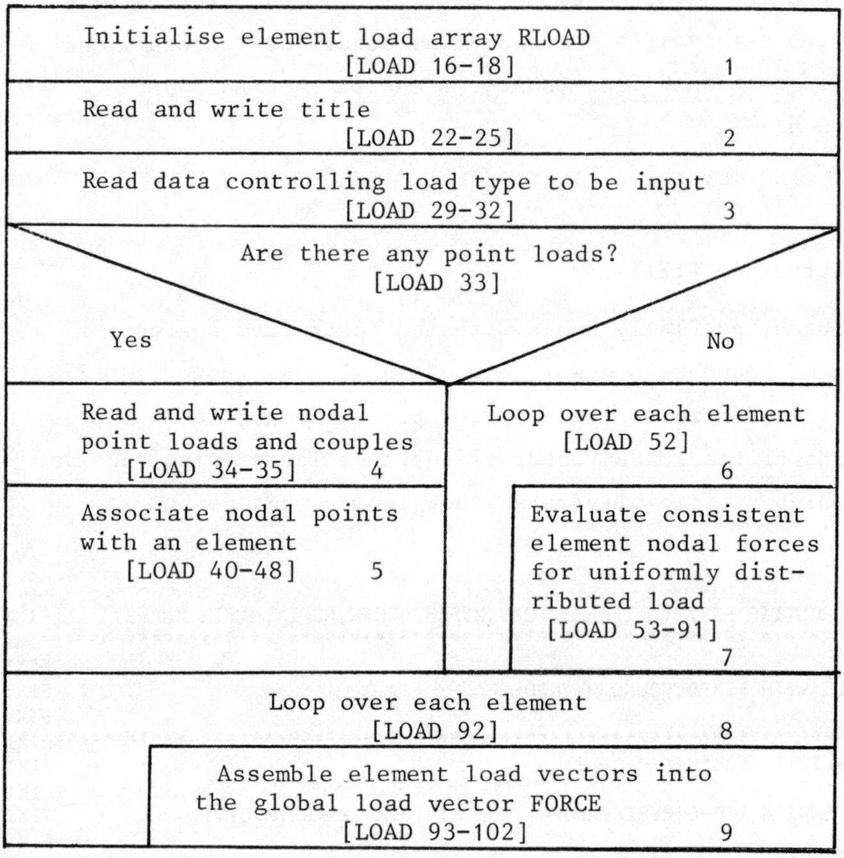

Figure 3.4 NS chart for consistent nodal force evaluation

Extract element uniform load, material set number and nodal coordinates
[LOAD 53-63] 7.1

Initialise Gauss point counter KGASP
[LOAD 67] 7.2

Call GAUSSQ to extract sampling positions and weights for 3-point Gauss-Legendre rule used to evaluate consistent nodal forces
[LOAD 68] 7.3

Loop over Gauss points in ξ direction
[LOAD 69] 7.4

Extract ξ sampling position
[LOAD 70] 7.5

Loop over Gauss points in η direction
[LOAD 71] 7.6

Extract η sampling position
[LOAD 72] 7.7

Increment Gauss point counter by 1
[LOAD 73] 7.8

Call SFR2 to evaluate N_i, $N_{i,\xi}$, $N_{i,\eta}$
[LOAD 78] 7.9

Call JACOB2 to evaluate det$\underline{J}$
[LOAD 79-80] 7.10

Evaluate DAREA = det$\underline{J}$ x Gauss point weights
[LOAD 81] 7.11

Loop over each element node
[LOAD 85] 7.12

Accumulate contribution to consistent load vector
[LOAD 86-90] 7.13

Figure 3.5 NS chart for consistent nodal force evaluation

```
      SUBROUTINE LOADPB (COORD,FORCE,LNODS,MATNO,MELEM,MMATS,MPOIN,
     .                   MTOTV,NDIME,NDOFN,NGAUB,NELEM,NEVAB,NNODE,
     .                   PROPS,RLOAD,NPOIN)
C**********************************************************************
C
C*** CALCULATE NODAL FORCES FOR PLATE ELEMENT
C
C**********************************************************************
      IMPLICIT REAL*8(A-H,O-Z)
C
      DIMENSION CARTD(2,9),COORD(MPOIN,NDIME),DERIV(2,9),ELCOD(2,9),
     .          FORCE(MTOTV),GPCOD(2,9),LNODS(MELEM,9),MATNO(MELEM),
     .          PROPS(MMATS,9),POINT(3),POSGP(3),RLOAD(MELEM,27),
     .          SHAPE(9),TITLE(20),WEIGP(3),XJACI(2,2),XJACM(2,2)
C
      DO 10 IELEM=1,NELEM
      DO 10 IEVAB=1,NEVAB
   10 RLOAD(IELEM,IEVAB) = 0.0
C
C*** READ DATA CONTROLLING LOADING TYPES TO BE INPUTTED
C
      READ(5,501) TITLE
  501 FORMAT(20A4)
      WRITE(6,601) TITLE
  601 FORMAT(/,1X,20A4)
C
C*** READ NODAL POINT LOADS
C
      READ(5,502) IPLOD
  502 FORMAT(I5)
      WRITE(6,602) IPLOD
  602 FORMAT(I5)
      IF(IPLOD.EQ.0) GO TO 500
   20 READ(5,915) LODPT,(POINT(IDOFN),IDOFN=1,NDOFN)
      WRITE(6,915) LODPT,(POINT(IDOFN),IDOFN=1,NDOFN)
  915 FORMAT(I5,3F10.3)
C
C*** ASSOCIATE THE NODAL POINT LOADS WITH AN ELEMENT
C
      DO 30 IELEM=1,NELEM
      DO 30 INODE=1,NNODE
      NLOCA=LNODS(IELEM,INODE)
   30 IF(LODPT.EQ.NLOCA) GO TO 40
   40 DO 50 IDOFN=1,NDOFN
      NGASH=(INODE-1)*NDOFN+IDOFN
   50 RLOAD(IELEM,NGASH) = POINT(IDOFN)
      IF(LODPT.NE.NPOIN) GO TO 20
  500 CONTINUE
C
C*** LOOP OVER EACH ELEMENT.
C
      DO 110 IELEM = 1,NELEM
      LPROP = MATNO(IELEM)
      UDLOD = PROPS(LPROP,9)
      IF(UDLOD.EQ.0.0) GO TO 110
C
C*** EVALUATE THE COORDINATES OF THE ELEMENT NODAL POINTS.
C
      DO 70 INODE = 1,NNODE
      LNODE = LNODS(IELEM,INODE)
      DO 70 IDIME = 1,NDIME
```

```
      ELCOD(IDIME,INODE) = COORD(LNODE,IDIME)
   70 CONTINUE
C
C*** ENTER LOOPS FOR NUMERICAL INTEGRATION.
C
      KGASP = 0
      CALL GAUSSQ (NGAUB,POSGP,WEIGP)
      DO 100 IGAUS = 1,NGAUB
      EXISP = POSGP(IGAUS)
      DO 100 JGAUS = 1,NGAUB
      ETASP = POSGP(JGAUS)
      KGASP = KGASP + 1
C
C*** EVALUATE THE SHAPE FUNCTIONS AT THE SAMPLING POINTS AND
C    THE ELEMENTAL AREA.
C
      CALL SFR2 (DERIV,ETASP,EXISP,NNODE,SHAPE)
      CALL JACOB2 (CARTD,DERIV,DJACB,ELCOD,GPCOD,IELEM,KGASP,
     .             NNODE,SHAPE,XJACI,XJACM)
      DAREA = DJACB*WEIGP(IGAUS)*WEIGP(JGAUS)
C
C*** CALCULATE LOADS AND ASSOCIATE WITH ELEMENT NODAL POINTS.
C
      DO 90 INODE = 1,NNODE
      NPOSN = (INODE-1)*NDOFN + 1
      RLOAD(IELEM,NPOSN) = RLOAD(IELEM,NPOSN) +
     .SHAPE(INODE)*UDLOD*DAREA
   90 CONTINUE
  100 CONTINUE
  110 CONTINUE
      DO 130 IELEM=1,NELEM
      NPOSN=0
      KEVAB=0
      DO 130 INODE=1,NNODE
      LNODE=LNODS(IELEM,INODE)
      NPOSN=(LNODE-1)*NDOFN
      DO 130 IDOFN=1,NDOFN
      KEVAB=KEVAB+1
      NPOSN=NPOSN+1
      FORCE(NPOSN)=FORCE(NPOSN)+RLOAD(IELEM,KEVAB)
  130 CONTINUE
      RETURN
      END
```

3.9 Function FUNCT

This function sets the value of the time varying function for a particular time step. The rectangular impulse shown in Figure 3.6 may be expressed by Heaviside function as

$$p(t) = 1.0\, p_o \quad , \quad t \leq t_1$$
$$p(t) = 0 \quad , \quad t > t_1 \qquad (3.1)$$

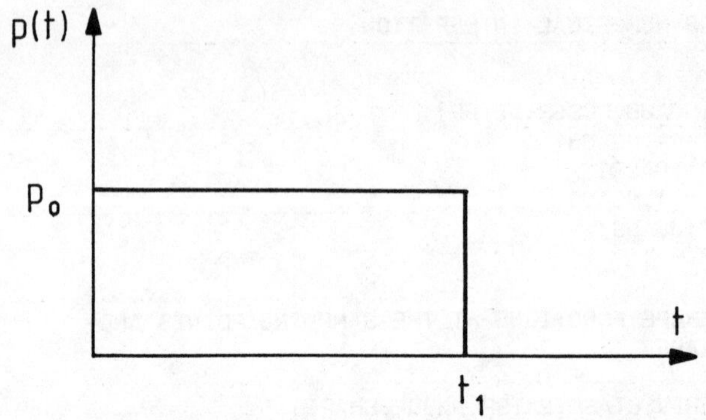

Figure 3.6 Rectangular (step) impulse

Other types of functions such as triangular impulse, harmonic functions etc. can be easily implemented into DYNAM.

```
      FUNCTION FUNCT(ISTEP,DTIME,DTEND)
C***********************************************************************
C
C*** HEAVISIDE TIME FUNCTION
C
C***********************************************************************
      FUNCT=1.0
      IF(FLOAT(ISTEP)*DTIME.GT.DTEND) FUNCT=0.0
      RETURN
      END
```

3.10 Subroutine STEP1

In subroutine STEP1 the starting algorithm for central difference method is implemented. The NS chart for STEP1 is shown in Figure 3.7.

Calculate $(\Delta t)^2$
[STEP 13] 1

Initialise location counter NPOSN
[STEP 14] 2

Loop over each nodal point
[STEP 15] 3

Loop over each degree of freedom
[STEP 16] 4

Increment location counter by 1
[STEP 17] 5

Calculate nodal displacements at time $t_1 (t_{n+1})$*
[STEP 18-22] 6

Store displacements at time $t_o (t_n)$* in vector DLAST
[STEP 23] 7

Figure 3.7 NS chart for STEP1 (STEPN)*

*Values in brackets are related to NS chart for subroutine STEPN

```
      SUBROUTINE STEP1 (DLAST,DTIME,FACTO,FORCE,MTOTV,NDOFN,NPOIN,       STEP    1
     .                  RESID,TDISP,VELOC,XMASS)                         STEP    2
C***********************************************************************STEP    3
C                                                                        STEP    4
C*** INITIAL PART OF TIME STEPPING                                       STEP    5
C                                                                        STEP    6
C***********************************************************************STEP    7
      IMPLICIT REAL*8(A-H,O-Z)                                           STEP    8
C                                                                        STEP    9
      DIMENSION DLAST(MTOTV),FORCE(MTOTV),RESID(MTOTV),TDISP(MTOTV),     STEP   10
     .          VELOC(MTOTV),XMASS(MTOTV)                                STEP   11
C                                                                        STEP   12
      DTIM2=DTIME*DTIME                                                  STEP   13
      NPOSN=0                                                            STEP   14
      DO 10 IPOIN = 1,NPOIN                                              STEP   15
      DO 10 IDOFN=1,NDOFN                                                STEP   16
      NPOSN=NPOSN+1                                                      STEP   17
      RESID(NPOSN)=0.0                                                   STEP   18
      DCURR=TDISP(NPOSN)                                                 STEP   19
      TDISP(NPOSN)=-(RESID(NPOSN)-FACTO*FORCE(NPOSN))                    STEP   20
     .*DTIM2*0.5/XMASS(NPOSN)+DCURR                                      STEP   21
     .+VELOC(NPOSN)*DTIME                                                STEP   22
      DLAST(NPOSN)=DCURR                                                 STEP   23
   10 CONTINUE                                                           STEP   24
      RETURN                                                             STEP   25
      END                                                                STEP   26
```

3.11 Subroutine STEPN

Subroutine STEPN is the time stepping routine for central difference approximation. The NS chart for STEPN is shown in Figure 3.7.

```
      SUBROUTINE STEPN (DLAST,DTIME,FACTO,FORCE,MTOTV,NDOFN,NPOIN,
     .                  RESID,TDISP,XMASS)
C***********************************************************************
C
C*** TIME STEPPING ROUTINE
C
C***********************************************************************
      IMPLICIT REAL*8(A-H,O-Z)
C
      DIMENSION DLAST(MTOTV),FORCE(MTOTV),RESID(MTOTV),TDISP(MTOTV),
     .          XMASS(MTOTV)
C
      DTIM2=DTIME*DTIME
      NPOSN=0
      DO 10 IPOIN=1,NPOIN
      DO 10 IDOFN=1,NDOFN
      NPOSN=NPOSN+1
      DCURR=TDISP(NPOSN)
      TDISP(NPOSN)=-(RESID(NPOSN)-FACTO*FORCE(NPOSN))
     .*DTIM2/XMASS(NPOSN)+2.0*DCURR
     .-DLAST(NPOSN)
      RESID(NPOSN)=0.0
      DLAST(NPOSN)=DCURR
   10 CONTINUE
      RETURN
      END
```

3.12 Subroutine RESIDU

Subroutine RESIDU evaluates the internal resisting force vector. The NS chart for this subroutine is given in Figure 3.8.

```
      SUBROUTINE RESIDU (ICONT,LNODS,MATNO,MELEM,MTOTV,NDOFN,NELEM,
     .                   NEVAB,NNODE,TDISP,RESID,RLOAD)
C***********************************************************************
C
C*** CALCULATE INTERNAL FORCES
C
C***********************************************************************
      IMPLICIT REAL*8(A-H,O-Z)
C
      DIMENSION ESTIF(27,27),EFDIS(27),GSTIF(27,27),
     .          LNODS(MELEM,9),MATNO(MELEM),TDISP(MTOTV),
     .          RESID(MTOTV),RLOAD(MELEM,27)
C
```

```
      REWIND 1                                                  RESI  14
      REWIND 2                                                  RESI  15
      DO 10 IELEM=1,NELEM                                       RESI  16
      DO 10 IEVAB=1,NEVAB                                       RESI  17
   10 RLOAD(IELEM,IEVAB)=0.0                                    RESI  18
C                                                               RESI  19
      DO 20 IELEM = 1,NELEM                                     RESI  20
C                                                               RESI  21
      READ(1) ESTIF                                             RESI  22
      IF(ICONT.EQ.1)GO TO 15                                    RESI  23
      READ(2) GSTIF                                             RESI  24
      DO 25 IEVAB=1,NEVAB                                       RESI  25
      DO 25 JEVAB=1,NEVAB                                       RESI  26
      ESTIF(IEVAB,JEVAB)=ESTIF(IEVAB,JEVAB)+GSTIF(IEVAB,JEVAB)  RESI  27
   25 CONTINUE                                                  RESI  28
   15 KEVAB=0                                                   RESI  29
      DO 30 INODE=1,NNODE                                       RESI  30
      LNODE=IABS(LNODS(IELEM,INODE))                            RESI  31
      NPOSN=(LNODE-1)*NDOFN                                     RESI  32
      DO 30 IDOFN=1,NDOFN                                       RESI  33
      KEVAB=KEVAB+1                                             RESI  34
      NPOSN=NPOSN+1                                             RESI  35
   30 EFDIS(KEVAB)=TDISP(NPOSN)                                 RESI  36
      DO 140 IEVAB=1,NEVAB                                      RESI  37
      DO 140 JEVAB=1,NEVAB                                      RESI  38
  140 RLOAD(IELEM,IEVAB)= RLOAD(IELEM,IEVAB)+ESTIF(IEVAB,JEVAB)  RESI  39
     . *EFDIS(JEVAB)                                            RESI  40
   20 CONTINUE                                                  RESI  41
      DO 5 IELEM=1,NELEM                                        RESI  42
      KEVAB=0                                                   RESI  43
      DO 5 INODE=1,NNODE                                        RESI  44
      LNODE=LNODS(IELEM,INODE)                                  RESI  45
      NPOSN=(LNODE-1)*NDOFN                                     RESI  46
      DO 5 IDOFN=1,NDOFN                                        RESI  47
      KEVAB=KEVAB+1                                             RESI  48
      NPOSN=NPOSN+1                                             RESI  49
      RESID(NPOSN)=RESID(NPOSN)+RLOAD(IELEM,KEVAB)              RESI  50
    5 CONTINUE                                                  RESI  51
      RETURN                                                    RESI  52
      END                                                       RESI  53
```

Rewind disc files 1 and 2 ready for reading operations
[RESI 14-15] 1

Initialise internal forces matrix array RLOAD
[RESI 16-19] 2

Loop over each element
[RESI 20] 3

Read element stiffness matrices from file 1 and if ICONT=2 read geometric stiffness matrices from file 2 and form sum $\underline{K}^e + \underline{K}_G^e$ otherwise continue
[RESI 21-28] 4

A

A

Calculate internal forces at element level RLOAD [RESI 29-41]	5
Assemble internal forces RLOAD to global internal force vector RESID [RESI 42-51]	6

Figure 3.8 NS chart for subroutine RESIDU

3.13 Subroutine OUTPUT

Subroutine OUTPUT prints out nodal displacements and rotations at every NOUTP(1) step and evaluates and prints out stresses by calling OUTSTR at every NOUTP(2) step. The NS charts for OUTPUT and OUTSTR are given in Figures 3.9 and 3.10 respectively.

Calculate counter values for output displacements and stresses (KOUTD and KOUTS) [OUTP 16-18]	1
If it is initial time step print out only displacements [OUTP 19]	2
If both counter values KOUTD and KOUTS differ from the current time step go to the end otherwise continue [OUTP 20]	3
Print out number of time steps and total time [OUTP 21-23]	4
Print out displacements if KOUTD is equal to time step otherwise jump to 8 [OUTP 24-33]	5
Print out displacements only at selective nodes [OUTP 34-40]	6
Print out displacements at all nodes [OUTP 41-45]	7
Call OUTSTR to evaluate and print out stresses if KOUTS is equal to time step otherwise go to end [OUTP 49-52]	8

Figure 3.9 NS chart for OUTPUT

```
      SUBROUTINE OUTPUT (COORD,DTIME,ISTEP,KOUNT,LNODS,LSELN,MATNO,
     .                   MELEM,MMATS,MSELN,MPOIN,MTOTV,NDOFN,NELEM,
     .                   NGAUB,NGAUS,NPOIN,NSELN,NOUTP,PROPS,STRND,
     .                   TDISP)
C***********************************************************************
C
C*** OUTPUTS DISPLACEMENTS AND STRESSES
C
C***********************************************************************
      IMPLICIT REAL*8(A-H,O-Z)
C
      DIMENSION COORD(MPOIN,2),KOUNT(MPOIN),LNODS(MELEM,9),LSELN(MSELN),
     .          MATNO(MELEM),NOUTP(2),PROPS(MMATS,9),STRND(MPOIN,5),
     .          TDISP(MTOTV)
C
      KSTEP=ISTEP+1
      KOUTD=(KSTEP/NOUTP(1))*NOUTP(1)
      KOUTS=(KSTEP/NOUTP(2))*NOUTP(2)
      IF(KSTEP.EQ.1)GO TO 5
      IF(KOUTD.NE.KSTEP.AND.KOUTS.NE.KSTEP)GO TO 50
      XTIME=FLOAT(KSTEP)*DTIME
      WRITE(6,890)KSTEP,XTIME
  890 FORMAT(//5X,22H RESULTS AT TIME STEP ,I10,5X,5HTIME ,E20.11)
    5 KOUTP=1
      IF(KOUTS.EQ.KSTEP) KOUTP=3
      IF(KOUTD.NE.KSTEP.AND.KSTEP.NE.1)GO TO 25
C
C*** OUTPUT DISPLACEMENTS
C
      WRITE(6,900)
  900 FORMAT(1H0,5X,13HDISPLACEMENTS)
      WRITE(6,950)
  950 FORMAT(1H0,6X,4HNODE,6X,1HW,10X,7HTHETA-X,7X,7HTHETA-Y)
      IF(NSELN.EQ.0) GO TO 15
      DO 10 ISELN=1,NSELN
      LNODE=LSELN(ISELN)
      NGASH=LNODE*NDOFN
      NGISH=NGASH-NDOFN+1
   10 WRITE(6,910)LNODE,(TDISP(IGASH),IGASH=NGISH,NGASH)
      GO TO 25
   15 DO 20 IPOIN= 1,NPOIN
      NGASH=IPOIN*NDOFN
      NGISH=NGASH-NDOFN+1
   20 WRITE(6,910) IPOIN,(TDISP(IGASH),IGASH=NGISH,NGASH)
  910 FORMAT(I10,3E14.6)
C
C*** OUTPUT STRESSES
C
   25 IF(KOUTP.LT.3) GO TO 50
      CALL OUTSTR (TDISP,COORD,KOUNT,LNODS,LSELN,MATNO,MELEM,
     .             MMATS,MSELN,MPOIN,MTOTV,NDOFN,NELEM,NGAUB,
     .             NGAUS,NPOIN,NSELN,PROPS,STRND)
   50 CONTINUE
      RETURN
      END
```

Write general title for stress results and initialise KOUNT and STRND [OUTS 15-18]	1
Loop over each element [OUTS 19]	2
Extract element material set, nodal coordinates and displacements [OUTS 20-30]	3
Evaluate and print out M_x, M_y, M_{xy} and M_1, M_2, and θ at 3x3 Gauss-Legendre points by calling BENDM [OUTS 34-50]	4*
Evaluate and print out M_x, M_y, M_{xy} and M_1, M_2, and θ at nodal points by calling BENDM. Accumulate bending moments at nodal points in STRND for future averaging. [OUTS 54-71]	5*
Evaluate and print out shear forces Q_x and Q_y at nodal points by calling SHEAR. Accumulate shear forces at nodal points in STRND for future averaging. [OUTS 75-97]	6*
Call AVERAG to calculate and print out the average nodal values for M_x, M_y, M_{xy} and M_1, M_2, θ and Q_x, Q_y [OUTS 101]	7

Figure 3.10 NS chart for subroutine OUTSTR

* printing suppressed by appropriate use of C in column 1

```
      SUBROUTINE OUTSTR(ASDIS,COORD,KOUNT,LNODS,LSELN,MATNO,MELEM,      OUTS
     .                  MMATS,MSELN,MPOIN,MTOTV,NDOFN,NELEM,NGAUB,      OUTS
     .                  NGAUS,NPOIN,NSELN,PROPS,STRND)                  OUTS
      IMPLICIT REAL*8(A-H,O-Z)                                          OUTS
      DIMENSION ASDIS(MTOTV),COORD(MPOIN,2),ELCOD(2,9),                 OUTS
     .ELDIS(3,9),KOUNT(MPOIN),LNODS(MELEM,9),MATNO(MELEM),              OUTS
     .PROPS(MMATS,9),POSGP(3),POSSP(3),SHEAV(9,2),STRES(5),             OUTS
     .STRND(MPOIN,5),STRSG(9,2),WEIGP(3),ICODE(9),                      OUTS
     .BMETA(6,27),BMEXI(6,27),LSELN(MSELN)                              OUTS
      DATA POSSP/-1.0,0.0,1.0/,ICODE/1,8,7,2,9,6,3,4,5/,                OUTS
     .     NNODE/9/                                                     OUTS
C                                                                       OUTS
C*** OUTPUT STRESS RESULTANTS AT GAUSS AND NODAL POINTS                 OUTS
C                                                                       OUTS
```

```
      WRITE(6,900)
  900 FORMAT(//1H0,5X,17HSTRESS RESULTANTS)
      CALL IVZERO(KOUNT,MPOIN)
      CALL RAZERO(STRND,MPOIN,5)
      DO 35 IELEM=1,NELEM
      LPROP=MATNO(IELEM)
      DO 10 INODE=1,NNODE
      LNODE=LNODS(IELEM,INODE)
      LNODE=IABS(LNODE)
      DO 5 IDIME=1,2
    5 ELCOD(IDIME,INODE)=COORD(LNODE,IDIME)
      NPOSN=(LNODE-1)*3
      DO 10 IDOFN=1,3
      NPOSN=NPOSN+1
      ELDIS(IDOFN,INODE)=ASDIS(NPOSN)
   10 CONTINUE
C
C*** EVALUATE BENDING MOMENTS AT GAUSS POINTS
C
      KSAMP=0
      CALL GAUSSQ(NGAUB,POSGP,WEIGP)
C     WRITE(6,905)IELEM
C905  FORMAT(//1H0,5X,13HELEMENT NO. =,I5)
C     WRITE(6,910)
C910  FORMAT(/,1X,31HBENDING MOMENTS AT GAUSS POINTS,/)
C     WRITE(6,915)
C915  FORMAT(1H0,2X,4HS.P.,2X,8HX-COORD.,1X,8HY-COORD.,3X,
C    .8HX-MOMENT,4X,8HY-MOMENT,3X,9HXY-MOMENT,4X,
C    .8HMAX P.M.,4X,8HMIN P.M.,6X,5HANGLE)
      DO 15 IGAUB=1,NGAUB
      EXISP=POSGP(IGAUB)
      DO 15 JGAUB=1,NGAUB
      ETASP=POSGP(JGAUB)
      CALL BENDM(ELCOD,ELDIS,ETASP,EXISP,IELEM,KSAMP,LPROP,
     .MMATS,NDOFN,PROPS,STRES)
   15 CONTINUE
C
C*** EVALUATE BENDING MOMENTS AT NODAL POINTS
C
      KSAMP=0
C     WRITE(6,920)
C920  FORMAT(/,1X,31HBENDING MOMENTS AT NODAL POINTS,/)
C     WRITE(6,915)
      DO 20 ISAMP=1,3
      EXISP=POSSP(ISAMP)
      DO 20 JSAMP=1,3
      ETASP=POSSP(JSAMP)
      CALL BENDM(ELCOD,ELDIS,ETASP,EXISP,IELEM,KSAMP,LPROP,
     .MMATS,NDOFN,PROPS,STRES)
      INODE=ICODE(KSAMP)
      LNODE=LNODS(IELEM,INODE)
      LNODE=IABS(LNODE)
      KOUNT(LNODE)=KOUNT(LNODE)+1
      DO 20 ISTRE=1,3
      STRND(LNODE,ISTRE)=STRND(LNODE,ISTRE)
     .+STRES(ISTRE)
   20 CONTINUE
C
C*** EVALUATE THE SHEAR FORCES AT NODAL POINTS
C
```

```
      CALL BSAMP(BMETA,BMEXI,ELCOD,IELEM,NNODE)
      KSAMP=0
C     WRITE(6,925)
C925  FORMAT(/,1X,28HSHEAR FORCES AT NODAL POINTS)
C     WRITE(6,930)
C930  FORMAT(/,2X,4HN.P.,2X,8HX-COORD.,2X,8HY-COORD.,
C    .4X,8HXZ-SHEAR,4X,8HYZ-SHEAR)
      DO 25 ISAMP=1,3
      EXISP=POSSP(ISAMP)
      DO 25 JSAMP=1,3
      ETASP=POSSP(JSAMP)
      CALL SHEAR(BMETA,BMEXI,ELCOD,ELDIS,ETASP,EXISP,IELEM,
     .           KSAMP,LPROP,MMATS,NDOFN,PROPS,STRES,STRSG)
   25 CONTINUE
      DO 30 ISAMP=1,9
      INODE=ICODE(ISAMP)
      LNODE=LNODS(IELEM,INODE)
      LNODE=IABS(LNODE)
      DO 30 ISTRE=1,2
      KSTRE=ISTRE+3
   30 STRND(LNODE,KSTRE)=STRND(LNODE,KSTRE)+
     .STRSG(ISAMP,ISTRE)
   35 CONTINUE
C
C*** EVALUATE AND PRINT AVERAGE NODAL VALUES
C
      CALL AVERAG(KOUNT,LSELN,MPOIN,MSELN,NPOIN,NSELN,STRES,STRND)
      RETURN
      END
```

The subsidiary subroutines IVZERO, RAZERO, BENDM, GRADPB, STRPB, SHEAR, AVERAG and PRINC are now listed for completeness.

```
      SUBROUTINE IVZERO(IVECT,NSIZE)
      IMPLICIT REAL*8(A-H,O-Z)
      DIMENSION IVECT(NSIZE)
C
C*** ZERO INTEGER VECTOR
C
      DO 5 ISIZE=1,NSIZE
      IVECT(ISIZE)=0
    5 CONTINUE
      RETURN
      END
```

```
      SUBROUTINE RAZERO(RVECT,NSIZE,MSIZE)
      IMPLICIT REAL*8(A-H,O-Z)
      DIMENSION RVECT(NSIZE,MSIZE)
C
C*** ZERO REAL ARRAY
C
      DO 5 ISIZE=1,NSIZE
      DO 5 JSIZE=1,MSIZE
      RVECT(ISIZE,JSIZE)=0.0
  5   CONTINUE
      RETURN
      END
```

```
      SUBROUTINE BENDM(ELCOD,ELDIS,ETASP,EXISP,IELEM,
     .KSAMP,LPROP,MMATS,NDOFN,PROPS,STRES)
      IMPLICIT REAL*8(A-H,O-Z)
      DIMENSION CARTD(2,9),DERIV(2,9),DFLEX(3,3),DGRAD(6),
     .DSHER(2,2),ELCOD(2,9),ELDIS(3,9),
     .PROPS(MMATS,9),SHAPE(9),SPCOD(2,9),STRES(5),
     .XJACI(2,2),XJACM(2,2)
      DATA NNODE/9/
C
C*** EVALUATES AND PRINTS BENDING MOMENTS MX MY MXY AND
C*** PRINCIPAL MOMENTS M1 M2 AND ANGLE.
C
      KSAMP=KSAMP+1
      CALL SFR2(DERIV,ETASP,EXISP,NNODE,SHAPE)
      CALL JACOB2(CARTD,DERIV,DJACB,ELCOD,SPCOD,
     .IELEM,KSAMP,NNODE,SHAPE,XJACI,XJACM)
      CALL MODPB(DFLEX,DSHER,LPROP,MMATS,
     .          PROPS,1,0)
      CALL STRPB(CARTD,DFLEX,DGRAD,DSHER,ELDIS,NDOFN,
     .          NNODE,SHAPE,STRES,1,0)
      CALL PRINC(ANGLE,PMMAX,PMMIN,STRES)
C     WRITE(6,900)KSAMP,(SPCOD(IDIME,KSAMP),IDIME=1,2),
C    .(STRES(ISTRE),ISTRE=1,3),PMMAX,PMMIN,ANGLE
C900  FORMAT(1X,I5,2F10.4,6E12.4)
      RETURN
      END
```

```
      SUBROUTINE GRADPB     (CARTD,DGRAD,ELDIS,NDOFN,NNODE)
C**********************************************************************
C
C*** FORM DISPLACEMENTS GRADIENTS
C
C**********************************************************************
      IMPLICIT REAL*8(A-H,O-Z)
      DIMENSION CARTD(2,9),DGRAD(6),ELDIS(3,9)
C
```

```
C*** ZERO DGRAD
C
      CALL RAZERO(DGRAD,6,1)
C
C*** FORM DISPLACEMENTS GRADIENTS
C
      DO 10 INODE=1,NNODE
      DNIDX=CARTD(1,INODE)
      DNIDY=CARTD(2,INODE)
      DO 10 IDOFN=1,NDOFN
      IPOSN=NDOFN+IDOFN
      CONST=ELDIS(IDOFN,INODE)
      DGRAD(IDOFN)=DGRAD(IDOFN)+DNIDX*CONST
   10 DGRAD(IPOSN)=DGRAD(IPOSN)+DNIDY*CONST
      RETURN
      END
```

```
      SUBROUTINE STRPB      (CARTD,DFLEX,DGRAD,DSHER,ELDIS,NDOFN,
     .                       NNODE,SHAPE,STRES,IFFLE,IFSHE)
C**********************************************************************
C
C*** EVALUATES STRESS RESULTANTS FOR MINDLIN PLATE
C
C**********************************************************************
      IMPLICIT REAL*8(A-H,O-Z)
      DIMENSION CARTD(2,9),DFLEX(3,3),DGRAD(6),DSHER(2,2),
     .          ELDIS(3,9),SHAPE(9),STRES(5)
C*** ZERO STRESS VECTOR
      CALL RAZERO(STRES,5,1)
      CALL GRADPB(CARTD,DGRAD,ELDIS,NDOFN,NNODE)
C
C*** EVALUATE ROTATIONS AT GAUSS POINT , IF NEEDED
C
      IF(IFSHE.EQ.0) GO TO 20
      XZROT=0.0
      YZROT=0.0
      DO 10 INODE=1,NNODE
      XZROT=XZROT+SHAPE(INODE)*ELDIS(2,INODE)
   10 YZROT=YZROT+SHAPE(INODE)*ELDIS(3,INODE)
C
C*** EVALUATE BENDING STRESS RESULTANTS
C
   20 IF(IFFLE.EQ.0) GOTO 30
      EFLXX=-DGRAD(2)
      EFLYY=-DGRAD(6)
      EFLXY=-(DGRAD(3)+DGRAD(5))
      STRES(1)=DFLEX(1,1)*EFLXX+DFLEX(1,2)*EFLYY
      STRES(2)=DFLEX(2,1)*EFLXX+DFLEX(2,2)*EFLYY
      STRES(3)=DFLEX(3,3)*EFLXY
C
C*** EVALUATE SHEAR STRESS RESULTANTS
C
   30 IF(IFSHE.EQ.0) RETURN
      ESHXX=DGRAD(1)-XZROT
      ESHYY=DGRAD(4)-YZROT
      STRES(4)=DSHER(1,1)*ESHXX
      STRES(5)=DSHER(2,2)*ESHYY
```

```
      RETURN
      END


      SUBROUTINE SHEAR(BMETA,BMEXI,ELCOD,ELDIS,ETASP,EXISP,IELEM,
     .                 KSAMP,LPROP,MMATS,NDOFN,PROPS,STRES,STRSG)
      IMPLICIT REAL*8(A-H,O-Z)
      DIMENSION CARTD(2,9),DERIV(2,9),DFLEX(3,3),DGRAD(6),
     .DSHER(2,2),ELCOD(2,9),ELDIS(3,9),
     .PROPS(MMATS,9),SHAPE(9),SPCOD(2,9),STRES(5),STRSG(9,2),
     .XJACI(2,2),XJACM(2,2),SHAP1(6),SHAP2(6),BMETA(6,27),BMEXI(6,27),
     .BSHEI(2,3),DBMAT(2,3)
      DATA NNODE/9/
C
C*** EVALUATES AND PRINTS SHEAR FORCES AT NODAL POINTS
C
      KSAMP=KSAMP+1
      CALL SFR2(DERIV,ETASP,EXISP,NNODE,SHAPE)
      CALL JACOB2(CARTD,DERIV,DJACB,ELCOD,SPCOD,IELEM,
     .KSAMP,NNODE,SHAPE,XJACI,XJACM)
      CALL SFRM(ETASP,EXISP,SHAP1,SHAP2)
      CALL MODPB(DFLEX,DSHER,LPROP,MMATS,PROPS,0,1)
      DO 5 ISTRE=4,5
      STRES(ISTRE)=0.0
    5 CONTINUE
      DO 30 INODE=1,9
      IPOSN=(INODE-1)*3
      CALL BMOTPB(BMETA,BMEXI,BSHEI,IPOSN,SHAP1,SHAP2,XJACI)
      CALL RAZERO(DBMAT,2,3)
      DO 10 ISTRE=1,2
      DO 10 JSTRE=1,2
      DO 10 IDOFN=1,3
      DBMAT(ISTRE,IDOFN)=DBMAT(ISTRE,IDOFN)+DSHER(ISTRE,JSTRE)*
     .                   BSHEI(JSTRE,IDOFN)
   10 CONTINUE
      DO 20 ISTRE=4,5
      KSTRE=ISTRE-3
      DO 20 IDOFN=1,3
      STRES(ISTRE)=STRES(ISTRE)+DBMAT(KSTRE,IDOFN)*
     .             ELDIS(IDOFN,INODE)
   20 CONTINUE
   30 CONTINUE
C     WRITE(6,900)KSAMP,(SPCOD(IDIME,KSAMP),IDIME=1,2),
C    .(STRES(ISTRE),ISTRE=4,5)
C900  FORMAT(1X,I5,2F10.4,2E12.5)
      STRSG(KSAMP,1)=STRES(4)
      STRSG(KSAMP,2)=STRES(5)
      RETURN
      END


      SUBROUTINE AVERAG(KOUNT,LSELN,MPOIN,MSELN,NPOIN,NSELN,STRES,
     .                  STRND)
      IMPLICIT REAL*8(A-H,O-Z)
      DIMENSION KOUNT(MPOIN),LSELN(MSELN),STRES(5),STRND(MPOIN,5)
C
C*** EVALUATES AND PRINTS AVERAGED NODAL STRESS RESULTANTS
C
      WRITE(6,900)
```

```
 900  FORMAT(/1X,24HBENDING MOMENTS AT NODES)
      WRITE(6,905)
 905  FORMAT(1X,5H NODE,2X,9HMX-MOMENT,4X,9HMY-MOMENT,
     .3X,10HMXY-MOMENT,2X,8HMAX-P.M.,4X,8HMIN-P.M.,
     .6X,5HANGLE)
      DO 40 IPOIN=1,NPOIN
      IF(NSELN.EQ.0)GO TO 20
      DO 10 ISELN=1,NSELN
      LNODE=LSELN(ISELN)
      IF(IPOIN.EQ.LNODE)GO TO 20
 10   CONTINUE
      GO TO 40
 20   EJOIN=FLOAT(KOUNT(IPOIN))
      DO 30 ISTRE=1,3
 30   STRES(ISTRE)=STRND(IPOIN,ISTRE)/EJOIN
      CALL PRINC(ANGLE,PMMAX,PMMIN,STRES)
      WRITE(6,910)IPOIN,(STRES(ISTRE),ISTRE=1,3),
     .PMMAX,PMMIN,ANGLE
 910  FORMAT(1X,I5,6E12.4)
 40   CONTINUE
      WRITE(6,915)
 915  FORMAT(/1X,21HSHEAR FORCES AT NODES)
      WRITE(6,920)
 920  FORMAT(1X,5H NODE,4X,8HXZ-SHEAR,4X,8HYZ-SHEAR)
      DO 80 IPOIN=1,NPOIN
      IF(NSELN.EQ.0) GO TO 60
      DO 50 ISELN=1,NSELN
      LNODE=LSELN(ISELN)
      IF(IPOIN.EQ.LNODE)GO TO 60
 50   CONTINUE
      GO TO 80
 60   EJOIN=FLOAT(KOUNT(IPOIN))
      DO 70 ISTRE=4,5
 70   STRES(ISTRE)=STRND(IPOIN,ISTRE)/EJOIN
      WRITE(6,925)IPOIN,(STRES(ISTRE),ISTRE=4,5)
 925  FORMAT(1X,I5,2E12.4)
 80   CONTINUE
      RETURN
      END
```

```
      SUBROUTINE PRINC(ANGLE,PMMAX,PMMIN,STRES)
      IMPLICIT REAL*8(A-H,O-Z)
      DIMENSION STRES(5)
C
C*** EVALUATE PRINCIPAL MOMENTS
C
      XXMOM=STRES(1)
      YYMOM=STRES(2)
      XYMOM=STRES(3)
      XXAYY=0.5*(XXMOM+YYMOM)
      XXMYY=0.5*(XXMOM-YYMOM)
      IF(XXMYY.EQ.0.0)XXMYY=0.000000001
      SUMMM=SQRT(XXMYY*XXMYY+XYMOM*XYMOM)
      PMMAX=XXAYY+SUMMM
      PMMIN=XXAYY-SUMMM
      ANGLE=ATAN(XYMOM/XXMYY)*0.5
      ANGLE=ANGLE*(180.0/3.141593)
      RETURN
      END
```

3.14 User Instructions for Program DYNAM

DATA SET 1		PROBLEM TITLE	(20A4) one record
Cols.	1 - 80	TITLE	title of the problem
DATA SET 2		CONTROL PARAMETER	(I5) one record
Cols.	1 - 5	ICONT	=1, transient dynamic analysis =2, initially stressed transient dynamic analysis
DATA SET 3		CONTROL DATA	(5I5) one record
Cols.	1 - 5	NPOIN	number of nodal points
	6 - 10	NELEM	number of elements
	11 - 15	NVFIX	number of restrained nodes
	16 - 20	NMATS	number of material sets
	21 - 25	NISTR	number of initial stress sets
DATA SET 4		ELEMENT CONNECTIONS	(12I5) NELEM records
Cols.	1 - 5	NUMEL	element number
	6 - 10	MATNO(NUMEL)	material set
	11 - 15	LNODS(NUMEL,1)	1st nodal connection number
	16 - 20	LNODS(NUMEL,2)	2nd nodal connection number
	⋮	⋮	⋮ ⋮
	51 - 55	LNODS(NUMEL,9)	9th nodal connection number
	56 - 60	ISTRN(NUMEL)	initial stress set number
DATA SET 5		NODAL COORDINATES	(I5,2F10.5) NPOIN records
Cols.	1 - 5	IPOIN	nodal point number
	6 - 15	COORD(IPOIN,1)	x-coordinate of node
	16 - 25	COORD(IPOIN,2)	y-coordinate of node

[N.B. Note that coordinates for midside nodes on straight edges may be omitted.]

DATA SET 6		RESTRAINED NODES	(I5,2X,3I1) NVFIX records
Cols.	1 - 5	NOFIX(IVFIX)	restrained node number
	8	IFPRE(IVFIX,1)	condition of restraint on nodal displacement w
	9	IFPRE(IVFIX,2)	condition of restraint on nodal rotation θ_x
	10	IFPRE(IVFIX,3)	condition of restraint on nodal rotation θ_y 0 - free 1 - fixed

DATA SET 7		MATERIAL SET DATA 1	(I5) one record
Cols.	1 - 5	NUMAT	material set number
DATA SET 8		MATERIAL SET DATA 2	(8F10.5) one record
Cols.	1 - 10	PROPS(NUMAT,1)	1st material property E or D_{11}
	11 - 20	PROPS(NUMAT,2)	2nd material property ν or D_{12}
	21 - 30	PROPS(NUMAT,3)	3rd material property h or D_{22}
	31 - 40	PROPS(NUMAT,4)	4th material property 0 or D_{66}
	41 - 50	PROPS(NUMAT,5)	5th material property 0 or D_{55}
	51 - 60	PROPS(NUMAT,6)	6th material property 0 or D_{44}
	61 - 70	PROPS(NUMAT,7)	7th material property 0 or h
	71 - 80	PROPS(NUMAT,8)	8th material property ρ-density per unit of volume
Cols.	1 - 10	PROPS(NUMAT,9)	uniform load intensity q

[N.B. Repeat DATA SETS 7 and 8 NMATS times.]

DATA SET 9 INITIAL STRESS SET DATA (I5,3F10.5) NISTR records

Cols.	1 - 5	NUSTR	initial stress set number
	6 - 15	STREM(NUSTR,1)	initial stress σ_x^o
	16 - 25	STREM(NUSTR,2)	initial stress σ_y^o
	26 - 35	STREM(NUSTR,3)	initial stress τ_{xy}^o

[N.B. Omit this data set if ICONT=1.]

DATA SET 10 TIME STEPPING DATA (3I5,2F10.3) one record

Cols.	1 - 5	NSTEP	total number of time steps
	6 - 10	NOUTP(1)	output for displacements at every NOUTP(1) time steps
	11 - 15	NOUTP(2)	output for stresses at every NOUTP(2) time steps
	16 - 25	DTIME	time step length
	26 - 35	DTEND	time at the end of the step impulse

DATA SET 11 INITIAL DISPLACEMENT CARD (I10,3F10.5) NPOIN records

Cols.	1 - 10	NGASH	nodal point
	11 - 20	ZGASH	initial w-displacement
	21 - 30	XGASH	initial θ_x-rotation
	31 - 40	YGASH	initial θ_y-rotation

[N.B. If all displacements are zero read data only for the last node.]

DATA SET 12 INITIAL VELOCITY CARD (I10,3F10.5) NPOIN records

Cols.	1 - 10	NGASH	nodal point
	11 - 20	ZGASH	initial w-velocity
	21 - 30	XGASH	initial θ_x-rotation velocity
	31 - 40	YGASH	initial θ_y-rotation velocity

[N.B. If all velocities are zero read data only for the last node.]

DATA SET 13 SELECTIVE OUTPUT DATA (I5) one record

Cols.	1 - 5	NSELN	number of nodes for selective output

DATA SET 14 NODE NUMBERS FOR SELECTIVE OUTPUT (14I5)

Cols.	1 - 5	LSELN(1)	1st node number for selective output
	6 - 10	LSELN(2)	2nd node number for selective output
	⋮	⋮	⋮
	.	LSELN(NSELN)	NSELN node number for selective output

[N.B. if NSELN=0 omit this data set.]

DATA SET 15		LOAD TITLE	(20A4) one record
Cols.	1 - 80	TITLE	load title
DATA SET 16		LOAD TYPE	(I5) one record
Cols.	1 - 5	IPLOD	load type indicator 0 - uniform load 1 - point load

DATA SET 17 NODAL LOADS (I5,3F10.3) one record for each loaded node

Cols.	1 - 5	LODPT	node number
	6 - 15	POINT(1)	lateral force
	16 - 25	POINT(2)	couple in xz-plane
	26 - 35	POINT(3)	couple in yz-plane

[N.B. This data set should be terminated by the highest node number even if it is not loaded. If IPLOD=0 omit this data set.]

4. SAMPLE SOLUTIONS

4.1 Simply Supported Initially Stressed Rectangular Plate

This example [7] presents the influence of prestress on the dynamic response of the rectangular simply supported plate of thickness/span ratio (h/a = 0.1) subjected to a rectangular (Heaviside) impulse acting as uniformly distributed load over a central area of the plate. A symmetric quadrant of the plate is idealized by 12 elements as shown in Figure 4.1. Typical input and output data for this example are given in Figures 4.2 and 4.3 respectively. Figures 4.4 and 4.5 show the time history of the plate centre deflection and bending moment, respectively, for several prestress conditions. The results are presented in dimensionless form and are compared with the results from the closed form solution in Chapter 1.

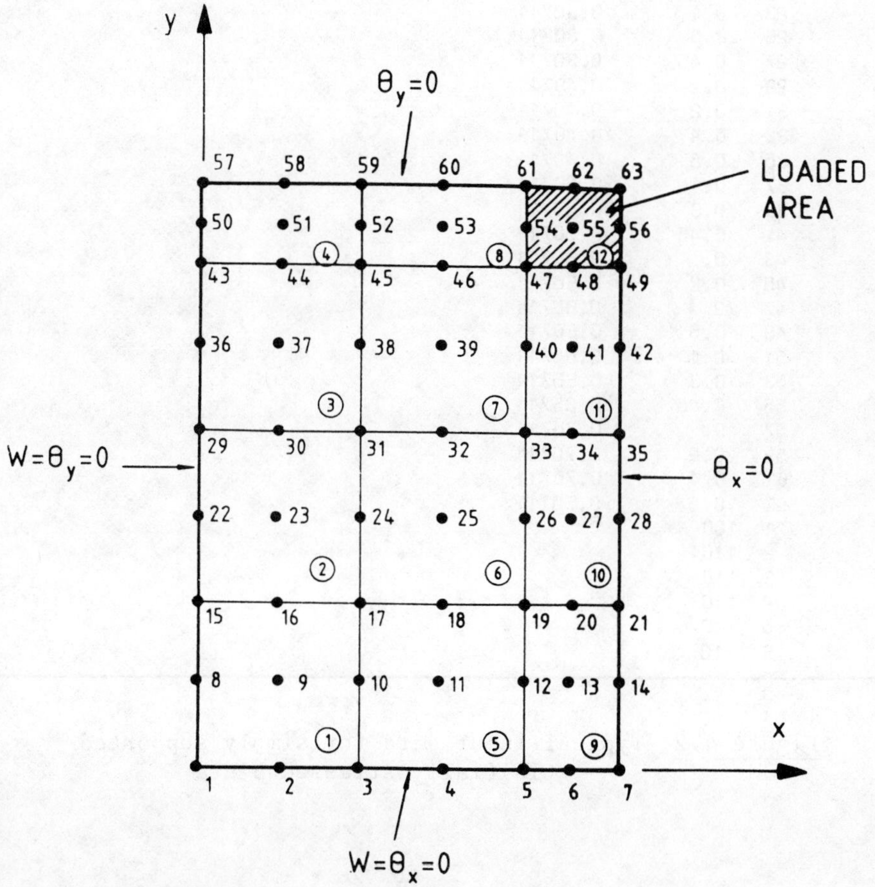

Figure 4.1 Quarter of a simply supported plate-mesh

```
** REISMANN AND TENDORF EXAMPLE H=0.1 **
 2
63   12   28    2    1
 1    1    1    2    3   10   17   16   15    8    9    1
 2    1   15   16   17   24   31   30   29   22   23    1
 3    1   29   30   31   38   45   44   43   36   37    1
 4    1   43   44   45   52   59   58   57   50   51    1
 5    1    3    4    5   12   19   18   17   10   11    1
 6    1   17   18   19   26   33   32   31   24   25    1
 7    1   31   32   33   40   47   46   45   38   39    1
 8    1   45   46   47   54   61   60   59   52   53    1
 9    1    5    6    7   14   21   20   19   12   13    1
10    1   19   20   21   28   35   34   33   26   27    1
11    1   33   34   35   42   49   48   47   40   41    1
12    2   47   48   49   56   63   62   61   54   55    1
 1   0.0       0.0
 3   0.2       0.
 5   0.4       0.
 7   0.5       0.
 9   0.1       0.10355
11   0.3       0.10355
13   0.45      0.10355
15   0.        0.20711
17   0.2       0.20711
19   0.4       0.20711
21   0.5       0.20711
23   0.1       0.30711
25   0.3       0.30711
27   0.45      0.30711
29   0.        0.40711
31   0.2       0.40711
33   0.4       0.40711
35   0.5       0.40711
37   0.1       0.50711
39   0.3       0.50711
41   0.45      0.50711
43   0.        0.60711
45   0.2       0.60711
47   0.4       0.60711
49   0.5       0.60711
51   0.1       0.65711
53   0.3       0.65711
55   0.45      0.65711
57   0.        0.70711
59   0.2       0.70711
61   0.4       0.70711
63   0.5       0.70711
 1  100
 2  110
 3  110
 4  110
 5  110
 6  110
```

Figure 4.2 Typical input data for simply supported initially stressed plate

```
    7  110
    8  101
   14  010
   15  101
   21  010
   22  101
   28  010
   29  101
   35  010
   36  101
   42  010
   43  101
   49  010
   50  101
   56  010
   57  101
   58  001
   59  001
   60  001
   61  001
   62  001
   63  011
    1
1.0         0.3         0.1         0.          0.          0.          0.          5.
0.
    2
1.0         0.3         0.1         0.          0.          0.          0.          5.
0.16
    1 -0.009757
 1700  100   100 0.0223607 120.
          63   0.0           0.0           0.0
          63   0.0           0.0           0.0
    1
   63
   UNIFORM DISTRIBUTED LOAD
    0
```

Figure 4.2 continued

** REISMANN AND TENDORF EXAMPLE H=0.1 **

THIS IS AN INITIALLY STRESSED TRANSIENT DYNAMIC ANALYSIS ICONT= 2

NPOIN = 63 NELEM = 12 NVFIX = 28 NMATS = 2

NISTR = 1

ELEM.	MAT.SET	NODE NUMBERS									STR.SET
1	1	1	2	3	10	17	16	15	8	9	1
2	1	15	16	17	24	31	30	29	22	23	1
3	1	29	30	31	38	45	44	43	36	37	1
4	1	43	44	45	52	59	58	57	50	51	1
5	1	3	4	5	12	19	18	17	10	11	1
6	1	17	18	19	26	33	32	31	24	25	1
7	1	31	32	33	40	47	46	45	38	39	1
8	1	45	46	47	54	61	60	59	52	53	1
9	1	5	6	7	14	21	20	19	12	13	1
10	1	19	20	21	28	35	34	33	26	27	1
11	1	33	34	35	42	49	48	47	40	41	1
12	2	47	48	49	56	63	62	61	54	55	1

NODAL POINT COORDINATES

NODE	X	Y
1	0.000	0.000
2	0.100	0.000
3	0.200	0.000
4	0.300	0.000
5	0.400	0.000
6	0.450	0.000
7	0.500	0.000
8	0.000	0.104
9	0.100	0.104
10	0.200	0.104
11	0.300	0.104
12	0.400	0.104
13	0.450	0.104
14	0.500	0.104
15	0.000	0.207
16	0.100	0.207
17	0.200	0.207
18	0.300	0.207
19	0.400	0.207
20	0.450	0.207
21	0.500	0.207
22	0.000	0.307
23	0.100	0.307
24	0.200	0.307
25	0.300	0.307
26	0.400	0.307
27	0.450	0.307
28	0.500	0.307
29	0.000	0.407
30	0.100	0.407
31	0.200	0.407
32	0.300	0.407
33	0.400	0.407

Figure 4.3 Typical output for simply supported initially stressed plate

34	0.450	0.407
35	0.500	0.407
36	0.000	0.507
37	0.100	0.507
38	0.200	0.507
39	0.300	0.507
40	0.400	0.507
41	0.450	0.507
42	0.500	0.507
43	0.000	0.607
44	0.100	0.607
45	0.200	0.607
46	0.300	0.607
47	0.400	0.607
48	0.450	0.607
49	0.500	0.607
50	0.000	0.657
51	0.100	0.657
52	0.200	0.657
53	0.300	0.657
54	0.400	0.657
55	0.450	0.657
56	0.500	0.657
57	0.000	0.707
58	0.100	0.707
59	0.200	0.707
60	0.300	0.707
61	0.400	0.707
62	0.450	0.707
63	0.500	0.707

RESTRAINED NODES

NODE	CODE
1	100
2	110
3	110
4	110
5	110
6	110
7	110
8	101
14	010
15	101
21	010
22	101
28	010
29	101
35	010
36	101
42	010
43	101
49	010
50	101
56	010
57	101
58	001
59	001
60	001
61	001
62	001
63	011

Figure 4.3 continued

```
  MATERIAL PROPERTIES
  NUMBER        PROPERTIES
     1          0.100000E+01  0.300000E+00  0.100000E+00
                0.000000E+00  0.000000E+00  0.000000E+00
                0.000000E+00  0.500000E+01  0.000000E+00
     2          0.100000E+01  0.300000E+00  0.100000E+00
                0.000000E+00  0.000000E+00  0.000000E+00
                0.000000E+00  0.500000E+01  0.160000E+00


 THE INITIAL IN-PLANE STRESSES
 NUMBER     SIGMA-X        SIGMA-Y       SIGMA-XY
    1  -0.975700E-02  0.000000E+00  0.000000E+00


 NSTEP =1700     NOUTP(1) = 100     NOUTP(2) = 100
 DTIME =  0.2236E-01      DTEND =  0.1200E+03


    NODE   INITIAL W-DISP.   INITIAL XZ-ROT.   INITIAL YZ-ROT.

      63      0.00000E+00      0.00000E+00      0.00000E+00


    NODE   INITIAL W-VELO.   INITIAL XZ-ROT.VEL   INITIAL YZ-ROT.VEL

      63      0.00000E+00      0.00000E+00      0.00000E+00

 NSELN=   1

 NODE NUMBERS FOR SELECTIVE OUTPUT

   63

    UNIFORM DISTRIBUTED LOAD

    0
      DISPLACEMENTS
       NODE         W            THETA-X         THETA-Y
        63  0.800001E-04  0.000000E+00  0.000000E+00



   RESULTS AT TIME STEP          100       TIME     0.22360700000E+01
   DISPLACEMENTS
    NODE         W            THETA-X         THETA-Y
     63  0.266393E+00  0.156914E-34  0.155941E-34


   STRESS RESULTANTS

BENDING MOMENTS AT NODES
 NODE  MX-MOMENT    MY-MOMENT    MXY-MOMENT  MAX-P.M.     MIN-P.M.      ANGLE
   63  0.9872E-03  0.9640E-03  0.3565E-19  0.9872E-03  0.9640E-03  0.8822E-13

SHEAR FORCES AT NODES
 NODE    XZ-SHEAR    YZ-SHEAR
   63 -0.2889E-03 -0.2814E-03
```

Figure 4.3 continued

```
RESULTS AT TIME STEP        900     TIME    0.20124630000E+02
DISPLACEMENTS
 NODE       W            THETA-X        THETA-Y
  63  0.370330E+01  0.540299E-32  0.468582E-32


STRESS RESULTANTS

BENDING MOMENTS AT NODES
 NODE  MX-MOMENT    MY-MOMENT   MXY-MOMENT  MAX-P.M.     MIN-P.M.       ANGLE
   63  0.4410E-02  0.3100E-02  0.9484E-19  0.4410E-02  0.3100E-02  0.4147E-14

SHEAR FORCES AT NODES
 NODE    XZ-SHEAR    YZ-SHEAR
   63  0.1251E-03 -0.1989E-03


RESULTS AT TIME STEP       1000     TIME    0.22360700000E+02
DISPLACEMENTS
 NODE       W            THETA-X        THETA-Y
  63  0.393698E+01  0.729458E-32  0.621448E-32


STRESS RESULTANTS

BENDING MOMENTS AT NODES
 NODE  MX-MOMENT    MY-MOMENT   MXY-MOMENT  MAX-P.M.     MIN-P.M.       ANGLE
   63  0.4669E-02  0.3653E-02  0.1202E-18  0.4669E-02  0.3653E-02  0.6777E-14


SHEAR FORCES AT NODES
 NODE    XZ-SHEAR    YZ-SHEAR
   63  0.5859E-03  0.1828E-03

RESULTS AT TIME STEP       1100     TIME    0.24596770000E+02
DISPLACEMENTS
 NODE       W            THETA-X        THETA-Y
  63  0.388504E+01  0.956033E-32  0.803452E-32


STRESS RESULTANTS

BENDING MOMENTS AT NODES
 NODE  MX-MOMENT    MY-MOMENT   MXY-MOMENT  MAX-P.M.     MIN-P.M.       ANGLE
   63  0.4419E-02  0.3612E-02  0.1221E-18  0.4419E-02  0.3612E-02  0.8669E-14

SHEAR FORCES AT NODES
 NODE    XZ-SHEAR    YZ-SHEAR
   63  0.3843E-03  0.8028E-04
```

Figure 4.3 continued

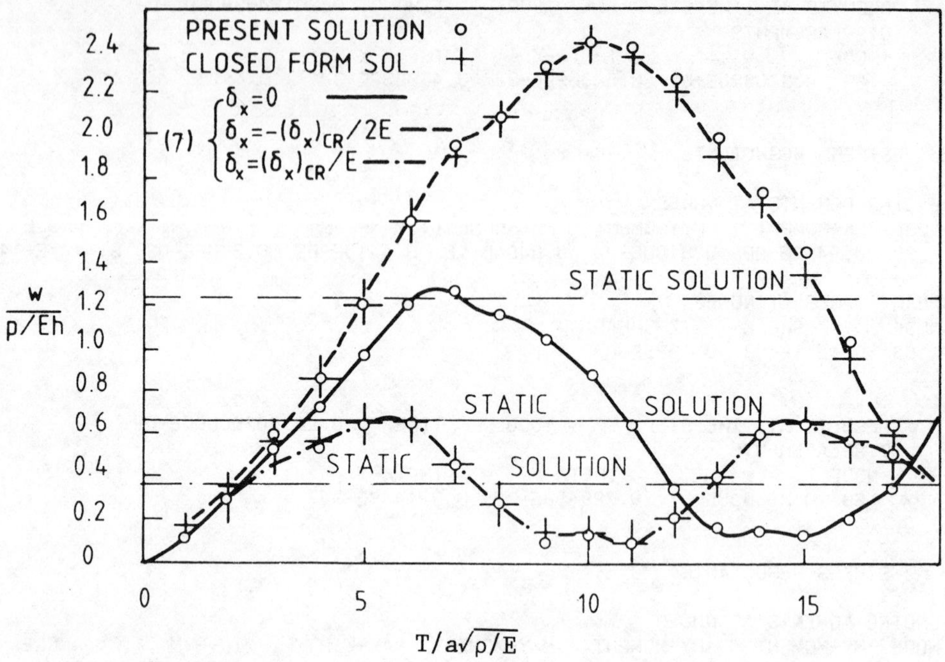

Figure 4.4 Centre deflection versus time

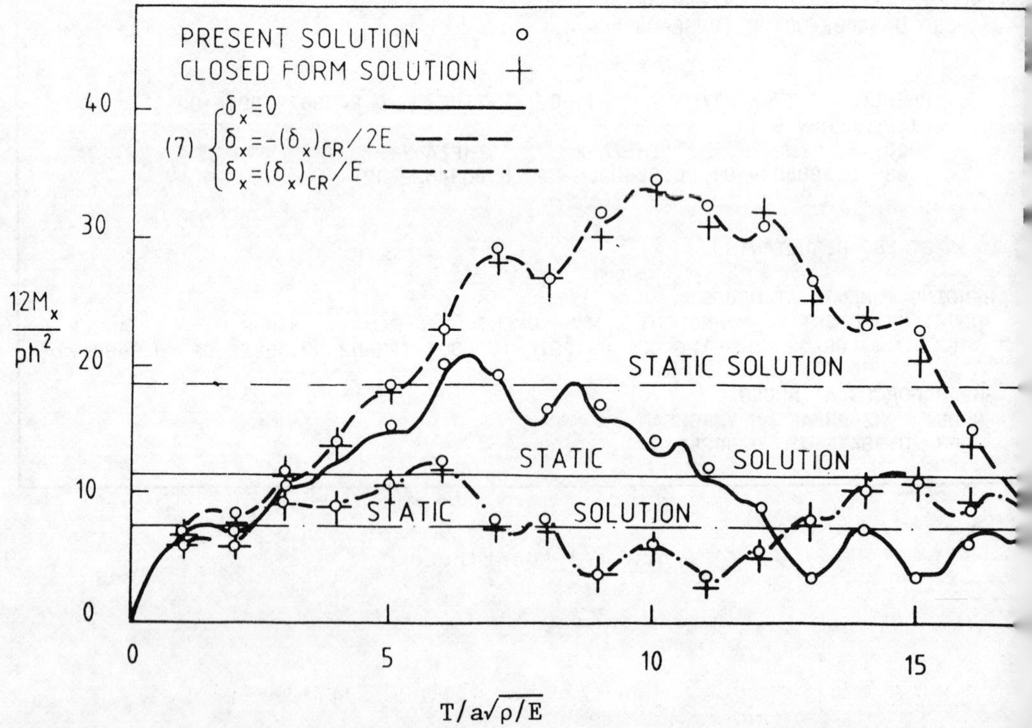

Figure 4.5 Centre bending moment versus time

4.2 Clamped Circular Plate

This example shows the results for a clamped circular plate which is subjected to a suddenly applied uniformly distributed load. A quarter of the plate shown in Figure 4.6 is idealized by 12 elements. Figures 4.7 and 4.8 present the time histories of the plate centre deflection and bending moment respectively. Typical input and output data for this example are given in Figures 4.9 and 4.10 respectively.

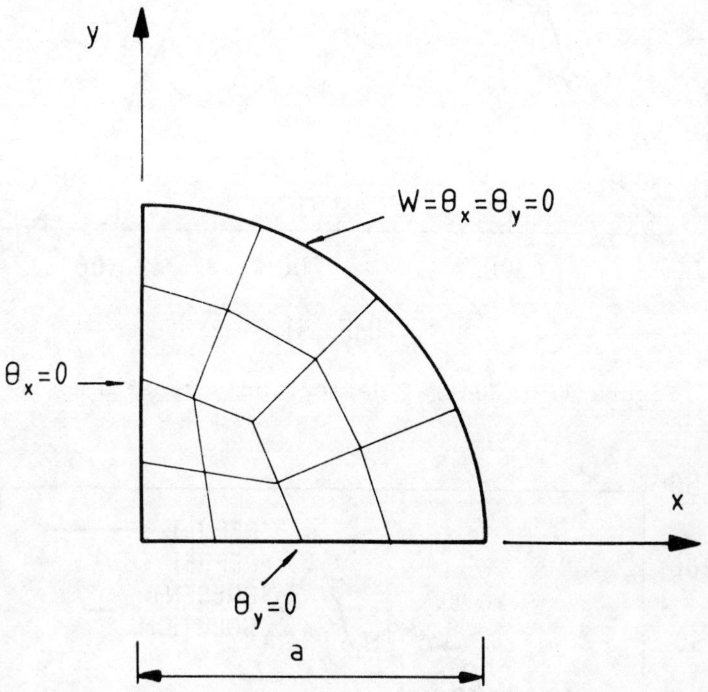

E =	100.0
ν =	0.3
h =	20.0
ρ =	10.0
a =	100.0
q =	0.1

Figure 4.6 Symmetric quadrant of clamped circular plate - geometry and mesh

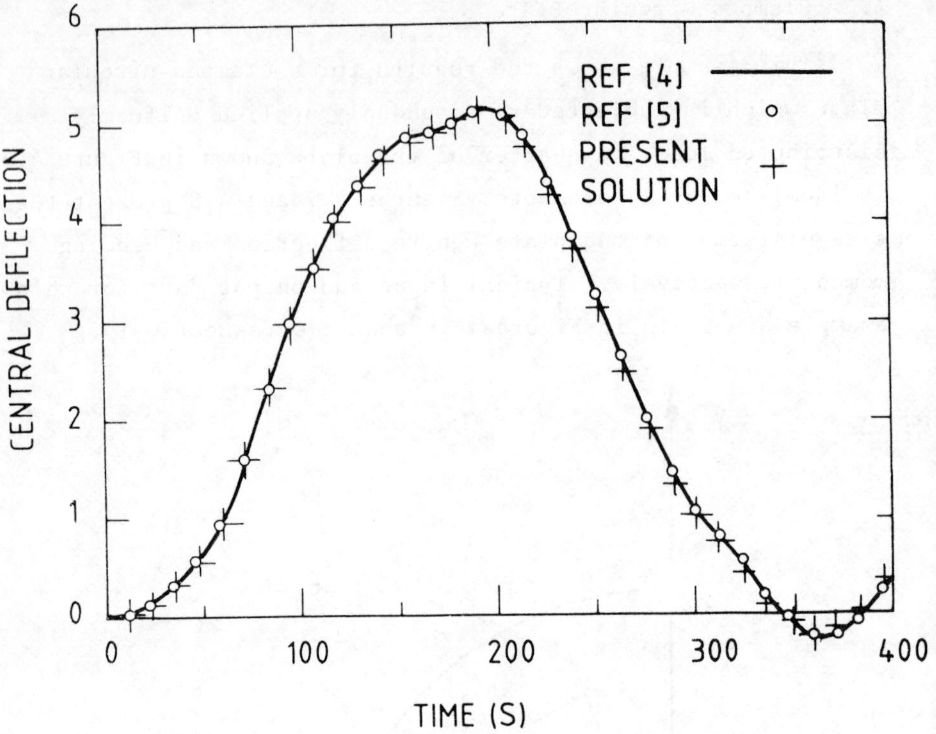

Figure 4.7 Central deflection versus time

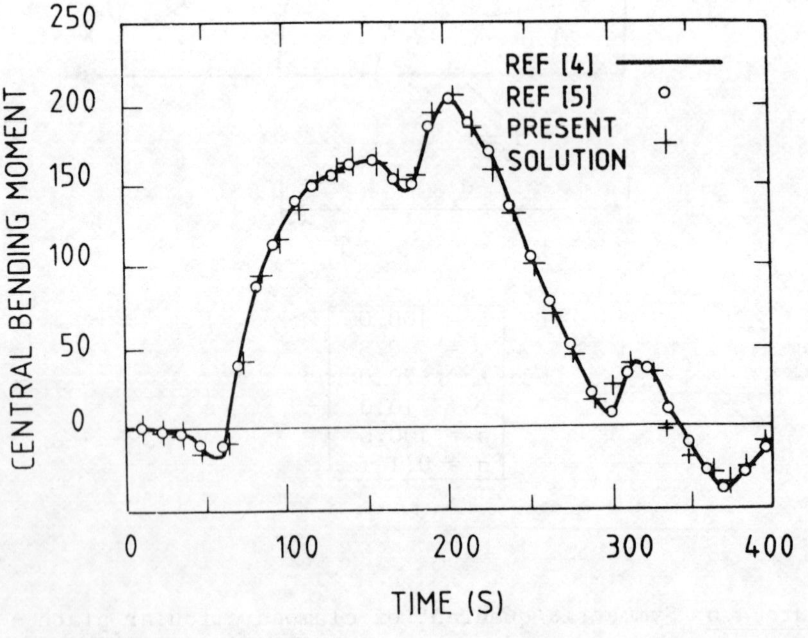

Figure 4.8 Central bending moment versus time

```
CLAMPED CIRCULAR PLATE
 1
61   12   24    1    0
 1    1    1    2    3   12   21   20   19   10   11
 2    1    3    4    5   14   23   22   21   12   13
 3    1   19   20   21   30   39   38   37   28   29
 4    1   21   22   23   32   41   40   39   30   31
 5    1    5    6    7   16   25   24   23   14   15
 6    1   23   24   25   34   43   42   41   32   33
 7    1   39   40   41   42   43   50   55   48   49
 8    1   37   38   39   48   55   54   53   46   47
 9    1    7    8    9   18   27   26   25   16   17
10    1   25   26   27   36   45   44   43   34   35
11    1   55   50   43   44   45   52   57   56   51
12    1   53   54   55   56   57   60   61   58   59
 1        0.0         0.0
 3       25.0         0.0
 5       50.0         0.0
 7       75.0         0.0
 9      100.0         0.0
11      10.67       10.67
13      33.84        8.84
15     57.925       11.05
17     82.852      16.198
18      98.08       19.51
19        0.0        25.0
21      17.68       17.68
23      42.68       17.68
25      64.02       26.52
27      92.39       38.27
29       8.84       33.84
31     28.348      28.348
33      48.77      33.145
35     70.038      47.132
36      83.15       55.56
37        0.0        50.0
39      17.68       42.68
41      35.35       35.35
43      53.03       53.03
45      70.71       70.71
47      11.05      57.925
49     33.145       48.77
51     47.132      70.038
52      55.56       83.15
53        0.0        75.0
55      26.52       64.02
57      38.27       92.39
59     16.198      82.852
60      19.51       98.08
61        0.0       100.0
```

Figure 4.9 Typical input data for clamped circular plate

```
    1  011
    2  001
    3  001
    4  001
    5  001
    6  001
    7  001
    8  001
    9  111
   10  010
   18  111
   19  010
   27  111
   28  010
   36  111
   37  010
   45  111
   46  010
   52  111
   53  010
   57  111
   58  010
   60  111
   61  111
    1
100.       0.3        20.        0.         0.         0.         0.         10.
0.1
  680   20    20 0.6       600.
        610.        0.         0.
        610.        0.         0.
    1
    1
  UNIFORM DISTRIBUTED LOAD
    0
```

Figure 4.9 continued

CLAMPED CIRCULAR PLATE

THIS IS A TRANSIENT DYNAMIC ANALYSIS   ICONT= 1

NPOIN = 61   NELEM = 12   NVFIX = 24   NMATS = 1

NISTR = 0

ELEM.	MAT.SET				NODE NUMBERS					STR.SET
1	1	1	2	3	12	21	20	19	10	11	0
2	1	3	4	5	14	23	22	21	12	13	0
3	1	19	20	21	30	39	38	37	28	29	0
4	1	21	22	23	32	41	40	39	30	31	0
5	1	5	6	7	16	25	24	23	14	15	0
6	1	23	24	25	34	43	42	41	32	33	0
7	1	39	40	41	42	43	50	55	48	49	0
8	1	37	38	39	48	55	54	53	46	47	0
9	1	7	8	9	18	27	26	25	16	17	0
10	1	25	26	27	36	45	44	43	34	35	0
11	1	55	50	43	44	45	52	57	56	51	0
12	1	53	54	55	56	57	60	61	58	59	0

NODAL POINT COORDINATES

NODE	X	Y
1	0.000	0.000
2	12.500	0.000
3	25.000	0.000
4	37.500	0.000
5	50.000	0.000
6	62.500	0.000
7	75.000	0.000
8	87.500	0.000
9	100.000	0.000
10	0.000	12.500
11	10.670	10.670
12	21.340	8.840
13	33.840	8.840
14	46.340	8.840
15	57.925	11.050
16	69.510	13.260
17	82.852	16.198
18	98.080	19.510
19	0.000	25.000
20	8.840	21.340
21	17.680	17.680
22	30.180	17.680
23	42.680	17.680
24	53.350	22.100
25	64.020	26.520
26	78.205	32.395
27	92.390	38.270
28	0.000	37.500
29	8.840	33.840
30	17.680	30.180
31	28.348	28.348
32	39.015	26.515
33	48.770	33.145

Figure 4.10 Typical output for clamped circular plate

34	58.525	39.775
35	70.038	47.132
36	83.150	55.560
37	0.000	50.000
38	8.840	46.340
39	17.680	42.680
40	26.515	39.015
41	35.350	35.350
42	44.190	44.190
43	53.030	53.030
44	61.870	61.870
45	70.710	70.710
46	0.000	62.500
47	11.050	57.925
48	22.100	53.350
49	33.145	48.770
50	39.775	58.525
51	47.132	70.038
52	55.560	83.150
53	0.000	75.000
54	13.260	69.510
55	26.520	64.020
56	32.395	78.205
57	38.270	92.390
58	0.000	87.500
59	16.198	82.852
60	19.510	98.080
61	0.000	100.000

RESTRAINED NODES

NODE	CODE
1	011
2	001
3	001
4	001
5	001
6	001
7	001
8	001
9	111
10	010
18	111
19	010
27	111
28	010
36	111
37	010
45	111
46	010
52	111
53	010
57	111
58	010
60	111
61	111

MATERIAL PROPERTIES

NUMBER	PROPERTIES		
1	0.100000E+03	0.300000E+00	0.200000E+02
	0.000000E+00	0.000000E+00	0.000000E+00
	0.000000E+00	0.100000E+02	0.100000E+00

Figure 4.10 continued

```
NSTEP = 680    NOUTP(1) =  20    NOUTP(2) =  20
DTIME =  0.6000E+00      DTEND =  0.6000E+03


    NODE   INITIAL W-DISP.   INITIAL XZ-ROT.   INITIAL YZ-ROT.

      61     0.00000E+00      0.00000E+00      0.00000E+00


    NODE   INITIAL W-VELO.   INITIAL XZ-ROT.VEL   INITIAL YZ-ROT.VEL

      61     0.00000E+00      0.00000E+00      0.00000E+00

NSELN=    1

NODE NUMBERS FOR SELECTIVE OUTPUT

   1

  UNIFORM DISTRIBUTED LOAD

   0
     DISPLACEMENTS
      NODE        W             THETA-X         THETA-Y
         1  0.900000E-04  0.000000E+00  0.000000E+00


     RESULTS AT TIME STEP          20      TIME     0.12000000000E+02
     DISPLACEMENTS
      NODE        W             THETA-X         THETA-Y
         1  0.359996E-01  0.689263E-32  0.689263E-32


     STRESS RESULTANTS

BENDING MOMENTS AT NODES
 NODE  MX-MOMENT     MY-MOMENT    MXY-MOMENT   MAX-P.M.      MIN-P.M.       ANGLE
    1  0.1487E-02  0.1487E-02  0.4678E-27  0.1487E-02  0.1487E-02 -0.5125E-10

 SHEAR FORCES AT NODES
  NODE     XZ-SHEAR    YZ-SHEAR
     1  0.1814E-03  0.1814E-03


     RESULTS AT TIME STEP          40      TIME     0.24000000000E+02
     DISPLACEMENTS
      NODE        W             THETA-X         THETA-Y
         1  0.143957E+00  0.203099E-29  0.203099E-29


     STRESS RESULTANTS

BENDING MOMENTS AT NODES
 NODE  MX-MOMENT     MY-MOMENT    MXY-MOMENT   MAX-P.M.      MIN-P.M.       ANGLE
    1 -0.2202E-01 -0.2202E-01 -0.3328E-25 -0.2202E-01 -0.2202E-01 -0.1262E-08

SHEAR FORCES AT NODES
 NODE     XZ-SHEAR    YZ-SHEAR
    1  0.2458E-02  0.2458E-02
```

Figure 4.10 continued

```
     RESULTS AT TIME STEP         300      TIME     0.18000000000E+03
     DISPLACEMENTS
      NODE        W             THETA-X          THETA-Y
         1  0.505370E+01 -0.291653E-23 -0.291653E-23


     STRESS RESULTANTS

BENDING MOMENTS AT NODES
 NODE   MX-MOMENT    MY-MOMENT    MXY-MOMENT   MAX-P.M.     MIN-P.M.       ANGLE
    1  0.1574E+03  0.1574E+03  0.6410E-19  0.1574E+03  0.1574E+03 -0.2479E-05

SHEAR FORCES AT NODES
 NODE     XZ-SHEAR     YZ-SHEAR
    1  0.4880E+00  0.4880E+00


     RESULTS AT TIME STEP         320      TIME     0.19200000000E+03
     DISPLACEMENTS
      NODE        W             THETA-X          THETA-Y
         1  0.518882E+01 -0.369476E-23 -0.369476E-23


     STRESS RESULTANTS

BENDING MOMENTS AT NODES
 NODE   MX-MOMENT    MY-MOMENT    MXY-MOMENT   MAX-P.M.     MIN-P.M.       ANGLE
    1  0.1989E+03  0.1989E+03  0.8110E-19  0.1989E+03  0.1989E+03  0.2913E-05

SHEAR FORCES AT NODES
 NODE     XZ-SHEAR     YZ-SHEAR
    1 -0.5466E+00 -0.5466E+00


     RESULTS AT TIME STEP         340      TIME     0.20400000000E+03
     DISPLACEMENTS
      NODE        W             THETA-X          THETA-Y
         1  0.509579E+01 -0.458752E-23 -0.458752E-23


     STRESS RESULTANTS

BENDING MOMENTS AT NODES
 NODE   MX-MOMENT    MY-MOMENT    MXY-MOMENT   MAX-P.M.     MIN-P.M.       ANGLE
    1  0.2047E+03  0.2047E+03  0.1005E-18  0.2047E+03  0.2047E+03  0.5035E-05

SHEAR FORCES AT NODES
 NODE     XZ-SHEAR     YZ-SHEAR
    1  0.8251E-01  0.8251E-01
```

Figure 4.10 continued

REFERENCES

1. BATHE,K.J. and WILSON, E.L.
"Numerical methods in finite element analysis",
Prentice-Hall, Englewood Cliffs, New Jersey, 1976.

2. OWEN, D.R.J. and HINTON, E.
"Finite Elements in Plasticity: Theory and Practice",
Pineridge Press, Swansea, 1981.

3. TSUI, T.Y. and TONG, P.
"Stability of transient solution of moderately thick plate by finite difference method",
American Institute of Aeronautics and Astronautics Journal, 9, 2062-2063, 1971.

4. HINTON, E., OWEN, D.R.J. and SHANTARAM, D.
"Dynamic transient linear and nonlinear behaviour of thick and thin plates",
in The Mathematics of Finite Element and Applications 11 (MAFELAP 1975), Academic Press, New York and London, 1976.

5. HINTON, E.
"The dynamic transient analysis of axisymmetric circular plates by the finite element method",
Journal of Sound and Vibration, 46(4), 465-472, 1976.

6. PICA, A. and HINTON, E.
"Transient and pseudo-transient analysis of Mindlin plates",
Int. J. Num. Meth. Engng., Vol.15, 189-208, 1980.

7. REISMANN, H. and TENDORF, Z.A.
"Dynamics of initially stressed plates",
J. Applied Mechanics, Trans. ASME6, 304-308, 1976.

A UNIFIED FINITE ELEMENT BASED METHOD FOR EVALUATING THE MODES OF VIBRATION OF COMPLETE SOLIDS OF REVOLUTION AND THEIR SECTORS

E. HINTON

University College of Swansea, U.K.

1. INTRODUCTION

Examples of bodies of revolution abound in contemporary society and in engineering practice: discs, circular and annular plates, domes, cylinders, tanks, hoppers, silos, cooling towers, chimneys, tubes and various instruments (e.g. cymbals, bells, etc.) – the list is almost endless. Our knowledge of the dynamic behaviour of these structures and components is vital for 'sound' design.

About two hundred years ago, Chladni [1] described a method of using sand sprinkled on circular plates and other structures to show the nodal lines. He found that a uniform flat circular plate with axially symmetric boundary conditions has normal bending modes with nodal patterns containing n uniformly spaced diameters (where $n = 0, 1, 2, \ldots$) and s concentric circles (where $s = 0, 1, 2, \ldots$) [2-5]. Other axially symmetric structures also have similar nodal patterns with n nodal diameters and s concentric circles [6].

The finite element method is now routinely used to gain insight into structural vibrations of bodies of revolution. Finite element methods were first applied to axisymmetric solids by Grafton and Strome [7], and to axisymmetric solids by Wilson [8]. Gladwell and Tahbildar [9] presented results for the finite element analysis for the free-free vibrations of right circular cylinders. Later, Gladwell and Vijay [10] presented results for the finite element vibration analysis of axisymmetric resonators.

Finite element techniques have been used to predict the resonant behavior of cooling towers. For example, Nelson and Thomas [11] have used a finite element method for rotationally periodic structures to obtain the resonant frequencies and mode shapes of a model cooling tower.

The prediction of the dynamic characteristics of discs is of considerable practical importance in the design of turbomachines. For example, Mota Soares and Petyt [12] have presented a finite element method for the prediction of such stress-free and initially-stressed discs.

The natural modes of various axisymmetric sections of certain musical instruments have been investigated using the finite element method. Perrin, Charnley and De Pont [13] have used finite elements to study the dynamic behaviour of English church bells.

In this chapter a finite element formulation is presented for the evaluation of the axisymmetric and asymmetric modes of vibration of complete solids of revolution.

Furthermore, it is shown that with relatively minor modifications it is also possible to use software based on this formulation for the vibration analysis of a sector of a solid of revolution with special (simple) boundary conditions on the two radial plane boundaries of the sector. This method is known as the finite prism method and is the three dimensional counterpart of the finite strip method [14].

Examples are included to illustrate the formulations. It is shown that rectangular plates may also be analysed by the finite prism method using a simple but effective artifice.

2. BASIC FORMULATION

This section provides the governing equations for the free vibrations of solids of revolution [15].

2.1 Solids of revolution

For the solid of revolution shown in Figure 2.1, the deformed shape can be defined by the displacement fields

$$\mathbf{u} = [\, u(r,y,\theta,t),\ v(r,y,\theta,t),\ w(r,y,\theta,t)\,]^T \tag{1}$$

where u, v and w are the displacements in the r, y and θ directions respectively.

In the absence of external loads, the virtual work expressions for dynamic analysis can be written as

$$\iiint \delta\,\boldsymbol{\epsilon}^T \mathbf{D}\,\boldsymbol{\epsilon}\, r\, dr\, dy\, d\theta + \iiint \delta \mathbf{u}^T \mathbf{P}\ddot{\mathbf{u}}\, r\, dr\, dy\, d\theta = 0 \tag{2}$$

where

$$\boldsymbol{\epsilon} = \begin{bmatrix} \partial u/\partial r \\ \partial v/\partial y \\ u/r + (1/r)\partial w/\partial \theta \\ \partial v/\partial r + \partial u/\partial y \\ \partial w/\partial r - w/r + (1/r)\partial u/\partial \theta \\ (1/r)\partial v/\partial \theta + \partial w/\partial r \end{bmatrix} \tag{3}$$

is the strain vector.

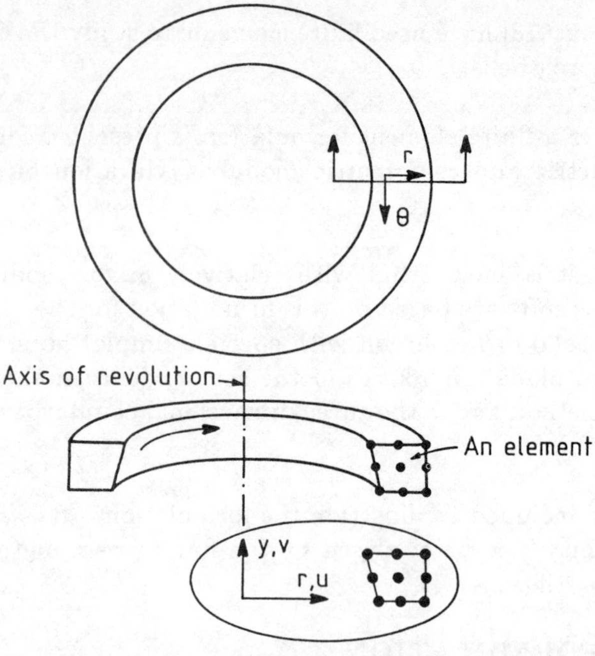

Figure 2.1 Finite element representation of a solid of revolution

It should also be noted that the constitutive matrix $\mathbf{D}$ has the form

$$\mathbf{D} = \begin{bmatrix} D_{11} & D_{12} & D_{13} & D_{14} & D_{15} & D_{16} \\ D_{21} & D_{22} & D_{23} & D_{24} & D_{25} & D_{26} \\ D_{31} & D_{32} & D_{33} & D_{34} & D_{35} & D_{36} \\ D_{41} & D_{42} & D_{43} & D_{44} & D_{45} & D_{46} \\ D_{51} & D_{52} & D_{53} & D_{54} & D_{55} & D_{56} \\ D_{61} & D_{62} & D_{63} & D_{64} & D_{65} & D_{66} \end{bmatrix} \tag{4}$$

For most cases,

$$\begin{aligned} &D_{15} = D_{16} = D_{25} = D_{26} = D_{35} = D_{36} = D_{45} = D_{46} = D_{56} = 0 \\ &D_{41} = D_{42} = D_{43} = D_{51} = D_{52} = D_{53} = D_{54} = D_{61} = D_{62} = 0 \\ &D_{63} = D_{64} = D_{65} = 0 \end{aligned} \tag{7}$$

Furthermore, for an isotropic material

$$\begin{aligned} D_{11} &= E(1-\nu)/((1+\nu)(1-2\nu)) \\ D_{12} &= \nu D_{11}/(1-\nu) \\ D_{55} &= (1-2\nu)D_{11}/(2(1-\nu)) \end{aligned} \tag{6}$$

where E is the elastic modulus and ν is Poisson's ratio. Note also that

$$\mathbf{P} = \rho\,\mathbf{I} \tag{7}$$

where ρ is the density of the material and $\mathbf{I}$ is a 3×3 identity matrix.

2.2 Solid of revolution (SOR) element

For the finite element analysis, the SOR is divided into a series of k-noded annular SOR elements as shown in Figure 2.1. The displacement field inside a typical element e can be expressed as products of polynomial two-dimensional shape functions on a typical radial plane of the structure and suitable Fourier expansions in the circumferential direction. Thus, the displacements can be expressed as

$$\mathbf{u} = \sum_{p=1}^{n} \sum_{i=1}^{k} \mathbf{N}_\mathrm{i}^\mathrm{p} \ \mathbf{a}_\mathrm{i}^\mathrm{p} \tag{8}$$

where

$$\mathbf{u} = [u,\ v,\ w]^T \tag{9}$$

is the displacement vector.

The vector of nodal displacement amplitudes for node i and the p-th harmonic term may be written as

$$\mathbf{a}_\mathrm{i}^\mathrm{p} = [u_i^p,\ v_i^p,\ w_i^p]^T \tag{10}$$

and the matrix of shape functions may be written as

$$\mathbf{N}_\mathrm{i}^\mathrm{p} = \begin{bmatrix} N_i C_p & 0 & 0 \\ 0 & N_i C_p & 0 \\ 0 & 0 & N_i S_p \end{bmatrix} \tag{11}$$

where N_i is the shape function associated with node i for the p-th harmonic term. In (11), $S_p = \sin p\theta$ and $C_p = \cos p\theta$.

The generalised strain vector can be written as

$$\boldsymbol{\epsilon} = \sum_{p=1}^{n} \sum_{i=1}^{k} \mathbf{B}_\mathrm{i}^\mathrm{p} \ \mathbf{a}_\mathrm{i}^\mathrm{p} \tag{12}$$

where $\mathbf{B}_\mathrm{i}^\mathrm{p}$ is the strain-displacement matrix associated with node i and harmonic p. This matrix may be written as

$$\mathbf{B}_\mathrm{i}^\mathrm{p} = \begin{bmatrix} (\partial N_i/\partial r)C_p & 0 & 0 \\ 0 & N_i C_p/r & 0 \\ N_i C_p/r & 0 & 0 \\ (\partial N_i/\partial y)C_p & (\partial N_i/\partial r)C_p & 0 \\ -pN_i S_p/r & 0 & (\partial N_i/\partial r - N_i/r)S_p \\ 0 & -pN_i S_p/r & (\partial N_i/\partial y)S_p \end{bmatrix} \tag{13}$$

By substituting (8-13) into (2) and by taking into account the orthogonality properties of the trigonometric functions chosen, i.e.

$$\int_0^{2\pi} \sin p\theta \sin m\theta \, d\theta = \pi/2 \quad \text{if} \quad p = m$$
$$= 0 \quad \text{if} \quad p \neq m \qquad (14a)$$

$$\int_0^{2\pi} \cos p\theta \cos m\theta \, d\theta = \pi/2 \quad \text{if} \quad p = m$$
$$= 0 \quad \text{if} \quad p \neq m \qquad (14b)$$

the following system of equations can be obtained:

$$\mathbf{Ka} + \mathbf{M\ddot{a}} = \mathbf{0} \qquad (15)$$

where the stiffness matrix is block-diagonal and has the form

$$\mathbf{K} = \begin{bmatrix} \mathbf{K^{11}} & \mathbf{0} & \dots & \mathbf{0} \\ \mathbf{0} & \mathbf{K^{22}} & \dots & \mathbf{0} \\ \vdots & \vdots & \ddots & \vdots \\ \mathbf{0} & \mathbf{0} & \dots & \mathbf{K^{nn}} \end{bmatrix} \qquad (16)$$

the mass matrix is also block-diagonal and has the form

$$\mathbf{M} = \begin{bmatrix} \mathbf{M^{11}} & \mathbf{0} & \dots & \mathbf{0} \\ \mathbf{0} & \mathbf{M^{22}} & \dots & \mathbf{0} \\ \vdots & \vdots & \ddots & \vdots \\ \mathbf{0} & \mathbf{0} & \dots & \mathbf{M^{nn}} \end{bmatrix} \qquad (17)$$

the vector of displacements is given as

$$\mathbf{a} = ([\mathbf{a^1}]^T, [\mathbf{a^2}]^T, \cdots, [\mathbf{a^n}]^T)^T \qquad (18)$$

and the vector of accelerations is given as

$$\mathbf{\ddot{a}} = ([\mathbf{\ddot{a}^1}]^T, [\mathbf{\ddot{a}^2}]^T, \cdots, [\mathbf{\ddot{a}^n}]^T)^T \qquad (19)$$

Details of matrices $\mathbf{K^{pp}}$ and $\mathbf{M^{pp}}$ will be given later in this section. Equation (15) is an uncoupled system of matrix equations which can be solved independently for each harmonic term. Thus for the p-th harmonic

$$\mathbf{K^{pp}}\,\mathbf{a^p} + \mathbf{M^{pp}}\,\mathbf{\ddot{a}^p} = \mathbf{0} \qquad (20)$$

The solution of each uncoupled matrix equation is obtained using standard procedures of structural dynamics. Thus, the general solution of (20) is written as

$$\mathbf{a^p} = \mathbf{\bar{a}^p}\, e^{i\omega_p t} \qquad (21)$$

where $e^{i\omega_p t} = cos\omega_p t + isin\omega_p t$ and ω_p and $\bar{\mathbf{a}}^{\mathbf{p}}$ are the natural frequency and vibration mode (eigen-vector) for the p-th harmonic term. Upon substitution of (21) into (20) the following classical eigenvalue equation is obtained

$$[\mathbf{K}^{\mathbf{pp}} - \omega_p^2 \mathbf{M}^{\mathbf{pp}}]\, \bar{\mathbf{a}}^{\mathbf{p}} = \mathbf{0} \tag{22}$$

The non-trivial solution of (22) implies

$$\det [\mathbf{K}^{\mathbf{pp}} - \omega_p^2 \mathbf{M}^{\mathbf{pp}}] = \mathbf{0} \tag{23}$$

from which the natural frequencies can be obtained. Finally, the corresponding eigenvectors $\bar{\mathbf{a}}^{\mathbf{p}}$ for each frequency are obtained from (22).

In conclusion, the free vibration analysis of SOR using the finite element method requires the solution of n uncoupled eigenvalue problems, n being the number of harmonic terms used in the analysis. The natural frequencies and the corresponding vibration modes for each harmonic term are obtained from (22).

The stiffness and mass matrices of a typical SOR element are given by the expressions

$$[\mathbf{K}_{\mathbf{ij}}^{\mathbf{pp}}]^e = \pi/2 \int\int [\mathbf{B}_{\mathbf{i}}^{\mathbf{p}}]^T \mathbf{D} \mathbf{B}_{\mathbf{j}}^{\mathbf{p}}\, rdrdy \tag{24}$$

and

$$[\mathbf{M}_{\mathbf{ij}}^{\mathbf{pp}}]^e = \pi/2 \int\int [\mathbf{N}_{\mathbf{i}}^{\mathbf{p}}]^T \mathbf{P} \mathbf{N}_{\mathbf{j}}^{\mathbf{p}}\, rdrdy \tag{25}$$

Note that

$$[\mathbf{K}_{\mathbf{ij}}^{\mathbf{pm}}]^e = [\mathbf{M}_{\mathbf{ij}}^{\mathbf{pm}}]^e = \mathbf{0} \quad \text{for} \quad p \neq m \tag{26}$$

where $\mathbf{B}_{\mathbf{i}}^{\mathbf{p}}$ and $\mathbf{N}_{\mathbf{i}}^{\mathbf{p}}$ are directly obtained from (13), (14) and (11) by making $S_p = C_p = 1$. Note that matrix $\mathbf{M}_{\mathbf{ij}}^{\mathbf{pp}}$ is independent of the harmonic number p and, therefore, the same matrix can be used for all the different harmonic equations.

Pedersen and co-workers [16,17] have presented an efficient method for the evaluation of the stiffness matrices for SOR elements using symbolic algebraic manipulation methods.

3. VIBRATION ANALYSIS OF SECTORS OF SOLIDS OF REVOLUTION USING THE FINITE PRISM METHOD

The previous section dealt with a formulation for the finite element analysis of the axisymmetric and asymmetric modes of vibration of complete solids of revolution. In this section, it is shown that this formulation may be used in a slightly modified form for the vibration analysis of a sector of a solid of revolution with special (simple) boundary conditions on the two radial plane boundaries of the sector. This approach is known as the finite prism method [14,18].

3.1 The finite prism method

Figure 3.1 shows a sector of a SOR. On the radial plane boundaries at $\theta = 0$ and $\theta = \alpha$, simple support conditions are assumed to apply, so that

$$u = v = \partial w/\partial\theta = 0 \tag{27}$$

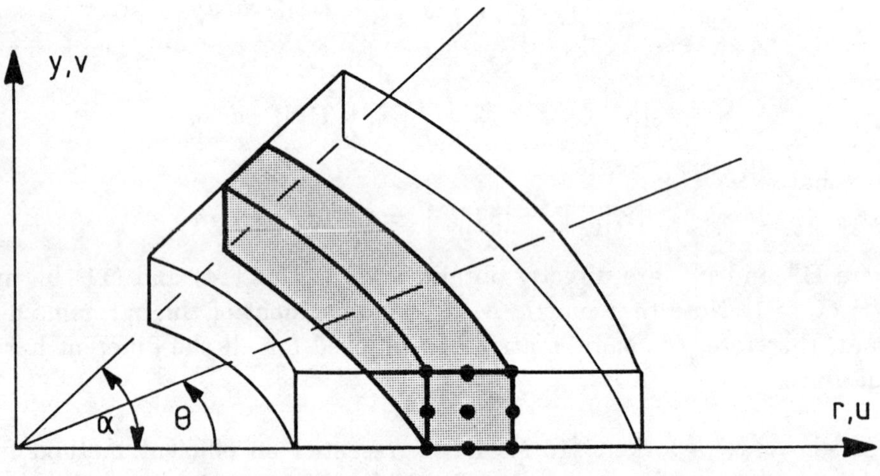

Figure 3.1 Finite prism representation of a solid of revolution

In the finite prism method [14,18], the SOR sector is divided into a series of k-noded finite prisms as shown in Figure 3.1. The displacement field inside a typical prism e can be expressed as products of polynomial two-dimensional shape functions on a typical radial plane of the structure and suitable Fourier expansions in the circumferential direction. Thus, the displacements can be expressed as

$$\mathbf{u} = \sum_{p=1}^{n} \sum_{i=1}^{k} \mathbf{N}_i^P \, \mathbf{a}_i^P \tag{28}$$

where $\mathbf{u}$ and $\mathbf{a}_i^P$ have the same meaning as for the SOR element and the matrix of shape functions may be written as

$$\mathbf{N}_i^P = \begin{bmatrix} N_i S_p & 0 & 0 \\ 0 & N_i S_p & 0 \\ 0 & 0 & N_i C_p \end{bmatrix} \tag{29}$$

where N_i is the shape function associated with node i for the p-th harmonic term. In (29), $S_p = \sin p\pi\theta/\alpha$ and $C_p = \cos p\pi\theta/\alpha$.

Note that the displacement representations of (28) and (29) automatically satisfy the boundary conditions given in (27).

The generalised strain vector can be written as

$$\boldsymbol{\epsilon} = \sum_{p=1}^{n} \sum_{i=1}^{k} \mathbf{B}_i^P \, \mathbf{a}_i^P \tag{30}$$

where $\mathbf{B}_i^P$ is the strain-displacement matrix associated with node i and harmonic p. This matrix may be written as

$$\mathbf{B}_i^P = \begin{bmatrix} (\partial N_i/\partial r) S_p & 0 & 0 \\ 0 & N_i S_p / r & 0 \\ N_i S_p / r & 0 & 0 \\ (\partial N_i/\partial y) S_p & (\partial N_i/\partial r) S_p & 0 \\ -p N_i C_p / r & 0 & (\partial N_i/\partial r - N_i/r) C_p \\ 0 & -p N_i C_p / r & (\partial N_i/\partial y) C_p \end{bmatrix} \tag{31}$$

The stress-strain relationships and virtual work expressions for the finite prism have the same form as those given for the SOR element in (2)-(7). By substituting (28-31) into (2) and by taking into account the orthogonality properties of the trigonometric functions chosen, i.e.

$$\int_0^\alpha \sin(p\pi\theta/\alpha)\sin(m\pi\theta/\alpha)\,d\theta = \alpha/2 \quad \text{if} \quad p = m$$
$$= 0 \quad \text{if} \quad p \neq m \tag{32a}$$

$$\int_0^\alpha \cos(p\pi\theta/\alpha)\cos(m\pi\theta/\alpha)\,d\theta = \alpha/2 \quad \text{if} \quad p = m$$
$$= 0 \quad \text{if} \quad p \neq m \tag{32b}$$

the following system of equations can be obtained:

$$\mathbf{K}\mathbf{a} + \mathbf{M}\ddot{\mathbf{a}} = \mathbf{0} \tag{33}$$

where **K** and **M** have the same block diagonal form as the matrices given in (16) and (17) for the SOR elements.

Thus, the free vibration analysis of SOR sectors using the finite prism method requires the solution of n uncoupled eigenvalue problems, n being the number of harmonic terms used in the analysis. The natural frequencies and the corresponding vibration modes for each harmonic term are obtained from (22).

The stiffness and mass matrices of a typical finite prism are given by the expressions

$$[\mathbf{K}_{ij}^{pp}]^e = \alpha/2 \iint [\mathbf{B}_i^p]^T \mathbf{D} \mathbf{B}_j^p \, r dr dy \tag{34a}$$

and

$$[\mathbf{M}_{ij}^{pp}]^e = \alpha/2 \iint [\mathbf{N}_i^p]^T \mathbf{P} \mathbf{N}_j^p \, r dr dy \tag{34b}$$

Note that

$$[\mathbf{K}_{ij}^{pm}]^e = [\mathbf{M}_{ij}^{pm}]^e = \mathbf{0} \quad \text{for} \quad p \neq m \tag{35}$$

where $\mathbf{B}_i^p$ and $\mathbf{N}_i^p$ are directly obtained from (31), (29) and (34) by making $S_p = C_p = 1$. Note also that the matrix $\mathbf{M}_{ij}^{pp}$ is independent of the harmonic number p and, therefore, the same matrix can be used for all the different harmonic equations.

The similarities with the SOR element described in the previous section are apparent and therefore software developed for SOR element analysis can be used with minor modification for finite prism analysis. In the next section, program VISOR, based on this concept, is described.

4. PROGRAM VISOR

4.1 Introduction

This section describes VISOR which is a program for the free vibration analysis of solids of revolution and their sectors in order to make all of the subroutines in VISOR modular in form a type of dynamic dimensioning has been used. Dimensions are fixed in the main routine and all necessary information is transmitted between routines by the use of arguments. This approach has the advantage that the maximum dimensions can be updated in a very simple manner. Only the DIMENSION statements in the main segment, which sets the maximum dimension sizes, need modification.

Program VISOR consists of four main modules:

(1) INSOR which reads in most of the input data,

(2) STISOR which evaluates the stiffness and mass matrices for solids of revolution and their sectors,

(3) BERKEL which is an eigenvalue solver, and

(4) OUTSOR which outputs the results.

Program VISOR is written in a modular form so that users can easily implement their own modules for eigenvalue solution and for output. Thus, BERKEL and OUTSOR are not compulsory routines in the program. They are routines which illustrate the implementation of the eigenvalue solver, described and coded by Bathe and Wilson [19], which employs a subspace iteration method with Sturm sequence checks.

4.2 Glossary of variable names

Main arrays

Array name: description

COORD(MPOIN,2): r- and y-coordinates of nodes

ESTIF(27,27): element stiffness matrix for a given harmonic

EMASS(27,27): element mass matrix

IFPRE(MVFIX,NDOFN): fixity code matrix, 0=free, 1=fixed

LNODS(MELEM,9): element nodal connectivities

MATNO(MELEM): material set numbers for each element

NOFIX(MVFIX): nodes with at least one prescribed variable

PROPS(MMATS,5): properties for each material set

Main variables

Array name: description

ALPHA: included angle for finite prism analysis

DENSE: density

IHARM: counter for harmonic terms

MELEM: maximum number of elements

MEVAB: = 27, maximum number of element variables

MMATS: maximum number of material sets

MPOIN: maximum number of nodal points

MVFIX: maximum number of restrained nodes

NDOFN: = 3, number of degrees of freedom per node

NEVAB: = 27, number of degrees of freedom per element

NELEM: number of elements

NHARM: number of harmonic terms to be used

NMATS: number of different material properties

NMODE: number of eigenvalues required

NNODE: = 9, number of nodes per element

NPOIN: number of nodes

NTYPE: indicator = 0 for axisymmetry, = 1 for asymmetry, = 2 for prism

POISS: Poisson's ratio

YOUNG: Young's modulus

4.3 Main segment

The main segment which controls the calling of the major subroutines is now described.

1. Initialise variables in DATA statements [MAIN 26-30].
2. Call INSOR to read in most of the data [MAIN 41-43].
3. Loop over each harmonic [MAIN 44].
   - 3.1 Call STISOR to evaluate **K** and **M** [MAIN 50-51].
   - 3.2 Call BERKEL to find eigenvalues [MAIN 55-59].
   - 3.3 Call OUTSOR to print the results [MAIN 63-64] .

4.4 Input module - Subroutine INSOR

The main function of INSOR is to read most of the input data. The basic structure of INSOR is of the following form.

1. Read and write problem title [INSO 14-15].
2. Read and write control data [INSO 21-29].
3. Read and write element connections and property set numbers [INSO 33-38].
4. Initialise array COORD [INSO 42-44].
5. Read and write nodal coordinates [INSO 48-61].
6. Read and write fixity conditions [INSO 65-94].
7. Read and write element properties [INSO 98-105].

4.5 Stiffness module - Subroutine STISOR

The main function of STISOR is to evaluate stiffness and mass matrices for SOR elements and SOR sectors. Subroutine STISOR has the following structure.

1. Rewind files 1 and 7 ready for writing **K** and **M** [STIS 16-17].
2. Set up Gauss sampling data [STIS 20].
3. Loop over each element [STIS 24].
   - 3.1 Put nodal coords. in local array [STIS 29-32].
   - 3.2 Set up element **D** matrix [STIS 36].
   - 3.3 Extract element density and included angle [STIS 37-38].
   - 3.4 Initialise **K** and **M** arrays [STIS 42-45].
   - 3.5 Evaluate stiffness and mass matrix [STIS 50-94].
   - 3.6 Make **K** and **M** symmetric [STIS 99-102].
   - 3.7 Write **K** and **M** to files 1 and 7 respectively [STIS 107-108].

4.6 Eigenvalue extraction module - Subroutine BERKEL

Subroutine BERKEL is the interface routine for the eigenvalue solver. It prepares all necessary data for subspace iteration coded in subroutine SSPACE.

BERKEL calls subroutine COLHT to calculate column heights and subroutine ADDRES to calculate addresses of diagonal elements in a banded matrix whose column heights are known. From files 1 and 7 BERKEL reads and rewrites in vector form strip stiffness and mass matrices, then calls ADDBAN to assemble the upper triangular part of those strip matices into the compacted global matrices.

BERKEL reads two indicators for subspace iteration as input data:

- IFSS - indicator for Sturn sequence check and
- IFPR - indicator for printing during iteration

NOTE: The following subroutines are fully described and listed in ' Numerica Methods in Finite Element Analysis' by K.J. Bathe and E.L. Wilson, Prentice-Hall, New Jersey, 1976.

COLHT, ADDRES AND ADDBAN	pages 227 - 229
SSPACE	pages 509 - 517

To match subroutine BERKEL with subroutine OUTSOR it is necessary to make some modifications in SSPACE and they are:

. Input DATA statement - DATA IOUT1/4/

. Substitute IOUT with IOUT1 in the following lines:

SPCE0292 and SPCE 0269 page 511

SPCE0292 page 512

4.7 Output module - Subroutine OUTSOR

Subroutine OUTSOR simply prints out eigenvalues, modes and error norms after reading from file 4. If printing during iteration is required (IFPR=1) then corresponding results are stored in file 3.

4.8 Input instructions

DATA SET 1	DATA TITLE (20A4) one record	
1- 80	TITLE	title of the problem
DATA SET 2	PROBLEM PARAMETERS (9I5) one record	
1 - 5	NPOIN	number of nodes
6 -10	NELEM	number of elements
11-15	NVFIX	number of prescribed nodes
16-20	NTYPE	analysis type indicator = 0 for axisymmetric analysis of solids of revolution = 1 for asymmetric analysis of solids of revolution = 2 for finite prism analysis
21-25	NMATS	number of different materials
26-30	NPROP	number of material properties (3 or 4)
31-35	NGAUS	number of Gauss points (3)
36-40	NHARM	number of harmonics
41-45	NMODE	number of eigenmodes per harmonic

DATA SET 3	NODAL CONNECTIONS (11I5) NELEM records	
1 - 5	NUMEL	element number
6 -10	MATNO (NUMEL)	material number for the element
11-15	LNODS (NUMEL, 1)	global number of node 1
⋮	⋮	⋮
51-55	LNODS (NUMEL, 9)	global number of node 9

DATA SET 4	NODAL COORDINATES (I5, 2F10.5) $\leq$ NPOIN records	
1 - 5	IPOIN	number of node
6 -15	COORD (IPOIN,1)	r-coordinate of node
16-25	COORD(IPOIN,2)	y-coordinate of node

DATA SET 5	FIXED VALUES (I5, 2X, 3I1) NVFIX records	
1 - 5	NOFIX (IVFIX)	number of fixed node
8	IFPRE (IVFIX,1)	indicator for constraint in u
9	IFPRE (IVFIX,2)	indicator for constraint in v
10	IFPRE (IVFIX,3)	indicator for constraint in w
	indicator = 1 constrained, = 0 free	

Note : NVFIX = 0 implies that for the prism analysis, the sector is simply supported at both ends. Also a constraint in a degree of freedom implies that the displacement associated with that degree of freedom is zero along the nodal line between the sector boundary planes. Other non-zero constraints are not allowed in this program.

DATA SET 6	MATERIAL SET NUMBER (I5)	
1 - 5	NUMAT	number associated with material set

DATA SET 7	MATERIAL PROPERTIES (5F10.5)	
1 -10	PROPS (NUMAT, 1)	Young's modulus
11-20	PROPS (NUMAT, 2)	Poisson's ratio
21-30	PROPS (NUMAT, 3)	density
31-40	PROPS (NUMAT, 4)	included angle in prism analysis

N.B. Data sets 6 and 7 are repeated for each separate material set.

DATA SET 8	STURM SEQUENCE INDICATORS (2I5) one record	
1 - 5	IFSS	indicator for Sturm sequence check = 0 no check, = 1 check applied
6 -10	IFPR	indicator for printing during iteration = 0 no printing, = 1 printing

4.9 Subroutine listings

Main segment

```
C**********************************************************************
C*
C*    FINITE ELEMENT PROGRAM FOR THE FREE VIBRATION ANALYSIS
C*    OF SOLIDS OF REVOLUTION AND THEIR SEGMENTS
C*
C**********************************************************************
      IMPLICIT REAL*8(A-H,O-Z)
C
C*** DIMENSIONS ASSOCIATED WITH SUBROUTINES INSOR AND STISOR
C
      DIMENSION COORD(150,2), IFPRE(150,3), LNODS(50,9), MATNO(50),
     .          NOFIX(150), PROPS(10,5)
C
C*** DIMENSIONS ASSOCIATED WITH SUBROUTINES BERKEL AND OUTSOR
C
      DIMENSION A(12150),AD(3,150),AR(171),B(12150),BR(171),BS(378),
     .          BUP(18),BLO(18),BUPC(18),D(18),ER(450,18),EIGV(18),
     .          ID(3,150),LM(27,50),MHT(450),MAXA(451),R(450,18),
     .          RTOLV(18),S(378),TT(150),VEC(18,18),W(450)
C**********************************************************************
C
C                  DYNAMIC  DIMENSIONING
C
C**********************************************************************
C
      DATA MPOIN/150/,MVFIX/150/MELEM/50/,MMATS/10/,
     .     NNODE/9/,NDOFN/3/,MPROP/5/,NEVAB/27/
C
      DATA MAHAM/378/,MAXNN/450/,MANNM/451/,MMODE/10/,MNEBS/12150/,
     .     MITEV/18/,MDISV/171/
C
C
C**  NDISV=MITEV*(MITEV+1)/2
C**  MAHAM=MEVAB*(MEVAB+1)/2
C**  MAXNN=MPOIN*NDOFN
C**  MANNM=MAXNN+1
C**  MNEBS=APPROX. MAXNN*MEVAB
C
C*** CALL SUBROUTINE WHICH READS IN THE DATA
C
      CALL   INSOR   (COORD,IFPRE,LNODS,MATNO,MELEM,MMATS,MPOIN,MPROP,
     .                MVFIX,NELEM,NGAUS,NHARM,NMATS,NMODE,NOFIX,NPOIN,
     .                NPROP,NTYPE,NVFIX,PROPS)
      DO 30 JHARM =1,NHARM
```

```
      IHARM=JHARM
      IF(NTYPE.EQ.0) IHARM=IHARM-1
C
C*** FORM THE ELEMENT STIFFNESS AND MASS MATRICES
C
      CALL  STISOR   (COORD,IHARM,LNODS,MATNO,MELEM,MMATS,MPOIN,MPROP,
     .                NELEM,NGAUS,NNODE,NTYPE,PROPS)
C
C*** SUBSPACE ITERATION
C
   10 CALL  BERKEL   (A,AR,B,BR,BS,BUP,BLO,BUPC,D,ER,EIGV,
     .                ID,IFPRE,LM,LNODS,MHT,MAXA,MAHAM,MAXNN,MANNM,
     .                MITEV,MDISV,MNEBS,MPOIN,MELEM,MVFIX,NMODE,
     .                NPOIN,NEQ,NVFIX,NOFIX,NDOFN,NELEM,NEVAB,
     .                NNODE,RTOLV,S,TT,VEC,W)
C
C*** CALL SUBROUTINE WHICH OUTPUTS THE RESULTS
C
      CALL  OUTSOR   (AD,D,EIGV,ID,IHARM,MPOIN,MAXNN,MITEV,NDOFN,
     .                NMODE,NEQ,NPOIN,R)
   30 CONTINUE
      STOP
      END
```

Subroutine INSOR

```
      SUBROUTINE INSOR(COORD,IFPRE,LNODS,MATNO,MELEM,MMATS,MPOIN,MPROP,
     .                 MVFIX,NELEM,NGAUS,NHARM,NMATS,NMODE,NOFIX,NPOIN,
     .                 NPROP,NTYPE,NVFIX,PROPS)
C************************************************************************
C
C*** INPUTS THE DATA FOR SOR FREE VIBRATIONS ANALYSIS
C
C************************************************************************
      IMPLICIT REAL*8(A-H,O-Z)
      DIMENSION COORD(MPOIN,2), IFPRE(MVFIX,3), LNODS(MELEM,9),
     .          MATNO(MELEM), NOFIX(MVFIX), PROPS(MMATS,MPROP),
     .          TITLE(20)
C
      READ(5,890) TITLE
      WRITE(6,895) TITLE
  890 FORMAT(20A4)
  895 FORMAT(////,1X,20A4)
C
C*** READ THE FIRST DATA CARD, AND ECHO IT IMMEDIATELY.
C
      READ(5,900) NPOIN,NELEM,NVFIX,NTYPE,NMATS,NPROP,NGAUS,NHARM,
```

```
                NMODE
  900 FORMAT(14I5)
      WRITE(6,905) NPOIN,NELEM,NVFIX,NTYPE,NMATS,NPROP,NGAUS,NHARM,
                NMODE
  905 FORMAT(//8H NPOIN =,I4,4X,8H NELEM =,I4,4X,8H NVFIX =,I4,4X,
     .8H NTYPE =,I4,//8H NMATS =,I4,
     .4X,8H NPROP =,I4,4X,8H NGAUS =,I4,4X,8H NHARM =,I4,
     .//8H NMODE =,I4)
C
C*** READ THE ELEMENT NODAL CONNECTIONS, AND THE PROPERTY NUMBERS.
C
      WRITE(6,910)
  910 FORMAT(//8H ELEMENT,3X,8HPROPERTY,6X,12HNODE NUMBERS)
      DO 10 IELEM=1,NELEM
      READ(5,900)NUMEL,MATNO(NUMEL),(LNODS(NUMEL,INODE),INODE=1,9)
   10 WRITE(6,915)NUMEL,MATNO(NUMEL),(LNODS(NUMEL,INODE),INODE=1,9)
  915 FORMAT(1X,I5,I9,6X,9I5)
C
C*** ZERO ALL THE NODAL COORDINATES, PRIOR TO READING SOME OF THEM.
C
      DO 20 IPOIN=1,NPOIN
      DO 20 IDIME=1,2
   20 COORD(IPOIN,IDIME)=0.0
C
C*** READ SOME NODAL COORDINATES, FINISHING WITH THE LAST NODE OF ALL.
C
      WRITE(6,920)
  920 FORMAT(//25H  NODAL POINT COORDINATES)
      WRITE(6,925)
  925 FORMAT(6H  NODE,7X,1HX,9X,1HY)
   30 READ(5,930) IPOIN,(COORD(IPOIN,IDIME),IDIME=1,2)
  930 FORMAT(I5,5F10.5)
      IF(IPOIN.NE.NPOIN) GO TO 30
C
C*** INTERPOLATE COORDINATES OF MID-SIDE NODES
C
      CALL NODEXY(COORD,LNODS,MELEM,MPOIN,NELEM)
      DO 50 IPOIN=1,NPOIN
   50 WRITE(6,935) IPOIN,(COORD(IPOIN,IDIME),IDIME=1,2)
  935 FORMAT(1X,I5,2F10.3)
C
C*** READ THE FIXED VALUES.
C
      WRITE(6,940)
  940 FORMAT(//17H RESTRAINED NODES)
      WRITE(6,945)
  945 FORMAT(5H NODE,1X,4HCODE,6X,12HFIXED VALUES)
```

```
C
C*** FOR SYMMETRIC CASE (I.E. NTYPE = 0), SET W EQUAL TO ZERO
C*** FOR EVERY NODE
C
      IF(NTYPE.NE.0) GO TO 75
      DO 60 IPOIN=1,NPOIN
      IFPRE(IPOIN,1)=0
      IFPRE(IPOIN,2)=0
      IFPRE(IPOIN,3)=1
      NOFIX(IPOIN)=IPOIN
   60 CONTINUE
C
      DO 65 IVFIX=1,NVFIX
      READ(5,955) I,(IFPRE(I,IDOFN),IDOFN=1,2)
   65 CONTINUE
C
      NVFIX=NPOIN
      DO 70 IVFIX=1,NVFIX
      WRITE(6,955) NOFIX(IVFIX),(IFPRE(IVFIX,IDOFN),IDOFN=1,2)
   70 CONTINUE
      GO TO 90
   75 DO 80 IVFIX=1,NVFIX
      READ(5,955) NOFIX(IVFIX),(IFPRE(IVFIX,IDOFN),IDOFN=1,3)
   80 WRITE(6,955) NOFIX(IVFIX),(IFPRE(IVFIX,IDOFN),IDOFN=1,3)
  955 FORMAT(1X,I4,2X,3I1,3F10.6)
   90 CONTINUE
C
C*** READ THE AVAILABLE SELECTION OF ELEMENT PROPERTIES.
C
      WRITE(6,960)
  960 FORMAT(//21H  MATERIAL PROPERTIES)
      WRITE(6,965)
  965 FORMAT(8H  NUMBER,7X,10HPROPERTIES)
      DO 100 IMATS=1,NMATS
      READ(5,930) NUMAT,(PROPS(NUMAT,IPROP),IPROP=1,NPROP)
  100 WRITE(6,970) NUMAT,(PROPS(NUMAT,IPROP),IPROP=1,NPROP)
  970 FORMAT(1X,I5,7X,5E14.6)
      RETURN
      END
```

Subroutine STISOR

```
      SUBROUTINE STISOR(COORD,IHARM,LNODS,MATNO,MELEM,MMATS,MPOIN,
     .                  MPROP,NELEM,NGAUS,NNODE,NTYPE,PROPS)
C************************************************************************
C
C*** CALCULATES ELEMENT STIFFNESS AND MASS MATRICES FOR
```

```
C     SOLIDS OF REVOLUTION ELEMENT AND THEIR SEGMENTS                   STIS   6
C                                                                       STIS   7
C***********************************************************************STIS   8
      IMPLICIT REAL*8(A-H,O-Z)                                          STIS   9
      DIMENSION BMATX(6,27),CARTD(2,9), COORD(MPOIN,2),                 STIS  10
     .          DBMAT(6,27), DERIV(2,9), DMATX(6,6), ELCOD(2,9),        STIS  11
     .          EMASS(27,27), ESTIF(27,27), GPCOD(2,9),                 STIS  12
     .          LNODS(MELEM,9), MATNO(MELEM), PROPS(MMATS,MPROP),       STIS  13
     .          POSGP(3), SHAPE(9), WEIGP(3)                            STIS  14
C                                                                       STIS  15
      REWIND 1                                                          STIS  16
      REWIND 7                                                          STIS  17
      TWOPI=3.1415927*2.0                                               STIS  18
      PI=3.1415927                                                      STIS  19
      CALL GAUSSQ(NGAUS,POSGP,WEIGP)                                    STIS  20
C                                                                       STIS  21
C*** LOOP OVER EACH ELEMENT                                             STIS  22
C                                                                       STIS  23
      DO 70 IELEM=1,NELEM                                               STIS  24
      LPROP=MATNO(IELEM)                                                STIS  25
C                                                                       STIS  26
C*** EVALUATE THE COORDINATES OF THE ELEMENT NODAL POINTS               STIS  27
C                                                                       STIS  28
      DO 10 INODE=1,NNODE                                               STIS  29
      LNODE=LNODS(IELEM,INODE)                                          STIS  30
      DO 10 IDIME=1,2                                                   STIS  31
   10 ELCOD(IDIME,INODE)=COORD(LNODE,IDIME)                             STIS  32
C                                                                       STIS  33
C*** EVALUATE THE D-MATRIX                                              STIS  34
C                                                                       STIS  35
      CALL MODSOR(DMATX,LPROP,MMATS,MPROP,PROPS)                        STIS  36
      DENSE=PROPS(LPROP,3)                                              STIS  37
      ALPHA=PROPS(LPROP,4)                                              STIS  38
C                                                                       STIS  39
C*** INITIALIZE THE ELEMENT STIFFNESS MATRIX                            STIS  40
C                                                                       STIS  41
      DO 20 IEVAB=1,27                                                  STIS  42
      DO 20 JEVAB=1,27                                                  STIS  43
      EMASS(IEVAB,JEVAB)=0.0                                            STIS  44
   20 ESTIF(IEVAB,JEVAB)=0.0                                            STIS  45
      KGASP=0                                                           STIS  46
C                                                                       STIS  47
C*** ENTER LOOPS FOR AREA NUMERICAL INTEGRATION                         STIS  48
C                                                                       STIS  49
      DO 50 IGAUS = 1,NGAUS                                             STIS  50
      EXISP = POSGP(IGAUS)                                              STIS  51
      DO 50 JGAUS = 1,NGAUS                                             STIS  52
```

```
      KGASP=KGASP+1
      ETASP = POSGP(JGAUS)
C
C*** EVALUATE THE SHAPE FUNCTIONS,ELEMENTAL VOLUME,ETC.
C
      CALL SFR2(DERIV,EXISP,9,SHAPE,ETASP)
      CALL JACOB2(CARTD,DERIV,DJACB,ELCOD,GPCOD,IELEM,KGASP,NNODE,
     .            SHAPE)
      DAREA = DJACB*WEIGP(IGAUS)*WEIGP(JGAUS)
      R=GPCOD(1,KGASP)
      IF(IHARM.EQ.0) DAREA=DAREA*TWOPI
      IF(NTYPE.EQ.1) DAREA=DAREA*PI
      IF(NTYPE.EQ.2) DAREA=DAREA*ALPHA/2.0
C
C*** EVALUATE THE B AND DB MATRICES
C
      CALL BMATSOR(ALPHA,BMATX,CARTD,IHARM,NNODE,NTYPE,R,SHAPE)
      CALL DBE(BMATX,DBMAT,DMATX)
C
C*** CALCULATE THE ELEMENT STIFFNESSES
C
      DO 30 IEVAB=1,27
      DO 30 JEVAB=IEVAB,27
      DO 30 ISTRE = 1,6
   30 ESTIF(IEVAB,JEVAB)=ESTIF(IEVAB,JEVAB)+BMATX(ISTRE,IEVAB)*
     .DBMAT(ISTRE,JEVAB)*DAREA*R
C
C*** EVALUATE MASS MATRICES
C
      IF(IHARM.GT.1) GO TO 50
      DO 40 INODE=1,NNODE
      IEVAB=(INODE-1)*3
      DO 40 IDOFN=1,3
      IEVAB=IEVAB+1
      DO 40 JNODE=INODE,NNODE
      JEVAB=(JNODE-1)*3
      DO 40 JDOFN=1,3
      JEVAB=JEVAB+1
      IF(IDOFN.EQ.JDOFN)
     .EMASS(IEVAB,JEVAB)= EMASS(IEVAB,JEVAB)+
     .SHAPE(INODE)*SHAPE(JNODE)*DENSE*DAREA*R
   40 CONTINUE
   50 CONTINUE
C
C*** CONSTRUCT THE LOWER TRIANGLE OF THE STIFFNESS AND
C    MASS MATRICES
C
```

```
      DO 60 IEVAB=1,27
      DO 60 JEVAB = IEVAB,27
      EMASS(JEVAB,IEVAB)=EMASS(IEVAB,JEVAB)
   60 ESTIF(JEVAB,IEVAB)=ESTIF(IEVAB,JEVAB)
C
C*** STORE THE STIFFNESS MATRIX,STRESS MATRIX AND SAMPLING POINT
C    COORDINATES FOR EACH ELEMENT ON DISC FILE
C
      WRITE(1) ESTIF
      IF(IHARM.LE.1) WRITE(7) EMASS
   70 CONTINUE
      RETURN
      END
```

Subroutine **BERKEL**

```
      SUBROUTINE BERKEL (A,AR,B,BR,BS,BUP,BLO,BUPC,D,ER,EIGV,
     .                   ID,IFPRE,LM,LNODS,MHT,MAXA,MAHAM,MAXNN,MANNM,
     .                   MITEV,MDISV,MNEBS,MPOIN,MELEM,MVFIX,NMODE,
     .                   NPOIN,NEQ,NVFIX,NOFIX,NDOFN,NELEM,NEVAB,
     .                   NNODE,RTOLV,S,TT,VEC,W)
C**********************************************************************
C
C*** INTERFACE ROUTINE FOR BERKELEY SOLVER AND SUBSPACE ITERATION
C
C**********************************************************************
      IMPLICIT REAL*8(A-H,O-Z)
C
      DIMENSION ESTIF(27,27),EMASS(27,27),
     .          IFPRE(MVFIX,NDOFN),LNODS(MELEM,9),NOFIX(MVFIX)
      DIMENSION A(MNEBS),AR(MDISV),B(MNEBS),BR(MDISV),BS(MAHAM),
     .          BUP(MITEV),BLO(MITEV),BUPC(MITEV),D(MITEV),
     .          ER(MAXNN,MITEV),EIGV(MITEV),ID(NDOFN,MPOIN),
     .          LM(27,MELEM),MHT(MAXNN),MAXA(MANNM),RTOLV(MITEV),
     .          S(MAHAM),TT(MAXNN),VEC(MITEV,MITEV),W(MAXNN)
      DATA IOUT/3/,NSTIF/8/,NITEM/16/,RTOL/0.000001/
      NEVAB=27
      REWIND 1
      REWIND 7
      NROOT=NMODE
C
C***  CREATION OF ID ARRAY
C
      DO 10 IPOIN=1,NPOIN
      DO 20 IVFIX=1,NVFIX
      IF(IPOIN.NE.NOFIX(IVFIX)) GO TO 20
      DO 30 IDOFN=1,NDOFN
```

```
   30 ID(IDOFN,IPOIN)=IFPRE(IVFIX,IDOFN)
      GO TO 11
   20 CONTINUE
      DO 40 IDOFN=1,NDOFN
   40 ID(IDOFN,IPOIN)=0
   11 CONTINUE
   10 CONTINUE
C
C***  NUMBER OF UNKNOWNS
C
      NEQ=0
      DO 100 IPOIN=1,NPOIN
      DO 60 IDOFN=1,NDOFN
      IF(ID(IDOFN,IPOIN)) 110,120,110
  120 NEQ=NEQ+1
      ID(IDOFN,IPOIN)=NEQ
      GO TO 60
  110 ID(IDOFN,IPOIN)=0
   60 CONTINUE
  100 CONTINUE
C
C***  ZERO A AND B
C
      DO 65 INEBS=1,MNEBS
      A(INEBS)=0.0
      B(INEBS)=0.0
   65 CONTINUE
C
C***  CONNECTIVITY ARRAY LM
C
      DO 50 IELEM=1,NELEM
      DO 70 IEVAB=1,NEVAB
   70 LM(IEVAB,IELEM)=0
      IEVAB=1
      DO 80 INODE=1,NNODE
      IDENT=LNODS(IELEM,INODE)
      DO 80 IDOFN=1,NDOFN
      LM(IEVAB,IELEM)=ID(IDOFN,IDENT)
   80 IEVAB=IEVAB+1
   50 CONTINUE
C
C***  LOOP OVER ALL ELEMENTS
C
      DO 90 IELEM=1,NELEM
      CALL COLHT(MHT,NEVAB,LM(1,IELEM))
   90 CONTINUE
C
```

```
C***  ADDRESES OF DIAGONAL ELEMENTS - MAXA ARRAY
C
      CALL ADDRES(MAXA,MHT,NEQ,NWK,MK)
C
C*** REWRITING OF ELEMENT STIFFNESS, ELEMENT MASS MATRIX AND
C*** GEOMETRIC STIFFNESS MATRIX IN VECTOR FORM
C
      DO 200 IELEM=1,NELEM
      READ(1) ESTIF
      READ(7) EMASS
  140 KOUNT=1
      DO 145 IEVAB=1,NEVAB
      DO 145 JEVAB=IEVAB,NEVAB
      S(KOUNT)=ESTIF(IEVAB,JEVAB)
      BS(KOUNT)=EMASS(IEVAB,JEVAB)
  145 KOUNT=KOUNT+1
C
C***  COMPACTED GLOBAL STIFFNESS MATRIX
C
  170 CALL ADDBAN(A,MAXA,S,LM(1,IELEM),NEVAB)
C
C***  COMPACTED GLOBAL MASS MATRIX
C
      CALL ADDBAN(B,MAXA,BS,LM(1,IELEM),NEVAB)
  200 CONTINUE
C
C***  PARAMETERS FOR SUBSPACE ITERATION
C
      NNM=1+NEQ
      NWM=NWK
      NN=NEQ
      READ(5,9)  IFSS,IFPR
    9 FORMAT(16I5)
      WRITE(6,3) IFSS,IFPR
    3 FORMAT(//,1X,20H*STURM SEQUENCE FLAG,I5,21H*ITERATION PRINT FLAG,
     .       I5)
      NC=2*NROOT
      NC2=NROOT+8
      IF(NC.GT.NC2) NC=NC2
      NNC=NC*(NC+1)/2
C
C***  SUBSPACE ITERATION
C
      CALL SSPACE (A,B,MAXA,ER,EIGV,TT,W,AR,BR,VEC,D,RTOLV,BUP,
     .BLO,BUPC,NN,NNM,NWK,NWM,NROOT,RTOL,NC,NNC,NITEM,IFSS,
     .IFPR,NSTIF,IOUT)
C
```

```
C***  EXIT OF SUBSPACE
C
      RETURN
      END
```

Subroutine OUTSOR

```
      SUBROUTINE OUTSOR(AD,D,EIGV,ID,IHARM,MPOIN,MAXNN,MITEV,NDOFN,
     .                  NMODE,NEQ,NPOIN,R)
C*********************************************************************
C
C*** OUTPUTS THE RESULTS FOR SOR ELEMENTS
C
C*********************************************************************
      IMPLICIT REAL*8(A-H,O-Z)
C
      DIMENSION AD(NDOFN,MPOIN),D(MITEV),EIGV(MITEV),ID(NDOFN,MPOIN),
     .          R(MAXNN,MITEV)
C
      REWIND 4
C
      READ(4,100)(EIGV(I),I=1,NMODE)
  100 FORMAT(1H0,6E22.14)
      DO 10 J=1,NMODE
   10 READ(4,110)(R(K,J),K=1,NEQ)
  110 FORMAT(1H ,12E11.4)
      READ(4,100)(D(I),I=1,NMODE)
      WRITE(6,120) IHARM
  120 FORMAT(///,1X,'THE CALCULATED VALUES FOR HARMONIC',I4,' ARE')
      WRITE(6,125)
  125 FORMAT(/,4X,'EIGENVALUES',5X,'FREQUENCIES',6X,'ERROR NORMS',/)
      DO 15 I=1,NMODE
      FREQ=SQRT(EIGV(I))
   15 WRITE(6,130)EIGV(I),FREQ,D(I)
  130 FORMAT(1X,3E16.7)
   26 WRITE(6,140)
  140 FORMAT(//,1X,'THE CALCULATED MODES ARE')
C
      DO 30 IMODE=1,NMODE
      DO 40 IPOIN=1,NPOIN
      DO 50 IDOFN=1,NDOFN
      IF(ID(IDOFN,IPOIN)) 60,70,60
   70 AD(IDOFN,IPOIN)=0.0
      GO TO 80
   60 M=ID(IDOFN,IPOIN)
      AD(IDOFN,IPOIN)=R(M,IMODE)
   80 CONTINUE
```

```
   50 CONTINUE
   40 CONTINUE
C
      WRITE(6,150)IMODE
  150 FORMAT(/,6H MODE=I3)
      WRITE(6,170)
  170 FORMAT(/,12X,'U',12X,'V',12X,'W',/)
      DO 90 IPOIN=1,NPOIN
   90 WRITE(6,160)IPOIN,(AD(IDOFN,IPOIN),IDOFN=1,NDOFN)
  160 FORMAT(1X,I5,3E12.4)
   30 CONTINUE
      REWIND 4
      RETURN
      END
```

Subroutine NODEXY

```
      SUBROUTINE NODEXY(COORD,LNODS,MELEM,MPOIN,NELEM)
C*********************************************************************
C
C*** SUBROUTINE TO INTERPOLATE MIDSIDE NODES FOR STRAIGHT EDGES
C
C*********************************************************************
      IMPLICIT REAL*8(A-H,O-Z)
      DIMENSION COORD(MPOIN,2), DERIV(2,9), LNODS(MELEM,9), SHAPE(9)
C
C*** LOOP OVER EACH ELEMENT
C
      DO 70 IELEM = 1,NELEM
C
C*** LOOP OVER EACH ELEMENT EDGE
C
      DO 80 INODE = 1,8,2
C
C*** COMPUTE THE NODE NUMBER OF THE FIRST NODE
C
      NODST = LNODS(IELEM,INODE)
      IGASH = INODE + 2
      IF(IGASH.GT.8) IGASH = 1
C
C*** COMPUTE THE NODE NUMBER OF THE LAST NODE
C
      NODFN = LNODS(IELEM,IGASH)
      MIDPT = INODE + 1
C
C*** COMPUTE THE NODE NUMBER OF THE INTERMEDIATE NODE
C
```

```
      NODMD = LNODS(IELEM,MIDPT)
      TOTAL = ABS(COORD(NODMD,1))+ ABS(COORD(NODMD,2))
C
C*** IF THE COORDINATE OF THE INTERMEDIATE NODE ARE BOTH ZERO
C    INTERPOLATE BY A STRAIGHT LINE.
C
      IF (TOTAL.GT.0.0) GO TO 80
      KOUNT = 1
   50 COORD(NODMD,KOUNT) = (COORD(NODFN,KOUNT) + COORD(NODST,KOUNT))/2
      KOUNT = KOUNT + 1
      IF(KOUNT.EQ.2) GO TO 50
   80 CONTINUE
C
C*** EVALUATE COORDINATES OF CENTRAL NODE
C
      NODMI=LNODS(IELEM,9)
      TOTAL=ABS(COORD(NODMI,1))+ABS(COORD(NODMI,2))
      IF(TOTAL.GT.0.0) GO TO 70
      CALL SFR2    (DERIV,0.0,8,SHAPE,0.0)
      DO 90 INODE=1,8
      NODEI=LNODS(IELEM,INODE)
      DO 90 IDIME=1,2
      COORD(NODMI,IDIME)=COORD(NODMI,IDIME)
     .                     +SHAPE(INODE)*COORD(NODEI,IDIME)
   90 CONTINUE
   70 CONTINUE
      RETURN
      END
```

Subroutine GAUSSQ

```
      SUBROUTINE GAUSSQ(LGAUS,POSGP,WEIGP)
C**********************************************************************
C
C***  SUBROUTINE SET UP GAUSS-LEGENDRE INTEGRATION CONSTANTS
C
C**********************************************************************
      IMPLICIT REAL*8(A-H,O-Z)
      DIMENSION POSGP(3), WEIGP(3)
C
      IF(LGAUS.NE.1) GO TO 50
      POSGP(1) = 0.0
      WEIGP(1) = 2.0
      RETURN
   50 IF(LGAUS.NE.2) GO TO 60
      POSGP(1) = 0.577350269
      POSGP(2) =-0.577350269
```

```
C
      WEIGP(1) = 1.0
      WEIGP(2) = 1.0
      RETURN
   60 IF(LGAUS.NE.3) RETURN
      POSGP(1) = 0.0
      POSGP(2) = 0.774596669
      POSGP(3) =-0.774596669
C
      WEIGP(1) = 0.8888888889
      WEIGP(2) = 0.5555555556
      WEIGP(3) = 0.5555555556
      RETURN
      END
```

Subroutine SFR2

```
      SUBROUTINE SFR2(DERIV, S,NNODE, SHAPE, T)
C**********************************************************************
C
C*** CALCULATES SHAPE FUNCTIONS AND THEIR DERIVATIVES FOR 2D ELEMENTS
C
C**********************************************************************
      IMPLICIT REAL*8(A-H,O-Z)
      DIMENSION DERIV(2,9), SHAPE(9)
      IF(NNODE.NE.8) GO TO 60
C
C*** SHAPE FUNCTIONS AND DERIVATIVES FOR THE 8 NODE QUADRATIC QUAD.
C
      SHAPE(1) = 0.25*(1-S)*(1-T)*(-S-T-1)
      SHAPE(2) = 0.5*(1-S*S)*(1-T)
      SHAPE(3) = 0.25*(1+S)*(1-T)*(S-T-1)
      SHAPE(4) = 0.5*(1-T*T)*(1+S)
      SHAPE(5) = 0.25*(1+S)*(1+T)*(S+T-1)
      SHAPE(6) = 0.5*(1-S*S)*(1+T)
      SHAPE(7) = 0.25*(1-S)*(1+T)*(-S+T-1)
      SHAPE(8) = 0.5*(1-T*T)*(1-S)
C
      DERIV(1,1) = 0.25*(T+2*S-2*S*T-T*T)
      DERIV(1,2) = -S+S*T
      DERIV(1,3) = 0.25*(-T+2*S-2*S*T+T*T)
      DERIV(1,4) = 0.5*(1-T*T)
      DERIV(1,5) = 0.25*(T+2*S+2*S*T+T*T)
      DERIV(1,6) = -S-S*T
      DERIV(1,7) = 0.25*(-T+2*S+2*S*T-T*T)
      DERIV(1,8) = 0.5*(-1+T*T)
C
```

```
      DERIV(2,1) = 0.25*(S+2*T-2*S*T-S*S)
      DERIV(2,2) = 0.5*(-1+S*S)
      DERIV(2,3) = 0.25*(-S+2*T-S*S+2*S*T)
      DERIV(2,4) = -T-S*T
      DERIV(2,5) = 0.25*(S+2*T+S*S+2*S*T)
      DERIV(2,6) = 0.5*(1-S*S)
      DERIV(2,7) = 0.25*(-S+2*T+S*S-2*S*T)
      DERIV(2,8) = -T+S*T
      RETURN
   60 CONTINUE
C
C*** SHAPE FUNCTIONS AND DERIVATIVES FOR THE 9 NODE QUADRATIC QUAD.
C
      SHAPE(1) = 0.25*S*(S-1)*T*(T-1)
      SHAPE(2) = 0.5*(1-S*S)*T*(T-1)
      SHAPE(3) = 0.25*S*(S+1)*T*(T-1)
      SHAPE(4) = 0.5*S*(S+1)*(1-T*T)
      SHAPE(5) = 0.25*S*(S+1)*T*(T+1)
      SHAPE(6) = 0.5*(1-S*S)*T*(T+1)
      SHAPE(7) = 0.25*(S-1)*S*T*(T+1)
      SHAPE(8) = 0.5*S*(S-1)*(1-T*T)
      SHAPE(9) = (1-S*S)*(1-T*T)
C
      DERIV(1,1) = 0.25*T*(T-1)*(-1+2*S)
      DERIV(1,2) =-0.5*2*S*T*(T-1)
      DERIV(1,3) = 0.25*(1+2*S)*T*(T-1)
      DERIV(1,4) = 0.5*(1+2*S)*(1-T*T)
      DERIV(1,5) = 0.25*(1+2*S)*T*(T+1)
      DERIV(1,6) =-S*T*(T+1)
      DERIV(1,7) = 0.25*(-1+2*S)*T*(T+1)
      DERIV(1,8) = 0.5*(-1+2*S)*(1-T*T)
      DERIV(1,9) =-2*S*(1-T*T)
C
      DERIV(2,1) = 0.25*(-1+2*T)*S*(S-1)
      DERIV(2,2) = 0.5*(1-S*S)*(-1+2*T)
      DERIV(2,3) = 0.25*S*(S+1)*(-1+2*T)
      DERIV(2,4) =-S*T*(S+1)
      DERIV(2,5) = 0.25*S*(S+1)*(1+2*T)
      DERIV(2,6) = 0.5*(1-S*S)*(1+2*T)
      DERIV(2,7) = 0.25*S*(S-1)*(1+2*T)
      DERIV(2,8) =-S*T*(S-1)
      DERIV(2,9) =-2*T*(1-S*S)
      RETURN
      END
```

Subroutine JACOB2

```
      SUBROUTINE JACOB2(CARTD,DERIV,DJACB,ELCOD,GPCOD,IELEM,KGASP,NNODE,
     .                  SHAPE)
C***********************************************************************
C
C***  CALCULATES COORDINATES OF GAUSS POINTS AND THE JACOBIAN MATRIX
C     AND ITS DETERMINANT AND THE INVERSE FOR 2D ELEMENTS
C
C***********************************************************************
      IMPLICIT REAL*8(A-H,O-Z)
      DIMENSION XJACM(2,2),XJACI(2,2),SHAPE(9)
      DIMENSION CARTD(2,9), ELCOD(2,9), GPCOD(2,9), DERIV(2,9)
C
C***  CALCULATE COORDINATES OF SAMPLING POINT
C
      DO 10 IDIME=1,2
      GPCOD(IDIME,KGASP)=0.0
      DO 10 INODE=1,NNODE
      GPCOD(IDIME,KGASP)=GPCOD(IDIME,KGASP)+ELCOD(IDIME,INODE)
     .*SHAPE(INODE)
   10 CONTINUE
C
C***  CREATE JACOBIAN MATRIX XJACM
C
      DO 20 IDIME=1,2
      DO 20 JDIME=1,2
      XJACM(IDIME,JDIME)=0.0
      DO 20 INODE=1,NNODE
      XJACM(IDIME,JDIME)=XJACM(IDIME,JDIME)+DERIV(IDIME,INODE)*
     .ELCOD(JDIME,INODE)
   20 CONTINUE
C
C***  CALCULATE DETERMINANT AND INVERSE OF JACOBIAN MATRIX
C
      DJACB=XJACM(1,1)*XJACM(2,2)-XJACM(1,2)*XJACM(2,1)
      IF(DJACB.GT.0.0) GO TO 30
      WRITE(6,900) IELEM
      STOP
   30 XJACI(1,1)=XJACM(2,2)/DJACB
      XJACI(2,2)=XJACM(1,1)/DJACB
      XJACI(1,2)=-XJACM(1,2)/DJACB
      XJACI(2,1)=-XJACM(2,1)/DJACB
C
C***  CALCULATE CARTESIAN DERIVATIVES
C
      DO 40 IDIME=1,2
```

```
      DO 40 INODE=1,NNODE
      CARTD(IDIME,INODE)=0.0
      DO 40 JDIME=1,2
      CARTD(IDIME,INODE)=CARTD(IDIME,INODE)+XJACI(IDIME,JDIME)*
     .DERIV(JDIME,INODE)
   40 CONTINUE
  900 FORMAT(//,36H PROGRAM HALTED IN SUBROUTINE JACOB2,/,11X,
     .22H ZERO OR NEGATIVE AREA,/,10X,16H ELEMENT NUMBER ,I5)
      RETURN
      END
```

Subroutine BMATSOR

```
      SUBROUTINE BMATSOR(ALPHA,BMATX,CARTD,IHARM,NNODE,NTYPE,R,SHAPE)
C***********************************************************************
C
C*** CALCULATES STRAIN MATRIX B FOR THE SOR ELEMENT
C
C***********************************************************************
      IMPLICIT REAL*8(A-H,O-Z)
      DIMENSION BMATX(6,27), CARTD(2,9), SHAPE(9)
      DO 10 ISTRE = 1,6
      DO 10 IEVAB = 1,27
      BMATX(ISTRE,IEVAB) = 0.0
   10 CONTINUE
      FHARM=FLOAT(IHARM)
      IF(NTYPE.EQ.2) FHARM=-FHARM*3.1415927
      IF(NTYPE.NE.2) ALPHA=1.0
      IGASH = 0
      DO 20 INODE = 1,NNODE
      IGASH=(INODE-1)*3+1
      BMATX(1,IGASH)=CARTD(1,INODE)
      BMATX(3,IGASH)=SHAPE(INODE)/R
      BMATX(4,IGASH)=CARTD(2,INODE)
      BMATX(5,IGASH)=-FHARM*SHAPE(INODE)/(ALPHA*R)
      IGASH=IGASH+1
      BMATX(2,IGASH)=CARTD(2,INODE)
      BMATX(4,IGASH)=CARTD(1,INODE)
      BMATX(6,IGASH)=-FHARM*SHAPE(INODE)/(ALPHA*R)
      IGASH=IGASH+1
      BMATX(3,IGASH)=FHARM*SHAPE(INODE)/(ALPHA*R)
      BMATX(5,IGASH)=CARTD(1,INODE)-SHAPE(INODE)/R
      BMATX(6,IGASH)=CARTD(2,INODE)
   20 CONTINUE
      RETURN
      END
```

Subroutine MODSOR

```
      SUBROUTINE MODSOR(DMATX,LPROP,MMATS,MPROP,PROPS)
C***********************************************************************
C
C*** EVALUATES THE D-MATRIX FOR SOR ELEMENT
C
C***********************************************************************
      IMPLICIT REAL*8(A-H,O-Z)
      DIMENSION DMATX(6,6), PROPS(MMATS,MPROP)
      DO 10 ISTRE = 1,6
      DO 10 JSTRE = 1,6
      DMATX(ISTRE,JSTRE) = 0.0
   10 CONTINUE
C
      YOUNG = PROPS(LPROP,1)
      POISS = PROPS(LPROP,2)
      FACTR = YOUNG*(1.-POISS)/((1.+POISS)*(1.-2.0*POISS))
      OFFDI = POISS*FACTR/(1.-POISS)
      SHEAR = FACTR*(1.-2.*POISS)/(2.*(1.-POISS))
C
      DMATX(1,1) = FACTR
      DMATX(1,2) = OFFDI
      DMATX(1,3) = OFFDI
      DMATX(2,2) = FACTR
      DMATX(2,1) = OFFDI
      DMATX(3,1) = OFFDI
      DMATX(2,3) = OFFDI
      DMATX(3,2) = OFFDI
      DMATX(3,3) = FACTR
      DMATX(4,4) = SHEAR
      DMATX(5,5) = SHEAR
      DMATX(6,6) = SHEAR
      RETURN
      END
```

Subroutine DBE

```
      SUBROUTINE DBE(BMATX,DBMAT,DMATX)
C***********************************************************************
C
C***  CALCULATE D X B
C
C***********************************************************************
      IMPLICIT REAL*8(A-H,O-Z)
      DIMENSION BMATX(6,27), DBMAT(6,27), DMATX(6,6)
      DO 10 ISTRE=1,6
      DO 10 IEVAB=1,27
      DBMAT(ISTRE,IEVAB)=0.0
      DO 10 JSTRE=1,6
      DBMAT(ISTRE,IEVAB)=DBMAT(ISTRE,IEVAB)+
```

```
      .DMATX(ISTRE,JSTRE)*BMATX(JSTRE,IEVAB)                             DBE  14
   10 CONTINUE                                                           DBE  15
      RETURN                                                             DBE  16
      END                                                                DBE  17
```

5 EXAMPLES

To demonstrate the use of the program VISOR for the free vibration of solids of revolution and their sectors, some examples are now presented.

5.1 Example 1: Simply supported circular plate

In the first example, the axisymmetric and asymmetric modes of vibration of a simply supported circular plate of thickness-to-radius ratio of $h/a = 0.1$ (shown in Figure 5.1) are evaluated using VISOR. Table 5.1 lists the frequency parameters $\lambda^2_{ns} = \omega_{ns} a^2 (\rho h/D)^{1/2}$ for nodal diameters $n = 0, 1, 2, 3$ and concentric circles $s = 0, 1, 2, 3$ obtained from VISOR using 5 and 10 SOR elements respectively. Note that ρ is the mass density per unit volume and D is the flexural rigidity of the plate expressed as $D = Eh^3/12(1-\nu^2)$ where E is the elastic modulus and ν is Poisson's ratio. As can be seen, these values are in good agreement with those obtained using a closed form Mindlin plate theory (MPT) solution [20].

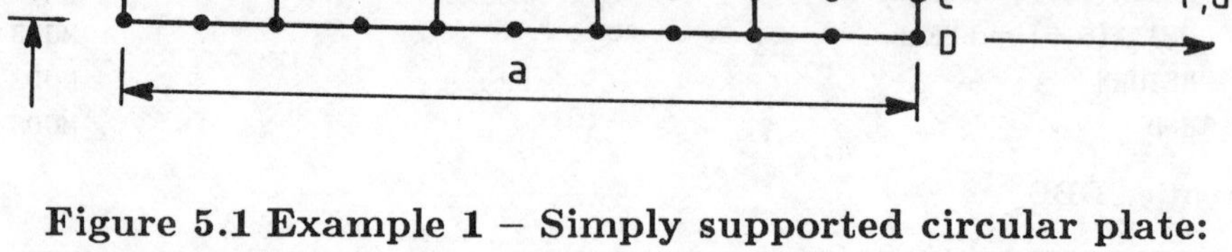

Figure 5.1 Example 1 – Simply supported circular plate: $h/a = 0.1$; boundary conditions $A \to C(u = w = 0), B(w = 0), C(u = v = w = 0), D(w = 0)$

Typical input data required by VISOR for the asymmetric analysis of the plate using 5 elements is listed in Figure 5.2. The corresponding output is given in Figure 5.3.

5.2 Example 2: Simply supported square plate

The second example demonstrates the use of VISOR for the finite prism analysis of a sector of a solid revolution with simple support conditions on the

```
 SIMPLY SUPPORTED CIRCULAR PLATE - ASYMMETRIC - H/A = 0.1
   33    5   13    1    1    3    3    3    3
    1    1    1    2    3    6    9    8    7    4    5
    2    1    7    8    9   12   15   14   13   10   11
    3    1   13   14   15   18   21   20   19   16   17
    4    1   19   20   21   24   27   26   25   22   23
    5    1   25   26   27   30   33   32   31   28   29
    1        0.0        0.1
    3        0.0        0.0
    7        0.2        0.1
    9        0.2        0.0
   13        0.4        0.1
   15        0.4        0.0
   19        0.6        0.1
   21        0.6        0.0
   25        0.8        0.1
   27        0.8        0.0
   31        1.0        0.1
   33        1.0        0.0
    2  101
    5  101
    8  101
   11  101
   14  101
   17  101
   20  101
   23  101
   26  101
   29  101
   31  001
   32  111
   33  001
    1        1.0        0.3        1.0
    1    1
    1    1
    1    1
```

Figure 5.2 Input data for Example 1

```
 SIMPLY SUPPORTED CIRCULAR PLATE - ASYMMETRIC - H/A = 0.1
NPOIN =  33     NELEM =   5     NVFIX =  13     NTYPE =   1
NMATS =   1     NPROP =   3     NGAUS =   3     NHARM =   3
NMODE =   3
ELEMENT   PROPERTY        NODE NUMBERS
    1         1           1    2    3    6    9    8    7    4    5
```

Figure 5.3 Output data for Example 1

2	1	7	8	9	12	15	14	13	10	11
3	1	13	14	15	18	21	20	19	16	17
4	1	19	20	21	24	27	26	25	22	23
5	1	25	26	27	30	33	32	31	28	29

NODAL POINT COORDINATES

NODE	X	Y
1	0.000	0.100
2	0.000	0.050
3	0.000	0.000
4	0.100	0.100
5	0.100	0.050
6	0.100	0.000
7	0.200	0.100
8	0.200	0.050
9	0.200	0.000
10	0.300	0.100
11	0.300	0.050
12	0.300	0.000
13	0.400	0.100
14	0.400	0.050
15	0.400	0.000
16	0.500	0.100
17	0.500	0.050
18	0.500	0.000
19	0.600	0.100
20	0.600	0.050
21	0.600	0.000
22	0.700	0.100
23	0.700	0.050
24	0.700	0.000
25	0.800	0.100
26	0.800	0.050
27	0.800	0.000
28	0.900	0.100
29	0.900	0.050
30	0.900	0.000
31	1.000	0.100
32	1.000	0.050
33	1.000	0.000

RESTRAINED NODES

NODE	CODE	FIXED VALUES
2	101	
5	101	
8	101	
11	101	
14	101	
17	101	

Figure 5.3 Output data for Example 1

```
 20  101
 23  101
 26  101
 29  101
 31  001
 32  111
 33  001
 MATERIAL PROPERTIES
 NUMBER        PROPERTIES
    1          0.100000E+01  0.300000E+00  0.100000E+01
*STURM SEQUENCE FLAG    1*ITERATION PRINT FLAG    1
UPPER BOUNDS ON EIGENVALUE CLUSTERS
  0.17206656237004E+00  0.19382907037321E+01  0.79862083958009E+01
 NO OF EIGENVALUES IN EACH CLUSTER
                      1                      1                      1
 NO OF EIGENVALUES LESS THAN UPPER BOUNDS
                      1                      2                      3
THE CALCULATED VALUES FOR HARMONIC   1 ARE
   EIGENVALUES      FREQUENCIES       ERROR NORMS
   0.1703629E+00    0.4127504E+00    0.2468618E-12
   0.1919100E+01    0.1385316E+01    0.2135507E-07
   0.7907137E+01    0.2811963E+01    0.3791889E-04
THE CALCULATED MODES ARE
MODE=  1
            U             V             W
    1 -0.5680E+00 -0.1234E-01  0.5651E+00
    2  0.0000E+00 -0.1052E-01  0.0000E+00
    3  0.5680E+00 -0.1234E-01 -0.5651E+00
    4 -0.5315E+00  0.1140E+01  0.5532E+00
    5  0.0000E+00  0.1149E+01  0.0000E+00
    6  0.5315E+00  0.1140E+01 -0.5532E+00
    7 -0.4492E+00  0.2153E+01  0.5236E+00
    8  0.0000E+00  0.2169E+01  0.0000E+00
    9  0.4492E+00  0.2153E+01 -0.5236E+00
   10 -0.3140E+00  0.2944E+01  0.4771E+00
   11  0.0000E+00  0.2966E+01  0.0000E+00
   12  0.3140E+00  0.2944E+01 -0.4771E+00
   13 -0.1543E+00  0.3430E+01  0.4167E+00
   14  0.0000E+00  0.3455E+01  0.0000E+00
   15  0.1543E+00  0.3430E+01 -0.4167E+00
   16  0.2090E-01  0.3567E+01  0.3468E+00
   17  0.0000E+00  0.3593E+01  0.0000E+00
   18 -0.2090E-01  0.3567E+01 -0.3468E+00
   19  0.1908E+00  0.3350E+01  0.2711E+00
   20  0.0000E+00  0.3375E+01  0.0000E+00
   21 -0.1908E+00  0.3350E+01 -0.2711E+00
   22  0.3325E+00  0.2807E+01  0.1947E+00
```

Figure 5.3 Output data for Example 1

```
   23  0.0000E+00  0.2829E+01  0.0000E+00
   24 -0.3325E+00  0.2807E+01 -0.1947E+00
   25  0.4431E+00  0.2007E+01  0.1216E+00
   26  0.0000E+00  0.2024E+01  0.0000E+00
   27 -0.4431E+00  0.2007E+01 -0.1216E+00
   28  0.4976E+00  0.1035E+01  0.5539E-01
   29  0.0000E+00  0.1046E+01  0.0000E+00
   30 -0.4976E+00  0.1035E+01 -0.5539E-01
   31  0.5110E+00 -0.3031E-02  0.0000E+00
   32  0.0000E+00  0.0000E+00  0.0000E+00
   33 -0.5110E+00 -0.3031E-02  0.0000E+00
MODE=  2
              U           V           W
    1  0.1381E+01  0.8846E-01 -0.1345E+01
    2  0.0000E+00  0.7744E-01  0.0000E+00
    3 -0.1381E+01  0.8846E-01  0.1345E+01
    4  0.1067E+01 -0.2745E+01 -0.1244E+01
    5  0.0000E+00 -0.2812E+01  0.0000E+00
    6 -0.1067E+01 -0.2745E+01  0.1244E+01
    7  0.4723E+00 -0.4465E+01 -0.1016E+01
    8  0.0000E+00 -0.4574E+01  0.0000E+00
    9 -0.4723E+00 -0.4465E+01  0.1016E+01
   10 -0.2716E+00 -0.4659E+01 -0.7098E+00
   11  0.0000E+00 -0.4769E+01  0.0000E+00
   12  0.2716E+00 -0.4659E+01  0.7098E+00
   13 -0.8854E+00 -0.3373E+01 -0.3826E+00
   14  0.0000E+00 -0.3452E+01  0.0000E+00
   15  0.8854E+00 -0.3373E+01  0.3826E+00
   16 -0.1070E+01 -0.1153E+01 -0.1059E+00
   17  0.0000E+00 -0.1180E+01  0.0000E+00
   18  0.1070E+01 -0.1153E+01  0.1059E+00
   19 -0.9157E+00  0.1079E+01  0.8226E-01
   20  0.0000E+00  0.1107E+01  0.0000E+00
   21  0.9157E+00  0.1079E+01 -0.8226E-01
   22 -0.3802E+00  0.2520E+01  0.1642E+00
   23  0.0000E+00  0.2580E+01  0.0000E+00
   24  0.3802E+00  0.2520E+01 -0.1642E+00
   25  0.2284E+00  0.2702E+01  0.1532E+00
   26  0.0000E+00  0.2768E+01  0.0000E+00
   27 -0.2284E+00  0.2702E+01 -0.1532E+00
   28  0.6626E+00  0.1680E+01  0.8466E-01
   29  0.0000E+00  0.1724E+01  0.0000E+00
   30 -0.6626E+00  0.1680E+01 -0.8466E-01
   31  0.8461E+00 -0.3595E-02  0.0000E+00
   32  0.0000E+00  0.0000E+00  0.0000E+00
   33 -0.8461E+00 -0.3595E-02  0.0000E+00
MODE=  3
```

Figure 5.3 Output data for Example 1

```
            U              V              W
    1  0.2401E+01  0.2380E+00 -0.2228E+01
    2  0.0000E+00  0.2121E+00  0.0000E+00
    3 -0.2401E+01  0.2380E+00  0.2228E+01
    4  0.1259E+01 -0.4503E+01 -0.1853E+01
    5  0.0000E+00 -0.4722E+01  0.0000E+00
    6 -0.1259E+01 -0.4503E+01  0.1853E+01
    7 -0.4160E+00 -0.5616E+01 -0.1155E+01
    8  0.0000E+00 -0.5875E+01  0.0000E+00
    9  0.4160E+00 -0.5616E+01  0.1155E+01
   10 -0.1532E+01 -0.2986E+01 -0.4200E+00
   11  0.0000E+00 -0.3124E+01  0.0000E+00
   12  0.1532E+01 -0.2986E+01  0.4200E+00
   13 -0.1587E+01  0.9451E+00  0.1007E+00
   14  0.0000E+00  0.9934E+00  0.0000E+00
   15  0.1587E+01  0.9451E+00 -0.1007E+00
   16 -0.3110E+00  0.3253E+01  0.2730E+00
   17  0.0000E+00  0.3401E+01  0.0000E+00
   18  0.3110E+00  0.3253E+01 -0.2730E+00
   19  0.9766E+00  0.2449E+01  0.1662E+00
   20  0.0000E+00  0.2560E+01  0.0000E+00
   21 -0.9766E+00  0.2449E+01 -0.1662E+00
   22  0.1134E+01 -0.3002E+00 -0.1753E-01
   23  0.0000E+00 -0.3138E+00  0.0000E+00
   24 -0.1134E+01 -0.3002E+00  0.1753E-01
   25  0.4625E+00 -0.2387E+01 -0.1252E+00
   26  0.0000E+00 -0.2498E+01  0.0000E+00
   27 -0.4625E+00 -0.2387E+01  0.1252E+00
   28 -0.5835E+00 -0.2142E+01 -0.9929E-01
   29  0.0000E+00 -0.2243E+01  0.0000E+00
   30  0.5835E+00 -0.2142E+01  0.9929E-01
   31 -0.1133E+01  0.3304E-02  0.0000E+00
   32  0.0000E+00  0.0000E+00  0.0000E+00
   33  0.1133E+01  0.3304E-02  0.0000E+00
*STURM SEQUENCE FLAG    1*ITERATION PRINT FLAG    1
UPPER BOUNDS ON EIGENVALUE CLUSTERS
  0.5658796900252E+00  0.3860093958805E+01  0.1287416972704 2E+02
 NO OF EIGENVALUES IN EACH CLUSTER
                    1                    1                    1
 NO OF EIGENVALUES LESS THAN UPPER BOUNDS
                    1                    2                    3
THE CALCULATED VALUES FOR HARMONIC   2 ARE
  EIGENVALUES       FREQUENCIES        ERROR NORMS
  0.5602851E+00    0.7485220E+00     0.2792387E-11
  0.3821875E+01    0.1954962E+01     0.1074784E-06
  0.1274670E+02    0.3570252E+01     0.5537340E-04
THE CALCULATED MODES ARE
```

Figure 5.3 Output data for Example 1

MODE= 1

	U	V	W
1	0.4186E-02	-0.1045E-01	-0.1842E-02
2	0.0000E+00	-0.9282E-02	0.0000E+00
3	-0.4186E-02	-0.1045E-01	0.1842E-02
4	-0.2150E+00	0.2335E+00	0.2201E+00
5	0.0000E+00	0.2362E+00	0.0000E+00
6	0.2150E+00	0.2335E+00	-0.2201E+00
7	-0.3799E+00	0.8616E+00	0.4124E+00
8	0.0000E+00	0.8740E+00	0.0000E+00
9	0.3799E+00	0.8616E+00	-0.4124E+00
10	-0.4331E+00	0.1739E+01	0.5509E+00
11	0.0000E+00	0.1762E+01	0.0000E+00
12	0.4331E+00	0.1739E+01	-0.5509E+00
13	-0.3923E+00	0.2620E+01	0.6234E+00
14	0.0000E+00	0.2655E+01	0.0000E+00
15	0.3923E+00	0.2620E+01	-0.6234E+00
16	-0.2252E+00	0.3283E+01	0.6245E+00
17	0.0000E+00	0.3326E+01	0.0000E+00
18	0.2252E+00	0.3283E+01	-0.6245E+00
19	-0.9564E-04	0.3530E+01	0.5590E+00
20	0.0000E+00	0.3577E+01	0.0000E+00
21	0.9564E-04	0.3530E+01	-0.5590E+00
22	0.2526E+00	0.3262E+01	0.4429E+00
23	0.0000E+00	0.3305E+01	0.0000E+00
24	-0.2526E+00	0.3262E+01	-0.4429E+00
25	0.4784E+00	0.2492E+01	0.2952E+00
26	0.0000E+00	0.2526E+01	0.0000E+00
27	-0.4784E+00	0.2492E+01	-0.2952E+00
28	0.6110E+00	0.1335E+01	0.1399E+00
29	0.0000E+00	0.1355E+01	0.0000E+00
30	-0.6110E+00	0.1335E+01	-0.1399E+00
31	0.6566E+00	-0.2865E-02	0.0000E+00
32	0.0000E+00	0.0000E+00	0.0000E+00
33	-0.6566E+00	-0.2865E-02	0.0000E+00

MODE= 2

	U	V	W
1	0.2600E-01	-0.8920E-01	-0.1539E-01
2	0.0000E+00	-0.8413E-01	0.0000E+00
3	-0.2600E-01	-0.8920E-01	0.1539E-01
4	-0.6302E+00	0.7908E+00	0.6792E+00
5	0.0000E+00	0.8160E+00	0.0000E+00
6	0.6302E+00	0.7908E+00	-0.6792E+00
7	-0.8628E+00	0.2527E+01	0.1118E+01
8	0.0000E+00	0.2618E+01	0.0000E+00
9	0.8628E+00	0.2527E+01	-0.1118E+01
10	-0.4183E+00	0.4070E+01	0.1193E+01

Figure 5.3 Output data for Example 1

11	0.0000E+00	0.4205E+01	0.0000E+00
12	0.4183E+00	0.4070E+01	-0.1193E+01
13	0.3028E+00	0.4251E+01	0.9294E+00
14	0.0000E+00	0.4392E+01	0.0000E+00
15	-0.3028E+00	0.4251E+01	-0.9294E+00
16	0.9316E+00	0.2760E+01	0.4879E+00
17	0.0000E+00	0.2851E+01	0.0000E+00
18	-0.9316E+00	0.2760E+01	-0.4879E+00
19	0.1174E+01	0.2975E+00	0.4034E-01
20	0.0000E+00	0.3055E+00	0.0000E+00
21	-0.1174E+01	0.2975E+00	-0.4034E-01
22	0.7162E+00	-0.1923E+01	-0.2417E+00
23	0.0000E+00	-0.1986E+01	0.0000E+00
24	-0.7162E+00	-0.1923E+01	0.2417E+00
25	-0.1988E-01	-0.2769E+01	-0.3033E+00
26	0.0000E+00	-0.2861E+01	0.0000E+00
27	0.1988E-01	-0.2769E+01	0.3033E+00
28	-0.6720E+00	-0.1914E+01	-0.1864E+00
29	0.0000E+00	-0.1981E+01	0.0000E+00
30	0.6720E+00	-0.1914E+01	0.1864E+00
31	-0.9720E+00	0.2545E-02	0.0000E+00
32	0.0000E+00	0.0000E+00	0.0000E+00
33	0.9720E+00	0.2545E-02	0.0000E+00

MODE= 3

	U	V	W
1	-0.4199E-01	0.3404E+00	0.4813E-01
2	0.0000E+00	0.3421E+00	0.0000E+00
3	0.4199E-01	0.3404E+00	-0.4813E-01
4	0.1124E+01	-0.1758E+01	-0.1338E+01
5	0.0000E+00	-0.1863E+01	0.0000E+00
6	-0.1124E+01	-0.1758E+01	0.1338E+01
7	0.8938E+00	-0.4503E+01	-0.1776E+01
8	0.0000E+00	-0.4782E+01	0.0000E+00
9	-0.8938E+00	-0.4503E+01	0.1776E+01
10	-0.6628E+00	-0.4727E+01	-0.1263E+01
11	0.0000E+00	-0.4999E+01	0.0000E+00
12	0.6628E+00	-0.4727E+01	0.1263E+01
13	-0.1776E+01	-0.1574E+01	-0.2947E+00
14	0.0000E+00	-0.1659E+01	0.0000E+00
15	0.1776E+01	-0.1574E+01	0.2947E+00
16	-0.1027E+01	0.2193E+01	0.3509E+00
17	0.0000E+00	0.2317E+01	0.0000E+00
18	0.1027E+01	0.2193E+01	-0.3509E+00
19	0.4443E+00	0.3070E+01	0.4030E+00
20	0.0000E+00	0.3245E+01	0.0000E+00
21	-0.4443E+00	0.3070E+01	-0.4030E+00
22	0.1183E+01	0.7209E+00	0.8404E-01

Figure 5.3 Output data for Example 1

```
   23  0.0000E+00  0.7616E+00  0.0000E+00
   24 -0.1183E+01  0.7209E+00 -0.8404E-01
   25  0.7933E+00 -0.2020E+01 -0.2049E+00
   26  0.0000E+00 -0.2137E+01  0.0000E+00
   27 -0.7933E+00 -0.2020E+01  0.2049E+00
   28 -0.4948E+00 -0.2292E+01 -0.2038E+00
   29  0.0000E+00 -0.2424E+01  0.0000E+00
   30  0.4948E+00 -0.2292E+01  0.2038E+00
   31 -0.1243E+01  0.1954E-02  0.0000E+00
   32  0.0000E+00  0.0000E+00  0.0000E+00
   33  0.1243E+01  0.1954E-02  0.0000E+00
*STURM SEQUENCE FLAG     1*ITERATION PRINT FLAG     1
UPPER BOUNDS ON EIGENVALUE CLUSTERS
   0.13235357900812E+01  0.66419696096344E+01  0.19132804592671E+02
 NO OF EIGENVALUES IN EACH CLUSTER
                       1                     1                     1
 NO OF EIGENVALUES LESS THAN UPPER BOUNDS
                       1                     2                     3
THE CALCULATED VALUES FOR HARMONIC    3 ARE
   EIGENVALUES      FREQUENCIES       ERROR NORMS
   0.1310431E+01    0.1144741E+01    0.1427208E-12
   0.6576208E+01    0.2564412E+01    0.4416857E-08
   0.1894337E+02    0.4352398E+01    0.3123860E-04
THE CALCULATED MODES ARE
MODE=  1
            U           V           W
    1  0.7865E-02  0.1851E-01 -0.1987E-02
    2  0.0000E+00  0.1746E-01  0.0000E+00
    3 -0.7865E-02  0.1851E-01  0.1987E-02
    4 -0.6202E-01  0.4017E-01  0.5972E-01
    5  0.0000E+00  0.4127E-01  0.0000E+00
    6  0.6202E-01  0.4017E-01 -0.5972E-01
    7 -0.2042E+00  0.3147E+00  0.2228E+00
    8  0.0000E+00  0.3209E+00  0.0000E+00
    9  0.2042E+00  0.3147E+00 -0.2228E+00
   10 -0.3656E+00  0.9439E+00  0.4367E+00
   11  0.0000E+00  0.9629E+00  0.0000E+00
   12  0.3656E+00  0.9439E+00 -0.4367E+00
   13 -0.4606E+00  0.1844E+01  0.6436E+00
   14  0.0000E+00  0.1881E+01  0.0000E+00
   15  0.4606E+00  0.1844E+01 -0.6436E+00
   16 -0.3895E+00  0.2790E+01  0.7754E+00
   17  0.0000E+00  0.2846E+01  0.0000E+00
   18  0.3895E+00  0.2790E+01 -0.7754E+00
   19 -0.1930E+00  0.3440E+01  0.7972E+00
   20  0.0000E+00  0.3509E+01  0.0000E+00
   21  0.1930E+00  0.3440E+01 -0.7972E+00
```

Figure 5.3 Output data for Example 1

```
   22  0.1316E+00  0.3512E+01  0.6974E+00
   23  0.0000E+00  0.3582E+01  0.0000E+00
   24 -0.1316E+00  0.3512E+01 -0.6974E+00
   25  0.4660E+00  0.2873E+01  0.4976E+00
   26  0.0000E+00  0.2931E+01  0.0000E+00
   27 -0.4660E+00  0.2873E+01 -0.4976E+00
   28  0.6933E+00  0.1600E+01  0.2456E+00
   29  0.0000E+00  0.1635E+01  0.0000E+00
   30 -0.6933E+00  0.1600E+01 -0.2456E+00
   31  0.7820E+00 -0.1668E-02  0.0000E+00
   32  0.0000E+00  0.0000E+00  0.0000E+00
   33 -0.7820E+00 -0.1668E-02  0.0000E+00
MODE=  2
             U           V           W
    1  0.5472E-01  0.5169E-01 -0.1950E-01
    2  0.0000E+00  0.5190E-01  0.0000E+00
    3 -0.5472E-01  0.5169E-01  0.1950E-01
    4 -0.2440E+00  0.1806E+00  0.2373E+00
    5  0.0000E+00  0.1885E+00  0.0000E+00
    6  0.2440E+00  0.1806E+00 -0.2373E+00
    7 -0.6569E+00  0.1198E+01  0.7849E+00
    8  0.0000E+00  0.1255E+01  0.0000E+00
    9  0.6569E+00  0.1198E+01 -0.7849E+00
   10 -0.6970E+00  0.2941E+01  0.1240E+01
   11  0.0000E+00  0.3069E+01  0.0000E+00
   12  0.6970E+00  0.2941E+01 -0.1240E+01
   13 -0.2465E+00  0.4149E+01  0.1316E+01
   14  0.0000E+00  0.4330E+01  0.0000E+00
   15  0.2465E+00  0.4149E+01 -0.1316E+01
   16  0.5987E+00  0.3690E+01  0.9408E+00
   17  0.0000E+00  0.3848E+01  0.0000E+00
   18 -0.5987E+00  0.3690E+01 -0.9408E+00
   19  0.1217E+01  0.1502E+01  0.3108E+00
   20  0.0000E+00  0.1564E+01  0.0000E+00
   21 -0.1217E+01  0.1502E+01 -0.3108E+00
   22  0.9696E+00 -0.1216E+01 -0.2201E+00
   23  0.0000E+00 -0.1268E+01  0.0000E+00
   24 -0.9696E+00 -0.1216E+01  0.2201E+00
   25  0.2112E+00 -0.2716E+01 -0.4307E+00
   26  0.0000E+00 -0.2832E+01  0.0000E+00
   27 -0.2112E+00 -0.2716E+01  0.4307E+00
   28 -0.6510E+00 -0.2109E+01 -0.2973E+00
   29  0.0000E+00 -0.2202E+01  0.0000E+00
   30  0.6510E+00 -0.2109E+01  0.2973E+00
   31 -0.1079E+01  0.5021E-03  0.0000E+00
   32  0.0000E+00  0.0000E+00  0.0000E+00
   33  0.1079E+01  0.5021E-03  0.0000E+00
```

Figure 5.3 Output data for Example 1

MODE= 3

	U	V	W
1	-0.2059E+00	-0.5398E-01	0.9215E-01
2	0.0000E+00	-0.5246E-01	0.0000E+00
3	0.2059E+00	-0.5398E-01	-0.9215E-01
4	0.5991E+00	-0.5336E+00	-0.6037E+00
5	0.0000E+00	-0.5735E+00	0.0000E+00
6	-0.5991E+00	-0.5336E+00	0.6037E+00
7	0.1151E+01	-0.2815E+01	-0.1634E+01
8	0.0000E+00	-0.3034E+01	0.0000E+00
9	-0.1151E+01	-0.2815E+01	0.1634E+01
10	0.1547E+00	-0.4798E+01	-0.1822E+01
11	0.0000E+00	-0.5135E+01	0.0000E+00
12	-0.1547E+00	-0.4798E+01	0.1822E+01
13	-0.1335E+01	-0.3362E+01	-0.9327E+00
14	0.0000E+00	-0.3590E+01	0.0000E+00
15	0.1335E+01	-0.3362E+01	0.9327E+00
16	-0.1407E+01	0.6700E+00	0.1501E+00
17	0.0000E+00	0.7163E+00	0.0000E+00
18	0.1407E+01	0.6700E+00	-0.1501E+00
19	-0.1984E+00	0.3085E+01	0.5866E+00
20	0.0000E+00	0.3296E+01	0.0000E+00
21	0.1984E+00	0.3085E+01	-0.5866E+00
22	0.1076E+01	0.1590E+01	0.2645E+00
23	0.0000E+00	0.1697E+01	0.0000E+00
24	-0.1076E+01	0.1590E+01	-0.2645E+00
25	0.1094E+01	-0.1595E+01	-0.2356E+00
26	0.0000E+00	-0.1705E+01	0.0000E+00
27	-0.1094E+01	-0.1595E+01	0.2356E+00
28	-0.3947E+00	-0.2431E+01	-0.3112E+00
29	0.0000E+00	-0.2597E+01	0.0000E+00
30	0.3947E+00	-0.2431E+01	0.3112E+00
31	-0.1352E+01	-0.3710E-03	0.0000E+00
32	0.0000E+00	0.0000E+00	0.0000E+00
33	0.1352E+01	-0.3710E-03	0.0000E+00

Figure 5.3 Output from Example 1

Table 5.1 Frequency parameters λ^2_{ns} of a uniform Mindlin circular plate with a simply supported edge; $\nu = 0.3, h/a = 0.1$

		λ^2_{ns}		
n	s	VISOR analysis (5 elmts.)	VISOR analysis (10 elmts.)	closed form MPT
0	0	4.904	4.901	4.894
	1	28.662	28.449	28.240
	2	68.645	67.039	65.942
1	0	13.639	13.611	13.510
	1	45.778	45.238	44.691
	2	92.992	89.921	87.994
2	0	24.735	24.654	24.313
	1	64.602	63.653	62.552
	2	117.980	113.653	110.658
3	0	37.828	37.691	36.962
	1	84.742	83.378	81.526
	2	143.827	138.028	133.769

radial plane boundaries. By using a very large average radius R and the special choice of included angle α so that $\alpha R = a$ it is possible to simulate quite accurately the behaviour of structures with rectangular planforms.

To illustrate this artifice, the square simply supported plate shown in Figure 5.4 is analysed using VISOR. An radius average of $R = 10,000.0$ is assumed and an included angle of $\alpha = 0.0001$ is used to represent a plate of span $a = \alpha R = 1.0$. By specifying NTYPE = 2 in the input for VISOR, the finite prism approach is adopted.

Table 5.2 lists the frequency parameters $\Omega_{mn} = \omega_{mn} a(\rho/G)^{1/2}$ for harmonics $m = 1,2,3$ and modes $n = 1,2,3$ obtained by VISOR using 5 and 10 prism elements respectively. Note that G is the shear modulus and ρ is the mass density per unit per unit volume. These values are in good agreement with frequencies obtained using the closed form Mindlin plate solution of Chapter 1 of this book (including rotatory inertia effects).

Typical input data required by VISOR for the analysis of the plate using 5 elements is listed in Figure 5.5 with the corresponding output provided in Figure 5.6.

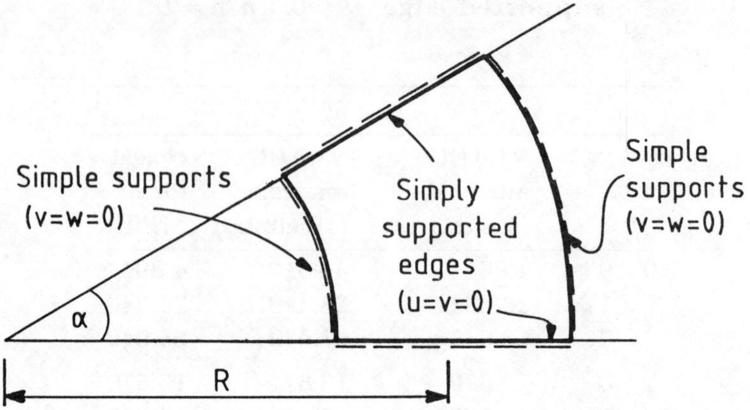

Figure 5.4 Example 2 – Simply supported square plate analysed using the curved finite prism method: $a = \alpha R = 1.0$, $\alpha = 0.0001$, $R = 10,000.0$

Table 5.2 Frequency parameters Ω_{mn} of a uniform square Mindlin plate with simply supported edges; $\nu = 0.3, h/a = 0.1$

m	n	Ω_{mn} VISOR analysis (5 elmts.)	VISOR analysis (10 elmts.)	closed form solution
1	1	0.9353	0.9343	0.932
	2	2.2670	2.2421	2.226
	3	4.3746	4.2284	4.171
2	1	2.2418	2.2412	2.226
	2	3.4719	3.4548	3.421
	3	5.4364	5.3181	5.239
3	1	4.2214	4.2208	4.171
	2	5.3247	5.3126	5.239
	3	7.1031	7.0114	6.889

5.3 Example 3 – Simply supported annular plate

The third example illustrates the use of VISOR for the analysis of the simply supported annular plate shown in Figure 5.7.

Table 5.3 lists the frequency parameters $\lambda_{ns}^2 = \omega_{ns} a^2 (\rho/D)^{1/2}$ for nodal di-

```
SIMPLY SUPPORTED SQUARE PLATE  BY FINITE PRISM METHOD H/A = 0.1
 33    5   15    2    1    4    3    3    3
  1    1    1    2    3    6    9    8    7    4    5
  2    1    7    8    9   12   15   14   13   10   11
  3    1   13   14   15   18   21   20   19   16   17
  4    1   19   20   21   24   27   26   25   22   23
  5    1   25   26   27   30   33   32   31   28   29
  1      999.5         0.1
  3      999.5         0.0
  7      999.7         0.1
  9      999.7         0.0
 13      999.9         0.1
 15      999.9         0.0
 19     1000.1         0.1
 21     1000.1         0.0
 25     1000.3         0.1
 27     1000.3         0.0
 31     1000.5         0.1
 33     1000.5         0.0
  1  001
  2  111
  3  001
  5  101
  8  101
 11  101
 14  101
 17  101
 20  101
 23  101
 26  101
 29  101
 31  001
 32  111
 33  001
  1    10920.0         0.3         10.0 0.001
  1    1
  1    1
  1    1
  1    1
  1    1
```

Figure 5.5 Input for Example 2

```
 SIMPLY SUPPORTED SQUARE PLATE  BY FINITE PRISM METHOD H/A = 0.1
NPOIN =  33       NELEM =   5       NVFIX =  15       NTYPE =   2
NMATS =   1       NPROP =   4       NGAUS =   3       NHARM =   3
```

Figure 5.6 Output for Example 2

NMODE = 3

ELEMENT	PROPERTY	NODE NUMBERS								
1	1	1	2	3	6	9	8	7	4	5
2	1	7	8	9	12	15	14	13	10	11
3	1	13	14	15	18	21	20	19	16	17
4	1	19	20	21	24	27	26	25	22	23
5	1	25	26	27	30	33	32	31	28	29

NODAL POINT COORDINATES

NODE	X	Y
1	999.500	0.100
2	999.500	0.050
3	999.500	0.000
4	999.600	0.100
5	999.600	0.050
6	999.600	0.000
7	999.700	0.100
8	999.700	0.050
9	999.700	0.000
10	999.800	0.100
11	999.800	0.050
12	999.800	0.000
13	999.900	0.100
14	999.900	0.050
15	999.900	0.000
16	1000.000	0.100
17	1000.000	0.050
18	1000.000	0.000
19	1000.100	0.100
20	1000.100	0.050
21	1000.100	0.000
22	1000.200	0.100
23	1000.200	0.050
24	1000.200	0.000
25	1000.300	0.100
26	1000.300	0.050
27	1000.300	0.000
28	1000.400	0.100
29	1000.400	0.050
30	1000.400	0.000
31	1000.500	0.100
32	1000.500	0.050
33	1000.500	0.000

RESTRAINED NODES

NODE	CODE	FIXED VALUES
1	001	
2	111	
3	001	

Figure 5.6 Output for Example 2

```
  5  101
  8  101
 11  101
 14  101
 17  101
 20  101
 23  101
 26  101
 29  101
 31  001
 32  111
 33  001
 MATERIAL PROPERTIES
 NUMBER         PROPERTIES
    1           0.109200E+05  0.300000E+00  0.100000E+02  0.100000E-02
*STURM SEQUENCE FLAG     1*ITERATION PRINT FLAG     1
UPPER BOUNDS ON EIGENVALUE CLUSTERS
   0.37110360065158E+03  0.21800536490823E+04  0.81181498584285E+04
 NO OF EIGENVALUES IN EACH CLUSTER
                        1                      1                      1
 NO OF EIGENVALUES LESS THAN UPPER BOUNDS
                        1                      2                      3
THE CALCULATED VALUES FOR HARMONIC   1 ARE
   EIGENVALUES      FREQUENCIES      ERROR NORMS
   0.3674293E+03   0.1916845E+02   0.1285133E-10
   0.2158469E+04   0.4645933E+02   0.6777165E-07
   0.8037772E+04   0.8965362E+02   0.6625699E-04
THE CALCULATED MODES ARE
MODE=  1
             U             V             W
    1 -0.2994E+00  0.1200E-02  0.0000E+00
    2  0.0000E+00  0.0000E+00  0.0000E+00
    3  0.2994E+00  0.1200E-02  0.0000E+00
    4 -0.2826E+00  0.6092E+00 -0.9216E-01
    5  0.0000E+00  0.6156E+00  0.0000E+00
    6  0.2826E+00  0.6092E+00  0.9216E-01
    7 -0.2426E+00  0.1159E+01 -0.1752E+00
    8  0.0000E+00  0.1171E+01  0.0000E+00
    9  0.2426E+00  0.1159E+01  0.1752E+00
   10 -0.1746E+00  0.1595E+01 -0.2412E+00
   11  0.0000E+00  0.1612E+01  0.0000E+00
   12  0.1746E+00  0.1595E+01  0.2412E+00
   13 -0.9270E-01  0.1876E+01 -0.2835E+00
   14  0.0000E+00  0.1895E+01  0.0000E+00
   15  0.9270E-01  0.1876E+01  0.2835E+00
   16 -0.3232E-04  0.1972E+01 -0.2981E+00
   17  0.0000E+00  0.1992E+01  0.0000E+00
```

Figure 5.6 Output for Example 2

18	0.3232E-04	0.1972E+01	0.2981E+00
19	0.9265E-01	0.1876E+01	-0.2835E+00
20	0.0000E+00	0.1895E+01	0.0000E+00
21	-0.9265E-01	0.1876E+01	0.2835E+00
22	0.1746E+00	0.1595E+01	-0.2411E+00
23	0.0000E+00	0.1612E+01	0.0000E+00
24	-0.1746E+00	0.1595E+01	0.2411E+00
25	0.2426E+00	0.1160E+01	-0.1752E+00
26	0.0000E+00	0.1171E+01	0.0000E+00
27	-0.2426E+00	0.1160E+01	0.1752E+00
28	0.2826E+00	0.6094E+00	-0.9210E-01
29	0.0000E+00	0.6157E+00	0.0000E+00
30	-0.2826E+00	0.6094E+00	0.9210E-01
31	0.2994E+00	0.1194E-02	0.0000E+00
32	0.0000E+00	0.0000E+00	0.0000E+00
33	-0.2994E+00	0.1194E-02	0.0000E+00

MODE= 2

	U	V	W
1	-0.5701E+00	0.2848E-02	0.0000E+00
2	0.0000E+00	0.0000E+00	0.0000E+00
3	0.5701E+00	0.2848E-02	0.0000E+00
4	-0.4436E+00	0.1141E+01	-0.1637E+00
5	0.0000E+00	0.1168E+01	0.0000E+00
6	0.4436E+00	0.1141E+01	0.1637E+00
7	-0.1764E+00	0.1848E+01	-0.2648E+00
8	0.0000E+00	0.1892E+01	0.0000E+00
9	0.1764E+00	0.1848E+01	0.2648E+00
10	0.1693E+00	0.1846E+01	-0.2647E+00
11	0.0000E+00	0.1890E+01	0.0000E+00
12	-0.1693E+00	0.1846E+01	0.2647E+00
13	0.4622E+00	0.1142E+01	-0.1637E+00
14	0.0000E+00	0.1170E+01	0.0000E+00
15	-0.4622E+00	0.1142E+01	0.1637E+00
16	0.5481E+00	0.4494E-03	-0.6474E-04
17	0.0000E+00	0.4600E-03	0.0000E+00
18	-0.5481E+00	0.4494E-03	0.6474E-04
19	0.4623E+00	-0.1141E+01	0.1635E+00
20	0.0000E+00	-0.1169E+01	0.0000E+00
21	-0.4623E+00	-0.1141E+01	-0.1635E+00
22	0.1694E+00	-0.1845E+01	0.2645E+00
23	0.0000E+00	-0.1890E+01	0.0000E+00
24	-0.1694E+00	-0.1845E+01	-0.2645E+00
25	-0.1763E+00	-0.1847E+01	0.2646E+00
26	0.0000E+00	-0.1892E+01	0.0000E+00
27	0.1763E+00	-0.1847E+01	-0.2646E+00
28	-0.4435E+00	-0.1140E+01	0.1635E+00
29	0.0000E+00	-0.1168E+01	0.0000E+00

Figure 5.6 Output for Example 2

```
   30  0.4435E+00 -0.1140E+01 -0.1635E+00
   31 -0.5699E+00 -0.2836E-02  0.0000E+00
   32  0.0000E+00  0.0000E+00  0.0000E+00
   33  0.5699E+00 -0.2836E-02  0.0000E+00
MODE=   3
            U            V            W
    1  0.8080E+00 -0.4725E-02  0.0000E+00
    2  0.0000E+00  0.0000E+00  0.0000E+00
    3 -0.8080E+00 -0.4725E-02  0.0000E+00
    4  0.4275E+00 -0.1548E+01  0.2054E+00
    5  0.0000E+00 -0.1617E+01  0.0000E+00
    6 -0.4275E+00 -0.1548E+01 -0.2054E+00
    7 -0.2507E+00 -0.1819E+01  0.2409E+00
    8  0.0000E+00 -0.1900E+01  0.0000E+00
    9  0.2507E+00 -0.1819E+01 -0.2409E+00
   10 -0.6913E+00 -0.5914E+00  0.7846E-01
   11  0.0000E+00 -0.6177E+00  0.0000E+00
   12  0.6913E+00 -0.5914E+00 -0.7846E-01
   13 -0.6555E+00  0.1124E+01 -0.1488E+00
   14  0.0000E+00  0.1174E+01  0.0000E+00
   15  0.6555E+00  0.1124E+01  0.1488E+00
   16 -0.6474E-04  0.1913E+01 -0.2537E+00
   17  0.0000E+00  0.1998E+01  0.0000E+00
   18  0.6474E-04  0.1913E+01  0.2537E+00
   19  0.6554E+00  0.1124E+01 -0.1488E+00
   20  0.0000E+00  0.1174E+01  0.0000E+00
   21 -0.6554E+00  0.1124E+01  0.1488E+00
   22  0.6912E+00 -0.5909E+00  0.7835E-01
   23  0.0000E+00 -0.6171E+00  0.0000E+00
   24 -0.6912E+00 -0.5909E+00 -0.7835E-01
   25  0.2507E+00 -0.1819E+01  0.2406E+00
   26  0.0000E+00 -0.1899E+01  0.0000E+00
   27 -0.2507E+00 -0.1819E+01 -0.2406E+00
   28 -0.4273E+00 -0.1547E+01  0.2052E+00
   29  0.0000E+00 -0.1616E+01  0.0000E+00
   30  0.4273E+00 -0.1547E+01 -0.2052E+00
   31 -0.8077E+00 -0.4709E-02  0.0000E+00
   32  0.0000E+00  0.0000E+00  0.0000E+00
   33  0.8077E+00 -0.4709E-02  0.0000E+00
*STURM SEQUENCE FLAG     1*ITERATION PRINT FLAG     1
UPPER BOUNDS ON EIGENVALUE CLUSTERS
   0.21319565996480E+04  0.51132891537925E+04  0.12536858684719E+05
 NO OF EIGENVALUES IN EACH CLUSTER
                      1                     1                     1
 NO OF EIGENVALUES LESS THAN UPPER BOUNDS
                      1                     2                     3
THE CALCULATED VALUES FOR HARMONIC    2 ARE
```

Figure 5.6 Output for Example 2

EIGENVALUES	FREQUENCIES	ERROR NORMS
0.2110848E+04	0.4594397E+02	0.1620529E-08
0.5062663E+04	0.7115239E+02	0.2225129E-06
0.1241273E+05	0.1114124E+03	0.6627913E-04

THE CALCULATED MODES ARE

MODE= 1

	U	V	W
1	-0.2774E+00	0.3908E-02	0.0000E+00
2	0.0000E+00	0.0000E+00	0.0000E+00
3	0.2774E+00	0.3908E-02	0.0000E+00
4	-0.2631E+00	0.5978E+00	-0.1717E+00
5	0.0000E+00	0.6126E+00	0.0000E+00
6	0.2631E+00	0.5978E+00	0.1717E+00
7	-0.2257E+00	0.1138E+01	-0.3263E+00
8	0.0000E+00	0.1165E+01	0.0000E+00
9	0.2257E+00	0.1138E+01	0.3263E+00
10	-0.1627E+00	0.1566E+01	-0.4491E+00
11	0.0000E+00	0.1604E+01	0.0000E+00
12	0.1627E+00	0.1566E+01	0.4491E+00
13	-0.8647E-01	0.1842E+01	-0.5280E+00
14	0.0000E+00	0.1886E+01	0.0000E+00
15	0.8647E-01	0.1842E+01	0.5280E+00
16	-0.2146E-03	0.1937E+01	-0.5552E+00
17	0.0000E+00	0.1983E+01	0.0000E+00
18	0.2146E-03	0.1937E+01	0.5552E+00
19	0.8611E-01	0.1843E+01	-0.5282E+00
20	0.0000E+00	0.1887E+01	0.0000E+00
21	-0.8611E-01	0.1843E+01	0.5282E+00
22	0.1626E+00	0.1568E+01	-0.4494E+00
23	0.0000E+00	0.1605E+01	0.0000E+00
24	-0.1626E+00	0.1568E+01	0.4494E+00
25	0.2258E+00	0.1140E+01	-0.3265E+00
26	0.0000E+00	0.1167E+01	0.0000E+00
27	-0.2258E+00	0.1140E+01	0.3265E+00
28	0.2635E+00	0.5987E+00	-0.1718E+00
29	0.0000E+00	0.6136E+00	0.0000E+00
30	-0.2635E+00	0.5987E+00	0.1718E+00
31	0.2779E+00	0.3904E-02	0.0000E+00
32	0.0000E+00	0.0000E+00	0.0000E+00
33	-0.2779E+00	0.3904E-02	0.0000E+00

MODE= 2

	U	V	W
1	-0.5328E+00	0.7719E-02	0.0000E+00
2	0.0000E+00	0.0000E+00	0.0000E+00
3	0.5328E+00	0.7719E-02	0.0000E+00
4	-0.4164E+00	0.1123E+01	-0.3073E+00
5	0.0000E+00	0.1165E+01	0.0000E+00

Figure 5.6 Output for Example 2

6	0.4164E+00	0.1123E+01	0.3073E+00
7	-0.1654E+00	0.1821E+01	-0.4971E+00
8	0.0000E+00	0.1887E+01	0.0000E+00
9	0.1654E+00	0.1821E+01	0.4971E+00
10	0.1587E+00	0.1819E+01	-0.4970E+00
11	0.0000E+00	0.1885E+01	0.0000E+00
12	-0.1587E+00	0.1819E+01	0.4970E+00
13	0.4338E+00	0.1126E+01	-0.3075E+00
14	0.0000E+00	0.1167E+01	0.0000E+00
15	-0.4338E+00	0.1126E+01	0.3075E+00
16	0.5142E+00	0.1500E-02	-0.4104E-03
17	0.0000E+00	0.1554E-02	0.0000E+00
18	-0.5142E+00	0.1500E-02	0.4104E-03
19	0.4342E+00	-0.1123E+01	0.3067E+00
20	0.0000E+00	-0.1164E+01	0.0000E+00
21	-0.4342E+00	-0.1123E+01	-0.3067E+00
22	0.1592E+00	-0.1817E+01	0.4964E+00
23	0.0000E+00	-0.1884E+01	0.0000E+00
24	-0.1592E+00	-0.1817E+01	-0.4964E+00
25	-0.1650E+00	-0.1820E+01	0.4966E+00
26	0.0000E+00	-0.1886E+01	0.0000E+00
27	0.1650E+00	-0.1820E+01	-0.4966E+00
28	-0.4163E+00	-0.1123E+01	0.3070E+00
29	0.0000E+00	-0.1165E+01	0.0000E+00
30	0.4163E+00	-0.1123E+01	-0.3070E+00
31	-0.5329E+00	-0.7701E-02	0.0000E+00
32	0.0000E+00	0.0000E+00	0.0000E+00
33	0.5329E+00	-0.7701E-02	0.0000E+00

MODE= 3

	U	V	W
1	0.7627E+00	-0.1120E-01	0.0000E+00
2	0.0000E+00	0.0000E+00	0.0000E+00
3	-0.7627E+00	-0.1120E-01	0.0000E+00
4	0.4049E+00	-0.1529E+01	0.3894E+00
5	0.0000E+00	-0.1615E+01	0.0000E+00
6	-0.4049E+00	-0.1529E+01	-0.3894E+00
7	-0.2380E+00	-0.1799E+01	0.4562E+00
8	0.0000E+00	-0.1897E+01	0.0000E+00
9	0.2380E+00	-0.1799E+01	-0.4562E+00
10	-0.6545E+00	-0.5849E+00	0.1488E+00
11	0.0000E+00	-0.6174E+00	0.0000E+00
12	0.6545E+00	-0.5849E+00	-0.1488E+00
13	-0.6216E+00	0.1110E+01	-0.2818E+00
14	0.0000E+00	0.1172E+01	0.0000E+00
15	0.6216E+00	0.1110E+01	0.2818E+00
16	-0.2834E-03	0.1891E+01	-0.4807E+00
17	0.0000E+00	0.1996E+01	0.0000E+00

Figure 5.6 Output for Example 2

```
   18  0.2834E-03  0.1891E+01  0.4807E+00
   19  0.6212E+00  0.1111E+01 -0.2821E+00
   20  0.0000E+00  0.1173E+01  0.0000E+00
   21 -0.6212E+00  0.1111E+01  0.2821E+00
   22  0.6545E+00 -0.5833E+00  0.1483E+00
   23  0.0000E+00 -0.6156E+00  0.0000E+00
   24 -0.6545E+00 -0.5833E+00 -0.1483E+00
   25  0.2383E+00 -0.1798E+01  0.4557E+00
   26  0.0000E+00 -0.1896E+01  0.0000E+00
   27 -0.2383E+00 -0.1798E+01 -0.4557E+00
   28 -0.4047E+00 -0.1529E+01  0.3889E+00
   29  0.0000E+00 -0.1614E+01  0.0000E+00
   30  0.4047E+00 -0.1529E+01 -0.3889E+00
   31 -0.7626E+00 -0.1117E-01  0.0000E+00
   32  0.0000E+00  0.0000E+00  0.0000E+00
   33  0.7626E+00 -0.1117E-01  0.0000E+00
*STURM SEQUENCE FLAG    1*ITERATION PRINT FLAG    1
UPPER BOUNDS ON EIGENVALUE CLUSTERS
   0.75591921721304E+04  0.12027332403906E+05  0.21402712433470E+05
 NO OF EIGENVALUES IN EACH CLUSTER
                      1                    1                    1
 NO OF EIGENVALUES LESS THAN UPPER BOUNDS
                      1                    2                    3
THE CALCULATED VALUES FOR HARMONIC   3 ARE
   EIGENVALUES      FREQUENCIES       ERROR NORMS
   0.7484349E+04    0.8651213E+02    0.1004066E-06
   0.1190825E+05    0.1091249E+03    0.1782716E-05
   0.2119080E+05    0.1455706E+03    0.1398226E-03
THE CALCULATED MODES ARE
MODE=  1
             U           V           W
    1 -0.2484E+00  0.7498E-02  0.0000E+00
    2  0.0000E+00  0.0000E+00  0.0000E+00
    3  0.2484E+00  0.7498E-02  0.0000E+00
    4 -0.2375E+00  0.5829E+00 -0.2324E+00
    5  0.0000E+00  0.6097E+00  0.0000E+00
    6  0.2375E+00  0.5829E+00  0.2324E+00
    7 -0.2034E+00  0.1111E+01 -0.4413E+00
    8  0.0000E+00  0.1159E+01  0.0000E+00
    9  0.2034E+00  0.1111E+01  0.4413E+00
   10 -0.1469E+00  0.1528E+01 -0.6077E+00
   11  0.0000E+00  0.1596E+01  0.0000E+00
   12  0.1469E+00  0.1528E+01  0.6077E+00
   13 -0.7825E-01  0.1797E+01 -0.7146E+00
   14  0.0000E+00  0.1877E+01  0.0000E+00
   15  0.7825E-01  0.1797E+01  0.7146E+00
   16 -0.4790E-03  0.1891E+01 -0.7518E+00
```

Figure 5.6 Output for Example 2

17	0.0000E+00	0.1975E+01	0.0000E+00
18	0.4790E-03	0.1891E+01	0.7518E+00
19	0.7743E-01	0.1800E+01	-0.7154E+00
20	0.0000E+00	0.1879E+01	0.0000E+00
21	-0.7743E-01	0.1800E+01	0.7154E+00
22	0.1466E+00	0.1532E+01	-0.6089E+00
23	0.0000E+00	0.1600E+01	0.0000E+00
24	-0.1466E+00	0.1532E+01	0.6089E+00
25	0.2037E+00	0.1115E+01	-0.4425E+00
26	0.0000E+00	0.1163E+01	0.0000E+00
27	-0.2037E+00	0.1115E+01	0.4425E+00
28	0.2383E+00	0.5852E+00	-0.2331E+00
29	0.0000E+00	0.6120E+00	0.0000E+00
30	-0.2383E+00	0.5852E+00	0.2331E+00
31	0.2494E+00	0.7513E-02	0.0000E+00
32	0.0000E+00	0.0000E+00	0.0000E+00
33	-0.2494E+00	0.7513E-02	0.0000E+00

MODE= 2

	U	V	W
1	-0.4823E+00	0.1436E-01	0.0000E+00
2	0.0000E+00	0.0000E+00	0.0000E+00
3	0.4823E+00	0.1436E-01	0.0000E+00
4	-0.3795E+00	0.1100E+01	-0.4202E+00
5	0.0000E+00	0.1162E+01	0.0000E+00
6	0.3795E+00	0.1100E+01	0.4202E+00
7	-0.1504E+00	0.1785E+01	-0.6792E+00
8	0.0000E+00	0.1882E+01	0.0000E+00
9	0.1504E+00	0.1785E+01	0.6792E+00
10	0.1443E+00	0.1782E+01	-0.6794E+00
11	0.0000E+00	0.1881E+01	0.0000E+00
12	-0.1443E+00	0.1782E+01	0.6794E+00
13	0.3953E+00	0.1104E+01	-0.4207E+00
14	0.0000E+00	0.1165E+01	0.0000E+00
15	-0.3953E+00	0.1104E+01	0.4207E+00
16	0.4683E+00	0.3256E-02	-0.1242E-02
17	0.0000E+00	0.3435E-02	0.0000E+00
18	-0.4683E+00	0.3256E-02	0.1242E-02
19	0.3961E+00	-0.1099E+01	0.4185E+00
20	0.0000E+00	-0.1159E+01	0.0000E+00
21	-0.3961E+00	-0.1099E+01	-0.4185E+00
22	0.1453E+00	-0.1779E+01	0.6781E+00
23	0.0000E+00	-0.1878E+01	0.0000E+00
24	-0.1453E+00	-0.1779E+01	-0.6781E+00
25	-0.1496E+00	-0.1784E+01	0.6786E+00
26	0.0000E+00	-0.1881E+01	0.0000E+00
27	0.1496E+00	-0.1784E+01	-0.6786E+00
28	-0.3794E+00	-0.1100E+01	0.4200E+00

igure 5.6 Output for Example 2

```
   29  0.0000E+00 -0.1163E+01  0.0000E+00
   30  0.3794E+00 -0.1100E+01 -0.4200E+00
   31 -0.4826E+00 -0.1434E-01  0.0000E+00
   32  0.0000E+00  0.0000E+00  0.0000E+00
   33  0.4826E+00 -0.1434E-01  0.0000E+00
MODE=  3
           U            V            W
    1  0.6992E+00 -0.2031E-01  0.0000E+00
    2  0.0000E+00  0.0000E+00  0.0000E+00
    3 -0.6992E+00 -0.2031E-01  0.0000E+00
    4  0.3734E+00 -0.1504E+01  0.5388E+00
    5  0.0000E+00 -0.1614E+01  0.0000E+00
    6 -0.3734E+00 -0.1504E+01 -0.5388E+00
    7 -0.2201E+00 -0.1770E+01  0.6308E+00
    8  0.0000E+00 -0.1895E+01  0.0000E+00
    9  0.2201E+00 -0.1770E+01 -0.6308E+00
   10 -0.6028E+00 -0.5760E+00  0.2060E+00
   11  0.0000E+00 -0.6175E+00  0.0000E+00
   12  0.6028E+00 -0.5760E+00 -0.2060E+00
   13 -0.5739E+00  0.1091E+01 -0.3896E+00
   14  0.0000E+00  0.1169E+01  0.0000E+00
   15  0.5739E+00  0.1091E+01  0.3896E+00
   16 -0.6182E-03  0.1861E+01 -0.6648E+00
   17  0.0000E+00  0.1994E+01  0.0000E+00
   18  0.6182E-03  0.1861E+01  0.6648E+00
   19  0.5731E+00  0.1094E+01 -0.3906E+00
   20  0.0000E+00  0.1173E+01  0.0000E+00
   21 -0.5731E+00  0.1094E+01  0.3906E+00
   22  0.6031E+00 -0.5725E+00  0.2047E+00
   23  0.0000E+00 -0.6138E+00  0.0000E+00
   24 -0.6031E+00 -0.5725E+00 -0.2047E+00
   25  0.2209E+00 -0.1769E+01  0.6297E+00
   26  0.0000E+00 -0.1893E+01  0.0000E+00
   27 -0.2209E+00 -0.1769E+01 -0.6297E+00
   28 -0.3731E+00 -0.1504E+01  0.5382E+00
   29  0.0000E+00 -0.1614E+01  0.0000E+00
   30  0.3731E+00 -0.1504E+01 -0.5382E+00
   31 -0.6993E+00 -0.2027E-01  0.0000E+00
   32  0.0000E+00  0.0000E+00  0.0000E+00
   33  0.6993E+00 -0.2027E-01  0.0000E+00
```

Figure 5.6 Output for Example 2

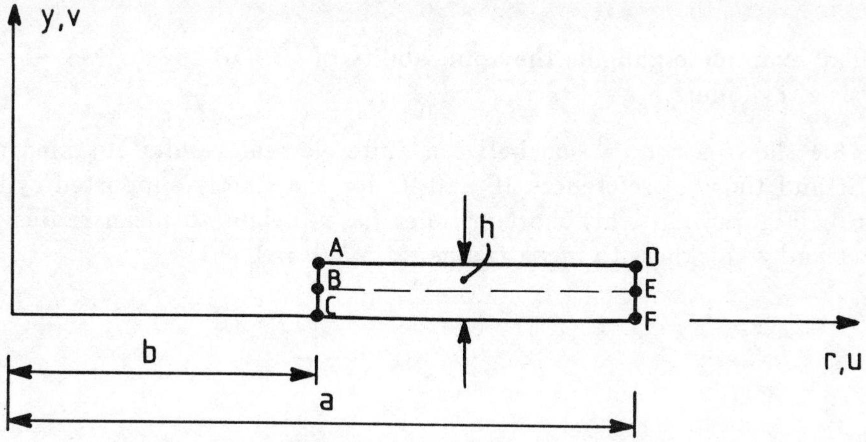

Figure 5.7 Simply supported, annular plate; $h/a = 0.1, b/a = 0.5$, $\nu = 0.3$; boundary conditions: $A(w = 0), B(u = v = w = 0)$, $C(w = 0), D(w = 0), E(u = v = w = 0), F(w = 0), B \rightarrow E(u = w = 0)$

ameters $n = 0, 1, 2$ and concentric circles $s = 1, 2$ obtained using meshes of 5 and 10 SOR elements. These values are in good agreement with frequencies obtained using Mindlin plate theory [21].

Table 5.3 Frequency parameters λ^2_{ns} for a uniform annular Mindlin plate with simple supports on the inner and outer edges; $\nu = 0.3, h/a = 0.1, b/a = 0.5$

		λ^2_{ns}		
n	s	VISOR analysis (5 elmts.)	VISOR analysis (10 elmts.)	closed form solution
0	1	37.657	37.577	37.33
	2	130.920	129.686	127.17
1	1	39.217	39.138	38.86
	2	136.249	131.025	128.46
2	1	43.880	43.803	43.45
	2	136.219	135.022	132.29

5.4 Example 4 – Short, simply supported cylinder

The final example highlights the applicability of VISOR to the free vibratio analysis of cylinders.

Table 5.4 shows a comparison between finite element results obtained usin VISOR and those of references 10 and 22 for the simply supported cylinde shown in Figure 5.8. This short cylinder has a height to mean radius rati $l/a = 1$ and a thickness to mean radius ratio $h/a = 1$.

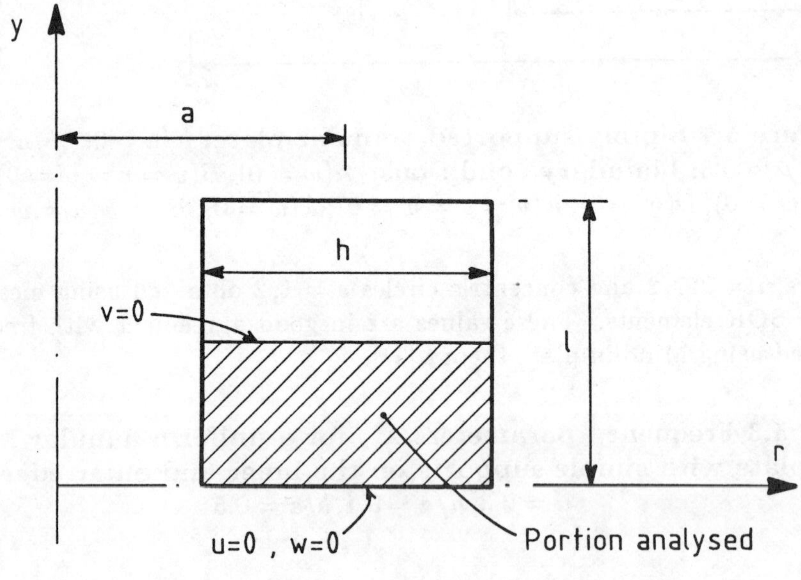

Figure 5.8 Short, simply supported cylinder

The VISOR results given in Table 5.4 were obtained using 4 elements in th thickness direction and 3 divisions of elements in a symmetric half of the cylir der (in the axial direction). There is excellent agreement between the freqer cies obtained by VISOR finite element analysis, the finite element analysis c Gladwell and Vijay [10] and the closed form solution of Armenakas, Gazis an Hermann [22].

Figure 5.9 shows the mode shapes for the case $n = 1$. The numbers in th round brackets are from reference 22 and those in square brackets are from th VISOR finite element analysis.

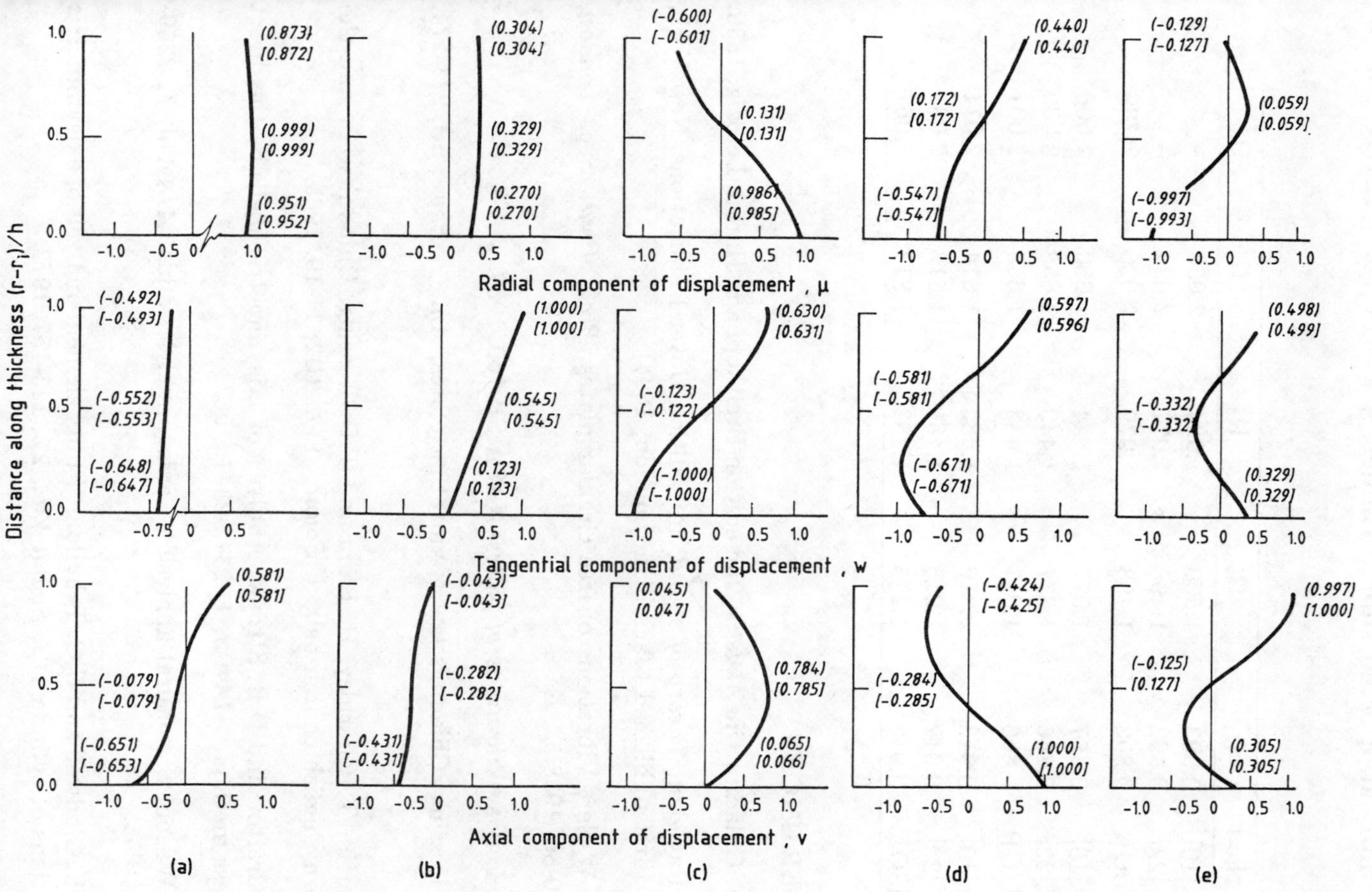

Figure 5.9 A comparison of mode shapes for a short, simply supported cylinder

Table 5.4 Frequency parameters $\Omega_i = \omega_i h(\rho/G)^{1/2}/\pi$ for a simply supported short cylinder; $h/a = 1.0, l/a = 1.0, \nu = 0.3$

n	method	Ω_1	Ω_2	Ω_3	Ω_4	Ω_5
0	f.e.[10]	0.893	1.500	1.984	2.035	–
	c.f.[22]	0.892	1.498	1.977	2.024	–
	VISOR	0.892	1.498	1.979	2.026	2.789
1	f.e.[10]	0.867	1.077	1.444	1.660	2.006
	c.f.[22]	0.866	1.077	1.443	1.658	2.000
	VISOR	0.866	1.077	1.443	1.658	2.001
2	f.e.[10]	0.913	1.216	1.483	1.814	2.071
	c.f.[22]	0.912	1.215	1.481	1.813	2.064
	VISOR	0.912	1.215	1.482	1.813	2.067

REFERENCES

1. E.F.F. Chladni, *Die Akustik*, 2nd edition Breitkopf and Hartel, Leipzig, 1830.

2. Lord Rayleigh, *Theory of sound*, 2nd edition Dover Publications, New York, 1945, (first published Macmillan, London, 1894).

3. M.D. Waller, Vibrations of free circular plates, *Proc. Phys. Soc. London*, **50**, 70-86, 1938.

4. A.W. Leissa, *Vibrations of plates*, NASA SP-160, 1969.

5. T.D. Rossing, Chladni's law of vibrating plates, *Am. J. Phys.*, **50**, 271-274, 1982.

6. R. Perrin, T. Charnley, H. Banu and T.D. Rossing, Chladni's law and the modern English church bell, *J. Sound. Vib.*, **102**, 11-19, 1985.

7. P.E. Grafton and D.R. Strome, Analysis of axisymmetric shells by the direct stiffness method, *AIAA J*, **1**, 2342-2347, 1963.

8. E.L. Wilson, Structural analysis of axisymmetric solids, *AIAA J*, **3**, 2269-2274, 1965.

9. G.M.L. Gladwell and U.C. Tahbildar, Finite element analysis of axisymmetric vibrations of cylinders, *J. Sound Vib.*, **22**, 143-157, 1972.

10. G.M.L. Gladwell and D.K. Vijay, Vibration analysis of axisymmetric resonators, *J. Sound Vib.*, **42**, 137-145, 1975.

11. D.L. Nelson and D.L. Thomas, Free vibration of cooling towers with column supports, *J. Sound Vib.*, **57**, 149-153, 1978.

12. C.A. Mota Soares and M. Petyt, Finite element dynamic analysis of practical disks, *J. Sound Vib.*, **61**, 547-560.

13. R. Perrin, T. Charnley and J. Depont, Normal modes of the modern English church bell, *J. Sound Vib.*, **90**, 29-49, 1983.

14. Y.K. Cheung, *The finite strip method in structural analysis*, Pergammon Press, Oxford, 1969.

15. B. M. Irons and S. Ahmad, *Techniques of finite elements*, Ellis Horwood, Chichester, 1980.

16. P.Pedersen and M.M. Megahed, Axisymmetric element analysis using analytical computing, *Computers and Structures*, **5**, 241-244, 1975.

17. P.Pedersen and J. Cederkvist, Analysis of non-axisymmetric vibrations and the use of basic element matrices, *Computers and Structures*, **14**, 255-260, 1981.

18. B. Duncan, User manual for finite prism program, Report to HECB, Dept. of Transport, Univ. College of Swansea, 1976.

19. K.J. Bathe and E.C. Wilson, *Numerical methods in finite element analysis*, Prentice-Hall, New Jersey, 1976.

20. T . Irie, G. Yamada and S. Aomura, Natural frequencies of Mindlin circular plates, *J. Appl. Mech.*, **47**, 652-655, 1980.

21. T. Irie, G. Yamada and K. Takagi, Natural frequencies of thick annular plates, *J. Appl. Mech.*, **49**, 633-638, 1982.

22. A.E. Armenakas, D.C. Gazis and G. Hermann, *Free vibrations of circular cylindrical shells*, Pergammon Press, New York, 1969.

NONLINEAR TRANSIENT DYNAMIC ANALYSIS OF THREE DIMENSIONAL STRUCTURES - A FINITE ELEMENT PROGRAM FOR STEEL AND REINFORCED CONCRETE MATERIALS

M.CERVERA, E. HINTON, J.BONET and N.BIĆANIĆ
Department of Civil Engineering,
University College of Swansea

1. INTRODUCTION

1.1 Main objectives

This chapter is concerned with three dimensional, nonlinear, transient dynamic analysis with special emphasis on plate and shell structures. Two types of structural material are considered: steel and reinforced concrete. Eight- and twenty-noded, hexahedral, isoparametric finite elements are used for the spatial discretisation. In the idealisation of the reinforced concrete structures, the steel reinforcement is incorporated in the concrete brick element by assuming perfect bond.

For steel structures, a classical elasto/viscoplastic constitutive model is adopted. A related model is used for concrete structures but allowance is made for rate dependency and damage accumulation in the concrete. Furthermore, tensile cracking is considered using the smeared crack approach and the constant fracture energy release concept, where the strain softening effect is related to the element size to make the response prediction mesh-size dependent.

1.2 Three dimensional models versus layered plate/ shell models

The usual method of modelling reinforced concrete shell structures is to make use of the so-called 'layered' shell elements. The elements are composed of a series of through-thickness 'layers', each assumed to be in a state of plane stress. This approach has several disadvantages:

(a) The quadrature rule used to integrate quantities such as the residual forces and the tangential stiffness through the thickness (i.e. the mid-ordinate rule) is not very accurate, and many layers (eight to twelve) must be used to ensure reasonable accuracy.

(b) The large number of sampling points used per element makes the evaluation of the tangential stiffness matrix and internal force vector quite expensive.

(c) The plane stress assumption in the layered plate or shell implies that the normal stress perpendicular to the midsurface is neglected. Furthermore, in most models, in-plane stresses are treated separately from transverse shear stresses, usually in an inconsistent way.

(d) The elements used are usually of the Mindlin type. This results in an 'a prori' imposed uniform distribution of transverse shear strains through the thickness.

(e) Cracks are assumed to form due to in-plane stresses only, the effect of the transverse shear stresses being disregarded when checking for cracking. As a result, cracks can only form in a direction perpendicular to the midsurface, which is an unrealistic constraint of the model that makes it unable to represent non-flexural failures.

(f) Concrete slabs are usually moderately thick, so consideration of transverse shear strains and stresses is not insignificant, especially near the supports.

(Some of the above comments (a)-(d) also apply to steel structures in which the monitoring of the spread of nonlinear behaviour through the thickness is of particular interest.)

All these considerations point to the necessity of developing fully three dimensional models which can be used to analyse reinforced concrete structures both efficiently and accurately. The use of a standard three dimensional approach for the analysis avoids the complexities associated with shell formulations, allows for a wider range of applications, and is free from the simplifying assumptions mentioned above. On the other hand, a 3D analysis usually involves a larger number of degrees of freedom for a given discretization than a shell formulation, and requires better mesh-generation and post-processing facilities than those of an essentially two dimensional analysis.

This chapter continues with a description of the spatial discretisation and then the various material models are described. The solution of the semi-discrete equilibrium equations using the Newmark method is then presented. The use of the present models is illustrated with the aid of some examples and finally, some finite element software is described, listed and fully documented with test examples.

2 STRUCTURAL IDEALIZATION

2.1 Three dimensional model - reinforced concrete and steel structures

The 8- and 20-node isoparametric elements shown in Figure 1 are used in this work. Standard interpolation functions [1] are used in the present formulation.

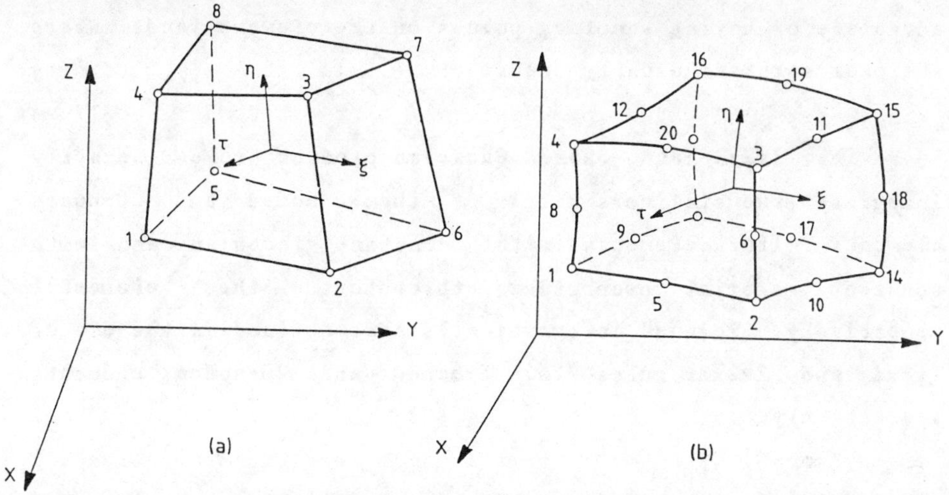

Figure 1 Linear and quadratic isoparametric solid elements

Isoparametric finite elements are highly effective in practice, although for linear problems a considerable proportion of the total computational effort is often absorbed in the numerical integration of the stiffness matrix coefficients. It is thus very important to choose suitable integration schemes that are both accurate and computationally efficient.

For nonlinear problems the previous observation is even more critical since evaluation of the stiffness matrix occurs frequently. Equally important is the fact that the integration points are also the sampling points for the stresses and material state determination. These points are used, in turn, in the evaluation of the internal resisting forces. On one hand, the use of few sampling points reduces the computation time, but on the other, the use of more stress sampling points provides more complete information about the material state throughout the element. Clearly, a compromise must be sought.

Usually, either Gauss-Legendre or Lobatto product rules are used with linear and quadratic solid elements. Gauss quadratures are more accurate, while Lobatto rules posess the advantage of having sampling points on the element faces, where the peak stresses usually occur.

The 2x2x2 and 3x3x3 Gaussian product rules exactly integrate the stiffness matrix of the 8-noded and 20-noded elements (for elements with constant Jacobian and with constant material properties throughout the element), repectively. Reduced integration is here defined as the use of 1x1x1 and 2x2x2 rules for 8-noded and 20-noded elements respectively.

Reduced integration is computationally attractive, because it greatly reduces the number of operations to be performed in the evaluation of the residual forces and tangential stiffness matrices. However, it is well-known that under-integrated matrices are rank deficient. This defect can lead to the development of spurious deformation mechanisms that affect the behaviour of a simple element and may, for certain meshes, propagate throughout the mesh. Much effort has been devoted to the development of 'stabilization' or 'mechanism suppression' techniques [2-4] that can be used at the element level to suppress the spurious mechanisms. As a result, highly efficient 8-noded elements with only one integration point are available.

Results presented by Crisfield [5] show that spurious mechanisms are more likely to occur where cracking or material softening is considered. Under-integration may seriously affect the computed results if material nonlinearity is to be considered.

In the present work, a different set of integration rules, first introduced by Irons [6], is used for the solid element. These Gaussian-type rules have proved to be both accurate and efficient [7].

The above integration rules are designed to integrate complete polynomials. They correctly integrate polynomials of the type $\sum C_{ijk} \; x^i y^j z^k$ (with $i+j+k \leq n$) while product Gauss rules, integrate correctly more terms, so that $i,j,k \leq n$ - an unnecessary accuracy. When these rules are used to integrate the stiffness matrix of the 20-noded element, no rank deficiency is observed. Furthermore, use of these rules alleviates the overstiff behaviour observed when the 3x3x3 rule is employed.

The rules can be expressed in the form

$$\int_{-1}^{+1}\int_{-1}^{+1}\int_{-1}^{+1} f(x,y,z)\, dx\, dy\, dz =$$

$$= A\, f(0,0,0) + \qquad (\text{1 term})$$

$$+ B\, [f(-b,0,0)+f(b,0,0)+f(0,-b,0)+\ldots] + \qquad (\text{6 terms})$$

$$+ C\, [\, f(-c,-c,-c) + f(c,-c,-c) + \ldots] \qquad (\text{8 terms})$$

(2.1)

The coefficients in (2.1) for the different rules are:

	A	B	C	b	c
Rule 15	1.564444	0.355556	0.537778	1.000000	0.674100
Rule 6	0.000000	1.333333	0.000000	1.000000	0.000000

The distribution of the sampling points over the volume of the 20-noded element can be seen in Figure 2. In the 8-noded element the sampling points are located at the centres of the faces.

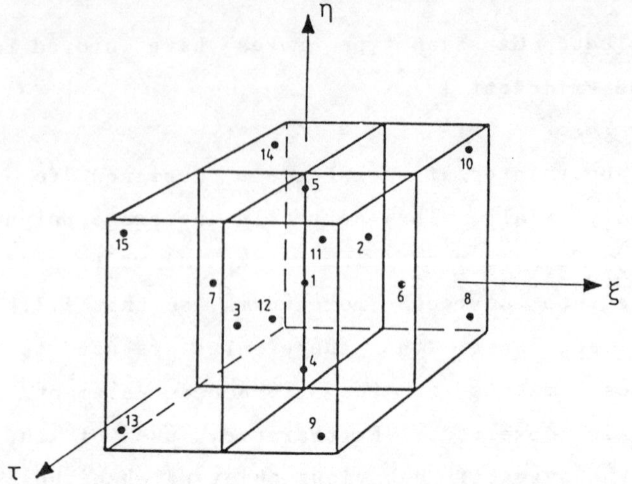

Figure 2 Three-dimensional concrete element with 20 nodes and 15 integration points

Both rules have the advantage of having sampling points at the centres of the element faces. These locations are convenient sampling positions for the stress peak values. Futhermore, the mismatch between the stress values at these points for two adjoining elements gives an estimate of the accuracy of the adopted mesh.

As the solid finite element is intended for use in the analysis of plates and shells of various thicknesses, some aspect ratio tests were carried out. A series of uniformly-loaded, linear elastic square plates of various span-to-thickness ratios, a/h, were analysed with two sets of boundary conditions: (i) simply supported on all edges, and (ii) clamped conditions on all edges.

Symmetric quadrants, idealised with regular meshes of 4, 9 and 16 twenty-noded elements were used for the analyses, and plots of normalised central deflection against log(a/h) for the individual elements are shown in Figures 3 and 4 for the two different boundary conditions, respectively. The central displacements are divided by the value predicted by thin plate

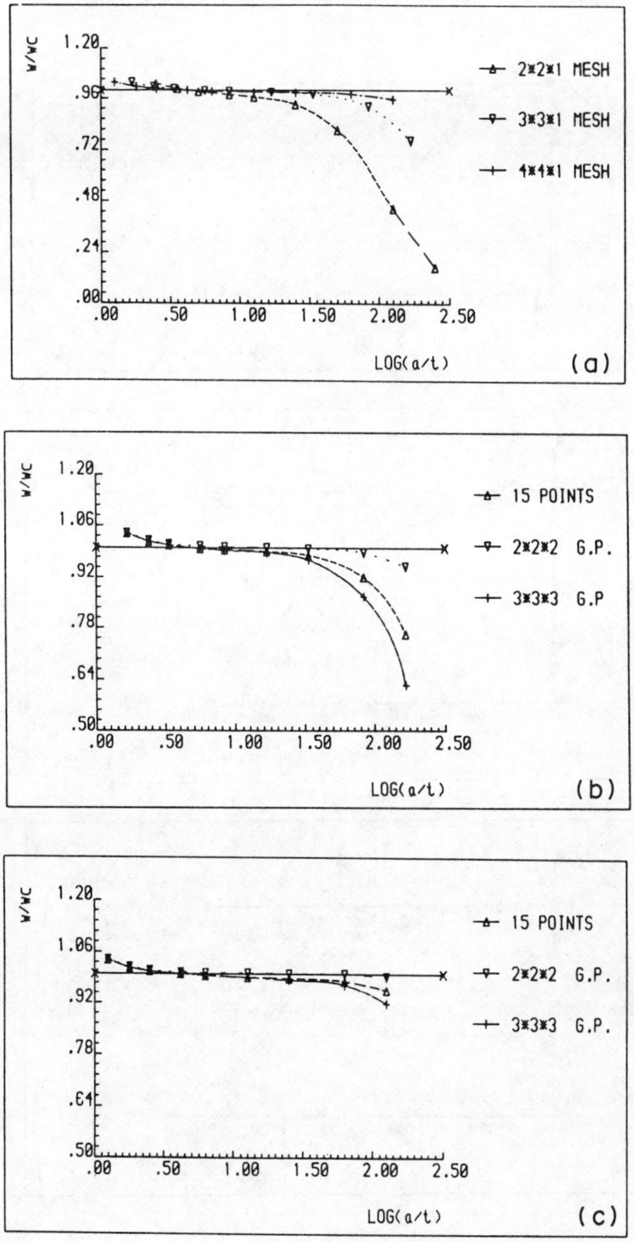

Figure 3 Aspect ratio study for a simply-supported plate: Central displacement (normalized with respect to thin plate theory) versus log(a/h)

(a) Influence of the mesh refinement

(b) Different integration rules for 3x3x1 mesh

(c) Different integration rules for 4x4x1 mesh

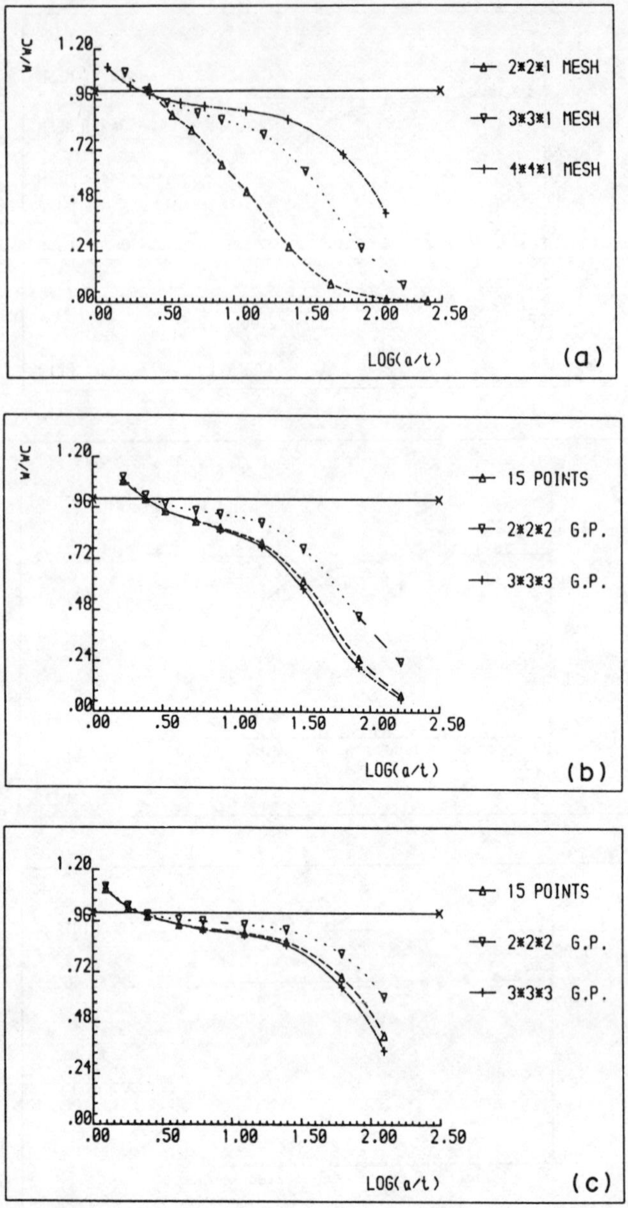

Figure 4 Aspect ratio study for a clamped plate:
Central displacement (normalized with respect to thin plate theory) versus log(a/h)
(a) Influence of the mesh refinement
(b) Different integration rules for 3x3x1 mesh
(c) Different integration rules for 4x4x1 mesh

theory. The solutions from the solid elements should become asymptotic to the thin plate solution as the aspect ratio, a/t, increases.

Figure 3(a) shows results for the simply supported plate using the integration rule 15 for the three different meshes. A locking-type behaviour is exhibited, but as expected, the problem is greatly alleviated by refinement of the mesh. Figures 3(b)-(c) show results for the same problem comparing the performance of the proposed rule against the traditional 2x2x2 and 3x3x3 Gaussian rules for the 9 and 16 element meshes, respectively. It can be observed that the 15 point rule, besides being computationally more economical than the equivalent 'exact' Gaussian rule, is less prone to locking. The results corresponding to the 2x2x2 rule show the benefits of reduced integration in alleviating locking behaviour. Although the 2x2x2 rule gives better results than the two other 'exact' rules, for very thin situations an oscillation in the lateral displacements was observed due to a spurious low energy mode. This is the reason why the 2x2x2 rule will not be used in this work for nonlinear analysis.

Figure 4 show similar results for the totally clamped plate. In this case the locking behaviour is more severe, and the previous conclusions are confirmed.

The reason for this locking behaviour can be explained. The transverse shear stresses are defined (up to the first order terms) as

$$\gamma_{xz} = \frac{\partial u}{\partial z} + \frac{\partial w}{\partial x}$$
$$\gamma_{yz} = \frac{\partial v}{\partial z} + \frac{\partial w}{\partial y} \qquad (2.2)$$

With the quadratic shape functions used in the 20-noded brick, displacements u, v and w are expressed as second order polynomials in x, y and z. Consequently, the terms $\partial u/\partial z$ and $\partial v/\partial z$ are quadratic in x and y, while the terms $\partial w/\partial x$ and $\partial w/\partial y$ are only linear in x and y, respectively. Therefore, due to the different order of the terms involved, it is impossible for the strains γ_{xz} and γ_{yz} to vanish for all points within the element, as they should in thin plate situations. The spurious shear strains are responsible for the shear-locking behaviour exhibited.

From a careful analysis of these and other results it appears wise to limit the aspect ratio of individual 20-node brick elements to a maximum of about 25 when bending action predominates and when adequate computational precision (at least 11 significant digits) is available.

2.2 Reinforcement representation

Analysis of reinforced concrete structures by the finite element method requires a simple, yet accurate way of representing the reinforcement.

Here, concrete and reinforcement are represented with a single element [8,9]. Perfect bond is assumed between the reinforcement and the surrounding concrete. The stiffness and internal forces associated with the reinforcement are integrated and added to those of the concrete to get the total stiffness and internal forces of the element.

Each set of reinforcing bars is smeared as a two-dimensional membrane 'layer' of equivalent thickness (and hence equal area). The layer is placed inside the solid element to coincide with the surface corresponding to (ξ, η, const.), (ξ, const, τ) or (const., η, τ) as appropriate. The resulting element is shown in Figure 5.

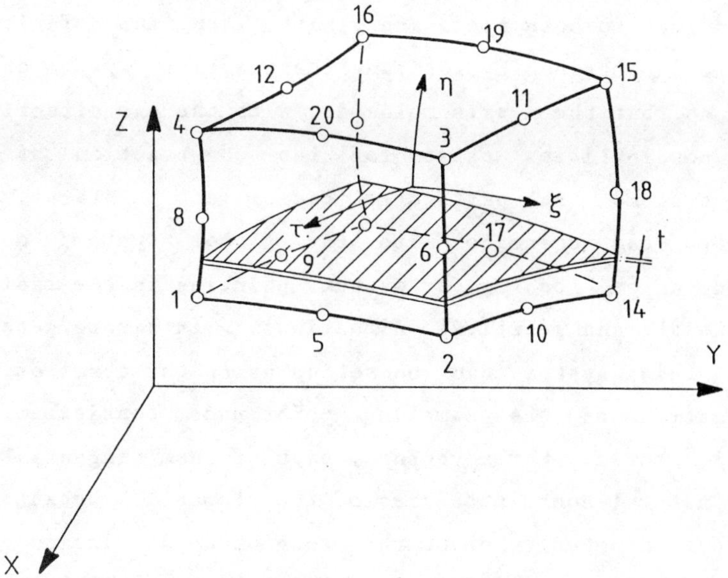

Figure 5 Isoparametric solid element with smeared reinforcement

Although this procedure does not allow the consideration of reinforcement in an arbitrary position inside the element, it covers most of the practical situations. The proposed restriction has the advantage of an easy definition of the sampling points used to perform the necessary surface integrations over the steel reinforcement membrane.

Reinforcing bars are assumed to only resist axial stresses in the bar direction. A local Cartesian coordinate system must be set up at each integration point in the reinforcment membrane with one of the axes pointing along the bar direction. Stresses and the local stiffness matrix for the reinforcement, are first evaluated in this local system, and then transformed into the global system. Finally, the contribution of the bar is added to that of the solid concrete.

The local system can be defined in two stages. First, an auxiliary system is set up so that the x- and y-axis are tangential to the membrane and are mutually orthogonal, and the z-axis is normal to both the x and y axes. Then, the definitive local system is obtained by rotating the auxiliary system about its z-axis so that the x-axis coincides with the bar direction. Different possibilities exist for the construction of the auxiliary system. In particular cases, such as plates, the local system can coincide with the global system, or be constructed as a local polar system, pointing in the radial, circumferential and vertical directions. In a more general situation, this system can be set up using the terms of the Jacobian matrix of the sampling point under consideration. This matrix provides three vectors, each of them tangential to one of the natural coordinate axes of the element. Because of the procedure adopted to place the reinforcement inside the element, two of these vectors will always be tangential to the reinforcement membrane, and they can be used to construct the auxiliary Cartesian system using a simple orthogonalisation procedure.

2.3 Dynamic equilibrium equations in semi-discrete form

The nonlinear dynamic equilibrium equations can be written in semi-discrete form as

$$\underline{M}\,\ddot{\underline{d}} + \underline{C}\,\dot{\underline{d}} + \underline{p}(\underline{d},\dot{\underline{d}}) = \underline{f} \tag{2.3}$$

where $\underline{d}$, $\dot{\underline{d}}$ and $\ddot{\underline{d}}$ are vectors of nodal displacements, velocities and accelerations, respectively. $\underline{M}$ and $\underline{C}$ are the mass and damping matrices, $\underline{p}(\underline{d},\dot{\underline{d}})$ is the vector of internal resisting forces, and $\underline{f}$ is the vector of external applied forces.

The global mass and damping matrices are defined as

$$\underline{M} = \int_V \underline{N}^T \rho\, \underline{N}\, dV \tag{2.4}$$

$$\underline{C} = \int_V \underline{N}^T c\, \underline{N}\, dV \tag{2.5}$$

where $\underline{N}$ is a matrix of shape functions, ρ is the mass density and c the damping parameter.

The vector of internal resisting forces, $\underline{p}(\underline{d},\dot{\underline{d}})$, is given by the expression

$$\underline{p} = \int_v \underline{B}^T \underline{\sigma} \, dv \tag{2.6}$$

where $\underline{B}$ is the strain-displacement matrix and $\underline{\sigma}$ is the vector of stresses.

2.3.1 Consistent and lumped mass matrices

The global mass matrix $\underline{M}$ is assembled from the element contributions $\underline{M}^e$ in the standard finite element manner [1] .

The mass matrices $\underline{M}$ and $\underline{M}^e$ are called 'consistent' when calculated using (2.4). The resulting element mass matrix is a full matrix, and the global matrix has the same structure as the stiffness matrix. A very convenient simplification is achieved by lumping the element mass to the nodes. For simple elements it is easy to devise lumping schemes based on intuitive reasoning [10]. However, with higher order elements a physically obvious lumping strategy is not always available. Several approaches have been proposed:

(i) The element nodes are chosen as the sampling points used for the numerical integration of $\underline{M}^e$. As in the standard finite element formulation the shape function corresponding to a particular node vanishes at all other node positions, this procedure yields a diagonal matrix. However, some of the matrix terms may be negative and this can lead to the computation of imaginary frequencies of vibration [11].

(ii) A set of shape functions is used for the evaluation of $\underline{M}^e$ which is different from the ones used for the stiffness matrix evaluation. Choosing piecewise constant functions, equal to unity in the vicinity of a node and zero elsewhere, leads to a diagonal matrix [12].

(iii) The diagonal term of the consistent mass matrix is scaled so that the total element mass M is preserved [13]:

$$M_i = \frac{M_{ii} M}{\sum_i M_{ii}} \tag{2.7}$$

This technique has been successfully used in the context of plane elements [14], Mindlin plate elements [15], degenerated shell elements [16], and heat capacity elements. It is interesting to note that this lumping technique gives results which are identical to those obtained using a 3x3 Lobatto integration rule for the biquadratic Lagrangian element [18]. This procedure will be used in the present study.

Lumping may distort the natural frequencies of the system. Comprehensive studies of this effect have been carried out by Bićanić [19] in the context of plane elements, and Surana [20] for degenerate shell elements. Results prove that mesh refinement significantly improves the frequencies for the lumped mass representation, but results obtained with coarse meshes are within acceptable engineering limits.

2.3.2 Modelling of damping

Usually the damping parameter c appearing in (2.5) is not known, so a different procedure has to be used to construct the $\underline{C}$ matrix. If the total damping in the structure is assumed to be a sum of the damping of the individual modes present in the system response, a reasonable numerical damping matrix can be derived as follows [21].

If two representative modes are considered then so-called Rayleigh damping is a linear combination of the mass and stiffness matrices so that

$$\underline{C} = a_o\underline{M} + a_1\underline{K} \tag{2.8}$$

The main advantage of Rayleigh damping is that it leads to a banded damping matrix, with the same structure as the stiffness matrix. Thus, consideration of damping does not cause any increase in computational time when solving the resulting set of equations. On the other hand, a disadvantage of Rayleigh damping is that the higher modes are considerably more damped than the lower modes, for which the Rayleigh constants have been selected. This implies that higher modes in the response of the structure will be artificially filtered out.

Here, a damping matrix of the form given by (2.8) is adopted.

3 MATERIAL MODELS

3.1 Mechanical properties of steel and concrete

Reinforced concrete has been the subject of extensive research over a considerable period of time. Despite this research effort our knowledge about the mechanical behaviour of reinforced concrete is rather deficient. The description of the behaviour of concrete as a composite structural material involves consideration of three main aspects: the behaviour of concrete, the reponse of the steel reinforcement, and the interaction between the steel and the surrounding concrete.

Although experimental data on dynamic behaviour of concrete are rather scarce, and almost nonexistent for multiaxial stress states, some features specific to dynamic behaviour can be observed. Phenomena such as strain-rate sensitivity and progressive degradation of strength should be included in a material model intended to be used for transient analysis.

In the following, an elasto/viscoplastic model that includes strain-rate sensitivity and progressive degradation of strength is described. Some aspects of the model implementation within a finite element computer program will also be discussed.

In this Section the experimental response of concrete and steel under dynamic loading will be considered, and some conclusions will be drawn which will be used as a basis for the development of the material model described in next section. The mechanics of bond-slip between steel and concrete will not be discussed here, because perfect bond is always assumed in our numerical model.

3.1.1 Concrete

Most of the experimental studies carried out on concrete are restricted to short term monotonic quasistatic loading conditions with strain-rates of about 10^{-6} sec^{-1} or less. However, some uniaxial and biaxial dynamic test results are available. The influence of loading rate for specimens with uniaxial compressive loads has been studied by many researchers [22-27]. Hatano [28] conducted some valuable direct tensile tests on notched cylinders under impulsive loading. He also studied fatigue failure under periodic compressive loads [29,30]. Nelissen [31] has performed biaxial tests under different rates of straining.

Typical experimental results from dynamic uniaxial tests are shown in Figure 6, where results for direct compressive tests [26,27], direct tensile tests [28] and low cycle fatigue tests [29,30] are plotted.

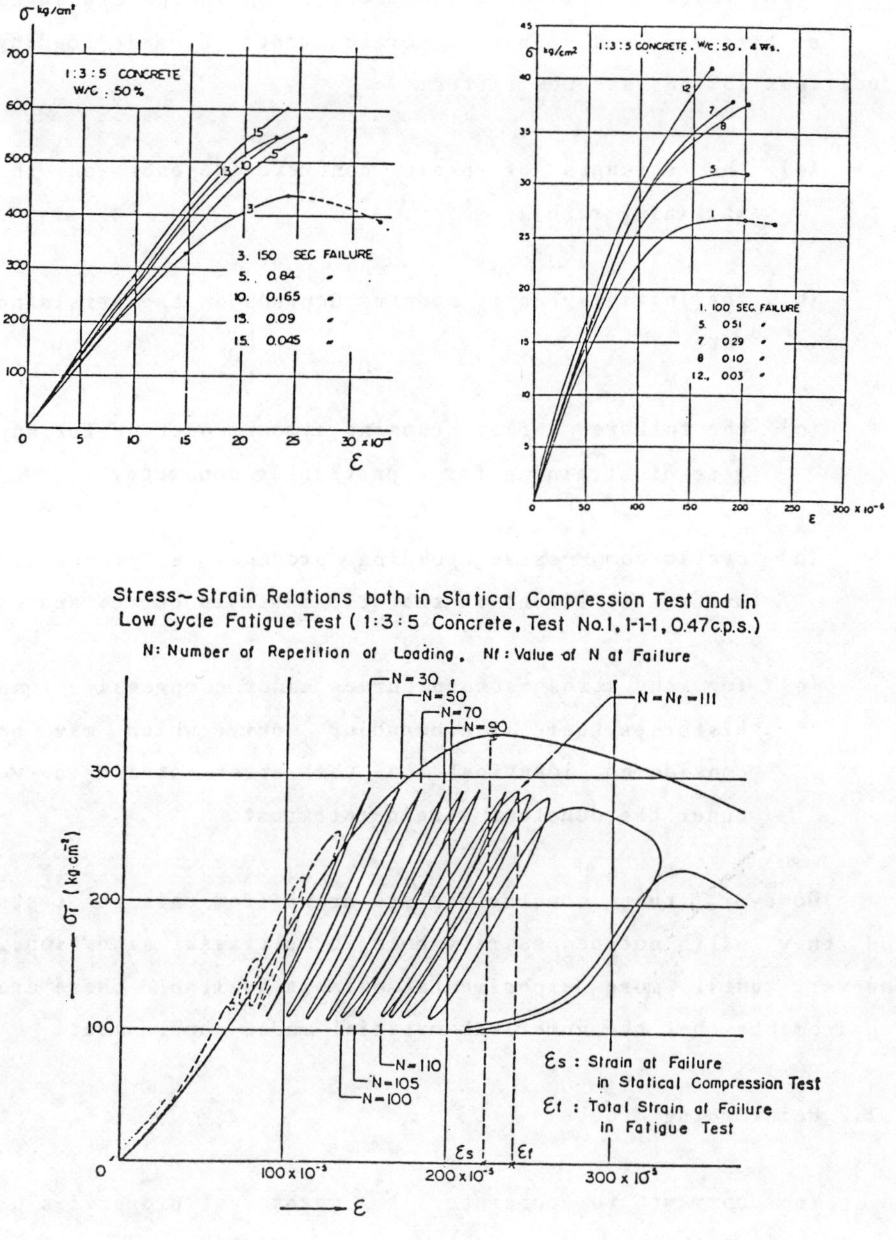

Figure 6 Typical experimental results from dynamic uniaxial tests

(a) compressive tests (1:3:5 concrete)

(b) tensile tests (1:3:5 concrete)

(c) stress-strain relations both in compression test and low cycle fatigue test (1:3:5 concrete)

From these experimental results, the principal features of the behaviour of plain concrete under dynamic loading conditions [32,33] are now listed:

(a) the strength of plain concrete depends on the straining rate,

(b) the initial elastic modulus depends on the straining rate,

(c) the failure strain remains almost constant for any rate of straining for a particular concrete,

(d) cyclic compressive loading produces a pronounced hysteresis effect in the stress-strain curve, and

(e) for the stress-strain curves under compressive load histories there is a bounding curve which may be considered identical to the stress-strain curve under the constant strain-rate test.

However, these conclusions are drawn from uniaxial tests and they will not necessarily hold in multiaxial situations. However, until more experimental data is available these are requirements that the numerical material model should meet.

3.1.2 Reinforcing Steel

In contrast to concrete, the mechanical properties of steel are well known, especially its uniaxial response. From dynamic uniaxial tests [34,35], some conclusions can be drawn, i.e.

(a) the yield stress and the ultimate stress of steel increase with the straining rate,

(b) the initial elastic modulus is relatively unaffected by the straining rate,

(c) ductility is observed to decrease with increasing straining rate, and

(d) the rate effects are approximately equal in tension and compression,

Figure 7 shows some of these features.

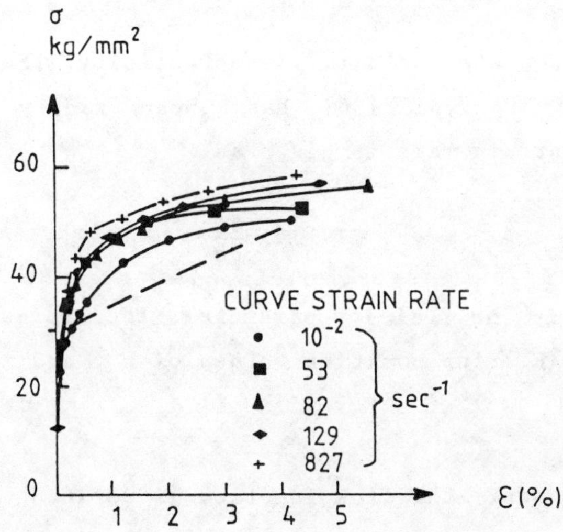

Figure 7 Dynamic stress-strain diagram of AISI 347

3.2 Traditional elasto/viscoplastic model

In the theory of elasto/viscoplasticity, the total strain $\underline{\varepsilon}$ and strain rate $\dot{\underline{\varepsilon}}$ are decomposed into elastic and viscoplastic parts as

$$\underline{\varepsilon} = \underline{\varepsilon}_e + \underline{\varepsilon}_{vp} \qquad (3.1)$$

$$\dot{\underline{\varepsilon}} = \dot{\underline{\varepsilon}}_e + \dot{\underline{\varepsilon}}_{vp}$$

The stress rate $\dot{\underline{\sigma}}$ is related to the elastic strain rate via the elasticity matrix $\underline{D}$ according to the expression

$$\dot{\underline{\sigma}} = \underline{D}\, \dot{\underline{\varepsilon}}_e \tag{3.2}$$

Viscoplastic flow occurs for positive values of a scalar yield function F_o

$$F_o(\underline{\sigma}) = f(\underline{\sigma}) - \sigma_o(k) \tag{3.3}$$

where σ_o is a value defining the position of the yield surface, and k is a hardening or softening parameter.

For associated elasto/viscoplasticity, the viscoplastic flow rule by Perzyna [36] has been widely used. The viscoplastic strain rate is given as

$$\dot{\underline{\varepsilon}}_{vp} = \gamma \langle \emptyset(F_o) \rangle \frac{\partial f}{\partial \underline{\sigma}} \tag{3.4}$$

in which γ is the fluidity parameter. The expression $\langle \emptyset(F_o) \rangle$ is equal to $\emptyset(F_o)$ for positive values of F_o, and zero otherwise.

In this work, the flow function is defined to be

$$\emptyset(F) = \frac{F_o}{\sigma_o} = \frac{f(\underline{\sigma}) - \sigma_o}{\sigma_o} \tag{3.5}$$

The term $\partial f/\partial \underline{\sigma}$ is a vector normal to the potential surface and it defines the direction of the viscoplastic flow.

3.3 Strain rate sensitive elasto/viscoplastic model for concrete

It is clear from the conclusions drawn in the previous section that any numerical model for reinforced concrete intended for transient analysis should be rate and history dependent [37]. Elasto/plastic and elasto/viscoplastic models in their basic formulations do not meet these requirements, but they can be modified to incorporate some of the features described above.

Bićanić [32,33] introduced a strain-rate sensitive, elasto/viscoplastic model with progressive degradation of the strength as a modification of Perzyna's elasto/viscoplastic model [36]. The original Bićanić model was extended to include tensile cracking in reference [38]. Here, similar concepts will be used to develop a viscoplastic model. The model has two main differences when compared with the traditional elasto-viscoplastic model.

(a) The fluidity parameter is not constant, and it is assumed to be dependent on the elastic strain rate (or stress rate).

(b) A variable strength limit surface is introduced to monitor the damage caused by viscoplastic flow. If the stress point reaches the strength limit surface, then the degradation of the yield surface is initiated.

3.3.1 Yield and strength limit surfaces

The yield surface F_o, defining the onset of viscoplastic behaviour, and the strength limit surface F_f, defining the initiation of material degradation, will be described in terms of the first and second invariants only. They can be expressed as

$$F_o(\underline{\sigma},\sigma_o) = cI_1 + (c^2I_1^2 + 3\beta J_2)^{1/2} - \sigma_o = 0$$

$$F_f(\underline{\sigma},\sigma_f) = cI_1 + (c^2I_1^2 + 3\beta J_2)^{1/2} - \sigma_f = 0 \qquad (3.6)$$

where I_1 and J_2 are the first and second stress invariants. The constants c, β are evaluated from experimental tests. The values

$$c=0.1775 \qquad \beta=1.355$$

correlate well with Kupfer's test results [39].

During inelastic straining both surfaces F_o and F_f change depending on the amount of accumulated damage, expressed as the viscoplastic energy density W_p

$$\begin{aligned} F_o(\underline{\sigma}, \sigma_o(W_p, k)) &= 0 \\ F_f(\underline{\sigma}, \sigma_f(W_p)) &= 0 \end{aligned} \tag{3.7}$$

where $\sigma_o(W_p, k)$ defines the change of the yield stress level in uniaxial compression σ_o,

$\sigma_f(W_p)$ defines the change of the failure stress level in uniaxial compression σ_f,

W_p is the viscoplastic energy density defined as

$$W_p = \int_o^t \underline{\sigma}^T \underline{\dot{\varepsilon}}_{vp} \, dt \quad , \tag{3.8}$$

k is the viscoplastic work density in the softening range. It is defined as

$$k = W_p - W_p^f = \int_{t_f}^t \underline{\sigma}^T \underline{\dot{\varepsilon}}_{vp} \, dt \quad , \tag{3.9}$$

and t_f and W_p^f are the time and viscoplastic energy density when the strength limit is reached.

While the stress path remains inside the yield surface, the behaviour of concrete is linearly elastic, no viscoplastic straining is developed, the yield and failure surfaces remain stationary. When the stress path is outside the yield surface, inelastic straining occurs, and the values of σ_o and σ_f vary. If hardening is considered, σ_o increases with the viscoplastic work and the yield surface expands. However, σ_f decreases with the increase of damage, and the strength limit surface shrinks. The strength limit surface is only a monitoring device to define where and when the failure occurs. When the stress path reaches the strength limit surface, degradation of the material is initiated. After that, the strength limit surface is no longer considered, and the yield surface begins to shrink according to the post-failure dissipated energy density k. Figure 8 summarizes the process.

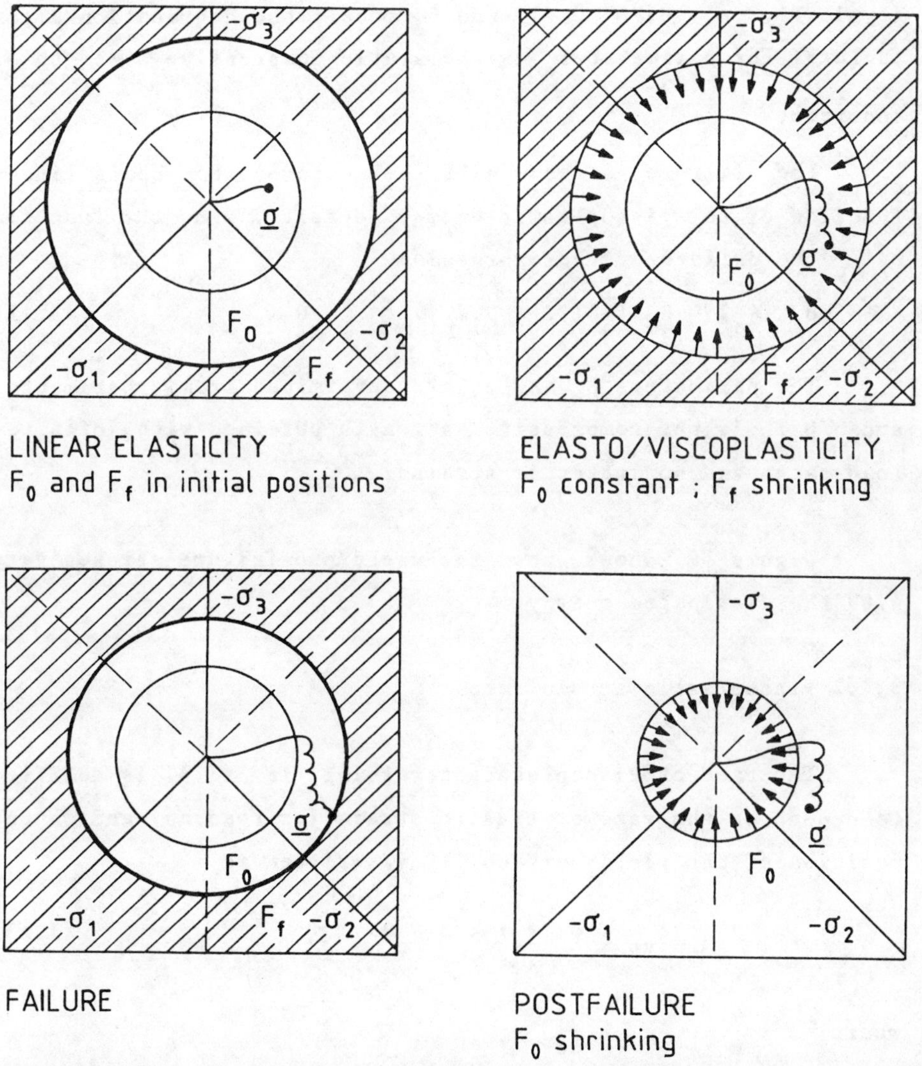

Figure 8 Evolution of the yield and failure surfaces

In this work, no hardening will be considered for concrete and an exponential function will be used to describe the post-failure behaviour. Therefore, the function $\sigma_o(W_p, k)$ is defined by the expression

$$\begin{aligned} \sigma_o\,(W_p, k) &= \alpha_1 f'_c & W_p &\leqq W_p^f \\ \sigma_o\,(W_p, k) &= \alpha_1 f'_c \exp(-\alpha_c k) & W_p &> W_p^f \end{aligned} \tag{3.10}$$

in which α_1, defines the limit for elastic behaviour (typically $\alpha_1 = 0.3 - 0.4$) and α_c models the degradation after failure. The parameter f'_c is the static compressive strength of concrete.

The failure stress will be assumed to be a linear function of the viscoplastic energy density, and the function $\sigma_f(W_p)$ be defined by the expression

$$\sigma_f\,(W_p) = \beta_o\, f'_c\, (1 - \beta_1 W_p) \qquad 0 < W_p \leqq W_p^f \tag{3.11}$$

The parameters β_o and β_1 are determined from experiments and $\beta_o f'_c$ is the compressive strength obtained with infinite load rates and no inelastic strains.

Figure 9 shows how the yield and failure streses vary with the dissipated energy.

3.3.2 Viscoplastic strain rate

The rate of viscoplastic straining in (3.4) is modified to depend on the rate of elastic strain (or loading) and on the position of the yield surface. It is written as

$$\underline{\dot{\varepsilon}}_{vp} = \gamma\,(\underline{\dot{\varepsilon}}_e)\,\langle\, \phi(F_o)\,\rangle\, \underline{n} \tag{3.12}$$

where $$\underline{n} = \frac{\partial f}{\partial \underline{\sigma}}$$

and $$\phi(F_o) = F_o \,/\, \alpha_1 f'_c$$

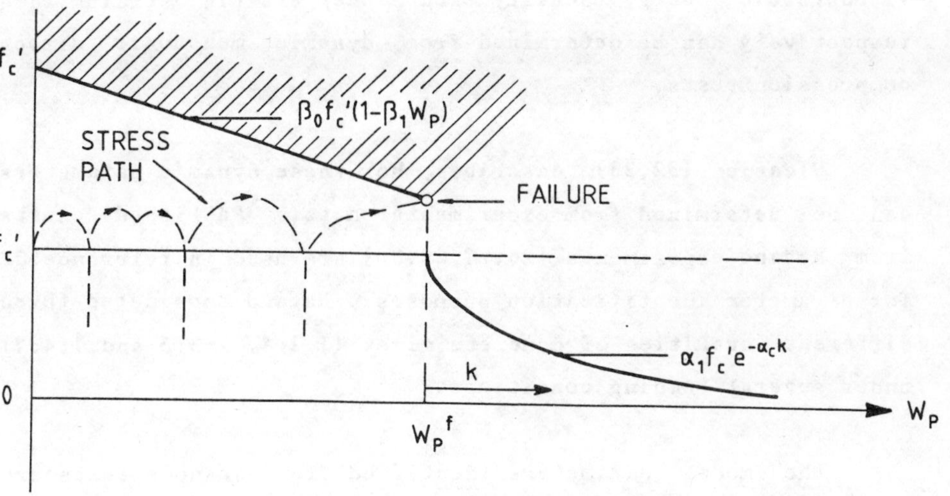

Figure 9 Variation of the yield and failure with the dissipated energy density

The fluidity parameter is related to the elastic strain rate through an exponential function of an effective elastic strain rate

$$\gamma\,(\dot{\underline{\varepsilon}}_e) = a_o\,(\dot{\underline{\varepsilon}}_e^{eff})^{a_1} \tag{3.13}$$

where a_o and a_1 are parameters which must be determined experimentally. The effective elastic strain is defined as

$$\varepsilon_e^{eff} = (\ 3J'_{2e}\ /\ (1+\nu)^2\ )^{1/2} \tag{3.14}$$

because deviatoric strains cause most damage to concrete and ε_e^{eff} is equal to the uniaxial elastic strain for a uniaxial stress state.

3.3.3 Determination of model parameters

The model requires only uniaxial tests to identify the material parameters needed. Parameters f_c', α_1 and α_c can be determined from uniaxial static tests. Whereas, parameters β_o,

β_1, a_o and a_1 defining σ_f and γ as functions of the viscoplastic energy density and the elastic strain rate respectively can be determined from dynamic monotonic direct compression tests.

Bićanić [32,33] describes how these dynamic parameters can be determined from experimental data. Published results from Hatano experiments [26,27,29,30] are used in reference 32 for parameter identification purposes. Hatano considered three different qualities of concrete mixes (1:2:4, 1:3:5 and 1:4:7) under several loading conditions.

The model parameters identified from Hatano's tests are shown in Table 3.1.

Table 3.1. Model parameters identified from Hatano's tests

Concrete mix	f'_c (kg/cm²)	a_o	a_1	β_o	β_1
1:2:4	605.	0.405	0.831	1.967	0.792
1:3:5	444.	0.306	0.760	1.836	1.088
1:4:7	275.	0.413	0.747	2.291	2.365

In reference 32, a linear relationship between the failure stress and the dissipated energy density is assumed but this is a crude approximation for all ranges of straining. When only moderate and fast strain rates are considered the assumed linear dependency appears to be satisfactory.

With the material parameters given in Table 3.1, a low cycle fatigue test (Figure 6) is performed, and predictions from the model are presented in Figure 10.

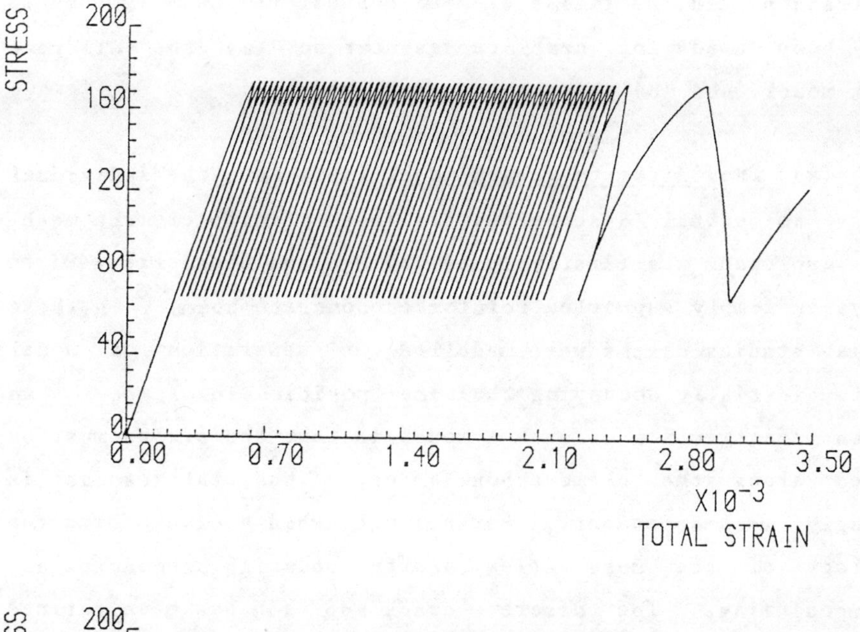

Figure 10 Prediction of the behaviour under cyclic loading for 1:4:7 concrete mix

3.4 Modelling of cracked concrete

Probably the main feature of plain concrete material behaviour is its low tensile strength, which results in tensile cracking at very low stress compared with the failure stress in

compression. In the finite element context two main approaches have been used for crack representation: (a) the discrete crack model, and (b) the smeared crack model.

(a) The <u>discrete crack model</u> represents the individual cracks as actual discontinuities in the finite element mesh. This approach was firstly used by Ngo and Scordelis [40] to analyse a simply supported reinforced concrete beam. In these initial studies cracks were modelled by separation of nodal points initially occupying the same position in space. An obvious restriction of such a model is that the cracks must be formed along the element boundaries. Thus, the response is strongly mesh-dependent. Furthermore, when a crack forms the topology of the mesh varies, and the updating procedures are time-consuming. The discrete crack approach has been refined [41] using adaptive methods so that new elements are introduced with boundaries along the spreading cracks. These developments reduce the mesh dependency of the model, but remeshing is necessary and the new elements introduced make the analysis increasingly expensive. These difficulties have resulted in a very limited acceptance of this model in general structural applications. However, the method seems appropriate for the problems involving only a few dominant cracks.

(b) The <u>smeared crack model</u> does not account for real discontinuities in the mesh. On the contrary, cracked concrete is assumed to remain a continuum and the material properties are modified to account for the damage due to cracking. Concrete is initially isotropic, but cracking induces anisotropy. After cracking, concrete is assumed to become orthotropic, with the principal material axes oriented along the directions of cracking. Material properties are varied depending on the state of strain and stress. The Young's modulus is reduced in the direction perpendicular to the crack plane, and Poisson's effect is usually neglected. The shear modulus parallel to the crack plane is also reduced. The smeared crack approach is computationally attractive, since the topology of the mesh is unchanged throughout the analysis, and only the stress-strain relationship need to be updated when cracking occurs.

The smeared approach is used for most structural engineering applications. This approach has been recently used by Nilsson and Oldenburg [42], Jiang [43], Bažant and Oh [44], Glemberg [45] and Rots et al. [46] among others. However, some concern has been expressed regarding the ability of the model to represent failure mechanisms with dominant discrete cracks [47]. Although for these cases the discrete crack model seems more adequate, the smeared approach using fine meshes of low order elements should be able to represent narrow mechanism bands leading to failure. Regarding this problem, interesting results have been presented by Rots et al. [46]. Although these authors favour the opinion that the smeared model can successfully model discrete cracks, their numerical results show that no objectivity is found regarding the orientation of the finite element mesh. The crack is found to prefer to propagate parallel to the element boundaries. This behaviour may be caused by the integration rule employed. Gustafsson [48] suggested that it could be meaningful to test the smeared model with a mesh updating procedure to overcome this undesired effect.

Figure 11 shows the two alternative models described for crack modelling for 'a priori' unknown crack paths.

A smeared crack model will be adopted in this work. To be fully described such a model requires the following items:

(a) a cracking criterion,
(b) a strain-softening (or tension-stiffening) rule, and
(c) a model for shear transfer

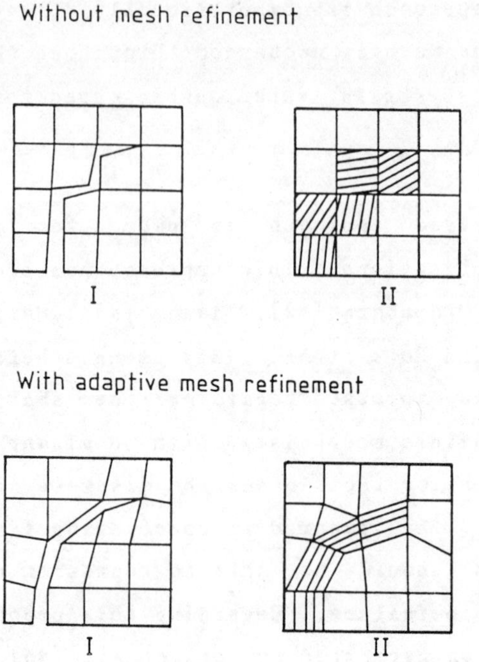

Figure 11 Alternatives for finite element modelling of unknown crack path:
I discrete crack approach
II smeared crack approach

3.4.1 Cracking criterion

The tensile strength of uncracked plain concrete can be obtained from laboratory tests. In the presence of reinforcment steel the prediction of crack initiation and crack direction is far more difficult. Simple criteria are favoured by most analysts to predict tensile fracture. Usually, a maximum tensile stress or maximum tensile strain criterion is used for this purpose.

In the present work concrete in tension is modelled as a linear elastic-strain softening material and the maximum tensile stress criterion will be employed to distinguish elastic behaviour from tensile fracture. For a previously uncracked sampling point, the principal stresses and their directions are evaluated. If the maximum principal stress exceeds a limiting value, a crack is formed in a plane orthogonal to this stress. Thereafter, the behaviour of the concrete is no longer isotropic - it becomes orthotropic, and the local material axes coincide with the principal stress directions. It should be noted that the direction of the crack remains fixed thereafter - this is known as the fixed crack approach.

A maximum of two sets of cracks are allowed to form at each sampling point. For simplicity, the crack directions are assumed to be orthogonal.

Under further loading, secondary cracking may occur at a sampling point that was originally cracked in one direction. Three variants are available to determine the direction of the second set of cracks.

(a) The principal material axes can be rotated to coincide with the current principal stress (or strain) directions, which is known as the rotating crack model [49]. Although this approach is reported to produce results which are in good agreement with experimental results, the model could be physically objectionable since it implies rotation of defects within the material [50].

(b) The material axes are fixed in the directions corresponding to the principal stress directions when the primary cracks occurred, irrespectively of the possible rotation of the stresses.

(c) Keeping the direction of the first set of cracks fixed, a search is performed to determine the maximum stress in the plane parallel to the existing crack. For this computation only the normal and shear stresses acting on that plane are considered. If this maximum stress exceeds the limiting value, then a new set of cracks is formed perpendicular to it, and the local material axes are fixed. This is the option that will be used here.

3.4.2 Strain-softening rule

The first studies done on numerical analysis of reinforced concrete structures assumed concrete to be an elastic-brittle material in tension. When cracking occurred, the stress normal to the crack direction was immediately released and dropped to zero. It was soon discovered that this procedure leads to great convergence difficulties, and more importantly, to results that strongly depend on the size of the finite elements used in the analysis.

It was then argued that due to bond forces, cracked concrete carries between the cracks a certain amount of tensile stress normal to the cracked plane. The concrete adheres to the reinforcing bars and contributes actively to the overall stiffness of the structure. This effect is known as tension-stiffening. It can be incorporated into the computational model in two indirect ways:

(a) assuming that the loss of tensile strength in concrete occurs gradually after cracking [51], or

(b) modifying the steel stress-strain curve [52].

The first option is equivalent to considering concrete as an elastic-strain softening material in tension, and has been extensively used in computational analysis of reinforced concrete structures. However, two main problems remained unsolved. The first one is that there is no objective way of measuring 'how much' tension-stiffening should be included in the model. It is easy to choose a tension-stiffening curve that will adequately fit experimental results, but very difficult to make any 'a priori' predictions. Secondly, the effect, if explained in terms of bond interaction with the reinforcing streel, cannot be applied to plain concrete structures, or, to concrete located at a certain distance from the reinforcement.

Considerable experimental research has recently been directed towards the study of the post-peak behaviour of cementitious materials. Servo-controlled testing with very stiff test devices have provided new experimental evidence which was not available earlier, from predominantly load-controlled test data. Fracture mechanics models have also been applied to the study of notch-sensitive problems in plain concrete [53,54]. These studies have shown the attractiveness of using some fracture energy concepts in the material modelling of concrete. Based on these concepts the composite damage models have been proposed for cementitious materials such as concrete [55,56]. The main concept borrowed from fracture mechanics to develop these models is the assumption that the fracture energy release rate, G_f, is a material property, rather than the local stress-strain curve. The implementation of the 'G_f = const.' concept leads to the important conclusion that the local strain-softening law depends on a characteristic length, l_c, depending on the finite element mesh. As a result, the fracture energy concept leads to a non-local format of the equivalent softening relation which is fundamentally different from the local constitutive formats of strain-softening plasticity and continuous damage mechanics [57].

In defining a curve to model the strain-softening effect, two aspects have to be considered: the shape of the adopted curve and the value of the parameters needed to define it. Different shapes of the descending branch of the stress-strain curve have been used by different authors. In most of the cases, either a simple straight line shape, or a bi-linear shape have been used. The bi-linear shape was recommended by Petersson [58] in the context of fracture mechanics and based on experimental tests. Nonlinear curves have been used by Nilsson and Oldenburg [42], Jiang [43], Glemberg [45] and others.

The assumptions used to select the parameters defining such a curve are more important than the shape of the strain-softening curve selected. It is now widely accepted that to make the constitutive model objective with regard to the size of the finite elements used in the mesh, the softening curve must be related to the fracture energy of the concrete.

Assuming that the stress, σ, across an opening crack is a function of the crack width, w, the fracture energy is defined as

$$G_f = \int_o^\infty \sigma(w)\, dw \qquad (3.15)$$

G_f represents the energy needed to seperate the two crack surfaces. Typical values of the fracture energy for normal concretes are in the range of 50 to 200 N/m.

The smeared approach does not represent individual cracks, so the crack width, w, must be smeared into an equivalent crack strain, ε_c, related to the physical crack opening by a characteristic length, l_c. Nilsson [42] derived this relation considering a control volume, V, containing a crack with an area S (see Figure 12). It is assumed that once the crack is formed, all inelastic deformation inside the

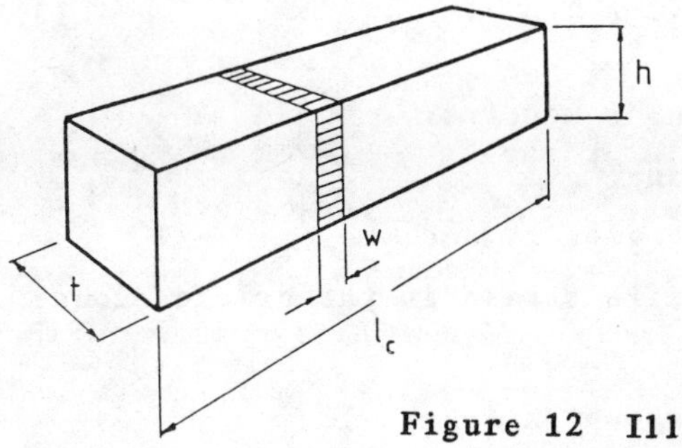

Figure 12 Illustration of characteristic length for a prismatic control volume

control volume takes place in the crack, the rest of the volume remaining elastic.

The rate of energy dissipation in the crack is

$$\dot{\pi}_S = \int_S \sigma \, \dot{w} \, dS \tag{3.16}$$

By assuming that control the volume is subjected to the same state of stress as the crack, but strained by the equivalent strain ε_c, the rate of energy dissipation in the volume is

$$\dot{\pi}_V = \int_V \sigma \, \dot{\varepsilon}_c \, dV \tag{3.17}$$

If the stress, strain and crack width are assumed to be constant inside the considered volume, then equating the rate of energy dissipation in the crack (3.16) to that in the control volume (3.17) gives the relationship between the crack width and the fictitious crack strain

$$w = (V/S) \, \varepsilon_c = l_c \varepsilon_c \tag{3.18}$$

This relation defines the characteristic length as the ratio between the control volume and the crack surface.

Here, an exponential function is used to simulate the strain-softening effect, so that

$$\sigma = E_o \varepsilon_o (\exp(-(\varepsilon-\varepsilon_o)/\alpha)) \tag{3.19}$$

where E_o is the elastic Young's modulus,

ε_o is strain at cracking,

α is the softening parameter, and

ε is the nominal tensile strain in the cracked zone.

The adopted curve is shown in Figure 13.

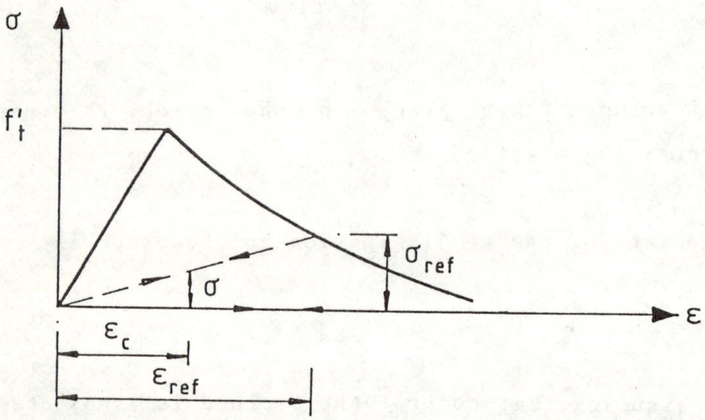

Figure 13 Strain-softening curve with secant unloading and re-loading

The softening parameter, α, is determined by the evaluation of the integral in (3.15) and by the introduction of the relation between the crack opening w and the fictitious crack strain ε_c (3.18). This yields

$$\sigma = (G_f - 1/2\ E_o \varepsilon_o{}^2\ l_c)/E_o \varepsilon_o l_c > 0 \tag{3.20}$$

In the context of finite element computations the control volume for crack monitoring is the volume associated with a sampling point in a given element. In the present work, the characteristic length is computed for each sampling point as

$$l_c = (dV)^{1/3} \tag{3.21}$$

where dV is the volume of concrete represented by the sampling point. Note that this definition does not account for directionality of the cracking or distortion of the element but it can be used as a first order approximation of the actual control length.

It should be noted that this approach to the computation of the strain-softening branch of the stress-strain curve is only directly applicable to plain concrete. The classical 'tension-stiffening' effect due to the presence of reinforcement has not been accounted for. However, the advantages of this approach regarding mesh objectivity for the modelling of localised fracture are unquestionable. The effect of the reinforcement can be heuristically included by assuming a higher fracture energy for reinforced concrete than for plain concrete.

The redistribution of stresses due to cracking in other sampling points, or further loading may force some of the previously-opened cracks to close partially or fully. This behaviour is allowed in the present model. If the current strain ε is smaller than the strain ε_{ref} recorded as the maximum tensile strain reached across the crack under consideration, the stress normal to the crack, σ, is calculated from

$$\sigma = \frac{\sigma_{ref}}{\varepsilon_{ref}} \varepsilon \tag{3.22}$$

in which σ_{ref} is the interpolated stress corresponding to the strain ε_{ref}. This secant 'unloading' path is shown in Figure 13. Re-opening of the crack follows the same path until ε_{ref} is exceeded. Then the stress is interpolated from (3.19).

3.4.3 Shear transfer across the crack

Experiments show that a considerable amount of shear stress can be transferred across the rough surfaces of cracked concrete. In plain concrete the main shear transfer mechanism is aggregate interlock and the main variables involved are the aggregate size and grading. In reinforced concrete dowel action will play a significant role, the main variables being the reinforcement ratio, the size of the bars and the angle between crack and bars. Both mechanisms are controlled by the width of the crack, the shear transfer capacity being reduced as the width increases.

The above-mentioned mechanisms cannot be directly included in the smeared crack model. A simplified approach is generally employed to take into account the shear transfer capacity of cracked concrete. The process consists of assigning to the shear modulus corresponding to the crack plane a reduced value, G_c, defined as

$$G_c = \beta G_o \qquad (3.23)$$

where G_o is the shear modulus of uncracked concrete and β is a reducing factor in the range of zero to one. A constant value for the reducing factor has been used in many analyses. It is, however, probably more realistic to relate the value of β to the tensile strain normal to the crack plane, a smeared measure of the crack width. In this work, the following value is used

$$\beta = 1 - (\varepsilon_t/0.005)^{k_1} \qquad (3.24)$$

where ε_t is the fictitous tensile strain normal to the crack plane, and

k_1 is a parameter in the range of 0.3 to 1.0 [59]

Figure 14 shows the variation of β with ε_t for different values of k_1.

3.5 Modelling of steel and reinforcing steel

3.5.1 Steel structures

The elasto-viscoplastic model described for concrete can

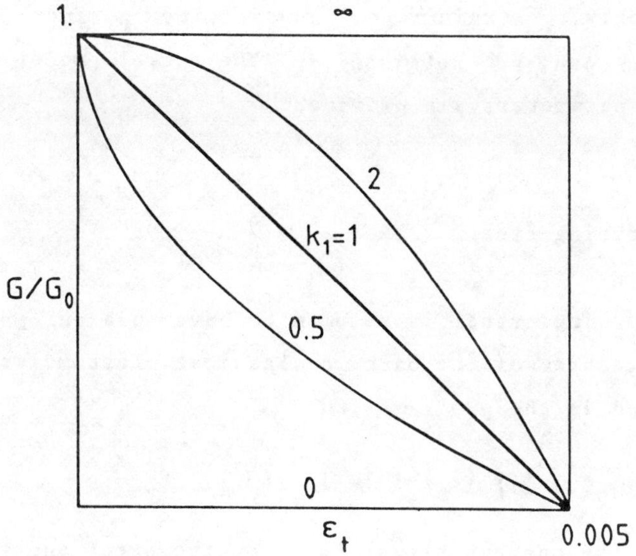

Figure 14 Variation of the shear modulus with the tensile strain across the crack

be directly used for steel if the appropriate material parameters are selected:

(a) If the constants $c = 0$ and $\beta = 1$ are used in the definition of the yield surface (3.6) then the criterion reduces to the classical Von Mises cylinder.

(b) A large value for the cracking strain and the crushing strain will ensure that steel does not 'crack' or 'crush' during the analysis.

(c) The expression for the fluidity parameter is

$$\gamma\ (\dot{\varepsilon}_e) = a_o\ (\dot{\varepsilon}_e)^{a_1} \qquad (3.25)$$

if a_1 is set to zero in (3.25), then the model is automatically strain-rate dependent and a_0 is then the usual fluidity parameter.

(d) A large value for β_o and a small one (or zero) for β_1 will ensure that the steel suffers no softening.

Obviously, strain-rate sensitivity and damage accumulation can be retained in the steel model if the appropriate parameters are provided.

3.5.2 Reinforcing steel

Reinforcing steel is assumed to have uniaxial properties in the direction of the bars. A classical elasto-viscoplastic model is used in the program with

$$\dot{\varepsilon}_{vps} = \pm \gamma\ (\dot{\varepsilon}_s)\ (\ |\sigma_s| - f_y\ )\ /\ f_y \qquad (3.26)$$

where σ_s is the current stress level in the steel and f_y is the yield stess of the material which is assumed constant. The fluidity parameter is assumed to be constant, although strain rate sensitivity may be readily included.

3.6 Computer implementation of the material model

3.6.1 Selection of the time step size

The viscoplastic flow rule

$$\dot{\underline{\varepsilon}}_{vp} = \gamma\ (\ \dot{\underline{\varepsilon}}_e\ )\ \langle\ \emptyset\ (F_o)\ \rangle\ \underline{n} \qquad (3.27)$$

is valid for all time t. In a step-by-step numerical procedure this relationship will only be satisfied for discrete time stations Δt apart. The viscoplastic strain is given by

$$\underline{\varepsilon}_{vp} = \int \dot{\underline{\varepsilon}}_{vp} \, dt \qquad (3.28)$$

which can be approximated numerically as

$$_{t+\Delta t}\underline{\varepsilon}_{vp} = {}_{t}\underline{\varepsilon}_{vp} + [(1-\beta) \; {}_{t}\dot{\underline{\varepsilon}}_{vp} + \beta \; {}_{t+\Delta t}\dot{\underline{\varepsilon}}_{vp}] \, \Delta t \qquad (3.29)$$

so that the change of viscoplastic straining within the interval is defined in terms of the viscoplastic flow rule at both ends of the interval. For $\beta=0$, the explicit Euler integration scheme is obtained, where only the flow rule at the beginning of the interval is relevant

$$_{t+\Delta t}\underline{\varepsilon}_{vp} = {}_{t}\underline{\varepsilon}_{vp} + {}_{t}\dot{\underline{\varepsilon}}_{vp} \, \Delta t \qquad (3.30)$$

Euler integration has been found computationally efficient for quasi-static analysis [60],[61] despite the stability limitations on the length of the time step, and will be adopted in this work.

The stability limit for equation (3.30) depends on the specific form of the viscoplastic potential used in the flow rule. Cormeau [61] derived theoretical stability limits for some yield criteria with linear flow functions, namely Von Mises, Tresca, Drucker-Prager and Mohr-Coulomb.

It should be noted that these stability limits were obtained for quasi-static elasto/visco-plasticity, with the flow rule being a function of stress only. As the flow rule used in this work involves both stresses and stress rates, the limits derived in [21] are not strictly applicable. However, an estimate of the allowable time step can be obtained by substituting some representative values from Hatano's tests into one of the criteria given in [21].

The stability limit for the Von Mises yield criterion (a particular case for the compression yield criterion, obtained using c=0 in (3.6)) is given by

$$\Delta t \leq 4\ (1+\nu)\ \sigma_o\ /\ 3\gamma E \tag{3.31}$$

Taking $\sigma_o = 0.3\ f'_c$ and elastic strain rates varying from 10^{-6} sec^{-1} to 10^{-1} sec^{-1} (the range in which the present material model is assumed to be valid) the critical time steps obtained are shown in Table 3.2.

Table 3.2. Critical time steps for some concrete mixes (assuming Von Mises yield criterion)

Concrete Mix	Δt_{cr} ($\dot{\varepsilon}_e = 10^{-6}$ sec^{-1})	Δt_{cr} ($\dot{\varepsilon}_e = 10^{-1}$ sec^{-1})
1:2:4	33.57	2.345-02
1:3:5	122.33	1.936-02
1:4:7	93.84	9.711-03

In dynamic analysis, however, these stability limits will rarely be decisive. As will be indicated later, if an explicit integration scheme is used, then the stability limit for the step-by-step integration of the equation of motion will normally govern the choice of the time step length. Implicit schemes are usually unconditionally stable, but the time step size is limited by accuracy considerations. In particular, when cracking is involved, the time step must be selected so that cracks spread progressively throughout the structure. If a large number of cracks are formed in the same interval, considerable difficulties in convergence may be encountered. From past experience, it appears that the time step size with implicit algorithms should be chosen to limit the speed at which the cracks spread.

4 SOLUTION OF SEMI-DISCRETE GOVERNING EQUATIONS

4.1 Introduction

In direct integration methods (2.3) is integrated, without any previous transformation, using a numerical step-by-step procedure. These schemes are based on two ideas [14]:

(i) Equation (2.3) is only satisfied for certain discrete time stations [62,63] or in a weighted sense for each time interval [64,65].

(ii) A variation of displacements, velocities and accelerations is assumed within each time interval. It is the form of this assumption (on the variation of displacements, velocities and accelerations within the time step) that determines the accuracy, stability and efficiency of each scheme.

Direct integration methods are generally divided into:

(a) Explicit integration algorithms, in which the solution at time $t+\Delta t$ is based on the equilibrium conditions at time t. They require little computer storage and are inexpensive per time step. However, they are only conditionally stable and stringent limits must be imposed on the time step size. The most popular of these methods is the central difference method [63,66].

(b) Implicit integration algorithms, in which equilibrium at time $t+\Delta t$ is imposed to obtain the corresponding solution. These methods are usually unconditionally stable, permitting larger time steps. However, the storage required and the cost per step is high because it is necessary to factorise the stiffness matrix. Some of the widely used implicit schemes are the Newmark method [62], the Houbolt [67] and the Wilson-θ method [68].

4.2 The Newmark method

The Newmark method [62], adopted in this work, is an extension of the linear acceleration method. The dynamic equilibrium equation is linearised and written at time t_{n+1} as

$$\underline{\underline{M}}\,\ddot{\underline{d}}_{n+1} + \underline{\underline{C}}\,\dot{\underline{d}}_{n+1} + \underline{\underline{K}}\,\underline{d}_{n+1} = \underline{f}_{n+1} \tag{4.1}$$

and the following assumptions on the variation of displacements and velocities are made within a typical time step:

$$\begin{aligned} \underline{d}_{n+1} &= \underline{d}_n + \Delta t\,\dot{\underline{d}}_n + \frac{\Delta t^2}{2}\,[(1-2\beta)\ddot{\underline{d}}_n + 2\beta\,\ddot{\underline{d}}_{n+1}] \\ \dot{\underline{d}}_{n+1} &= \dot{\underline{d}}_n + \Delta t\,[(1-\gamma)\ddot{\underline{d}}_n + \gamma\ddot{\underline{d}}_{n+1}] \end{aligned} \tag{4.2}$$

where $\underline{d}_n$, $\dot{\underline{d}}_n$ and $\ddot{\underline{d}}_n$ are values of displacement, velocity and acceleration known at time t. Parameters β and γ control the stability and accuracy of the method. Stability conditions are given by [69]:

-unconditional stability $\quad 2\beta \geq \gamma \geq 1/2$

-conditional stability $\quad \gamma > 1/2$

$\beta < \gamma/2$

$\omega\Delta t < \Omega_{crit}$

where $\Omega_{crit} = [\xi(\gamma-1/2)+[\gamma/2-\beta+\xi^2(\gamma-1/2)^2]^{1/2}]/(\gamma/2-\beta)$

ω is the undamped frequency of vibration and

ξ is the damping ratio (given by (2.9) if Rayleigh damping is used)

The Newmark family includes, as particular cases, many well known integration schemes. Some of these are summarized in Table 4.1 [69]. The average acceleration method is one of the most effective and widely used, because of its unconditional stability.

Table 4.1. Some methods of the Newmark family.

SCHEME	PARAMETER β	γ	STABILITY CONDITION
average acceleration	1/4	1/2	unconditional
linear acceleration	1/6	1/2	$\Omega_{crit} = 3^{1/2}$
Fox-Goodwin	1/12	1/2	$\Omega_{crit} = 6^{1/2}$
central difference	0	1/2	$\Omega_{crit} = 2$

Notes (1) The central difference method is explicit with $\underline{M}$ and $\underline{C}$ diagonal

(2) Stability conditions are derived for $\xi = 0$

To start the step-by-step procedure the values for initial displacements $\underline{d}_o$ and velocities $\dot{\underline{d}}_o$ must be given. Initial accelerations $\ddot{\underline{d}}_o$ can be obtained by solving (4.1) for time t=0 .

$$\ddot{\underline{d}}_o = \underline{M}^{-1} \left(\underline{f}_o - \underline{C}\,\dot{\underline{d}}_o - \underline{K}\,\underline{d}_o \right) \tag{4.3}$$

A recent study on the effect of the starting algorithms for a simple 1-D problem [70] concluded that the values given by (4.3) produce very good results. It should be noted that (4.3) requires another step in the solution procedure (i.e. one elimination and back-substitution).

4.3 Predictor-corrector form of Newmark's method

Hughes et al [71-73] have developed a predictor-corrector form of the Newmark method which is most suitable for non-linear transient analysis.

The Newmark formulae (4.2) can be rewritten in terms of predictor and corrector values as

$$\underline{d}_{n+1} = \underline{d}^{p}_{n+1} + \Delta t^2 \beta\, \ddot{\underline{d}}_{n+1}$$
$$\dot{\underline{d}}_{n+1} = \dot{\underline{d}}^{p}_{n+1} + \Delta t\ \gamma\, \ddot{\underline{d}}_{n+1} \tag{4.4}$$

with predictor values given as

$$\underline{d}^{p}_{n+1} = \underline{d}_{n} + \Delta t\, \dot{\underline{d}}_{n} + \frac{\Delta t^2}{2} (1-2\beta)\, \ddot{\underline{d}}_{n}$$
$$\dot{\underline{d}}^{p}_{n+1} = \dot{\underline{d}}_{n} + \Delta t\ (1-\gamma)\, \ddot{\underline{d}}_{n} \tag{4.5}$$

The terms $\underline{d}_{n+1}$, $\dot{\underline{d}}_{n+1}$ are corrector values and $\underline{d}^{p}_{n+1}$, $\dot{\underline{d}}^{p}_{n+1}$ are the predictor values. The corrector values for the acceleration values can be obtained from (4.4) as

$$\ddot{\underline{d}}_{n+1} = (\, \underline{d}_{n+1} - \underline{d}^{p}_{n+1}\,)/(\beta \Delta t^2) \tag{4.6}$$

Substituting (4.4)-(4.6) into (4.1) an 'effective static problem' is formed in terms of the unknown $\Delta \underline{d}$ [74]

$$\underline{K}^{*} \Delta \underline{d} = \underline{\Psi} \tag{4.7}$$

where the 'effective stiffness matrix' is

$$\underline{K}^{*} = \underline{M}\ /\ (\beta \Delta t^2) + \gamma\ \underline{C}_{T}\ /\ (\beta \Delta t) + \underline{K}_{T} \tag{4.8}$$

and the residual forces are

$$\underline{\Psi} = \underline{f}_{n+1} - \underline{M}\, \ddot{\underline{d}}^{p}_{n+1} - \underline{C}_{T}\, \dot{\underline{d}}^{p}_{n+1} - \underline{p}(\underline{d}^{p}_{n+1}) \tag{4.9}$$

When solving non-linear problems, the linearization involved in writing (4.1) will make it necessary to perform iterative corrections to $\Delta \underline{d}$ to achieve equilibrium at time $t+\Delta t$. A Newton-Raphson type scheme will be used in this work, although most solution techniques employed in static analysis can probably also be used effectively in direct integration.

The computational algorithms for the implicit, explicit and implicit-explicit forms of the Newmark method will be given in the next sections.

4.4 Computational algorithm for the implicit form of the Newmark method

The computations needed in a typical time step of the implicit form of the Newmark method can be summarized as follows [74].

(1) set iteration counter i=0

(2) Enter the predictor phase

$$\underline{d}^{i}_{n+1} = \underline{d}^{p}_{n+1}$$
$$\dot{\underline{d}}^{i}_{n+1} = \dot{\underline{d}}^{p}_{n+1} \tag{4.10}$$
$$\ddot{\underline{d}}^{i}_{n+1} = \underline{0}$$

(3) Solve the incremental 'effective static problem'

$$\underline{K}^{*}\Delta\underline{d}^{i} = \underline{\Psi}^{i} \tag{4.11}$$

where

$$\underline{K}^{*} = \underline{M} \,/\, (\beta\Delta t^{2}) + \gamma\, \underline{C}_{T} / \,(\beta\Delta t) + \underline{K}_{T}$$

and (4.12)

$$\underline{\Psi}^{i} = \underline{f}_{n+1} - \underline{M}\, \ddot{\underline{d}}^{i}_{n+1} - \underline{C}_{T}\, \dot{\underline{d}}^{i}_{n+1} - \underline{p}(\underline{d}^{i}_{n+1})$$

are, respectively, the effective stiffness matrix, and the residual force vector, with

$$\underline{K}_{T} = \partial\underline{p}/\partial\underline{d} \tag{4.13}$$

being the tangential stiffness matrix.

(4) Perform the corrector phase

$$\underline{d}_{n+1}^{i+1} = \underline{d}_{n+1}^{i} + \Delta\underline{d}^{i}$$

$$\ddot{\underline{d}}_{n+1}^{i+1} = (\underline{d}_{n+1}^{i+1} - \underline{d}_{n+1}^{p})/(\beta\Delta t^2) \qquad (4.14)$$

$$\dot{\underline{d}}_{n+1}^{i+1} = \dot{\underline{d}}_{n+1}^{p} + \Delta t\ \gamma\ \ddot{\underline{d}}_{n+1}^{i+1}$$

(5) If the convergence criterion selected is not satisfied, then set i=i+1 and go to (3)

(6) Set the solution at time t

$$\underline{d}_{n+1} = \underline{d}_{n+1}^{i+1}$$

$$\dot{\underline{d}}_{n+1} = \dot{\underline{d}}_{n+1}^{i+1} \qquad (4.15)$$

$$\ddot{\underline{d}}_{n+1} = \ddot{\underline{d}}_{n+1}^{i+1}$$

for use in the next time step. Also set n=n+1 and go to (1).

[NOTE:

When the mesh involves only implicit elements and large time steps are adopted with $\gamma = 1/2$, a set of alternative predictor values is recommended in reference 74:

$$\underline{d}_{n+1}^{o} = \underline{d}_{n}$$

$$\dot{\underline{d}}_{n+1}^{o} = \dot{\underline{d}}_{n} \qquad (4.16)$$

$$\ddot{\underline{d}}_{n+1}^{o} = (\underline{d}_{n+1}^{o} - \underline{d}_{n+1}^{p})/(\beta\Delta t^2)$$

where $\underline{d}_{n+1}^{p}$ is given by (4.5)]

5. NUMERICAL APPLICATIONS

5.1 Introduction

Sections 6 and 7 provide a listing and full documentation of a program called DARC3 which is based on the computational model described in the previous sections. DARC3 is now used to analyse various reinforced concrete structures under dynamic loading. This study has the following objectives:

(a) to verify the validity of the material model adopted, and to study its sensitivity to the main parameters involved in the description of the material behaviour,

(b) to demonstrate the possibility of analysing moderately thin and moderately thick plate/shell - type structures using a single layer of isoparametric three dimensional elements, and

(c) to show the versatility and generality of DARC3.

For all the examples presented in this section the convergence criterion adopted is the following

$$|\underline{\Psi}_t^i| \;/\; |\underline{\Psi}_t^1| \leq \varepsilon \qquad (5.1)$$

where $\underline{\Psi}_t^i$ and $\underline{\Psi}_t^1$ are the vectors of residual forces for the i-th and first iteration of time step t, respectively. The tolerance ε is equal to 0.05.

5.2 Simply supported beam

5.2.1 Geometry, material properties and loading

A simply supported reinforced concrete beam subjected to two symmetrically applied concentrated loads (see Figure 15)

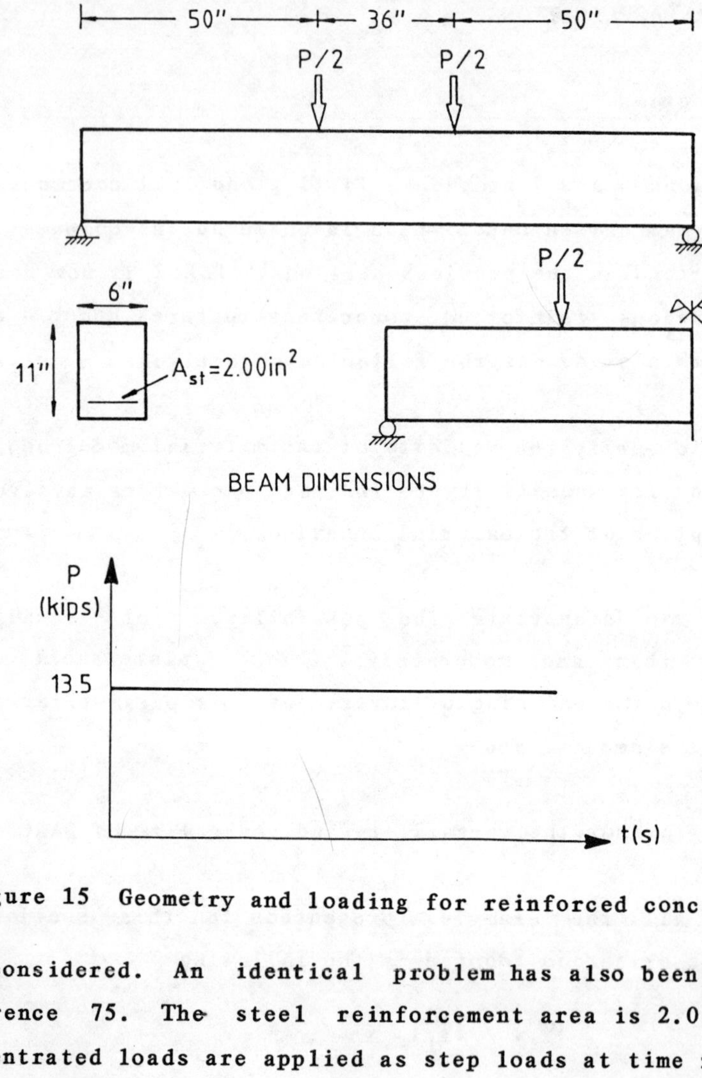

Figure 15 Geometry and loading for reinforced concrete beam

is considered. An identical problem has also been solved in reference 75. The steel reinforcement area is 2.0 in². The concentrated loads are applied as step loads at time zero, each with magnitude of P = 13.5 kips. The material properties are given in Table 5.1.

Using symmetry conditions only one-half of the structure needs to be considered. Five 20-noded elements are used and the mesh can be seen in Figure 17.

The dynamic response is evaluated using the trapezoidal rule (the Newmark method with β=0.25 and γ =0.50) with a time step of 0.0005 sec. (1/40 of the elastic fundamental period). No viscous damping is considered.

Table 5.1 Material properties for simply supported beam (in, kips)

Concrete		
Young's modulus	E_c =	6100.0
Poisson's ratio	υ =	0.20
Ultimate compressive stress	f'_c =	3.74
Ultimate compressive strain	ε_{cu} =	0.0035
Mass density	ρ =	0.217E−06
Cracking tensile strain	ε_{cr} =	0.750E−04
Fracture energy	G_f =	0.600E−03
Fluidity parameter	a_0 =	0.3055
	a_1 =	0.7600
Yield surface function	α_1 =	Variable
	α_c =	10.0
Failure surface function	β_0 =	1.84
	β_1 =	1.09
Steel		
Young's modulus	E_s =	30 000.0
Yield stress	f_y =	44.0
Fluidity parameter	a_0 =	1.539
	a_1 =	0.971

5.2.2 Results

Firstly, an elastic analysis was performed, and the results are found to be in full agreement with those given in reference 75. Figure 16 shows the time history of the midspan deflection for the linear case and two different nonlinear cases: one with the yielding surface defined by $\sigma_o = 0.3\ f'_c$ and the other with $\sigma_o = f'_c$. Three phenomena can be observed from Figure 16 in the nonlinear response:

(a) The deflection is considerably amplified (in this example, almost 50 %.

(b) The period of vibration is elongated.

(c) Energy is dissipated by the material model so the amplitude of the oscillations diminishes, when compared with the linear case.

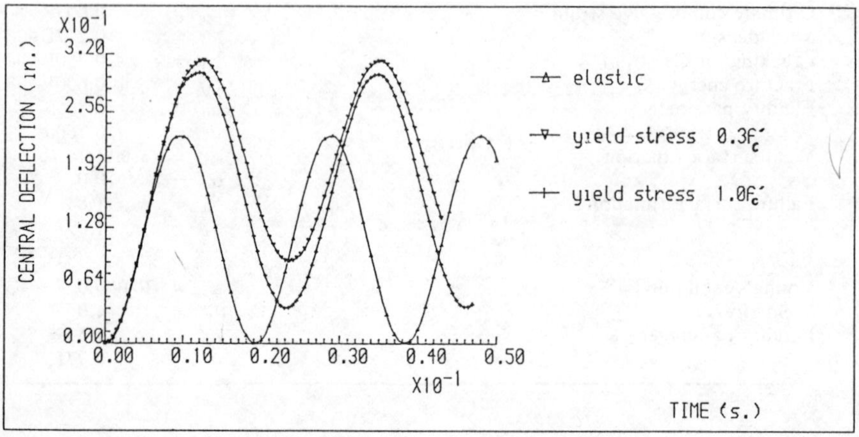

Figure 16 Nonlinear response of reinforced concrete beam

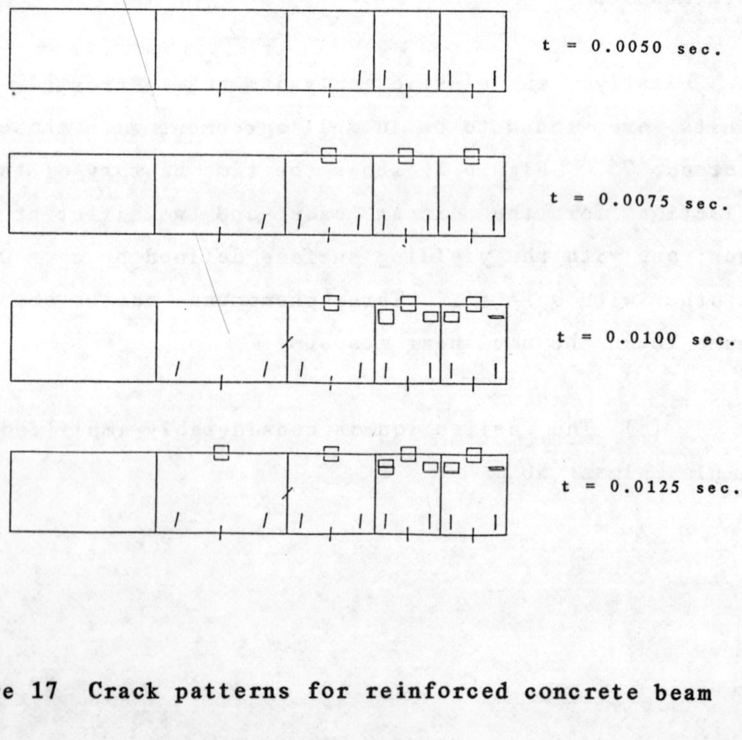

Figure 17 Crack patterns for reinforced concrete beam

In the case with $\sigma_o = f'_c$, no viscoplastic behaviour is observed, so the nonlinear effects are only due to the cracking of the concrete. It can be seen that lowering the yield stress to a more realistic value ($\sigma_o = 0.3\ f'_c$) does not significantly affect the deflections or the period, but it considerably decreases the amplitude of the oscillations.

Figure 16 shows how the cracks spread in the beam for different time stations.

5.3 Clamped circular reinforced concrete slab

5.3.1 Geometry, material properties and loading

The reinforced concrete slab shown in Figure 18 is subjected to a uniformly distributed load of intensity 1.4 kg/cm². The plate has a radius of 10 m. and a thickness of 1 m. The load is applied with a rise time equal to half of the elastic fundamental period (T=0.060 sec.). The material properties used in the analysis are the same as those of reference 76 (see Table 5.2). The percentage of reinforcement placed near the upper and lower surfaces in the radial and tangential directions is 1% which in the adopted model implies a layer of equivalent thickness of 1 cm.

From symmetry, it is sufficient to analyse a plate segment (adopted included angle 4°). Nine 20-noded elements are used in the finite element mesh, as can be seen in Figure 20. Note that a specially modified version of DARC3 was used to allow locally directed boundary degrees of freedom.

The Newmark method with $\beta = 0.25$ and $\gamma = 0.50$ is used to integrate the dynamic equations, with a time step of $5\text{x}10^{-4}$ sec. (approximately 1/100 of the elastic fundamental period). No viscous damping is considered.

Table 5.2 Material properties for clamped circular reinforced concrete slab and nuclear containment shell (cm, kg)

Concrete	
Young's modulus	E_c = 200 000.0
Poisson's ratio	v = 0.17
Ultimate compressive stress	f'_c = 350.0
Ultimate compressive strain	ε_{cu} = 0.0035
Mass density	ρ = 0.245E–05
Cracking tensile strain	ε_{cr} = Variable
Fracture energy	G_f = Variable
Fluidity parameter	a_0 = 0.3055
	a_1 = 0.7600
Yield surface function	α_1 = 0.40
	α_c = 10.0
Failure surface function	β_0 = 1.84
	β_1 = 1.09
Steel	
Young's modulus	E_s = 210 000.0
Yield stress	f_y = 4600.0
Fluidity parameter	a_0 = 1.539
	a_1 = 0.971

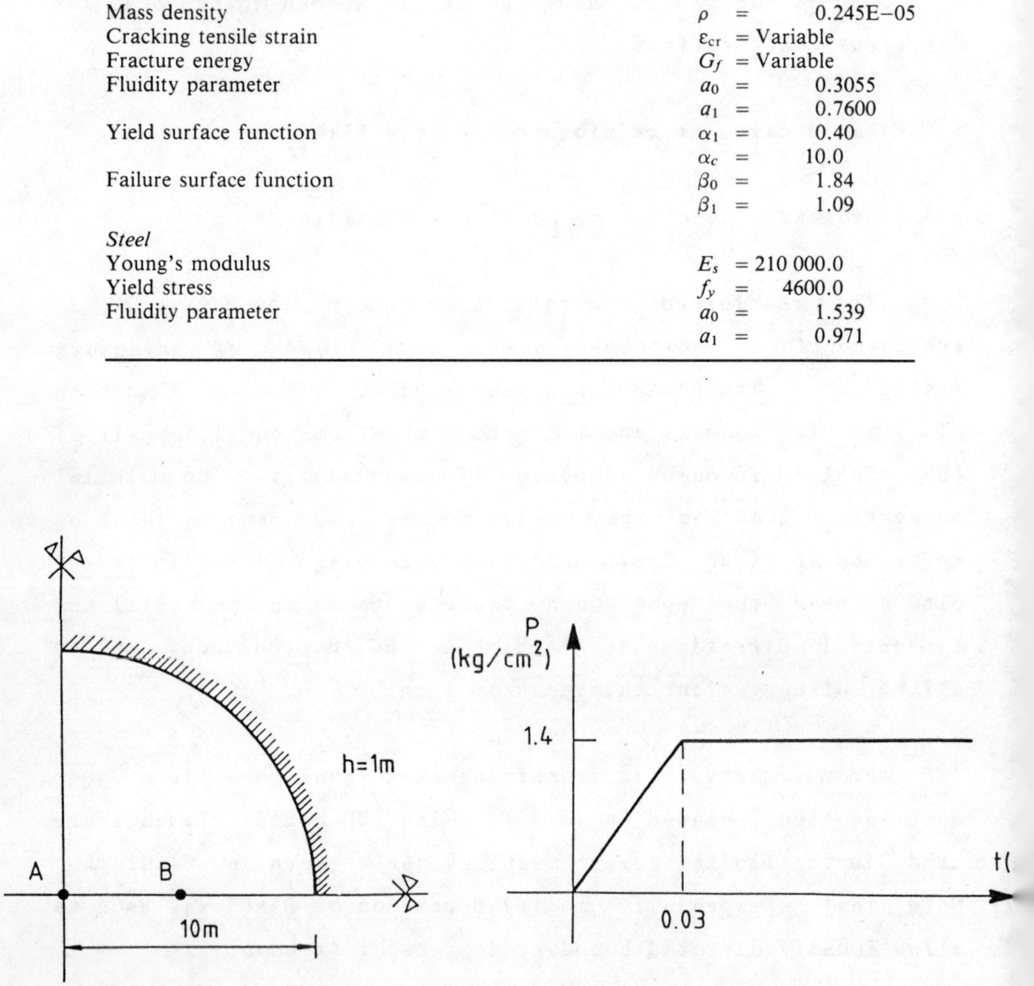

Figure 18 Clamped circular reinforced concrete slab: (a) symmetric quadrant and (b) loading time history

5.3.2 Results

In the linear analysis, complete agreement with the analytical results for a system with one degree of freedom is obtained. The nonlinear response is plotted in Figure 19 for three different values of the cracking strain. It is clear from these results that although the resulting central deflection varies significantly with the value of the cracking strain, this is not observed in the response of point B, located at a distance of 5 metres from the centre of the slab.

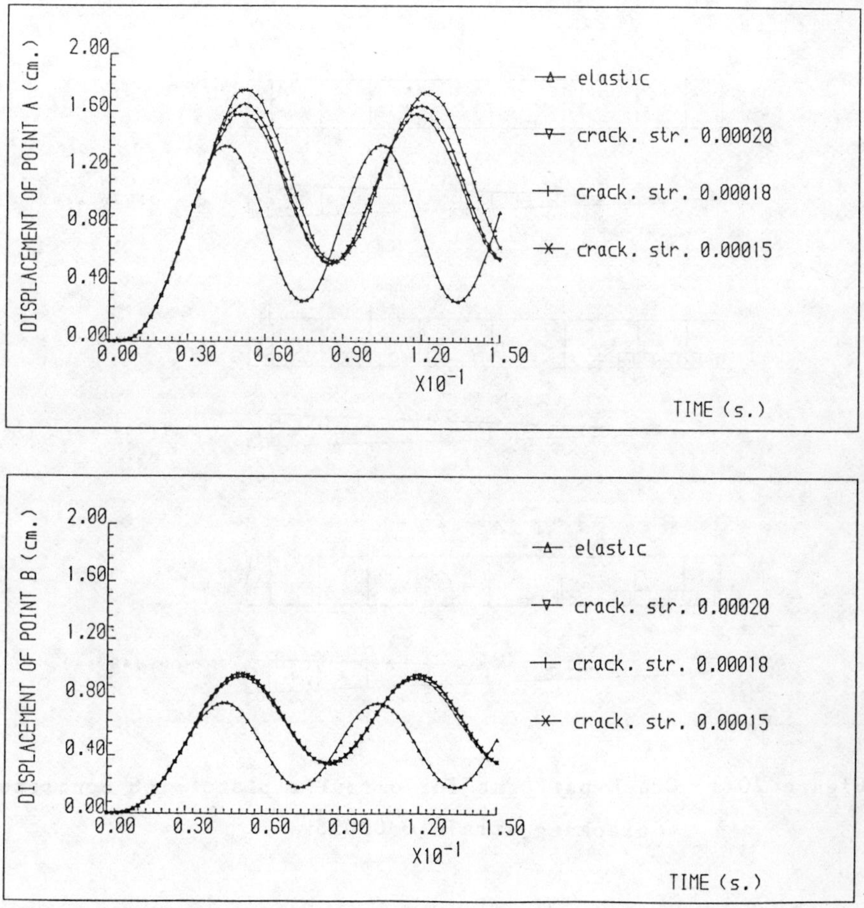

Figure 19 Nonlinear dynamic response of clamped circular reinforced concrete plate: (a) displacement history at point A and (b) displacement history at point B

The curve obtained for $\varepsilon_{cr} = 0.00018$ is almost identical to the response in reference 76. However, unlike the result in reference 76, no decay of the subsequent peak amplitude is observed. This is probably due to the fact that a smaller time step was used in the present analysis, thus avoiding numerical damping.

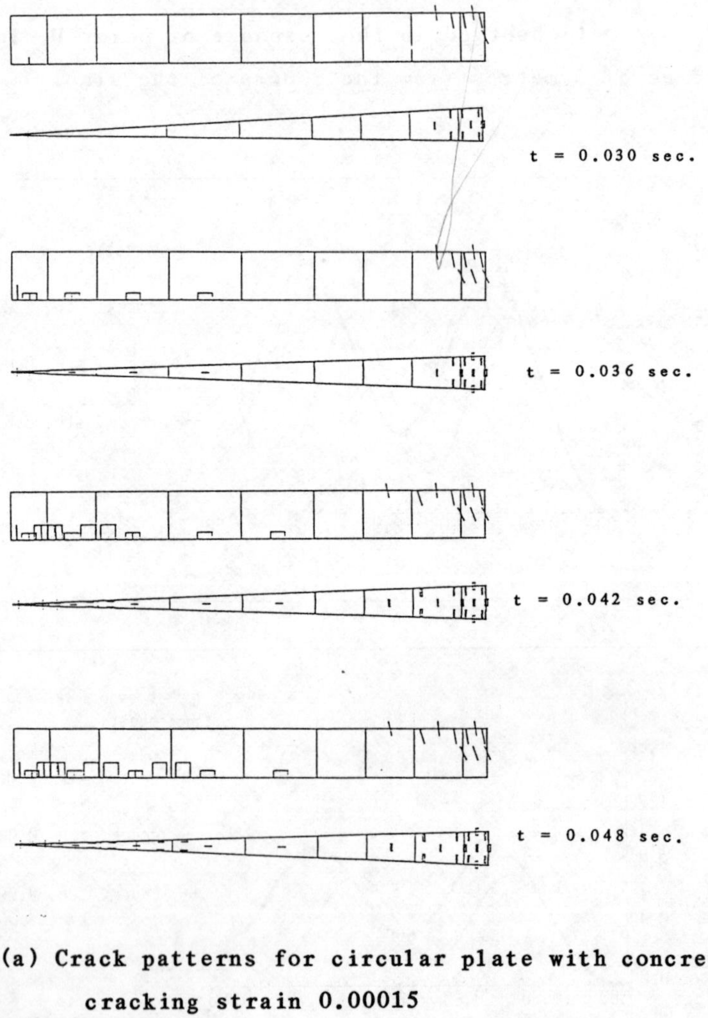

Figure 20(a) Crack patterns for circular plate with concrete cracking strain 0.00015

Figures 20 (a) and (b) show the crack patterns obtained for different time stations and two different cracking strain values. Tangential cracks develop first at the clamped edge (upper surface), and later, both tangential and radial cracks spread from the centre (bottom surface).

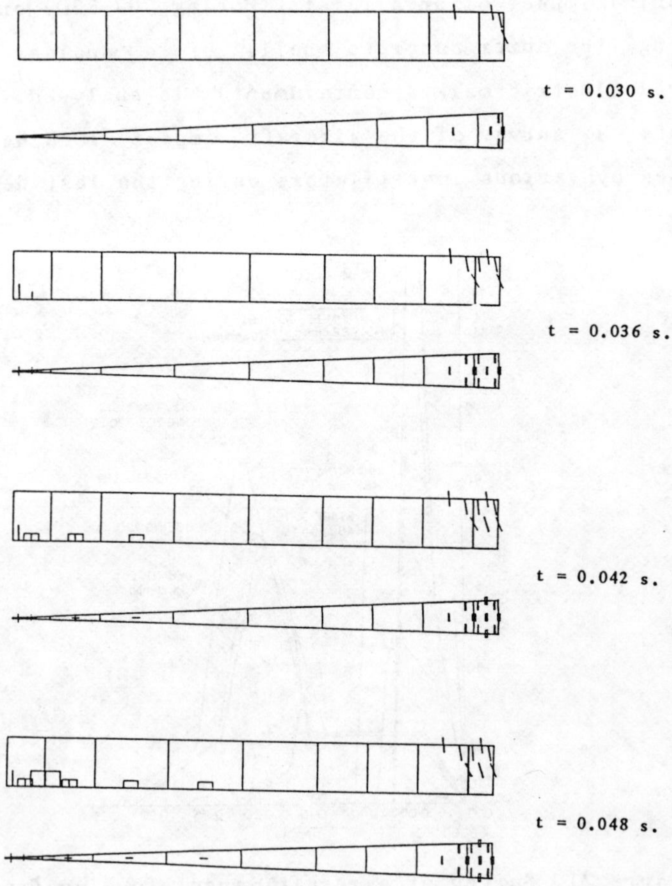

Figure 20(b) Crack patterns for circular plate with concrete cracking strain 0.00020

5.4 Reactor containment shell subjected to aircraft impact

5.4.1 Geometry, material properties and loading

The problem considered here has been previously studied by Rebora et al [76], Liu [77] and Crutzen et al [78,79]. The horizontal impact of an aircraft (Boeing 707-320) on the shield building (the outer concrete shell) of a nuclear power plant (General Electric mark 3 containment) is analysed. Figure 21 presents a survey of the aircraft impact loading functions proposed by various investigators during the last decade [80].

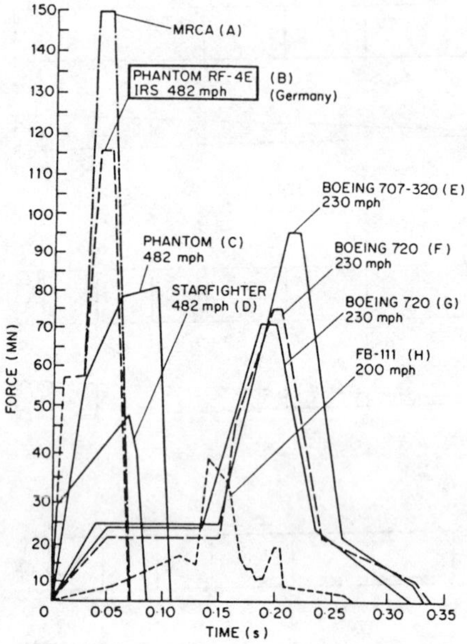

Figure 21 Survey of aircraft impact loading functions

The geometry, the loading function and the reinforcement are specified in Figure 22. The built-in reinforced concrete shell is composed of cylindrical and spherical parts of constant thickness. The reinforcement, placed circumferentially and meridionally on the interior and exterior surfaces, consists of bars of 40 mm diameter, spaced at 8 cm.

The material properties are the same as those used for the slab in Section 5.3 (see Table 5.2).

The impact is assumed to occur horizontally. The location of the area of impact of 28 m² is shown in Figure 22. The load history is also indicated and it is noted that the load has a maximum value of 9,000 t.

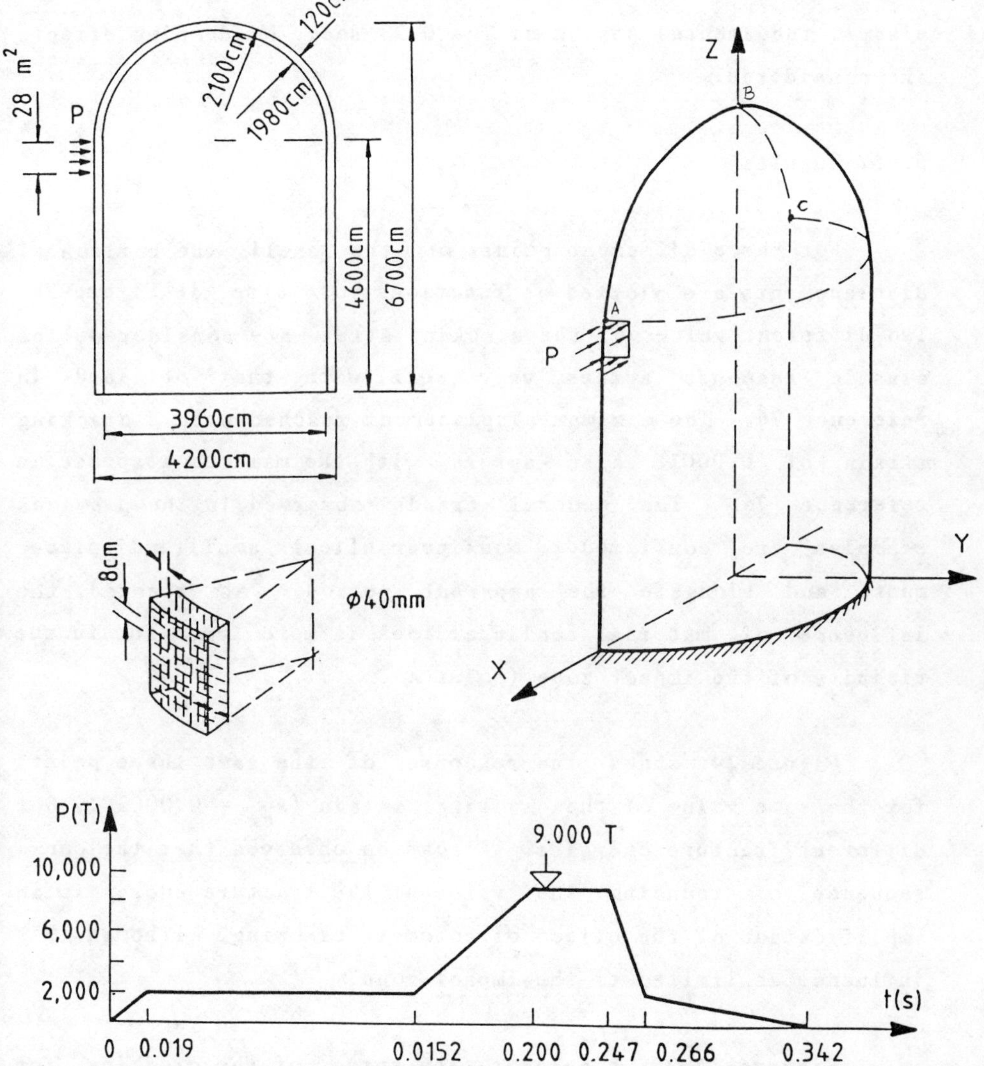

Figure 22 Nuclear containment structure: (a) general layout and (b) loading time history for aircraft impact

Since the loading and geometry of the shell are symmetric, only one half of the structure is considered. A mesh of 52 solid elements is used in the analysis (see Figure 25), with a local refinement in the vicinity of the impact zone.

The implicit Newmark algorithm with $\beta = 0.25$ and $\gamma = 0.50$ is used to integrate the governing equations in time. The time step selected is $\Delta t = 0.00475$ sec. which is about 1/50 of the elastic fundamental period of $T = 0.23$ sec. No damping effects are considered.

5.4.2 Results

For three different points on the shell, the horizontal displacements are plotted as functions of time in Figure 23. Two different values of the cracking strain are considered. The elastic response agrees very well with that obtained in reference 76. The maximum displacement reached with a cracking strain of 0.00018 also agrees with the maximum response in reference 76. The general trends observed in the previous examples are confirmed. Nonlinear effects amplify displacements and elongate the apparent period. As expected, the influence of material nonlinearities is more important in the vicinity of the impact zone (point A).

Figure 24 shows the response of the same three points for the same value of the cracking strain ($\varepsilon_{cr} = 0.00020$), but different fracture energies. It can be observed that the consequence of reducing the value of the fracture energy is an amplification of the effect of concrete cracking, although this influence is limited to the impact zone.

Figures 25-27 highlight the spread of the cracking for different time stations and three different values of the cracking strain. For a cracking strain of 0.00020, cracking

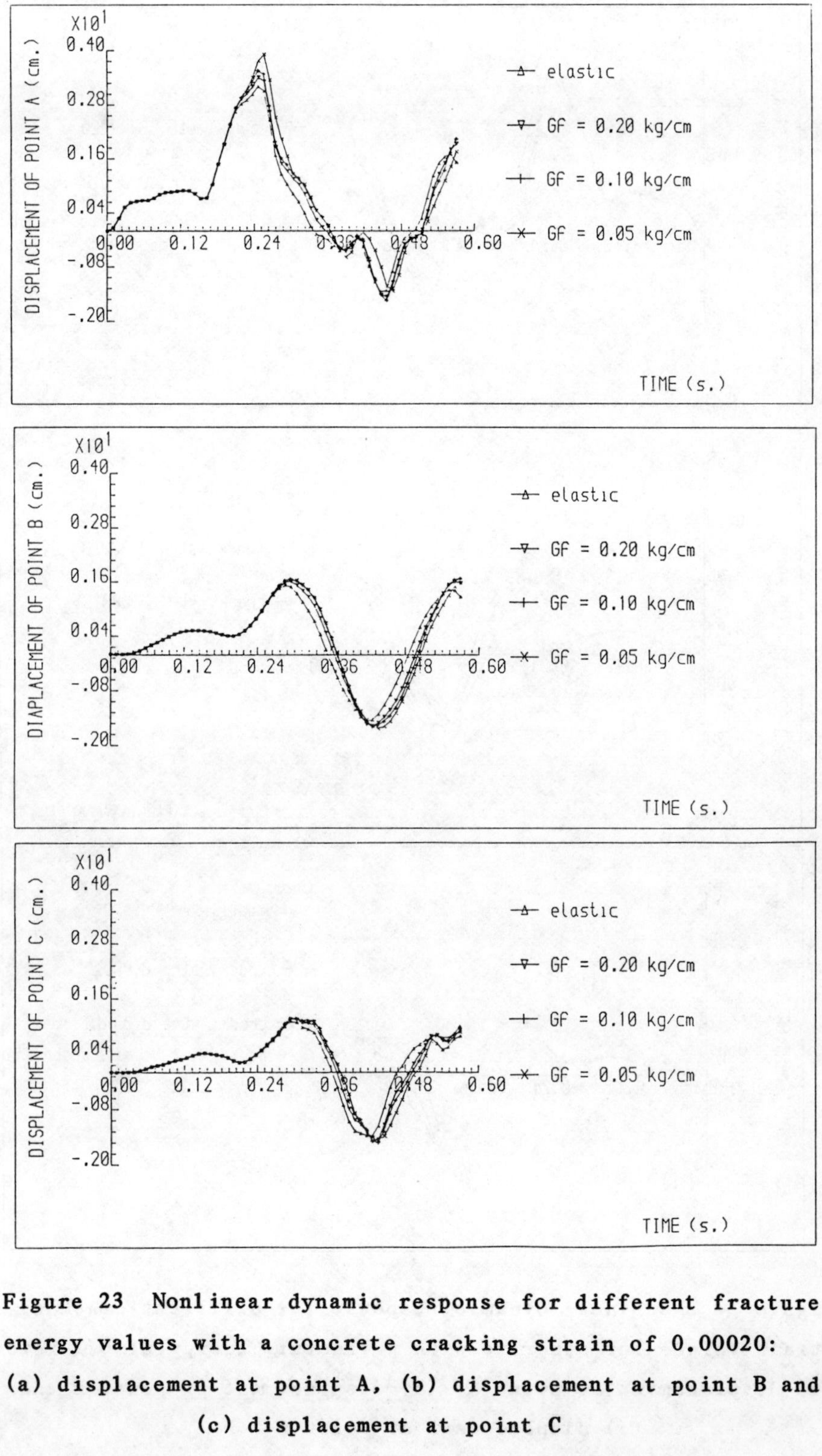

Figure 23 Nonlinear dynamic response for different fracture energy values with a concrete cracking strain of 0.00020: (a) displacement at point A, (b) displacement at point B and (c) displacement at point C

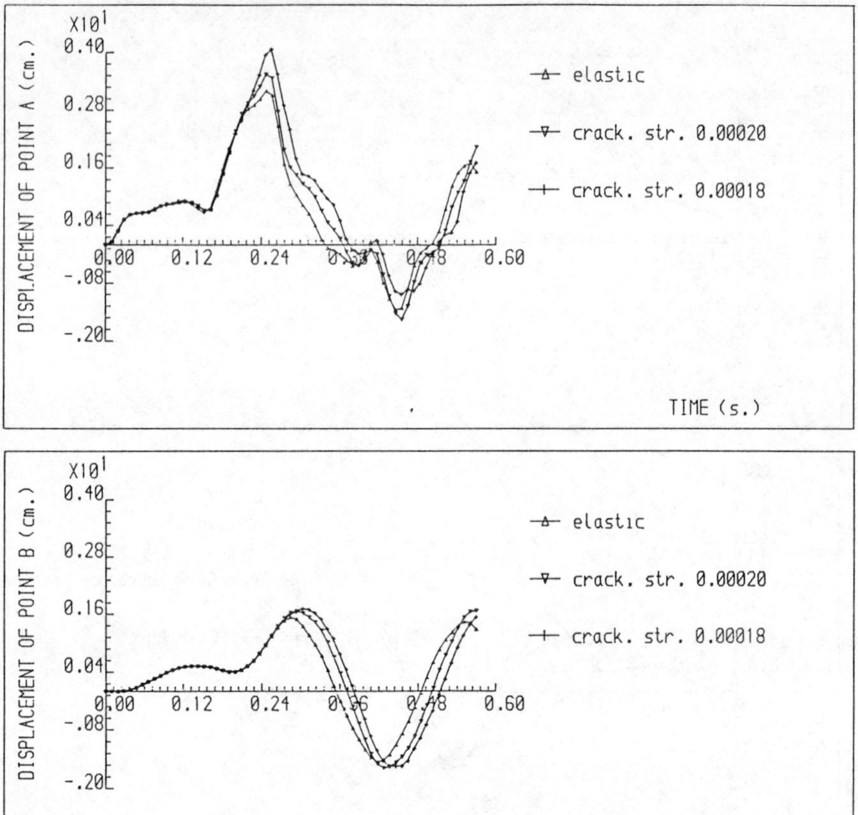

Figure 24 Nonlinear dynamic response for different cracking strain values for concrete with a fracture energy of 0.1 kg/cm (a) displacement at point A, (b) displacement at point B and (c) displacement at point C

mostly affects the impact zone and part of the base of the shell, where cracks in both surfaces of the shell can be observed. For the value $\varepsilon_{cr} = 0.00018$, cracks in both surfaces appear in the impact zone, and cracking spreads widely over the cylindrical and spherical parts of the shell. For the lowest

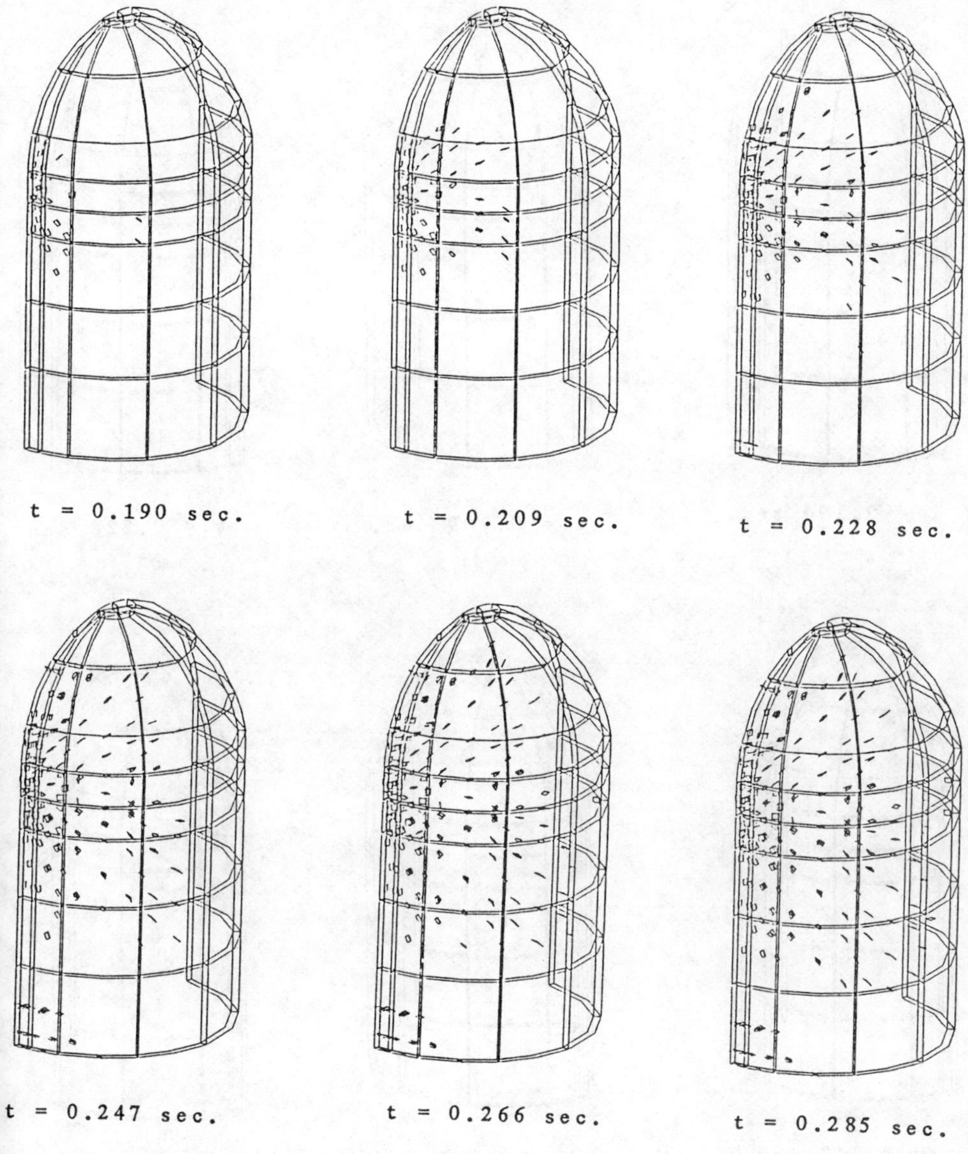

Figure 25 Crack patterns at different times for concrete with a cracking strain of 0.00015

values ε_{cr} = 0.00015 cracks are spread over almost the entire front hemisphere of the shell. The impact zone is cracked throughout and many parts of the structure can be seen to be doubly-cracked.

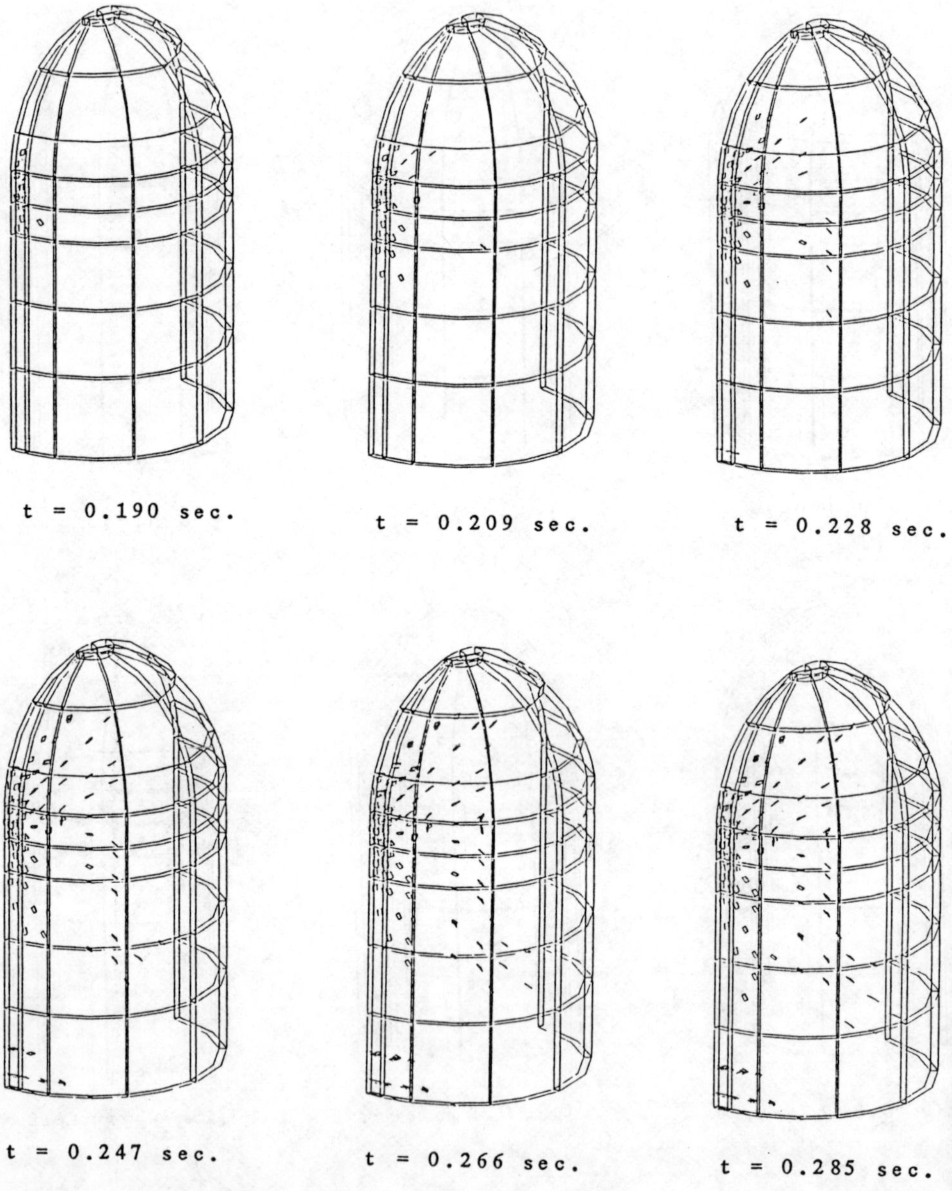

Figure 26 Crack patterns at different times for concrete with a cracking strain of 0.00018

5.5 Reactor containment shell under earthquake loading

In this example, the containment shell considered in Section 5.4.1 is subjected to the action of the horizontal

t = 0.190 sec.   t = 0.209 sec.   t = 0.228 sec.

t = 0.247 sec.   t = 0.266 sec.   t = 0.285 sec.

Figure 27 Crack pattern at different times for concrete with a cracking strain of 0.00020

components of acceleration of an earthquake. A similar problem has been considered in reference 77.

The cost of a time history analysis increases linearly with the accelerogram duration. This has motivated the development of short duration accelerograms which are - in some sense - compatible with the design response spectrum. Here, the Johnson-Epstein sinesweep analytic earthquake [81] will be used as a prescribed horizontal acceleration history. A maximum acceleration level of 0.33g is prescribed.

The sinesweep accelerogram which is equivalent to the El Centro NS accelerogram is shown in Figure 28.

When the structure is subjected to earthquake loading, the external applied forces are defined by

$$\underline{f} = - \underline{M}\, \underline{I}\, \ddot{d}_g(t) \tag{5.2}$$

where $\underline{M}$ is the mass matrix and $\underline{I}$ is a vector indicating the direction of the earthquake excitation.

The geometry and material properties are the same as those described in Section 5.4. The finite element mesh is redesigned for this example. One half of the structure is discretized using 40 solid elements.

5.5.1 Results

Firstly, a linear elastic analysis is performed. The implicit Newmark algorithm with β=0.25 and γ=0.50 is used. A time step of Δt = 0.010 sec. is selected. Figure 29 shows the horizontal displacement-time curves for two different points in the shell in three different situations: with no damping considered, with 1% of mass damping (α=0.546) and with

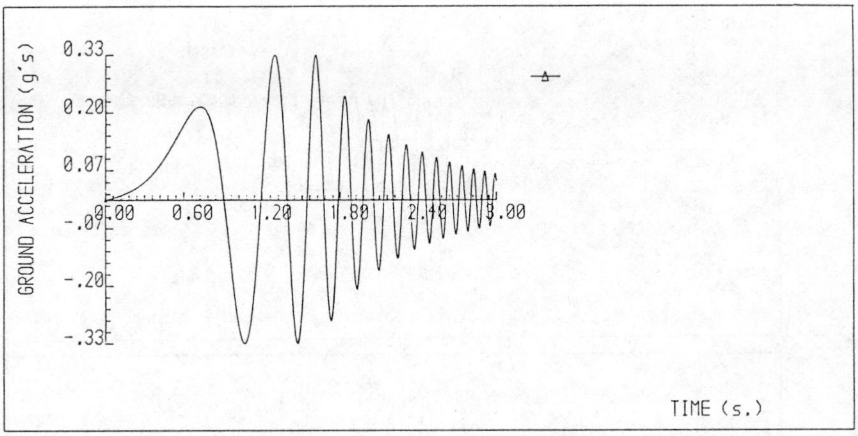

Figure 28 Sine sweep earthquake

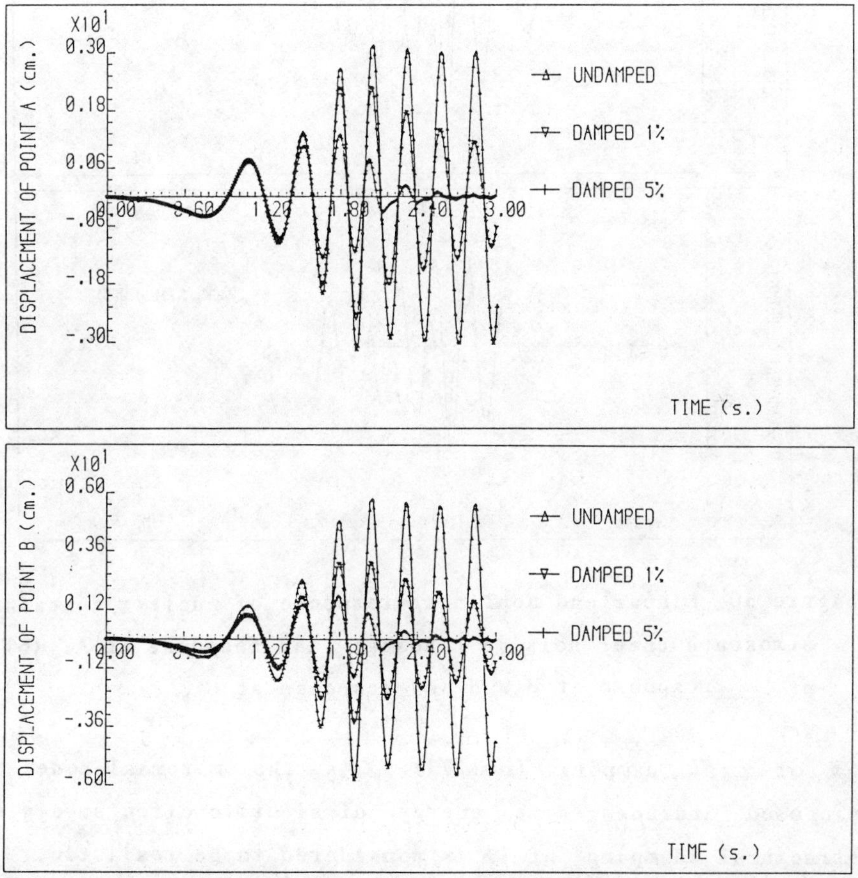

Figure 29 Nuclear containment structure under seismic loading: (a) linear response at A and (b) linear response at B

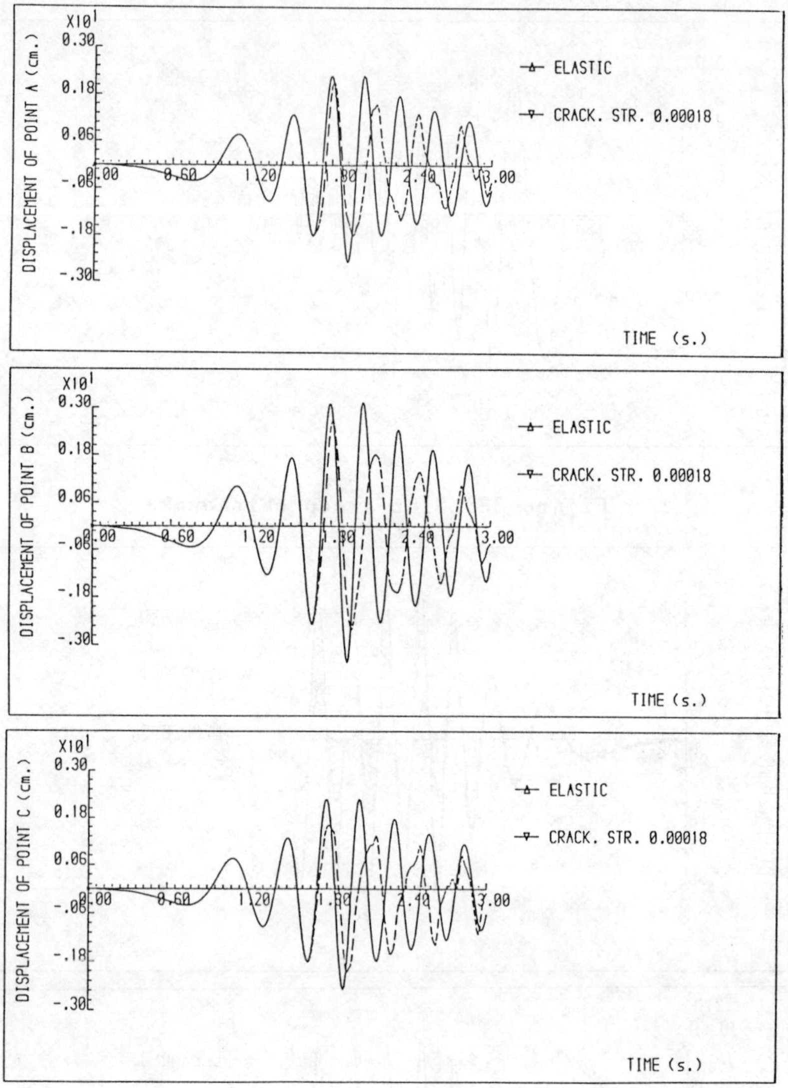

Figure 30 Linear and nonlinear response of nuclear containment structure under seismic loading: (a) response at A, (b) response at B and (c) response at C

5% of mass damping (α=2.73). As the material model here proposed includes some energy dissipative effects, a global structural damping of 1% is considered to be realistic.

Figure 30 shows the displacement histories for three different points on the shell when a nonlinear analysis is

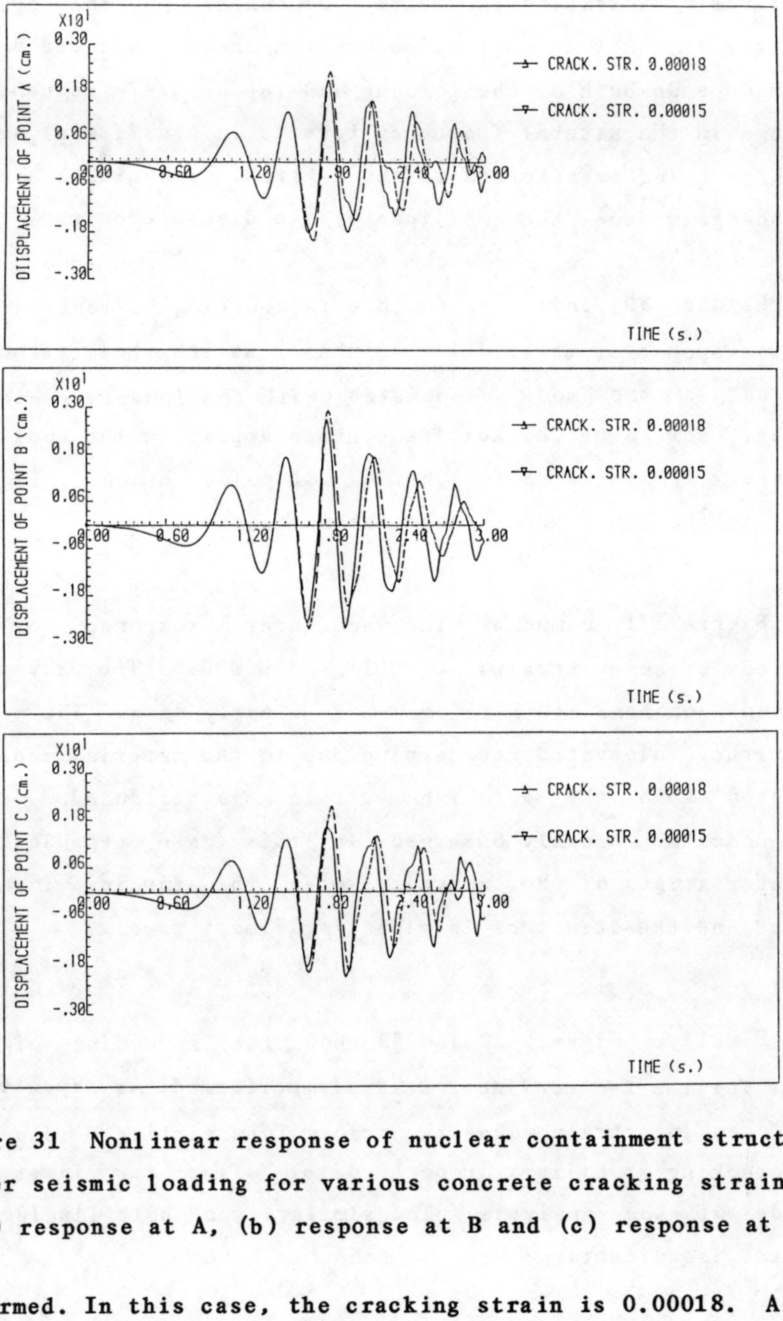

Figure 31 Nonlinear response of nuclear containment structure under seismic loading for various concrete cracking strains: (a) response at A, (b) response at B and (c) response at C

performed. In this case, the cracking strain is 0.00018. As in the previous examples, the period of vibration is elongated and some dissipation due to nonlinear effects is evident. However, here, the amplitude is smaller in the nonlinear analysis than in the linear case. Cracking affects the stiffness of the structure, thus changing its fundamental period. The response to a seismic excitation is greatly dependent on the dynamic characteristics of the structure, as the energy absorbed by the system depends both on the forcing and the natural frequencies. A change in the natural frequency results in a different amount of energy being transferred to the system, and in this case, this change reduces the amplitude of the displacements.

Figure 30 indicates another interesting effect. The linear response is essentially in phase, as the whole structure vibrates in the mode associated with the lowest frequency. However, some other higher frequencies appear in the nonlinear response. This is more obvious for points B and C, located closer to the base, where the cracking occurs.

Figure 31 compares the nonlinear response for two different cracking strains, 0.00018 and 0.00015. The previously observed phenomena are here even more clearly seen. The period is further elongated and damping due to the material model is increased when the cracking strain is reduced. High frequencies are clearly observed in this case, especially in the later stages of the analysis, when the forcing force is reduced and the structure is vibrating almost freely.

Finally, Figures 32 and 33 show the spreading of the cracks for the two nonlinear analysis performed. As expected, a lower cracking strain makes the cracks form earlier. However, the cracking stabilizes in both cases after the first two seconds of the analysis. The similarity of both final crack patterns is evident.

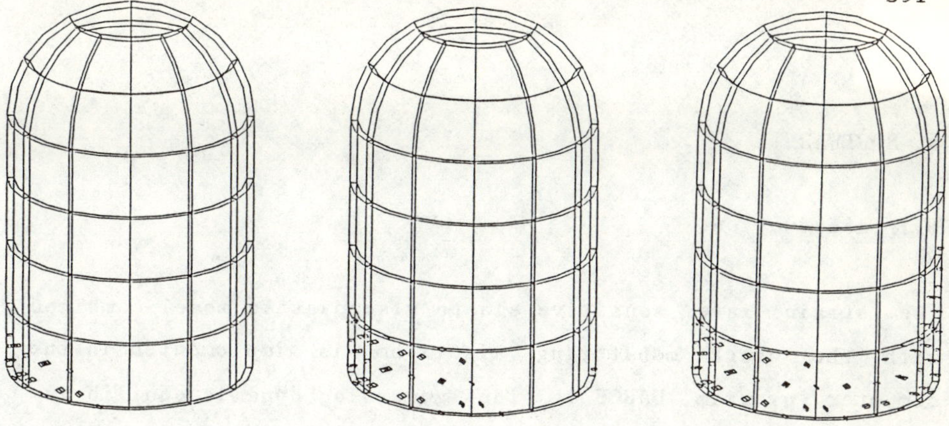

t = 1.65 sec. t = 1.80 sec. t = 1.95 sec.

Figure 32 Crack patterns at different times for concrete with a cracking strain of 0.00018

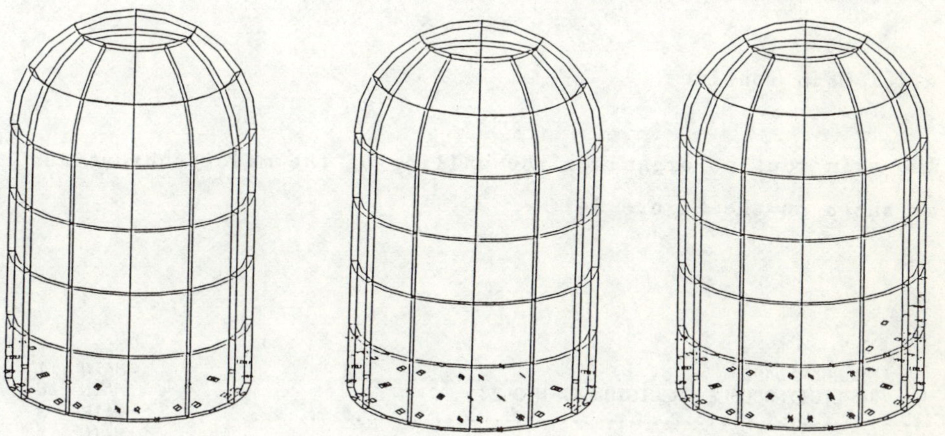

t = 1.65 sec. t = 1.80 sec. t = 1.95 sec.

Figure 33 Crack patterns at different times for concrete with a cracking strain of 0.00020

6. SOFTWARE

6.1 Introduction

The strain rate sensitive elasto/viscoplastic model combined with the crack monitoring algorithm is implemented in the computer program DARC3 . The governing dynamic equilibrium equations are solved using the implicit Newmark algorithm. Numerical examples using the program are presented later in section 7.

6.2 Overall design and main routine

6.2.1 Main routine

The main routine organises the calling of the major subroutines as shown on the Figure 34.

```
      PROGRAM DARC3
      IMPLICIT DOUBLE PRECISION (A-H,O-Z)
C.............................................................
C
C     PROGRAM FOR THE 3D DYNAMIC ANALYSIS OF
C     REINFORCED STRUCTURES ( STEEL & CONCRETE)
C
C     LUMPED MASS MATRIX
C     NEWMARK'S IMPLICIT ALGORITHM
C     ELASTO/VISCOPLASTIC MATERIAL MODEL
C                                M. CERVERA & J. BONET
C.............................................................
      PARAMETER(MLARG= 200000 , MNODE =    20 , MELEM =    60 ,
     .          MMATS =     5 , MPOIN =   500 , MDOFN =     3 ,
     .          MTOTV =  1500 , MVFIX =   200 , MPROP =    15 ,
     .          MEVAB =    60 , MDIME =     3 , MSTRE =     6 ,
     .          MGAUS =     3 , MGPCO =    16 , MTOTG =   960 ,
     .          MREIN =     5 , MLAYR =     5 , INDE1 =     4 ,
     .          INDE2 =     2 , INDE3 =     2 , INDE4 =     3 ,
     .          MOUTP =    50 , MTOTS =   960 , MACCE =  3000 )
```

Parameter, dimension and common statement
[MAIN 13-58]

Call routine INPUT0 to read control variables
[MAIN 60] 1

Call routine INPUT to read geometry, topology,
boundary conditions, material properties and reinforcement data
[MAIN 62-63] 2

Call routine INIT which initiates main arrays
[MAIN 65-66] 3

Call routine INTIME which reads data for time
integration and initial displacements and velocities
[MAIN 68] 4

Call routine LINKIN which sets up vectors for
use with profile solver
[MAIN 70] 5

Call routine LUMASS which computes mass matrix
and sets up shape function and their derivatives for use
to evaluate the stiffness matrix and force vector
[MAIN 72-74] 6

Call routine LOADPL which reads data associated
with load and computes reference load vector
[MAIN 76-77] 7

Loop over each timestep
[MAIN 81] 8

Loop over each iteration
[MAIN 83] 9

A

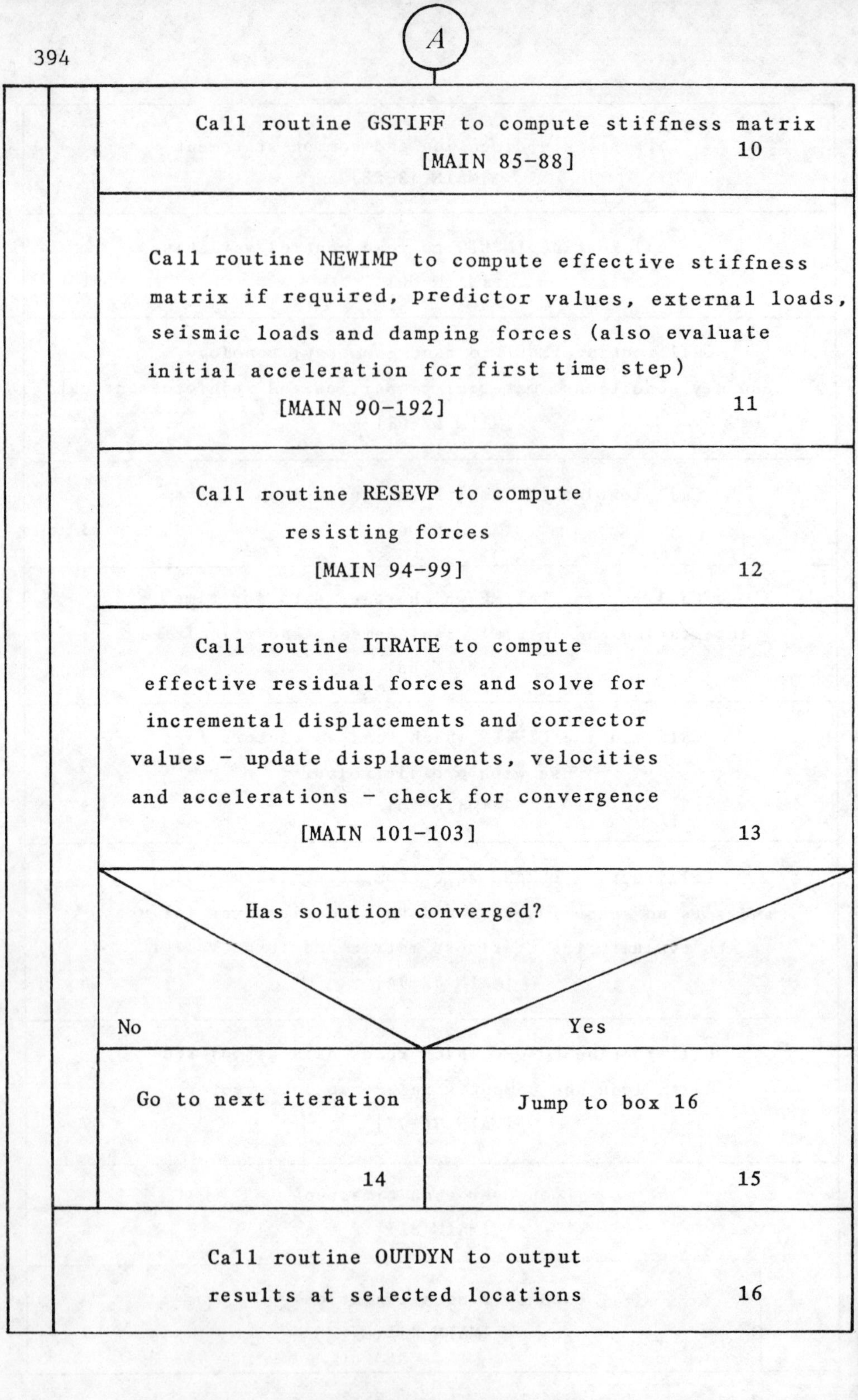

Figure 34. Nassi - Schneiderman (NS) chart for main routine

```
C
      DIMENSION ACCEH(MACCE) , ACCEI(MTOTV) , ACCEK(MTOTV) ,
     .          ACCEL(MTOTV) , ACCEV(MACCE) , DISPI(MTOTV) ,
     .          DISPL(MTOTV) , DISPQ(MTOTV) , DISPT(MTOTV) ,
     .          DVOLS(MTOTS) , DVOLU(MTOTG) , FORCE(MTOTV) ,
     .          ISTAT(MTOTV) , MATNO(MELEM) , MAXAI(MTOTV) ,
     .          MHIGH(MTOTV) , MPATT(MELEM) , NGRQS(MOUTP) ,
     .          NOCAP(MREIN) , NPRQD(MOUTP) , POSGP(MGAUS) ,
     .          RESID(MTOTV) , STIFF(MLARG) , STIFS(MLARG) ,
     .          VELOI(MTOTV) , VELOL(MTOTV) , VELOT(MTOTV) ,
     .          WEIGN(MGPCO) , WEIGP(MGAUS) , YMASS(MTOTV)
      DIMENSION ALPHI(INDE1,MTOTG), COORD(MDIME,MPOIN),
     .          CRVAL(INDE1,MTOTG),
     .          DMATX(MSTRE,MSTRE), ELAST(INDE4,MMATS),
     .          EFFST(INDE2,MTOTG), EFFSS(INDE2,MTOTS),
     .          ELCOD(MDIME,MNODE), ELDIS(MDOFN,MNODE),
     .          GPCOD(MDIME,MTOTG), GPCOS(MDIME,MTOTS),
     .          IFPRE(MDOFN,MPOIN), LEQNS(MEVAB,MELEM),
     .          LNODS(MNODE,MELEM), POSGN(MDIME,MGPCO),
     .          PROPS(MPROP,MMATS), RLOAD(MEVAB,MELEM),
     .          SHAPE(MNODE,MGPCO), STREF(MSTRE,MTOTS),
     .          STRES(MSTRE,MTOTG), WORKF(INDE2,MTOTG),
     .          WORKP(INDE2,MTOTG), XJACM(MDIME,MDIME)
      DIMENSION CARDS(MDIME,MNODE,MTOTS), CARTD(MDIME,MNODE,MTOTG),
     .          DERIV(MDIME,MNODE,MGPCO), MBARS(INDE3,MLAYR,MREIN),
     .          STRVP(INDE2,MSTRE,MTOTG), STRAF(INDE2,MSTRE,MTOTS),
     .          TMATC(MDIME,MDIME,MTOTG), TMATX(MDIME,MDIME,MTOTS),
     .          VBARS(INDE4,MLAYR,MREIN)
C
      COMMON/CTRL/ NDIME,NDOFN,NECHO,NELEM,NEVAB,NGASN,NGAUS,NMATS,
     &             NNODE,NPOIN,NPROP,NREIN,NSIZE,NSTRE,NTOTG,NTOTV,
     &             NVFIX,NWKTL,NYIEL
      COMMON/RUN/  IFUNC,IPRED,KSTEP,MITER,NACCE,NOUTD,NOUTP,NREQD,
     &             NREQS,NSTEP
      COMMON/CONST/AALFA,BEETA,GAAMA,DELTA,AZERO,BZERO,OMEGA,TMAXR,
     &             DTEND,DTIME,AFACT,TOLER,ADISP,AVELO,CONSD,CONSF
      COMMON/FILE/ NDATA,NRESU
      COMMON/STAT/ IITER,ISTEP,KTOLE
C
      CALL      INPUT0
C
      CALL      INPUT (COORD,LNODS,MATNO,IFPRE,PROPS,ELAST,MLAYR,
     .                 NOCAP,MBARS,VBARS,MPATT)
C
      CALL      INIT   (ISTAT,EFFST,WORKP,WORKF,STRVP,STRES,CRVAL,
     .                 ALPHI,STRAF,STREF,MGPCO,EFFSS)
C
      CALL      INTIME(ACCEH,ACCEV,NGRQS,NPRQD,DISPI,VELOI,IFPRE)
C
      CALL      LINKIN(LNODS,IFPRE,LEQNS,MAXAI,MHIGH,MLARG)
C
      CALL      LUMASS(COORD,LNODS,MATNO,PROPS,DVOLU,IFPRE,ELCOD,
     .                 CARTD,GPCOD,WEIGN,DERIV,SHAPE,POSGN,WEIGP,
     .                 XJACM,POSGP,YMASS)
C
      CALL      LOADPL(COORD,LNODS,MATNO,POSGP,PROPS,RLOAD,SHAPE,
     .                 ELCOD,IFPRE,XJACM,FORCE,DVOLU,WEIGP)
C
      KTOLE=0
      IINCS=0
      DO 510 ISTEP=1,NSTEP
C
      DO 500 IITER=1,MITER
C
      CALL      GSTIFF(COORD,LNODS,MATNO,DMATX,XJACM,POSGP,PROPS,
     .                 WEIGP,ELCOD,CARTD,MPATT,MLAYR,NOCAP,MBARS,
     .                 VBARS,ISTAT,DVOLS,TMATX,TMATC,CRVAL,LEQNS,
     .                 MAXAI,DVOLU,STIFF,CARDS,GPCOS)
```

```
C
      CALL      NEWIMP(ACCEH,ACCEI,ACCEK,ACCEL,ACCEV,DISPI,DISPL,
     .                 DISPT,IFPRE,MAXAI,FORCE,STIFF,VELOI,VELOL,
     .                 STIFS,VELOT,YMASS)
C
      CALL      RESEVP(COORD,LNODS,CRVAL,ELAST,MATNO,DVOLU,DVOLS,
     .                 CARDS,POSGP,PROPS,WEIGP,ELDIS,TMATX,TMATC,
     .                 CARTD,XJACM,STRES,DMATX,MPATT,MREIN,MLAYR,
     .                 NOCAP,MBARS,VBARS,STREF,ISTAT,ALPHI,EFFST,
     .                 DISPT,LEQNS,RESID,STRVP,STRAF,IFPRE,WORKP,
     .                 WORKF,EFFSS)
C
      CALL      ITRATE(ACCEI,ACCEL,YMASS,DISPI,DISPL,DISPT,MAXAI,
     .                 NCHEK,RESID,STIFS,VELOI,VELOL,VELOT,SUMP1,
     .                 RATIO)
C
      PRINT 888,ISTEP,RATIO
  888 FORMAT(5X,'ISTEP =',I5,5X,'RATIO =',E20.5)
      IF(NCHEK.EQ.1) GO TO 520
C
  500 CONTINUE
C
  520 CALL      OUTDYN(DISPT,NGRQS,NPRQD,MGPCO,DISPQ,ISTAT,IFPRE,
     .                 STRES,EFFST,WORKP,WORKF,GPCOD,STRVP,STRAF,
     .                 ALPHI,EFFSS)
C
  510 CONTINUE
      STOP
      END
```

6.2.2 Common blocks, main arrays and variables

In the program DARC3 most of the information is passed on through the argument lists, thereby allowing a form of dynamic dimensioning. However, mainly to avoid over-long argument lists, five labelled common blocks are included and these are now discussed.

<u>Common blocks</u>

<u>COMMON/CTRL/</u>

NDIME - number of dimensions of the problem (=3)

NDOFN - number of degrees of freedom per node (=3)

NECHO - parameter controlling echo of data

= 1, then load data suppressed

= 2, then all data suppressed

NELEM - number of elements

NEVAB - number of degrees of freedom per element

NGASN - number of sampling points per element

NMATS - number of different materials

NNODE - number of nodes per element

NPOIN - number of nodes

NPROP - number of properties per material

NREIN - number of reinforcing patterns

NSIZE - number of equations

= NTOTV - number of constrained degrees of freedom

NSTRE - number of components of stress vector

NTOTG - number of sampling points

NTOTV - number of degrees of freedom

NVFIX - number of constrained nodes

NWKTL - length of profile of K* matrix

NYIEL - type of yield surface

= 1 for Von Mises

= 2 for concrete (compressive behaviour)

COMMON/RUN/

IFUNC - time function code

= 0 for acceleration time history (e.g. seismic)

= 1 for Heaviside function, f(t) =1

= 2 for harmonic excitation, $f(t)=a_o + b_o \sin \omega t$

= 3 for linear-constant time history

= 4 for arbitrary time history

= 5 for linear-harmonic time history

IFRED - algorithm parameter

= 1 for standard algorithm

= 2 for modified algorithm

KSTEP - number of steps after which the stiffness matrix is reformed

MITER - maximum number of iterations

NACCE - number of acceleration of load history coordinates (if IFUNC $\neq 0$ and IFUNC $\neq 4$ then it is not used)

NOUTD - number of time steps between concrete state output

NOUTP - number of time steps between displacement and stress output

NREQD - number of nodes for selective output

NREQS - number of integration points for selective output

NSTEP - total number of time steps

COMMON/CONST/

AALFA - damping parameter $C = \alpha M + \beta K$

BEETA - damping parameter $C = \alpha M + \beta K$

GAAMA - Newmark's integration parameter $\gamma > 0.5$ for stable solution

DELTA - Newmark's integration parameter $\delta = 0.25(\gamma + 0.5)$

AZERO, BZERO, OMEGA - constants for harmonic excitation $f(t) = a_0 + b_0 \sin \omega t$

TMAXR - time to end of linear rise f(t)= t/TMAXR

DTEND - time at end of the excitation force

DTIME - time step length

AFACT - DTREC/DTIME

TOLER - specified tolerance on norm of residual forces

ADISP - norm of the initial displacements

AVELO - norm of the initial velocities

CONSD - GAAMA*DTIME

CONSF - 1./DTIME*DELTA

COMMON/FILE/

NDATA - input file number

NRESU - output file number

COMMON /STAT/

IITER	Current iteration number
ISTEP	Current time step number
KTOLE	Indicator of the material linearity (=0 linear , =1 nonlinear)

(b) Arrays

The main arrays are now described

ACCEH (MACCE), ACCEV (MACCE)	Base acceleration or load histories in two orthogonal directions
ACCEI (MTOTV)	
ACCEK (MTOTV)	Global working vectors
ACCEL (MTOTV)	
ALPHI (4,MTOTG)	Gauss point cracking information
CARDS (NDIME,MNODE,MTOTS)	Cartesian derivatives for the reinforcement
CARTD (NDIME,MNODE,MTOTG)	Cartesian derivatives for the reinforcement
COORD (NDIME,NPOIN)	Nodal point coordinates
CRVAL (4,MTOTG)	Crack reference values of stress and strain
DERIV (NDIME,MNODE,MGPCO)	Shape function derivatives
DISPI (MTOTV)	
DISPL (MTOTV)	Global working vectors
DISPQ (MTOTV)	
DISPT (MTOTV)	Total displacements
DMATX (NSTRE,NSTRE)	Material matrix
DVOLS (MTOTS)	Differential volume of reinforcement
DVOLU (MTOTG)	Differential volume

EFFST (MTOTG)	Effective elastic strain
EFFSS (MTOTS)	Effective strain in reinforcement
ELAST (4,MMATS)	Elastic material constants
ELCOD (NDIME,MNODE)	Element node coordinates
ELDIS (NDOFN,MNODE)	Element node displacements
FORCE (MTOTV)	Global force vector
GPCOD (NDIME,MTOTG)	Coordinates of integration points
GPCOS (NDIME,MTOTS)	Coordinates of integration points for the reinforcement
IFPRE (NDOFN,MPOIN)	Flags for constrained dof's
ISTAT (MTOTG)	Material state indicators
LEQNS (MEVAB,MELEM)	Equation addresses
LNODS (MNODE,MELEM)	Element connectivity array
MATNO (MELEM)	Element material identification
MAXAI (MTOTV)	Addresses of diagonal elements
MBARS (2,MLAYR,MREIN)	Reinforcement information
MHIGH (MTOTV)	Solver pointer
MPATT (MREIN)	Reinforcement pattern indicator
NGRQS (MOUTP)	Integration points for selective output
NOCAP (MREIN)	Number of layers of reinforcement patterns
NPRQD (NOUTP)	Nodes for selective output
POSGN (NDIME,MGPCO)	Integration points locations
POSGP (MGAUS)	Gauss point locations
PROPS (NPROP,MMATS)	Material properties
RESID (MTOTV)	Resisting forces global vector
RLDAD (MEVAB,MELEM)	Reference load vector
SHAPE (MNODE,MGPCO)	Shape functions
STIFF (MLARG)	Stiffness matrix
STIFS (MLARG)	Effective stiffness matrix (K*)
STRAF (2,NSTRE,MTOTS)	Viscoplastic strains in reinforcement
STREF (NSTRE,MTOTS)	Stresses in reinforcement
STRES (NSTRE,MTOTG)	Stresses
STRVP (2,NSTRE,MTOTG)	Viscoplastic strains

TMATC (NDIME,NDIME,MTOTG)	Transformation matrix for the integration points
TMATX (NDIME,NDIME,MTOTS)	Transformation matrix for the reinforcement integration points
VBARS (3,MLAYR,MREIN)	Reinforcement information
VELOI (MTOTV)	Working vector
VELOL (MTOTV)	Working vector
VELOT (MTOTV)	Nodal velocities
WEIGN (MGPCO)	Integration point weightings
WEIGP (MGAUS)	Gauss point weightings
WORKF (2,MTOTG)	Viscoplastic work at time of failure
WORKP (2,MTOTG)	Viscoplastic work
XJACM (NDIME,NDIME)	Jacobian matrix
YMASS (MTOTV)	Mass matrix

(c) Parameters

To enable a certain degree of flexibility in the use of the program DARC3 - in other words to allow problem of various sizes to be solved - the dimensions of the main arrays are defined using variables in the list of parameters given in the main routine. These variables are now defined

MLARG	Maximum profile length
MNODE	Maximum number of element nodes
MELEM	Maximum number of elements
MMATS	Maximum number of materials
MPOIN	Maximum number of nodal points
MDOFN	Maximum number of degrees of freedom
MTOTV	Maximum number of unknowns
MVFIX	Maximum number of nodes having constrained dofs
MPROP	Maximum number of material properties
MEVAB	Maximum number of unknowns per element

MDIME	Maximum analysis dimension
MSTRE	Maximum number of stress components
MGAUS	Maximum number of Gauss points for the one dimensional numerical integration
MGPCO	Maximum number of integration points for the volume integration (=16)
MTOTG	Maximum number of Gauss points for the whole structure
MREIN	Maximum number of reinforcement patterns
MLAYR	Maximum number of layers for reinforcement patterns
MOUTP	Maximum number of Gauss points or nodes for selective output
MTOTS	Maximum number of Gauss points or nodes for selective output for reinforcement
MACCE	Maximum number of acceleration or load history points

6.3 Main input and initialisation routines

In this section the main input and initialisation routines are listed.

```
      SUBROUTINE INPUTO
      IMPLICIT DOUBLE PRECISION (A-H,O-Z)
      COMMON/CTRL/ NDIME,NDOFN,NECHO,NELEM,NEVAB,NGASN,NGAUS,NMATS,
     &             NNODE,NPOIN,NPROP,NREIN,NSIZE,NSTRE,NTOTG,NTOTV,
     &             NVFIX,NWKTL,NYIEL
      COMMON/FILE/ NDATA,NRESU
C
C*********************************************************************
C
C**** THIS SUBROUTINE ACCEPTS THE CONTROL INPUT DATA
C
C*********************************************************************
      DIMENSION TITLE(40)
C
      READ(NDATA,900)  TITLE
      WRITE(NRESU,910) TITLE
```

```
C
C*** READ THE FIRST DATA CARD, AND ECHO IT INMEDIATELY.
C
      READ(NDATA,920) NPOIN,NELEM,NVFIX,NNODE,NMATS,NYIEL,
     .                NECHO,NREIN
      IF(NECHO. GE. 1) WRITE(NRESU,930)
      IF(NECHO. GE. 2) WRITE(NRESU,940)
      NEVAB=NDOFN*NNODE
      NTOTV=NPOIN*NDOFN
      NGASN=15
      IF(NNODE.EQ.8) NGASN=6
      NGAUS=2
      NTOTG=NELEM*NGASN
      IF(NECHO.LT.2) WRITE(NRESU,950) NPOIN, NELEM, NVFIX
      IF(NECHO.LT.2) WRITE(NRESU,960) NNODE, NMATS, NYIEL, NREIN
      RETURN
 900   FORMAT(40A2)
 910   FORMAT(1H0,10X,'TITLE OF RUN.    ',40A2/11X,12('=')//10X,
     .        'ECHO OF INPUT DATA.'/10X,19('-'))
 920   FORMAT(15I5)
 930   FORMAT(1H0,10X,'TOTAL LOAD MATRIX OUTPUT SUPPRESED.')
 940   FORMAT(1H0,10X,'ECHO OF DATA ALSO SUPPRESED.')
 950   FORMAT(//20X,'TOTAL NUMBER OF NODAL POINTS............',I5//
     .           ,20X,'TOTAL NUMBER OF ELEMENTS................',I5//
     .           ,20X,'TOTAL NUM. OF RESTRAINED BOUNDARY NDS...',I5)
 960   FORMAT(//20X,'NUMBER OF NODES PER ELEMENT.............',I5//
     .           ,20X,'NUMBER OF DIFFERENT MATERIALS...........',I5//
     .           ,20X,'NUMBER OF YIELD CRITERION SELECTED......',I5//
     .           ,20X,'NUM OF DIFFERENT REINFORCEMENT PATTERNS.',I5)
      END
```

```
      SUBROUTINE INPUT(COORD,LNODS,MATNO,IFPRE,PROPS,ELAST,MLAYR,
     .                 NOCAP,MBARS,VBARS,MPATT)
      IMPLICIT DOUBLE PRECISION (A-H,O-Z)
      COMMON/CTRL/ NDIME,NDOFN,NECHO,NELEM,NEVAB,NGASN,NGAUS,NMATS,
     &             NNODE,NPOIN,NPROP,NREIN,NSIZE,NSTRE,NTOTG,NTOTV,
     &             NVFIX,NWKTL,NYIEL
      COMMON/FILE/ NDATA,NRESU
C**********************************************************************
C
C**** THIS SUBROUTINE ACCEPTS  MOST OF THE INPUT DATA
C
C**********************************************************************
      DIMENSION COORD(NDIME,*),LNODS(NNODE,*),
     .          MATNO(*)       ,IFPRE(NDOFN,*),
     .          PROPS(NPROP,*),ELAST(3,*),
     .          NOCAP(*)       ,MPATT(*),
     .          VBARS(3,MLAYR,*),MBARS(2,MLAYR,*)
C
C*** READ THE ELEMENT NODAL CONNECTIONS, AND THE PROPERTY NUMBERS.
C
      IF(NECHO.LT.2) WRITE(NRESU,901)
      DO 2 IELEM=1,NELEM
      READ(NDATA,900) NUMEL,MATNO(NUMEL),MPATT(NUMEL),
     .                (LNODS(INODE,NUMEL),INODE=1,NNODE)
    2 IF(NECHO.LT.2) WRITE(NRESU,902) NUMEL,MATNO(NUMEL),MPATT(NUMEL),
     .                (LNODS(INODE,NUMEL),INODE=1,NNODE)
C
C*** ZERO ALL THE NODAL COORDINATES, PRIOR TO READING SOME OF THEM.
C
      DO 4 IPOIN=1,NPOIN
      DO 4 IDIME=1,NDIME
    4 COORD(IDIME,IPOIN)=0.0
```

```
C
C*** READ SOME NODAL COORDINATES, FINISHING WITH THE LAST NODE OF ALL.
C
      IF(NECHO.LT.2) WRITE(NRESU,903)
    6 READ(NDATA,904) IPOIN,(COORD(IDIME,IPOIN),IDIME=1,NDIME)
      IF(IPOIN.NE.NPOIN) GO TO 6
C
      IF(NNODE.EQ.20) CALL NODXYZ(COORD,LNODS,NDIME,NELEM,NNODE)
C
      DO 10 IPOIN=1,NPOIN
   10 IF(NECHO.LT.2) WRITE(NRESU,905) IPOIN,(COORD(IDIME,IPOIN),
     .                                IDIME=1,NDIME)
C
C*** READ THE FIXED VALUES.
C
      PI=4.*ATAN(1.)
      IF(NECHO.LT.2) WRITE(NRESU,906)
      DO 30 IPOIN=1,NPOIN
      DO 30 IDOFN=1,NDOFN
 30   IFPRE(IDOFN,IPOIN)=0
      DO 31 IVFIX=1,NVFIX
      READ(NDATA,907) IPOIN,(IFPRE(IDOFN,IPOIN),IDOFN=1,NDOFN)
      IF(NECHO.LT.2) WRITE(NRESU,908) IPOIN,(IFPRE(IDOFN,IPOIN),
     .                                IDOFN=1,NDOFN)
 31   CONTINUE
C
C*** READ THE AVAILABLE SELECTION OF ELEMENT PROPERTIES.
C
      IF(NECHO.LT.2) WRITE(NRESU,909)
      DO 18 IMATS=1,NMATS
      READ(NDATA,900) NUMAT
      READ(NDATA,910) (PROPS(IPROP,NUMAT),IPROP=1,NPROP)
C
C     COMPUTE ELASTIC CONSTANTS
C
      YOUNG=PROPS(1,IMATS)
      POISS=PROPS(2,IMATS)
      CONST=YOUNG*(1.-POISS)/((1.+POISS)*(1.-2.*POISS))
      ELAST(1,IMATS)=CONST
      ELAST(2,IMATS)=CONST*POISS/(1.-POISS)
      ELAST(3,IMATS)=CONST*(1.-2.*POISS)/(2.*(1.-POISS))
 18   CONTINUE
       IF(NECHO.GE.2) GOTO 19
       WRITE(NRESU,911)(I, I= 1, NMATS)
       WRITE(NRESU,912) (PROPS(1,IMATS), IMATS= 1,NMATS)
       WRITE(NRESU,913) (PROPS(2,IMATS), IMATS= 1,NMATS)
       WRITE(NRESU,914) (PROPS(3,IMATS), IMATS= 1,NMATS)
       WRITE(NRESU,915) (PROPS(4,IMATS), IMATS= 1,NMATS)
       WRITE(NRESU,916) (PROPS(5,IMATS), IMATS= 1,NMATS)
       WRITE(NRESU,917) (PROPS(6,IMATS), IMATS= 1,NMATS)
       WRITE(NRESU,918) (PROPS(7,IMATS), IMATS= 1,NMATS)
       WRITE(NRESU,919) (PROPS(8,IMATS), IMATS= 1,NMATS)
       WRITE(NRESU,920) (PROPS(9,IMATS), IMATS= 1,NMATS)
       WRITE(NRESU,921) (PROPS(10,IMATS), IMATS= 1,NMATS)
       WRITE(NRESU,922) (PROPS(11,IMATS), IMATS= 1,NMATS)
       WRITE(NRESU,923) (PROPS(12,IMATS), IMATS= 1,NMATS)
       WRITE(NRESU,924) (PROPS(13,IMATS), IMATS= 1,NMATS)
       WRITE(NRESU,925) (PROPS(14,IMATS), IMATS= 1,NMATS)
       WRITE(NRESU,926) (PROPS(15,IMATS), IMATS= 1,NMATS)
  19   CONTINUE
C
C*** READ THE AVAILABLE SELECTION OF REINFORCEMENT PATTERNS
C
      IF(NREIN.EQ.0) GO TO 26
      IF(NECHO.LT.2) WRITE(NRESU,927)
      DO 20 IREIN=1,NREIN
      READ(NDATA,900) KREIN,NOCAP(KREIN)
      NLAYR=NOCAP(KREIN)
```

```
      DO 21 ILAYR=1,NLAYR
        READ(NDATA,928) (MBARS(I,ILAYR,KREIN),I=1,2),
     .                  (VBARS(I,ILAYR,KREIN),I=1,3)
      VBARS(3,ILAYR,KREIN)=VBARS(3,ILAYR,KREIN)*ATAN(1.0)/45.
 21   CONTINUE
 20   CONTINUE
      IF(NECHO.GE.2) GOTO 332
       DO 333 IREIN=1,NREIN
       NLAYR=NOCAP(IREIN)
       WRITE(NRESU,929) IREIN
       WRITE(NRESU,930)(I, I= 1, NLAYR)
       WRITE(NRESU,931) (MBARS(1,ILAYR,IREIN),ILAYR=1,NLAYR)
       WRITE(NRESU,932) (MBARS(2,ILAYR,IREIN),ILAYR=1,NLAYR)
       WRITE(NRESU,933) (VBARS(1,ILAYR,IREIN),ILAYR=1,NLAYR)
       WRITE(NRESU,934) (VBARS(2,ILAYR,IREIN),ILAYR=1,NLAYR)
       WRITE(NRESU,935) (VBARS(3,ILAYR,IREIN),ILAYR=1,NLAYR)
  333  CONTINUE
  332  CONTINUE
   26  CONTINUE
       RETURN
C
900    FORMAT(13I5/15X,10I5)
901    FORMAT(///10X,' NODAL CONNECTION    ANTI-CLOCKWISE AROUND',
     .         ' ELEMENT.  RIGHT HAND SCREW RULE.'/11X,16('*')//12X,
     . 'ELEMENT      PROPERTY    REINFORC.      NODE NUMBERS.'/12X,
     . 'NUMBER.        SET.           PATTERN     N1    N2    N3    N4    N5    N6'
     . 'N7    N8    N9   N10')
902    FORMAT(10X,I5,3X,I9,6X,I5,6X,10I5/44X,10I5)
903    FORMAT(///10X,'NODAL CO-ORDINATES DATA.'/10X,24('*')//20X,
     .         '       NODE NUMBER          X CO-ORDINATE.  Y CO-ORDINATE.',
     .         '  Z CO-ORDINATE.')
904    FORMAT(I5,3F10.5)
905    FORMAT(25X,I5,6X,3(6X,F10.3))
906    FORMAT(///10X,'RESTRAINED NODES RELATIVE TO THE',
     . '  X-Y-Z  CO-ORDINATE SYSTEM, AND THEIR ORIGINAL POSITION.'/10X,
     . 100('*')//8X,'  NODE      X RESTRAINT        ',
     .'Y RESTRAINT          Z RESTRAINT ')
907    FORMAT(1X,I4,7X,3I1,F10.5)
908    FORMAT(8X,I5,3(6X,I5,7X),F10.5)
909    FORMAT(///10X,'MATERIAL PROPERTY SETS.'/10X,23('*')//)
910    FORMAT(5E10.4/5E10.4/5E10.4)
911    FORMAT(1H0,71X,5('  SET',I2,'      '))
912    FORMAT(1H ,20X,'YOUNG MODULUS.................................',
     .   5(3X,E10.4))
913    FORMAT(1H ,20X,'POISSON RATIO.................................',
     .   5(3X,E10.4))
914    FORMAT(1H ,20X,'COMPRESSION FLOW STRESS.......................',
     .   5(3X,E10.4))
915    FORMAT(1H ,20X,'CRACKING STRESS ( YOUNG*CRACKING STRAIN )....',
     .   5(3X,E10.4))
916    FORMAT(1H ,20X,'CRUSHING STRAIN...............................',
     .   5(3X,E10.4))
917    FORMAT(1H ,20X,'FRACTURE ENERGY...............................',
     .   5(3X,E10.4))
918    FORMAT(1H ,20X,'FACTOR FOR SHEAR REDUCTION....................',
     .   5(3X,E10.4))
919    FORMAT(1H ,20X,'NOT USED......................................',
     .   5(3X,E10.4))
920    FORMAT(1H ,20X,'MATERIAL DENSITY..............................',
     .   5(3X,E10.4))
921    FORMAT(1H ,20X,'FACTOR FOR END OF ELASTICITY..................',
     .   5(3X,E10.4))
922    FORMAT(1H ,20X,'A0 FOR FLUIDITY PARAMETER.....................',
     .   5(3X,E10.4))
923    FORMAT(1H ,20X,'A1 FOR FLUIDITY PARAMETER.....................',
     .   5(3X,E10.4))
924    FORMAT(1H ,20X,'ALFA-C FOR STRAIN-SOFTENING...................',
     .   5(3X,E10.4))
```

```
925   FORMAT(1H ,20X,'BETA0 FOR MONITORING SURFACE.................',
     . 5(3X,E10.4))
926   FORMAT(1H ,20X,'BETA1 FOR MONITORING SURFACE.................',
     . 5(3X,E10.4))
927   FORMAT(///10X,'REINFORCEMENT SETS.'/10X,23('*')//)
928   FORMAT(2I5,3F10.5)
929   FORMAT(//10X,'REINFORCEMENT SET NO.',I3)
930   FORMAT(1H0,54X,5('LAYER',I2,'      '))
931   FORMAT(1H ,10X,'MATERIAL NUMBER.........................',
     . 5(8X,I5))
932   FORMAT(1H ,10X,'COORDINATE NUMBER.......................',
     . 5(8X,I5))
933   FORMAT(1H ,10X,'COORDINATE POSITION.....................',
     . 5(3X,F10.5))
934   FORMAT(1H ,10X,'THICKNESS...............................',
     . 5(3X,F10.5))
935   FORMAT(1H ,10X,'ANGLE FROM EXI-AXIS.....................',
     . 5(3X,F10.5))
      END
```

```
      SUBROUTINE INIT   (ISTAT,EFFST,WORKP,WORKF,STRVP,STRES,CRVAL,
     .                    ALPHI,STRAF,STREF,MGPCO,EFFSS)
      IMPLICIT DOUBLE PRECISION (A-H,O-Z)
      COMMON/CTRL/ NDIME,NDOFN,NECHO,NELEM,NEVAB,NGASN,NGAUS,NMATS,
     &             NNODE,NPOIN,NPROP,NREIN,NSIZE,NSTRE,NTOTG,NTOTV,
     &             NVFIX,NWKTL,NYIEL
C
C.....................................................................
C
C     ROUTINE TO INITIALISE MATERIAL STATE ARRAYS
C
C.....................................................................
C
      DIMENSION ISTAT(*)   ,EFFST(2,*),WORKP(2,*),WORKF(2,*),
     .          STRES(6,*),STREF(6,*),CRVAL(4,*),ALPHI(4,*),
     .          EFFSS(2,*),STRAF(2,6,*),STRVP(2,6,*)
      NTOTS=NELEM*MGPCO
      DO 10 ITOTG=1,NTOTG
         ISTAT(ITOTG)=0
         EFFST(1,ITOTG)=0.0
         WORKP(1,ITOTG)=0.0
         WORKF(1,ITOTG)=0.0
           DO 20 ISTRE=1,NSTRE
              STRVP(1,ISTRE,ITOTG)=0.0
              STRES(ISTRE,ITOTG)=0.0
   20      CONTINUE
           DO 30 INDEX=1,4
              CRVAL(INDEX,ITOTG)=0.0
              ALPHI(INDEX,ITOTG)=0.0
   30      CONTINUE
   10 CONTINUE
C
      DO 40 ITOTS=1,NTOTS
        EFFSS(1,ITOTS)=0.0
           DO 50 ISTRE=1,NSTRE
             STRAF(1,ISTRE,ITOTS)=0.0
             STREF(ISTRE,ITOTS)=0.0
   50      CONTINUE
   40 CONTINUE
      RETURN
      END
```

```
      SUBROUTINE NODXYZ ( COORD, LNODS, NDIME, NELEM , NNODE )
      IMPLICIT DOUBLE PRECISION (A-H,O-Z)
C *******************************************************
C *                                                     *
C *    A SUBROUTINE TO INTERPOLATE NON SPECIFIED        *
C *               MID-SIDE NODES.                       *
C *                                                     *
C *******************************************************
C
       DIMENSION COORD(NDIME,*), LNODS(NNODE,*)
C
C ****  LOOP OVER EACH ELEMENT.
C
      DO 100 IELEM = 1,NELEM
      KOUNT = 0
      NODEB = 0
C
C***  COMPUTE THE NUMBER OF THE MIDSIDE NODE
C
   10 KOUNT = KOUNT+1
      NODEB = NODEB+2
      IF(KOUNT.EQ.5) NODEB = 14
      IF(KOUNT.GT.8) NODEB = KOUNT
      NODMD = LNODS(NODEB,IELEM)
C
C***  CHECK IF THE COORDINATES OF THE MIDSIDE NODE HAVE BEEN INPUT
C
      TOTAL =ABS(COORD(1,NODMD))+ABS(COORD(2,NODMD))+ABS(COORD(3,
     .NODMD))
      IF(TOTAL.NE.0.0) GO TO 30
C
C***  COMPUTE THE NUMBERS OF THE CORNER NODES OF THE CURRENT EDGE
C
      NODEA = NODEB-1
      IF(KOUNT.GT.8) NODEA = 2*KOUNT-17
      NODEC = NODEA+2
      IF(KOUNT.EQ.4.OR.KOUNT.EQ.8) NODEC = NODEC-8
      IF(KOUNT.GT.8) NODEC = NODEA+12
      NODST = LNODS(NODEA,IELEM)
      NODFN = LNODS(NODEC,IELEM)
C
C***  INTERPOLATE BY A STRAIGHT LINE
C
      DO 20 IDIME = 1,NDIME
   20 COORD(IDIME,NODMD) = (COORD(IDIME,NODST)+COORD(IDIME,NODFN))*0.5
C
   30 IF(KOUNT.NE.12) GO TO 10
  100 CONTINUE
C
      RETURN
      END
```

```
      SUBROUTINE INTIME(ACCEH,ACCEV,NGRQS,NPRQD,TDISP,VELOC,IFPRE)
C**********************************************************
C
C  INPUT INITIAL VALUES AND TIME INTEGRATION DATA
C
C**********************************************************
      IMPLICIT DOUBLE PRECISION (A-H,O-Z)
      COMMON/CTRL/ NDIME,NDOFN,NECHO,NELEM,NEVAB,NGASN,NGAUS,NMATS,
     &             NNODE,NPOIN,NPROP,NREIN,NSIZE,NSTRE,NTOTG,NTOTV,
     &             NVFIX,NWKTL,NYIEL
      COMMON/RUN/  IFUNC,IPRED,KSTEP,MITER,NACCE,NOUTD,NOUTP,NREQD,
     &             NREQS,NSTEP
```

```
      COMMON/CONST/AALFA,BEETA,GAAMA,DELTA,AZERO,BZERO,OMEGA,TMAXR,
     &             DTEND,DTIME,AFACT,TOLER,ADISP,AVELO,CONSD,CONSF
      COMMON/FILE/ NDATA,NRESU
      DIMENSION TDISP(*),ACCEH(*),NPRQD(*),
     .          VELOC(*),ACCEV(*),NGRQS(*),IFPRE(3,*)
C
C***  READ TIME STEPPING AND SELECTIVE OUTPUT PARAMETERS
C
      READ(NDATA,900) NSTEP,NOUTD,NOUTP,NREQD,NREQS,NACCE,IFUNC,
     .                IFIXD,MITER,KSTEP,IPRED
      READ(NDATA,901) DTIME,DTEND,DTREC,AALFA,BEETA,DELTA,GAAMA,
     .                AZERO,BZERO,OMEGA,TOLER,TMAXR
      WRITE(NRESU,902) NSTEP,NOUTD,NOUTP,NREQD,NREQS,NACCE,IFUNC,
     .                 IFIXD,MITER,KSTEP,IPRED
      WRITE(NRESU,903) DTIME,DTEND,DTREC,AALFA,BEETA,DELTA,GAAMA,
     .                 AZERO,BZERO,OMEGA,TOLER,TMAXR
C
C***  SELECTED NODES AND GAUSS POINTS FOR OUTPUT
C
      IF(NREQD.NE.0) READ(NDATA,900) (NPRQD(IREQD),IREQD=1,NREQD)
      IF(NREQS.NE.0) READ(NDATA,900) (NGRQS(IREQS),IREQS=1,NREQS)
      WRITE(NRESU,904)
      IF(NREQD.NE.0) WRITE (NRESU,905) (NPRQD(IREQD),IREQD=1,NREQD)
      IF(NREQS.NE.0) WRITE (NRESU,906) (NGRQS(IREQS),IREQS=1,NREQS)
C
C***  INITIAL DISPLACEMENTS
C
      JPOIN=0
      DO 500 IPOIN=1,NPOIN
      DO 500 IDOFN=1,NDOFN
      JPOIN=JPOIN+1
      TDISP(JPOIN)=0.
  500 VELOC(JPOIN)=0.
      WRITE(NRESU,908)
  200 READ(NDATA,907) NGASH,XGASH,YGASH,ZGASH
      NPOSN=(NGASH-1)*NDOFN+1
      TDISP(NPOSN)=XGASH
      NPOSN=NPOSN+1
      TDISP(NPOSN)=YGASH
      NPOSN=NPOSN+1
      TDISP(NPOSN)=ZGASH
      WRITE(NRESU,909) NGASH,XGASH,YGASH,ZGASH
      IF(NGASH.NE.NPOIN) GO TO 200
C
C***  INITIAL VELOCITIES
C
      WRITE(NRESU,910)
  210 READ(NDATA,907) NGASH,XGASH,YGASH,ZGASH
      NPOSN=(NGASH-1)*NDOFN+1
      VELOC(NPOSN)=XGASH
      NPOSN=NPOSN+1
      VELOC(NPOSN)=YGASH
      NPOSN=NPOSN+1
      VELOC(NPOSN)=ZGASH
      WRITE(NRESU,909) NGASH,XGASH,YGASH,ZGASH
      IF(NGASH.NE.NPOIN) GO TO 210
C
C***  REARRANGE INITIAL DISPLACEMENTS AND VELOCITY VECTORS
C
      KOUNT=0
      KOUND=0
      ADISP=0.
      AVELO=0.
      DO 510 IPOIN=1,NPOIN
      DO 510 IDOFN=1,NDOFN
      KOUNT=KOUNT+1
      IF(IFPRE(IDOFN,IPOIN).NE.0) GO TO 510
```

```
      KOUND=KOUND+1
      TDISP(KOUND)=TDISP(KOUNT)
      ADISP=ADISP+TDISP(KOUND)**2
      VELOC(KOUND)=VELOC(KOUNT)
      AVELO=AVELO+VELOC(KOUND)**2
  510 CONTINUE
C
C***  READ ACCELEROGRAM DATA, FROM TAPE 12
C
      IF(IFUNC.NE.0) GO TO 250
      AFACT=DTREC/DTIME
      READ(12,911) (ACCEV(I),I=1,NACCE)
      WRITE(NRESU,913) DTREC
      WRITE(NRESU,912) (ACCEV(I),I=1,NACCE)
  250 CONTINUE
C
C***  READ LOAD TIME HISTORY, FROM TAPE 12
C
      IF(IFUNC.NE.4) GO TO 260
      READ(12,914) (ACCEH(I),ACCEV(I),I=1,NACCE)
      WRITE(NRESU,915)
      WRITE(NRESU,916) (ACCEH(I),ACCEV(I),I=1,NACCE)
  260 CONTINUE
C
      RETURN
C
  900 FORMAT(16I5)
  901 FORMAT(8F10.4)
  902 FORMAT(/5X,'TIME STEPPING PARAMETERS'/
     .       /5X,'NSTEP=',I5,12X,'NOUTD=',I5,12X,'NOUTP=',I5,/
     .       /5X,'NREQD=',I5,12X,'NREQS=',I5,12X,'NACCE=',I5,/
     .       /5X,'IFUNC=',I5,12X,'IFIXD=',I5,12X,'MITER=',I5,/
     .       /5X,'KSTEP=',I5,12X,'IPRED=',I5)
  903 FORMAT(/5X,'DTIME=',G12.4,4X,'DTEND=',G12.4,4X,'DTREC=',G12.4,/
     .       /5X,'AALFA=',G12.4,4X,'BEETA=',G12.4,4X,'DELTA=',G12.4,/
     .       /5X,'GAAMA=',G12.4,4X,'AZERO=',G12.4,4X,'BZERO=',G12.4,/
     .       /5X,'OMEGA=',G12.4,4X,'TOLER=',G12.4,4X,'TMAXR=',G12.4)
  904 FORMAT(//5X,' SELECTIVE OUTPUT REQUESTED FOR FOLLOWING')
  905 FORMAT(/5X,' NODES',10I5)
  906 FORMAT(5X,' GAUSS POINTS',10I5)
  907 FORMAT(I5,3F10.5)
  908 FORMAT(//5X,' NODE',2X,' INITIAL X-DISP.',2X,
     .       ' INITIAL Y-DISP.',2X,' INITIAL Z-DISP.',/)
  909 FORMAT(I10,3E18.5)
  910 FORMAT(//5X,' NODE',2X,' INITIAL X-VELO.',2X,
     .       ' INITIAL Y-VELO.',2X,' INITIAL Z-VELO.',/)
  911 FORMAT(F10.3)
  912 FORMAT(7F10.3)
  913 FORMAT(/5X,' ACCELERATION ORDINATES AT',F9.4,2X,'SEC'/)
  914 FORMAT(2F10.5)
  915 FORMAT(/5X,'TIME DEFINITION OF LOAD',
     .       /,11X,'TIME',4X,'LOAD FACTOR')
  916 FORMAT(5X,F10.5,5X,F10.5)
      END
```

```
      BLOCK DATA
      COMMON/CTRL/ NDIME,NDOFN,NECHO,NELEM,NEVAB,NGASN,NGAUS,NMATS,
     &             NNODE,NPOIN,NPROP,NREIN,NSIZE,NSTRE,NTOTG,NTOTV,
     &             NVFIX,NWKTL,NYIEL
      COMMON/FILE/ NDATA,NRESU
C
      DATA NDIME,NDOFN,NSTRE,NPROP,NDATA,NRESU/3,3,6,15,5,6/
      END
```

6.4 Profile addressing routines

A profile solver is used to solve the linearised set of equations in the Newmark time stepping scheme. Subroutine LINKIN organises the evaluation of certain key parameters defining the packing of the effective stiffness matrix into a vector form. For further details see the software in reference [74], on which these routines are based. The details of the computer implementation are given in Figure 34.

Subroutine LINKIN calls subroutines COLMHT and ADDRES

6.4.1. Subroutine LINKIN

```
      SUBROUTINE LINKIN(LNODS,IFPRE,LEQNS,MAXAI,MHIGH,MLARG)
C
      IMPLICIT DOUBLE PRECISION (A-H,O-Z)
      COMMON/CTRL/ NDIME,NDOFN,NECHO,NELEM,NEVAB,NGASN,NGAUS,NMATS,
     &             NNODE,NPOIN,NPROP,NREIN,NEQNS,NSTRE,NTOTG,NTOTV,
     &             NVFIX,NWKTL,NYIEL
      COMMON/FILE/ NDATA,NRESU
      DIMENSION LNODS(NNODE,*),IFPRE(NDOFN,*),
     .          LEQNS(NEVAB,*),MHIGH(*),MAXAI(*)
C
C***  NUMBER OF UNKNOWNS
C
      NEQNS=0
      DO 100 IPOIN=1,NPOIN
      DO 100 IDOFN=1,NDOFN
      IF(IFPRE(IDOFN,IPOIN)) 110,120,110
  120 NEQNS=NEQNS+1
      IFPRE(IDOFN,IPOIN)=NEQNS
      GO TO 150
  110 IFPRE(IDOFN,IPOIN)=0
  150 CONTINUE
  100 CONTINUE
      MEQNS=NEQNS+1
C
C***  CONNECTIVITY ARRAY LEQNS
C
      DO 70 IELEM=1,NELEM
      DO 70 IEVAB=1,NEVAB
   70 LEQNS(IEVAB,IELEM)=0
C
      DO 50 IELEM=1,NELEM
      IEVAB=1
      DO 80 INODE=1,NNODE
      IDENT=LNODS(INODE,IELEM)
      DO 80 IDOFN=1,NDOFN
      LEQNS(IEVAB,IELEM)=IFPRE(IDOFN,IDENT)
   80 IEVAB=IEVAB+1
      CALL COLMHT(MHIGH,NEVAB,LEQNS(1,IELEM))
   50 CONTINUE
```

```
C
C***  ADDRESSES OF DIAGONAL ELEMENTS - MAXA ARRAY
C
      CALL ADDRES(MAXAI,MHIGH,NEQNS,NWKTL,MKOUN)
      WRITE(NRESU,920) NEQNS,NWKTL
      IF(NWKTL.GT.MLARG) THEN
         WRITE(NRESU,910)
         STOP
      ENDIF
      RETURN
C
  910 FORMAT(/'SET DIMENSION EXCEEDED - CHECK LINKIN '/)
  920 FORMAT(/5X,'NEQNS=',I5,5X,'NWKTL=',I7)
C
      END
```

```
      SUBROUTINE COLMHT (MHIGH,NEVAB,LEQNS)
      IMPLICIT DOUBLE PRECISION (A-H,O-Z)
      DIMENSION LEQNS(*),MHIGH(*)
C
      MAXAM=2000000
      DO 100 IEVAB=1,NEVAB
      IF(LEQNS(IEVAB)) 110,100,110
  110 IF(LEQNS(IEVAB)-MAXAM) 120,100,100
  120 MAXAM=LEQNS(IEVAB)
  100 CONTINUE
      DO 200 IEVAB=1,NEVAB
      IEQNS=LEQNS(IEVAB)
      IF(IEQNS.EQ.0) GO TO 200
      JHIGH=IEQNS-MAXAM
      IF(JHIGH.GT.MHIGH(IEQNS)) MHIGH(IEQNS)=JHIGH
  200 CONTINUE
      RETURN
      END
```

```
      SUBROUTINE ADDRES(MAXAI,MHIGH,NEQNS ,NWKTL ,MKOUN )
      IMPLICIT DOUBLE PRECISION (A-H,O-Z)
      DIMENSION MAXAI(*),MHIGH(*)
C
      NEQNN=NEQNS+1
      DO 20 IEQNN=1,NEQNN
   20 MAXAI(IEQNN)=0
      MAXAI(1)=1
      MAXAI(2)=2
      MKOUN=0
      IF(NEQNS.EQ.1) GO TO 30
      DO 10 IEQNS=2,NEQNS
      IF(MHIGH(IEQNS).GT.MKOUN) MKOUN=MHIGH(IEQNS)
   10 MAXAI(IEQNS+1)=MAXAI(IEQNS)+MHIGH(IEQNS)+1
   30 MKOUN=MKOUN+1
      NWKTL=MAXAI(NEQNS+1)-MAXAI(1)
      RETURN
      END
```

6.5 Lumped mass matrix routines

This section lists the routines to evaluate the global lumped mass matrix for 3D elements. The routine also calculates the shape function and derivative values at the 15 point integration positions - for use in later subroutines LOADPL, GSTIFF and RESEVP - see Figure 35.

6.5.1 Subroutine LUMASS

```
      SUBROUTINE LUMASS(COORD,LNODS,MATNO,PROPS,DVOLU,IFPRE,ELCOD,
     .                  CARTD,GPCOD,WEIGN,DERIV,SHAPE,POSGN,WEIGP,
     .                  XJACM,POSGP,YMASS)
C*****************************************************************
C
C*    CALCULATES THE LUMPED MASS MATRIX
C
C*****************************************************************
      IMPLICIT DOUBLE PRECISION (A-H,O-Z)
      COMMON/CTRL/ NDIME,NDOFN,NECHO,NELEM,NEVAB,NGASN,NGAUS,NMATS,
     &             NNODE,NPOIN,NPROP,NREIN,NSIZE,NSTRE,NTOTG,NTOTV,
     &             NVFIX,NWKTL,NYIEL
      DIMENSION COORD(NDIME,*),ELCOD(NDIME,*),
     .          LNODS(NNODE,*),CARTD(NDIME,NNODE,*),
     .          PROPS(NPROP,*),GPCOD(NDIME,*),
     .          DERIV(NDIME,NNODE,*),SHAPE(NNODE,*),
     .          POSGN(NDIME,*),WEIGN(*),WEIGP(*),
     .          MATNO(*),DIAGM(20),XJACM(NDIME,*),
     .          POSGP(*),YMASS(*),DVOLU(*),IFPRE(NDOFN,*),
     .          CARLC(3,20),DERLC(3,20),SHALC(20),GPCLC(3),
     .          POSG3(3),WEIG3(3)
C
C     INITIALISE MASS MATRIX
C
      DO 1 ITOTV=1,NTOTV
      YMASS(ITOTV)=0.0
    1 CONTINUE
C
C     SET UP SHAPE FUNCTIONS, SHAPE FUNCTIONS DERIVATIVES
C     AND DIFFERENTIAL VOLUME FOR INTEGRATION POINTS NEEDED
C     FOR STIFFNESS COMPUTATION
C
      CALL GAUSSQ(NGAUS,POSGP,WEIGP)
      CALL GAUSSN(NGASN,POSGN,WEIGN,NDIME)
C
      DO 2 IGAUN=1,NGASN
        EXISP=POSGN(1,IGAUN)
        ETASP=POSGN(2,IGAUN)
        ZETSP=POSGN(3,IGAUN)
        CALL SHAPE3(DERIV(1,1,IGAUN),ETASP,EXISP,ZETSP,NNODE,
     &              SHAPE(1,IGAUN),NDIME)
    2 CONTINUE
      KGASP=0
      DO 3 IELEM=1,NELEM
        DO 4 INODE=1,NNODE
          LNODE=LNODS(INODE,IELEM)
            DO 5 IDIME=1,NDIME
              ELCOD(IDIME,INODE)=COORD(IDIME,LNODE)
    5       CONTINUE
    4   CONTINUE
C
```

```
      DO 6 IGAUN=1,NGASN
        KGASP=KGASP+1
        CALL JACOB3(CARTD(1,1,KGASP),DERIV(1,1,IGAUN),
     &              DVOLU(KGASP),ELCOD,IELEM,
     .              NNODE,SHAPE(1,IGAUN),GPCOD(1,KGASP),
     .              NDIME,XJACM,NRESU)
        DVOLU(KGASP)=DVOLU(KGASP)*WEIGN(IGAUN)
    6   CONTINUE
    3 CONTINUE
C
C     COMPUTE ELEMENTAL LUMPED MASS MATRIX USING
C     GAUSSIAN INTEGRATION
C
      NGASS=3
      IF(NNODE.EQ.8) NGASS=2
      CALL GAUSSQ(NGASS,POSG3,WEIG3)
C
      DO 100 IELEM=1,NELEM
C
      LPROP=MATNO(IELEM)
      RHOEL=PROPS(9,LPROP)
      DO 10 INODE=1,NNODE
      DIAGM(INODE)=0.0
      LNODE=LNODS(INODE,IELEM)
      DO 10 IDIME=1,NDIME
      ELCOD(IDIME,INODE)=COORD(IDIME,LNODE)
   10 CONTINUE
C
      TMASS=0.0
      DO 11 IGAUS=1,NGASS
         EXISP=POSG3(IGAUS)
      DO 11 JGAUS=1,NGASS
         ETASP=POSG3(JGAUS)
      DO 11 KGAUS=1,NGASS
         ZETSP=POSG3(KGAUS)
         CALL SHAPE3(DERLC,ETASP,EXISP,ZETSP,NNODE,SHALC,NDIME)
         CALL JACOB3(CARLC,DERLC,DVOLC,ELCOD,IELEM,
     .               NNODE,SHALC,GPCLC,NDIME,XJACM,NRESU)
         DVOLC=DVOLC*WEIG3(IGAUS)*WEIG3(JGAUS)*WEIG3(KGAUS)
         DMASS=DVOLC*RHOEL
         TMASS=TMASS+DMASS
C
         DO 20 INODE=1,NNODE
         SHAPI=SHALC(INODE)
   20    DIAGM(INODE)=DIAGM(INODE)+SHAPI*SHAPI*DMASS
   11 CONTINUE
C
C    GENERATE LUMPED MASS MATRIX PROPORTIONAL TO DIAGONAL
C
      SUMAS=0.
      DO 40 INODE=1,NNODE
   40 SUMAS=SUMAS+DIAGM(INODE)
      SUMAS=TMASS/SUMAS
      DO 50 INODE=1,NNODE
      LNODE=LNODS(INODE,IELEM)
      IPOSN=(LNODE-1)*NDOFN
      DO 50 IDOFN=1,NDOFN
      IPOSN=IPOSN+1
      YMASS(IPOSN)=YMASS(IPOSN)+DIAGM(INODE)*SUMAS
   50 CONTINUE
  100 CONTINUE
C
C     GLOBAL MASS VECTOR
C
      NPOSM=0
      DO 200 IPOIN=1,NPOIN
        DO 201 IDOFN=1,NDOFN
          NPOSM=NPOSM+1
          NPOSN=IFPRE(IDOFN,IPOIN)
```

```
      IF(NPOSN.NE.0) YMASS(NPOSN)=YMASS(NPOSM)                        LUMA 121
201     CONTINUE                                                      LUMA 122
200   CONTINUE                                                        LUMA 123
C                                                                     LUMA 124
      RETURN                                                          LUMA 125
      END                                                             LUMA 126
```

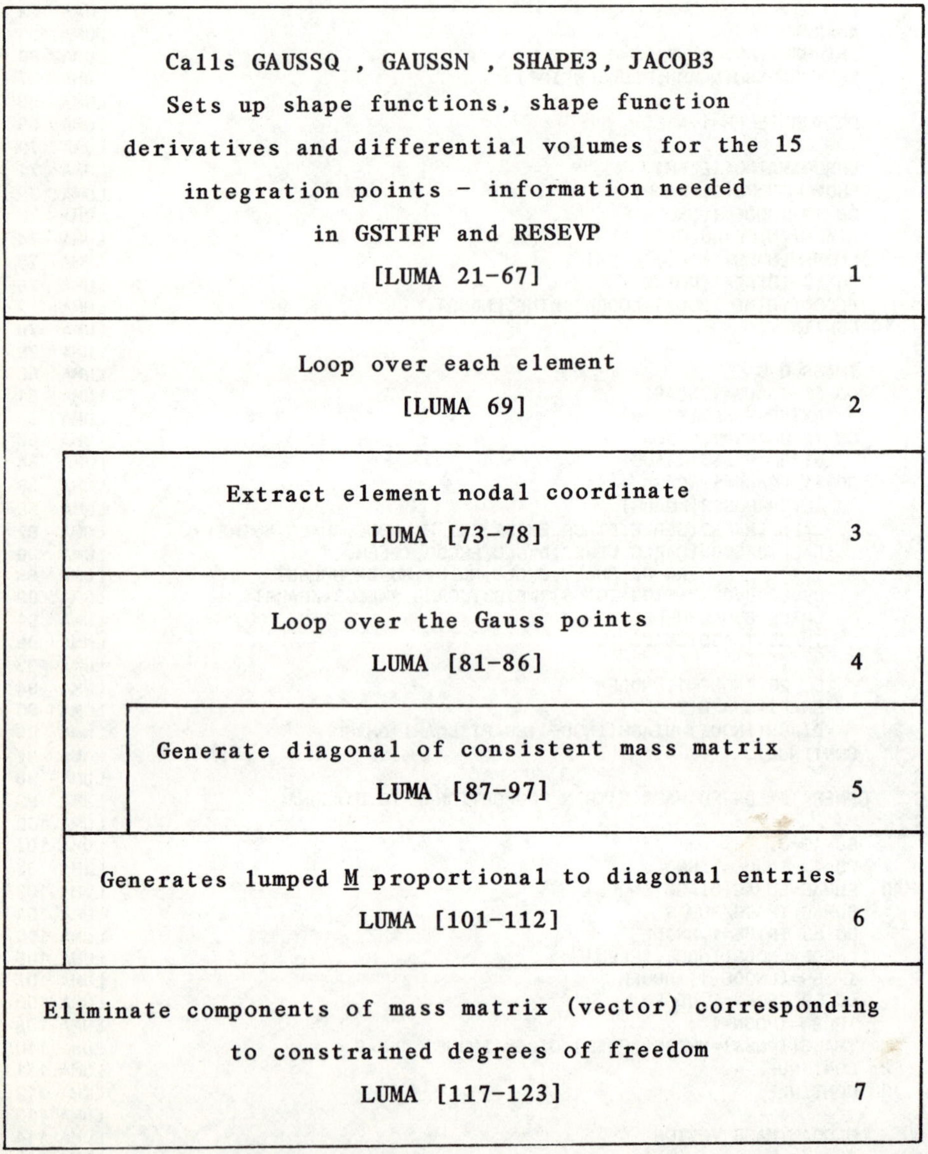

Figure 35. NS chart for lumped mass matrix routine

6.5.2 Subroutine GAUSSQ

```
      SUBROUTINE GAUSSQ(NGAUS,POSGP,WEIGP)
      IMPLICIT DOUBLE PRECISION (A-H,O-Z)
C***********************************************************************
C
C**** THIS SUBROUTINE SETS UP THE GAUSS-LEGENDRE INTEGRATION CONSTANTS
C
C**********************************************************************
      DIMENSION POSGP(*),WEIGP(*)
      POSGP(1)=0.
      WEIGP(1)=2.
      IF(NGAUS.EQ.1)RETURN
      IF(NGAUS.GT.2) GO TO 4
2       POSGP(1) = -1.0 / SQRT(3.0)
      WEIGP(1)=1.0
        POSGP(2) = -POSGP(1)
        WEIGP(2) = 1.0
        RETURN
 4      POSGP(1) = -SQRT(3.0 / 5.0)
      POSGP(2)=0.0
        POSGP(3) = -POSGP(1)
        WEIGP(1) = 5.0/9.0
        WEIGP(2) = 8.0/9.0
        WEIGP(3) = 5.0/9.0
       RETURN
        END
```

6.5.3 Subroutine GAUSSN

```
      SUBROUTINE GAUSSN(NGASN,POSGN,WEIGP,NDIME)
      IMPLICIT DOUBLE PRECISION (A-H,O-Z)
      DIMENSION POSGN(NDIME,*),WEIGP(*)
C
      IF(NGASN.EQ.15) THEN
        A1=1.564444444444D+0
        A2=0.355555555556D+0
        A3=0.537777777778D+0
         WEIGP(1)=A1
         DO 1 I=2,7
   1     WEIGP(I)=A2
         DO 2 I=8,15
   2     WEIGP(I)=A3
      ELSE
        A1=8./6.
        DO 3 I=1,6
   3    WEIGP(I)=A1
      ENDIF
C
      DO 4 IGAUN=1,NGASN
      DO 4 IDIME=1,NDIME
   4  POSGN(IDIME,1)=0.0
C
      IF(NGASN.EQ.15) THEN
        B=1.0D+00
        C=(1.0D+0/(9.0D+0*A3))**0.25D+0
C
        I=2
        DO 5 IDIME=1,NDIME
        POSGN(IDIME,I  )= B
        POSGN(IDIME,I+1)=-B
        I=I+2
   5    CONTINUE
```

```
C
      I=8
      C1=C
      DO 6 J=1,2
      C2=C
      DO 7 K=1,2
      C3=C
      DO 8 L=1,2
      POSGN(1,I)=C1
      POSGN(2,I)=C2
      POSGN(3,I)=C3
      C3=-C
    8 I=I+1
      C2=-C
    7 CONTINUE
      C1=-C
    6 CONTINUE
     ELSE
      B=1.
C
      I=1
      DO 9 IDIME=1,NDIME
      POSGN(IDIME,I  )= B
      POSGN(IDIME,I+1)=-B
      I=I+2
    9 CONTINUE
     ENDIF
     RETURN
     END
```

6.5.4 Subroutine SHAPE3

```
      SUBROUTINE SHAPE3(DERIV,T,S,Z,NNODE,SHAPE,NDIME)
      IMPLICIT DOUBLE PRECISION (A-H,O-Z)
C**********************************************************************
C
C**** THIS SUBROUTINE EVALUATES SHAPE FUNCTIONS AND THEIR DERIVATIVES
C     FOR LINEAR AND QUADRATIC SERENDIPITY 3D ELEMENTS
C
C**********************************************************************
      DIMENSION DERIV(NDIME,*),SHAPE(*)
C
C***  SOME CONSTANTS
C
      SM = 0.5*(1.-S)
      TM = 0.5*(1.-T)
      ZM = 0.5*(1.-Z)
C
      SP = 0.5*(1.+S)
      TP = 0.5*(1.+T)
      ZP = 0.5*(1.+Z)
C
C***  8 NODED BRICK ELEMENT
C
      IF(NNODE.NE.8) GO TO 10
C
      SHAPE(   1) = +    SM*TM*ZM
      DERIV(1, 1) = -.5     *TM*ZM
      DERIV(2, 1) = -.5*SM     *ZM
      DERIV(3, 1) = -.5*SM*TM
C
      SHAPE(   2) = +    SP*TM*ZM
      DERIV(1, 2) = +.5     *TM*ZM
      DERIV(2, 2) = -.5*SP     *ZM
      DERIV(3. 2) = -.5*SP*TM
```

```
C
      SHAPE(   3) = +   SP*TP*ZM
      DERIV(1, 3) = +.5   *TP*ZM
      DERIV(2, 3) = +.5*SP   *ZM
      DERIV(3, 3) = -.5*SP*TP
C
      SHAPE(   4) = +   SM*TP*ZM
      DERIV(1, 4) = -.5   *TP*ZM
      DERIV(2, 4) = +.5*SM   *ZM
      DERIV(3, 4) = -.5*SM*TP
C
      SHAPE(   5) = +   SM*TM*ZP
      DERIV(1, 5) = -.5   *TM*ZP
      DERIV(2, 5) = -.5*SM   *ZP
      DERIV(3, 5) = +.5*SM*TM
C
      SHAPE(   6) = +   SP*TM*ZP
      DERIV(1, 6) = +.5   *TM*ZP
      DERIV(2, 6) = -.5*SP   *ZP
      DERIV(3, 6) = +.5*SP*TM
C
      SHAPE(   7) = +   SP*TP*ZP
      DERIV(1, 7) = +.5   *TP*ZP
      DERIV(2, 7) = +.5*SP   *ZP
      DERIV(3, 7) = +.5*SP*TP
C
      SHAPE(   8) = +   SM*TP*ZP
      DERIV(1, 8) = -.5   *TP*ZP
      DERIV(2, 8) = +.5*SM   *ZP
      DERIV(3, 8) = +.5*SM*TP
C
      RETURN
C
C***  SOME MORE CONSTANTS
C
   10 SS = 0.5*(1.-S*S)
      TT = 0.5*(1.-T*T)
      ZZ = 0.5*(1.-Z*Z)
C
      S2 = -2.*S
      T2 = -2.*T
      Z2 = -2.*Z
C
C***  20 NODED BRICK ELEMENTS
C
      AA          = +SM+TM+ZM-   2.5
      SHAPE(   1) = +SM*TM*ZM*(AA+AA)
      DERIV(1, 1) = -   TM*ZM*(AA+SM)
      DERIV(2, 1) = -SM   *ZM*(AA+TM)
      DERIV(3, 1) = -SM*TM   *(AA+ZM)
C
      SHAPE(   2) = +SS*TM*ZM*2.
      DERIV(1, 2) = +S2*TM*ZM
      DERIV(2, 2) = -SS   *ZM
      DERIV(3, 2) = -SS*TM
C
      AA          = +SP+TM+ZM-   2.5
      SHAPE(   3) = +SP*TM*ZM*(AA+AA)
      DERIV(1, 3) = +   TM*ZM*(AA+SP)
      DERIV(2, 3) = -SP   *ZM*(AA+TM)
      DERIV(3, 3) = -SP*TM   *(AA+ZM)
C
      SHAPE(   4) = +SP*TT*ZM*2.
      DERIV(1, 4) = +   TT*ZM
      DERIV(2, 4) = +SP*T2*ZM
      DERIV(3, 4) = -SP*TT
C
```

```
      AA          = +SP+TP+ZM-   2.5
      SHAPE(   5) = +SP*TP*ZM*(AA+AA)
      DERIV(1, 5) = +   TP*ZM*(AA+SP)
      DERIV(2, 5) = +SP    *ZM*(AA+TP)
      DERIV(3, 5) = -SP*TP    *(AA+ZM)
C
      SHAPE(   6) = +SS*TP*ZM*2.
      DERIV(1, 6) = +S2*TP*ZM
      DERIV(2, 6) = +SS    *ZM
      DERIV(3, 6) = -SS*TP
C
      AA          = +SM+TP+ZM-   2.5
      SHAPE(   7) = +SM*TP*ZM*(AA+AA)
      DERIV(1, 7) = -   TP*ZM*(AA+SM)
      DERIV(2, 7) = +SM    *ZM*(AA+TP)
      DERIV(3, 7) = -SM*TP    *(AA+ZM)
C
      SHAPE(   8) = +SM*TT*ZM*2.
      DERIV(1, 8) = -   TT*ZM
      DERIV(2, 8) = +SM*T2*ZM
      DERIV(3, 8) = -SM*TT
C
      SHAPE(   9) = +SM*TM*ZZ*2.
      DERIV(1, 9) = -   TM*ZZ
      DERIV(2, 9) = -SM    *ZZ
      DERIV(3, 9) = +SM*TM*Z2
C
      SHAPE(  10) = +SP*TM*ZZ*2.
      DERIV(1,10) = +   TM*ZZ
      DERIV(2,10) = -SP    *ZZ
      DERIV(3,10) = +SP*TM*Z2
C
      SHAPE(  11) = +SP*TP*ZZ*2.
      DERIV(1,11) = +   TP*ZZ
      DERIV(2,11) = +SP    *ZZ
      DERIV(3,11) = +SP*TP*Z2
C
      SHAPE(  12) = +SM*TP*ZZ*2.
      DERIV(1,12) = -   TP*ZZ
      DERIV(2,12) = +SM    *ZZ
      DERIV(3,12) = +SM*TP*Z2
C
      AA          = +SM+TM+ZP-   2.5
      SHAPE(  13) = +SM*TM*ZP*(AA+AA)
      DERIV(1,13) = -   TM*ZP*(AA+SM)
      DERIV(2,13) = -SM    *ZP*(AA+TM)
      DERIV(3,13) = +SM*TM    *(AA+ZP)
C
      SHAPE(  14) = +SS*TM*ZP*2.
      DERIV(1,14) = +S2*TM*ZP
      DERIV(2,14) = -SS    *ZP
      DERIV(3,14) = +SS*TM
C
      AA          = +SP+TM+ZP-   2.5
      SHAPE(  15) = +SP*TM*ZP*(AA+AA)
      DERIV(1,15) = +   TM*ZP*(AA+SP)
      DERIV(2,15) = -SP    *ZP*(AA+TM)
      DERIV(3,15) = +SP*TM    *(AA+ZP)
C
      SHAPE(  16) = +SP*TT*ZP*2.
      DERIV(1,16) = +   TT*ZP
      DERIV(2,16) = +SP*T2*ZP
      DERIV(3,16) = +SP*TT
C
      AA          = +SP+TP+ZP-   2.5
      SHAPE(  17) = +SP*TP*ZP*(AA+AA)
      DERIV(1,17) = +   TP*ZP*(AA+SP)
      DERIV(2.17) = +SP    *ZP*(AA+TP)
```

```
      DERIV(3,17) = +SP*TP   *(AA+ZP)
C
      SHAPE(  18) = +SS*TP*ZP*2.
      DERIV(1,18) = +S2*TP*ZP
      DERIV(2,18) = +SS   *ZP
      DERIV(3,18) = +SS*TP
C
      AA          = +SM+TP+ZP-   2.5
      SHAPE(  19) = +SM*TP*ZP*(AA+AA)
      DERIV(1,19) = -    TP*ZP*(AA+SM)
      DERIV(2,19) = +SM    *ZP*(AA+TP)
      DERIV(3,19) = +SM*TP    *(AA+ZP)
C
      SHAPE(  20) = +SM*TT*ZP*2.
      DERIV(1,20) = -    TT*ZP
      DERIV(2,20) = +SM*T2*ZP
      DERIV(3,20) = +SM*TT
C
      RETURN
      END
```

6.5.5 Subroutine JACOB3

```
      SUBROUTINE JACOB3(CARTD,DERIV,DJACB,ELCOD,KELEM,NNODE,
     .                  SHAPE,GPCOD,NDIME,XJACM,NRESU)
      IMPLICIT DOUBLE PRECISION (A-H,O-Z)
C***********************************************************************
C
C**** THIS SUBROUTINE EVALUATES THE JACOBIAN MATRIX AND THE CARTESIAN
C     SHAPE FUNCTION DERIVATIVES
C
C***********************************************************************
        DIMENSION CARTD(NDIME,*), DERIV(NDIME,*),
     .            ELCOD(NDIME,*), GPCOD(NDIME), SHAPE(*),
     .            XJACM(NDIME,*), XJACI(3,3)
C
C***  CALCULATE COORDINATES OF SAMPLING POINT
C
      DO 10 IDIME=1,NDIME
        GPCOD(IDIME)=0.0
        DO 20 INODE=1,NNODE
          GPCOD(IDIME)=GPCOD(IDIME)
     &                  +ELCOD(IDIME,INODE)*SHAPE(INODE)
   20   CONTINUE
   10 CONTINUE
C
C***  CREATE JACOBIAN MATRIX XJACM
C
      DO 30 IDIME=1,NDIME
        DO 40 JDIME=1,NDIME
          XJACM(IDIME,JDIME)=0.0
          DO 50 INODE=1,NNODE
            XJACM(IDIME,JDIME)=XJACM(IDIME,JDIME)
     &                   +DERIV(IDIME,INODE)*ELCOD(JDIME,INODE)
   50     CONTINUE
   40   CONTINUE
   30 CONTINUE
      IF(KELEM.EQ.0) RETURN
C
C***  CALCULATE DETERMINANT AND INVERSE OF JACOBIAN MATRIX
C
      CALL DETMX3(XJACM, DJACB)
      IF(DJACB.LE.0.0) THEN
```

```
      WRITE(NRESU,600) KELEM
      STOP
    END IF
    CALL INVMX3 ( XJACM,XJACI,DJACB)
C
C***  CALCULATE CARTESIAN DERIVATIVES
C
    DO 60 IDIME=1,NDIME
      DO 70 INODE=1,NNODE
        CARTD(IDIME,INODE)=0.0
        DO 80 JDIME=1,NDIME
          CARTD(IDIME,INODE)=CARTD(IDIME,INODE)
     &                     +XJACI(IDIME,JDIME)*DERIV(JDIME,INODE)
  80    CONTINUE
  70  CONTINUE
  60 CONTINUE
C
    RETURN
 600 FORMAT(//,36H PROGRAM HALTED IN SUBROUTINE JACOB2,/,11X,
    .22H ZERO OR NEGATIVE AREA,/,10X,16H ELEMENT NUMBER ,I5)
    END
```

6.5.6 Subroutine DETMX3

```
      SUBROUTINE DETMX3 ( XMATX, DETMX)
      IMPLICIT DOUBLE PRECISION (A-H,O-Z)
C     *****************************************************
C     *                                                   *
C     *    A SUBROUTINE TO FIND THE DETERMINATE OF A      *
C     *                 3 * 3  MATRIX.                    *
C     *                                                   *
C     *****************************************************
C
      DIMENSION XMATX(3,3)
      DETMX = XMATX(1,1)*(XMATX(2,2)*XMATX(3,3) - XMATX(2,3)*
     . XMATX(3,2))  -  XMATX(1,2)*(XMATX(2,1)*XMATX(3,3) - XMATX(2,3)
     . *XMATX(3,1))  +  XMATX(1,3)*(XMATX(2,1)*XMATX(3,2) - XMATX(2,2)
     . *XMATX(3,1))
      RETURN
      END
```

6.5.7 Subroutine INVMX3

```
      SUBROUTINE INVMX3 ( XMATX, XMATI, DETMX)
      IMPLICIT DOUBLE PRECISION (A-H,O-Z)
C     *****************************************************
C     *                                                   *
C     *       A SUBROUTINE TO INVERT A 3*3 MATRIX.        *
C     *                                                   *
C     *****************************************************
C
      DIMENSION XMATX(3,3), XMATI(3,3)
      DO 100 I = 1,3
     IP1 = I + 1 - I/3*3
      IP2 = IP1+1 - IP1/3*3
      DO 100 J = 1,3
      JP1 = J+1 - J/3*3
      JP2 = JP1+1 - JP1/3*3
 100  XMATI(J,I) = ( XMATX(IP1,JP1)*XMATX(IP2,JP2) - XMATX(IP2,JP1)*
     .               XMATX(IP1,JP2)) / DETMX
      RETURN
      END
```

6.6 Consistent nodal force routine

6.6.1 Subroutine LOADPL

This routine evaluates the consistent nodal forces RLOAD for each element and assembles them into the global force vector FORCE. The NS - chart is shown in Figure 36.

```
      SUBROUTINE LOADPL(COORD,LNODS,MATNO,POSGP,PROPS,RLOAD,SHAPE,
     .                  ELCOD,IFPRE,XJACM,FORCE,DVOLU,WEIGP)
      IMPLICIT DOUBLE PRECISION (A-H,O-Z)
      COMMON/CTRL/ NDIME,NDOFN,NECHO,NELEM,NEVAB,NGASN,NGAUS,NMATS,
     &             NNODE,NPOIN,NPROP,NREIN,NSIZE,NSTRE,NTOTG,NTOTV,
     &             NVFIX,NWKTL,NYIEL
      COMMON/FILE/ NDATA,NRESU
C*********************************************************************
C
C**** THIS SUBROUTINE EVALUATES THE CONSISTENT NODAL FORCES FOR EACH
C     ELEMENT
C
C*********************************************************************
      DIMENSION CARTD(3,20),PVECT(3),COORD(NDIME,*),
     .          PROPS(NPROP,*),VAREA(3),GPCOD(3),
     .          DERIV(3,20),NOPRS(8),LNODS(NNODE,*),
     .          ELCOD(NDIME,*),GVECT(3),RLOAD(NEVAB,*),
     .          XJACM(NDIME,NDIME),POSGP(*),WEIGP(*),
     .          SHAPE(NNODE,*),MATNO(*),PRESS(8, 3),TITLE(40),
     .          FORCE(*),SHAPL(20),IFPRE(NDOFN,*)
C
C***  INITIALISE THE TOTAL LOAD ARRAY
C
      DO 9 ITOTV=1,NTOTV
    9 FORCE(ITOTV)=0.
      DO 10 IELEM=1,NELEM
      DO 10 IEVAB=1,NEVAB
   10 RLOAD(IEVAB,IELEM)=0.0
C
      READ(NDATA,901) TITLE
      IF(NECHO.LT.1) WRITE(NRESU,902) TITLE
C
C*** READ DATA CONTROLLING LOADING TYPES TO BE INPUT
C
      READ(NDATA,903) IPLOD,IGRAV,IFACE
      IF(NECHO.LT.2) WRITE(NRESU,904) IPLOD,IGRAV,IFACE
C
C***  READ DATA CONTROLLING LOADING TYPES TO BE INPUT
C
      IF(IPLOD.EQ.0) GO TO 500
      IF(NECHO.LT.1) WRITE(NRESU,905)
   20 READ (NDATA,*) LODPT,(PVECT(IDIME),IDIME=1,NDIME)
      IF(NECHO.LT.1) WRITE(NRESU,907) LODPT,(PVECT(IDIME),IDIME=1,NDIME)
C
C***  ASSOCIATE THE NODAL POINT LOADS WITH AN ELEMENT
C
      DO 30 IELEM = 1,NELEM
      DO 30 INODE = 1,NNODE
```

```
      LNODE = LNODS(INODE,IELEM)
      IF(LODPT.EQ.LNODE) GO TO 40
   30 CONTINUE
   40 IEVAB = (INODE-1)*NDIME
      DO 50 IDIME = 1,NDIME
      IEVAB = IEVAB+1
   50 RLOAD(IEVAB,IELEM) = PVECT(IDIME)
      IF(LODPT.LT.NPOIN) GO TO 20
C
C***  GRAVITY LOADING SECTION AND ASSOCIATED VECTORS.
C
  500 IF(IGRAV.EQ.0) GO TO 600
C
C***  READ GRAVITY DATA
C
      READ(NDATA,908) (GVECT(IDIME),IDIME=1,NDIME),GCONS
      GSIZE =SQRT(GVECT(1)*GVECT(1)+GVECT(2)*GVECT(2)+GVECT(3)*GVECT(3))
      DO 55 IDIME = 1,NDIME
   55 GVECT(IDIME) = GVECT(IDIME)/GSIZE
      IF(NECHO.LT.1) WRITE(NRESU,909)(GVECT(IDIME),IDIME=1,NDIME),GCONS
C
C***  LOOP OVER EACH ELEMENT
C
      KGAST=0
      DO 90 IELEM = 1,NELEM
C
C***  SET UP PRELIMINARY CONSTANTS
C
      LPROP = MATNO(IELEM)
      DENSE = PROPS(9,LPROP)
      IF(DENSE.EQ.0.0) GO TO 90
      DO 75 IDIME = 1,NDIME
   75 PVECT(IDIME) = DENSE*GVECT(IDIME)*GCONS
C
C***  STORE THE COORDINATES OF THE ELEMENT NODAL POINTS
C
      DO 60 INODE = 1,NNODE
      LNODE = LNODS(INODE,IELEM)
      DO 60 IDIME = 1,NDIME
   60 ELCOD(IDIME,INODE) = COORD(IDIME,LNODE)
C
C***  ENTER LOOPS FOR VOLUME NUMERICAL INTEGRATION
C
      DO 70 IGAUS=1,NGASN
      KGAST=KGAST+1
C
C***  CALCULATE LOADS AND ASSOCIATE WITH ELEMENT NODAL POINTS
C
      IEVAB = 0
      DO 70 INODE = 1,NNODE
      SHVOL = SHAPE(INODE,IGAUS)*DVOLU(KGAST)
      DO 70 IDIME = 1,NDIME
      IEVAB = IEVAB+1
   70 RLOAD(IEVAB,IELEM) = RLOAD(IEVAB,IELEM)+PVECT(IDIME)*SHVOL
   90 CONTINUE
C
C***  DISTRIBUTED FACE LOADS SECTION
C
  600 IF(IFACE.EQ.0) GO TO 700
      READ(NDATA,910) NFCES
      IF(NECHO.LT.1) WRITE(NRESU,911)NFCES
      IF(NECHO.LT.1) WRITE(NRESU,912)
C
C***  LOOP OVER EACH LOADED FACE
C
      NODFC = 8
      IF(NNODE.EQ.8) NODFC = 4
      DO 160 KFACE = 1,NFCES
```

```
C
C***  READ DATA DEFINING THE LOADED FACE AND APPLIED LOAD
C
      READ(NDATA,913) NEASS,(NOPRS(JODFC),JODFC=1,NODFC)
      IF(NECHO.LT.1) WRITE(NRESU,914)NEASS,(NOPRS(JODFC),JODFC=1,NODFC)
      READ(NDATA,915) ((PRESS(JODFC,IDIME),IDIME=1,NDIME),JODFC=1,NODFC)
      IF(NECHO.LT.1) WRITE(NRESU,915) ((PRESS(JODFC,IDIME),IDIME=1,
     .                          NDIME),JODFC=1,NODFC)
C
C***  STORE THE COORDINATES OF THE NODES OF THE ELEMENT FACE
C
      DO 100 JODFC = 1,NODFC
      LNODE = NOPRS(JODFC)
      DO 100 IDIME = 1,NDIME
  100 ELCOD(IDIME,JODFC) = COORD(IDIME,LNODE)
C
C***  ENTER LOOP FOR AREA NUMERICAL INTEGRATION
C
      KGASP = 0
      ZETSP = -1.0
      DO 150 IGAUS = 1,NGAUS
      EXISP = POSGP(IGAUS)
      DO 150 JGAUS = 1,NGAUS
      ETASP = POSGP(JGAUS)
      KGASP=KGASP+1
C
C***  COMPUTE THE SHAPE FUNCTIONS AT THE SAMPLING POINT, THE "AREA"
C     VECTOR AND SOME VECTOR NORMS
C
      CALL SHAPE3(DERIV,ETASP,EXISP,ZETSP,NNODE,SHAPL,NDIME)
      CALL JACOB3(CARTD,DERIV,DJACB,ELCOD,     0,
     .                  NNODE,SHAPL,GPCOD,NDIME,XJACM,
     .                  NRESU)
C
      DAREA = 0.0
      SNORM = 0.0
      TNORM = 0.0
      DO 105 IDOFA = 1,NDIME
      IDOFB = IDOFA+1-IDOFA/3*3
      IDOFC = IDOFB+1-IDOFB/3*3
      VAREA(IDOFA) = XJACM(1,IDOFB)*XJACM(2,IDOFC)-
     .               XJACM(2,IDOFB)*XJACM(1,IDOFC)
      DAREA = DAREA+VAREA(IDOFA)*VAREA(IDOFA)
      SNORM = SNORM+XJACM(1,IDOFA)*XJACM(1,IDOFA)
  105 TNORM = TNORM+XJACM(2,IDOFA)*XJACM(2,IDOFA)
      DAREA = SQRT(DAREA)
      SNORM = SQRT(SNORM)
      TNORM = SQRT(TNORM)
C
C***  COMPUTE THE LOCAL LOAD COMPONENTS AT THE CURRENT GAUSS POINT
C
      DO 110 IDIME = 1,NDIME
      GVECT(IDIME) = 0.0
      DO 110 JODFC = 1, NODFC
  110 GVECT(IDIME) = GVECT(IDIME)+PRESS(JODFC,IDIME)*SHAPL(JODFC)
C
C***  COMPUTE THE CARTESIAN LOAD COMPONENTS AT THE CURRENT GAUSS POINT
C
      DO 120 IDIME = 1,NDIME
  120 PVECT(IDIME) = GVECT(1)*XJACM(1,IDIME)/SNORM+
     .               GVECT(2)*XJACM(2,IDIME)/TNORM+
     .               GVECT(3)*VAREA( IDIME)/DAREA
C
C***  COMPUTE THE ELEMENTAL AREA
C
      DAREA = DAREA*WEIGP(IGAUS)*WEIGP(JGAUS)
C
C***  ASSOCIATE THE EQUIVALENT NODAL FACE LOADS WITH AN ELEMENT
C
```

```
      DO 140 JODFC = 1,NODFC
      LNODE = NOPRS(JODFC)
      DO 130 INODE = 1,NNODE
      IF(LNODS(INODE,NEASS).EQ.LNODE) GO TO 135
  130 CONTINUE
  135 IEVAB = (INODE-1)*NDIME
      SAREA = SHAPL(JODFC)*DAREA
      DO 140 IDIME = 1,NDIME
      IEVAB = IEVAB+1
  140 RLOAD(IEVAB,NEASS) = RLOAD(IEVAB,NEASS)+PVECT(IDIME)*SAREA
  150 CONTINUE
  160 CONTINUE
C
C***  WRITE THE TOTAL NODAL FORCES FOR EACH ELEMENT
C
  700 IF(NECHO.GE.1) GOTO 999
      WRITE(NRESU,916)
      DO 290 IELEM = 1,NELEM
  290 WRITE(NRESU,917) IELEM,(RLOAD(IEVAB,IELEM),IEVAB=1,NEVAB)
  999 CONTINUE
C
C*** ASSEMBLE INTO GLOBAL LOAD VECTOR
C
      DO 5 IELEM=1,NELEM
      KEVAB=0
      DO 5 INODE=1,NNODE
      LNODE=LNODS(INODE,IELEM)
      NPOSN=(LNODE-1)*NDOFN
      DO 5 IDOFN=1,NDOFN
      KEVAB=KEVAB+1
      NPOSN=NPOSN+1
      FORCE(NPOSN)=FORCE(NPOSN)+RLOAD(KEVAB,IELEM)
    5 CONTINUE
C
C     GLOBAL FORCE VECTOR
C
      NPOSM=0
      DO 6 IPOIN=1,NPOIN
        DO 7 IDOFN=1,NDOFN
          NPOSM=NPOSM+1
          NPOSN=IFPRE(IDOFN,IPOIN)
          IF(NPOSN.NE.0) FORCE(NPOSN)=FORCE(NPOSM)
    7   CONTINUE
    6 CONTINUE
C
      RETURN
C
  901 FORMAT(40A2)
  902 FORMAT(//10X,'TITLE    ',40A2)
  903 FORMAT(12I5)
  904 FORMAT(//10X,'APPLIED LOADING TO STRUCTURE.'/10X,29('*')//20X,
     .  'POINT LOAD PARAMETER...................=',I5//20X,
     .  'GRAVITY LOAD PARAMETER.................=',I5//20X,
     .  'FACE LOADS PARAMETER...................=',I5//20X)
  905 FORMAT(//20X,'POINT LOADING.'/20X,14('-')/20X,'NODE.',
     .             18X,'PX',18X,'PY',18X,'PZ')
  906 FORMAT(I5,3F10.5)
  907 FORMAT(20X,I5,3(5X,F15.3))
  908 FORMAT(4F10.5)
  909 FORMAT(/' GRAVITY UNIT VECTOR = (',3F10.5,')  G.CONSTANT =',F10.5)
  910 FORMAT(I5)
  911 FORMAT(1H0,5X,21HNO. OF LOADED FACES =,I5)
  912 FORMAT(1H0,5X,38HLIST OF LOADED FACES AND APPLIED LOADS)
  913 FORMAT(9I5)
  914 FORMAT(I10,5X,8I5)
  915 FORMAT(6F10.3)
  916 FORMAT(//6X,36H TOTAL NODAL FORCES FOR EACH ELEMENT,/)
  917 FORMAT(I5,/(3(4X,3E12.4)))
      END
```

Initialise element and global force arrays RLOAD and FORCE and loading control data [LOAD 21-39]	1
If point loads occur read and write relevant data and insert into correct position in RLOAD [LOAD 40-56]	2
If gravity loading occurs, read and write relevant data and evaluate consistent nodal forces using a 15 point rule [LOAD 60-103]	3
If distributed force load occurs, read and write relevant data and evaluate consistent nodal forces using a Gauss-Legendre rule [LOAD 107-197]	4
If required, write the consistent nodal force for each element [LOAD 201-205]	5
Assemble element force vectors RLOAD into global force vector FORCE and eliminate contribution associated with restrained degrees of freedom [LOAD 209-229]	6

Figure 36. NS Chart for subroutine LOADPL

6.7 Stiffness matrix routines

This section list the routines needed to evaluate the stiffness matrix for 3D elements

6.7.1 Subroutine GSTIFF

The NS - chart for this subroutine is given in Figure 37.

```
      SUBROUTINE GSTIFF(COORD,LNODS,MATNO,DMATX,XJACM,POSGP,PROPS,
     .                  WEIGP,ELCOD,CARTD,MPATT,MLAYR,NOCAP,MBARS,
     .                  VBARS,ISTAT,DVOLS,TMATX,TMATC,CRVAL,LEQNS,
     .                  MAXAI,DVOLU,STIFF,CARDS,GPCOS)
      IMPLICIT DOUBLE PRECISION (A-H,O-Z)
      COMMON/CTRL/ NDIME,NDOFN,NECHO,NELEM,NEVAB,NGASN,NGAUS,NMATS,
     &             NNODE,NPOIN,NPROP,NREIN,NSIZE,NSTRE,NTOTG,NTOTV,
     &             NVFIX,NWKTL,NYIEL
      COMMON/RUN/  IFUNC,IPRED,KSTEP,MITER,NACCE,NOUTD,NOUTP,NREQD,
     &             NREQS,NSTEP
      COMMON/FILE/ NDATA,NRESU
      COMMON/STAT/ IITER,ISTEP,KTOLE
C***********************************************************************
C
C**** THIS SUBROUTINE EVALUATES THE STIFFNESS MATRIX FOR EACH ELEMENT
C     IN TURN
C
C***********************************************************************
      DIMENSION CARTD(NDIME,NNODE,*),ELCOD(NDIME,*),
     .          COORD(NDIME,*),
     .          DMATX(NSTRE,*),ESTIF(3,3,210),
     .          LNODS(NNODE,*),
     .          MATNO(*),POSGP(*),PROPS(NPROP,*),
     .          WEIGP(*),MPATT(*),XJACM(NDIME,*),
     .          NOCAP(*),MBARS(2,MLAYR,*),
     .          VBARS(3,MLAYR,*),ISTAT(*),
     .          TMATC(NDIME,NDIME,*),CRVAL(4,*),
     .          LEQNS(NEVAB,*),MAXAI(*),STIFF(*)
      DIMENSION DVOLS(*),DVOLU(*),CARDS(NDIME,NNODE,*),
     .          GPCOS(NDIME,*),TMATX(NDIME,NDIME,*)
C
C     CHECK IF IT IS NECESSARY TO EVALUATE THE STIFFNESS MATRIX
C
      IF(ISTEP.EQ.1) GO TO 200
      KOUNT=(ISTEP/KSTEP)*KSTEP
      IF(KOUNT.NE.ISTEP) RETURN
      IF(KTOLE.EQ.0) RETURN
  200 CONTINUE
      IF(IITER.GT.1) RETURN
C
      KGAST=0
      KGREF=0
C
      DO 81 I=1,NWKTL
   81 STIFF(I)=0.
C
C*** LOOP OVER EACH ELEMENT
C
```

```
      DO 70 IELEM=1,NELEM
C
C*** EVALUATE THE COORDINATES OF THE ELEMENT NODAL POINTS
C
      DO 10 INODE=1,NNODE
      LNODE=LNODS(INODE,IELEM)
      DO 10 IDIME=1,NDIME
      ELCOD(IDIME,INODE)=COORD(IDIME,LNODE)
   10 CONTINUE
C
C      INITIALIZE THE ELEMENT STIFFNESS MATRIX.
C
      DO 20 INODE=1,210
      DO 20 IDOFN=1,NDOFN
      DO 20 JDOFN=1,NDOFN
   20 ESTIF(IDOFN,JDOFN,INODE)=0.0
C
      DO 50 IGAUN=1,NGASN
      KGAST=KGAST+1
C
C ****  EVALUATE THE D-MATRIX.
C
      INDIC=0
      CALL MOD3 (DMATX,NSTRE,IELEM,PROPS,MATNO,NPROP,
     .           ISTAT,TMATC(1,1,KGAST) ,KGAST,CRVAL,INDIC)
C
C    FORM THE ELEMENT STIFFNESS MATRIX
C
      INDIC=1
      IF(ISTAT(KGAST).GE.10) INDIC=2
      KNODE=0
      DO 100 JNODE=1,NNODE
      DO 100 INODE=1,JNODE
      KNODE=KNODE+1
      CALL FORMK(INODE,JNODE,ESTIF(1,1,KNODE),CARTD(1,1,KGAST),
     .           DMATX,DVOLU(KGAST),INDIC)
  100 CONTINUE
C
   50 CONTINUE
C
C*** ADD REINFORCEMENT CONTRIBUTION TO ELEMENT STIFFNESS
C
      CALL       REINF3(IELEM,LNODS,MATNO,DMATX,ELCOD,POSGP,PROPS,
     .                  WEIGP,CARDS,GPCOS,XJACM,ESTIF,MPATT,MLAYR,
     .                  NOCAP,MBARS,VBARS,KGREF,DVOLS,TMATX)
C
C***  GENERATES GLOBAL STIFFNESS MATRIX IN COMPACTED COLUMN FORM
C
      CALL ADDBAN(STIFF,MAXAI,ESTIF,LEQNS(1,IELEM),NNODE,NDOFN)
   70 CONTINUE
      RETURN
      END
```

Check if it is necessary to evaluate the stiffness matrix
[GSTI 31-39] 1

Initialise stiffness matrix 'vector' STIFF
[GSTI 44-45] 2

Loop over each element
[GSTI 49] 3

Extract element nodal coordinates and
initialise element stiffness matrix ESTIF
[GSTI 50-64] 4

Loop over each integration point
[GSTI 66] 5

Call MOD3 to evaluate $\underline{D}$ matrix
[GSTI 72-73] 6

Call FORMK to evaluate $\underline{B}^T \underline{D} \underline{B}$ dV
[GSTI 80-85] 7

Call REINF3 to add reinforcement contribution
to element stiffness
[GSTI 91-93] 8

Call ADDBAN to generate global stiffness 'matrix' STIFF
in compacted form for element stiffness ESTIF 9

Figure 37. NS chart for subroutine GSTIFF

6.7.2 Subroutine MOD3

```
      SUBROUTINE MOD3(DMATX,NSTRE,IELEM,PROPS,MATNO,NPROP,
     .                ISTAT,TMATC,KGAST,CRVAL,INDIC)
      IMPLICIT DOUBLE PRECISION (A-H,O-Z)
C*********************************************************************
C
C**** THIS SUBROUTINE EVALUATES THE DMATX-MATRIX
C
C*********************************************************************
      DIMENSION DMATX(NSTRE,*),MATNO(*),PROPS(NPROP,*),
     .          ISTAT(*),DLOCA(6,6),BETAM(3,3),T(6,6),CRVAL(4,*)
C
      DO 10 ISTRE=1,NSTRE
      DO 10 JSTRE=1,NSTRE
   10 DMATX(ISTRE,JSTRE)=0.0
C
C***  D MATRIX FOR ELASTIC CASE
C
       LPROP=MATNO(IELEM)
       YOUNG=PROPS(1,LPROP)
       POISS=PROPS(2,LPROP)
       ALFA1=YOUNG*(1.-POISS)/((1.+POISS)*(1.-2*POISS))
       ALFA2=ALFA1*POISS/(1.-POISS)
       ALFA3=ALFA1*(1.-2.*POISS)/(2.*(1.-POISS))
C
       DMATX(1,1)=ALFA1
       DMATX(2,2)=ALFA1
       DMATX(3,3)=ALFA1
       DMATX(1,2)=ALFA2
       DMATX(1,3)=ALFA2
       DMATX(2,3)=ALFA2
       DMATX(4,4)=ALFA3
       DMATX(5,5)=ALFA3
       DMATX(6,6)=ALFA3
C
      IF(INDIC.EQ.1) GO TO 60
C
C***CHECK IF THE CONCRETE IS ELASTIC
C
      IT=ISTAT(KGAST)
      IF(IT.EQ.0.OR.IT.EQ.2) GO TO 60
C
C*** IF THE CONCRETE IS CRACKED,CALCULATE THE D-MATRIX
C
      DO 21 ISTRE=1,NSTRE
      DO 21 JSTRE=ISTRE,NSTRE
   21 DMATX(ISTRE,JSTRE)=0.0
      IF(IT.EQ.13) GO TO 60
C
C ***BUILD UP THE SYSTEM CHANGE MATRICES
C
      CALL DTMAT (BETAM,    T)
C
      ALPHA=0.5
      DO 34 I=1,NSTRE
      DO 34 J=1,NSTRE
   34 DLOCA(I,J)=0.0
         STIFF=YOUNG
         IF(CRVAL(1,KGAST).NE.0.0)
     .     STIFF=CRVAL(2,KGAST)/CRVAL(1,KGAST)
           IF(STIFF.GT.0.0.AND.STIFF.LT.YOUNG) THEN
             DLOCA(1,1)=STIFF
         ELSE
```

```
              DLOCA(1,1)=YOUNG
           ENDIF
         STIFF=YOUNG
         IF(CRVAL(3,KGAST).NE.0.0)
     .      STIFF=CRVAL(4,KGAST)/CRVAL(3,KGAST)
            IF(STIFF.GT.0.0.AND.STIFF.LT.YOUNG) THEN
              DLOCA(2,2)=STIFF
           ELSE
              DLOCA(2,2)=YOUNG
           ENDIF
      DLOCA(3,3)=YOUNG
      DLOCA(4,4)=ALPHA*YOUNG/2.
      DLOCA(5,5)=ALPHA*YOUNG/2.
      DLOCA(6,6)=ALPHA*YOUNG/2.
C
      IF(IT.NE.10.AND.IT.NE.110) GO TO 35
      DLOCA(2,2)=YOUNG
      DLOCA(5,5)=YOUNG/2.
C
   35 CONTINUE
      DO 12 I=1,NSTRE
      DO 12 J=I,NSTRE
      DO 12 K=1,NSTRE
   12 DMATX(I,J)=DMATX(I,J)+T(K,I)*DLOCA(K,K)*T(K,J)
C
60    DO 100 ISTRE = 1, NSTRE
      DO 100 JSTRE = ISTRE, NSTRE
100   DMATX(JSTRE,ISTRE) = DMATX(ISTRE,JSTRE)
      RETURN
      END
```

6.7.3 Subroutine FORMK

```
      SUBROUTINE FORMK(I,J,A,S,D,V,IF)
C.........................................................................
C
C                                T
C   ROUTINE TO PERFORM THE PRODUC B * D * B * dV
C
C.........................................................................
      IMPLICIT DOUBLE PRECISION (A-H,O-Z)
      DIMENSION E(3,3),S(3,*),D(6,6),A(3,3)
C
      IF(IF.EQ.0) THEN
      E(1,1)=S(1,I)*(D(1,1)*S(1,J)+D(1,4)*S(2,J)+D(1,6)*S(3,J))+
     .       S(2,I)*(D(4,1)*S(1,J)+D(4,4)*S(2,J)+D(4,6)*S(3,J))+
     .       S(3,I)*(D(6,1)*S(1,J)+D(6,4)*S(2,J)+D(6,6)*S(3,J))
      E(2,1)=S(2,I)*(D(2,1)*S(1,J)+D(2,4)*S(2,J)+D(2,6)*S(3,J))+
     .       S(1,I)*(D(4,1)*S(1,J)+D(4,4)*S(2,J)+D(4,6)*S(3,J))+
     .       S(3,I)*(D(5,1)*S(1,J)+D(5,4)*S(2,J)+D(5,6)*S(3,J))
      E(3,1)=S(3,I)*(D(3,1)*S(1,J)+D(3,4)*S(2,J)+D(3,6)*S(3,J))+
     .       S(2,I)*(D(5,1)*S(1,J)+D(5,4)*S(2,J)+D(5,6)*S(3,J))+
     .       S(1,I)*(D(6,1)*S(1,J)+D(6,4)*S(2,J)+D(6,6)*S(3,J))
      E(1,2)=S(1,I)*(D(1,2)*S(2,J)+D(1,4)*S(1,J)+D(1,5)*S(3,J))+
     .       S(2,I)*(D(4,2)*S(2,J)+D(4,4)*S(1,J)+D(4,5)*S(3,J))+
     .       S(3,I)*(D(6,2)*S(2,J)+D(6,4)*S(1,J)+D(6,5)*S(3,J))
      E(2,2)=S(2,I)*(D(2,2)*S(2,J)+D(2,4)*S(1,J)+D(2,5)*S(3,J))+
     .       S(1,I)*(D(4,2)*S(2,J)+D(4,4)*S(1,J)+D(4,5)*S(3,J))+
     .       S(3,I)*(D(5,2)*S(2,J)+D(5,4)*S(1,J)+D(5,5)*S(3,J))
      E(3,2)=S(3,I)*(D(3,2)*S(2,J)+D(3,4)*S(1,J)+D(3,5)*S(3,J))+
     .       S(2,I)*(D(5,2)*S(2,J)+D(5,4)*S(1,J)+D(5,5)*S(3,J))+
     .       S(1,I)*(D(6,2)*S(2,J)+D(6,4)*S(1,J)+D(6,5)*S(3,J))
```

```
      E(1,3)=S(1,I)*(D(1,3)*S(3,J)+D(1,5)*S(2,J)+D(1,6)*S(1,J))+
     .       S(2,I)*(D(4,3)*S(3,J)+D(4,5)*S(2,J)+D(4,6)*S(1,J))+
     .       S(3,I)*(D(6,3)*S(3,J)+D(6,5)*S(2,J)+D(6,6)*S(1,J))
      E(2,3)=S(2,I)*(D(2,3)*S(3,J)+D(2,5)*S(2,J)+D(2,6)*S(1,J))+
     .       S(1,I)*(D(4,3)*S(3,J)+D(4,5)*S(2,J)+D(4,6)*S(1,J))+
     .       S(3,I)*(D(5,3)*S(3,J)+D(5,5)*S(2,J)+D(5,6)*S(1,J))
      E(3,3)=S(3,I)*(D(3,3)*S(3,J)+D(3,5)*S(2,J)+D(3,6)*S(1,J))+
     .       S(2,I)*(D(5,3)*S(3,J)+D(5,5)*S(2,J)+D(5,6)*S(1,J))+
     .       S(1,I)*(D(6,3)*S(3,J)+D(6,5)*S(2,J)+D(6,6)*S(1,J))
      END IF
C
      IF(IF.EQ.1) THEN
      E(1,1)=S(1,I)*D(1,1)*S(1,J)+
     .                            S(2,I)*D(4,4)*S(2,J)+
     .                                    S(3,I)*D(6,6)*S(3,J)
      E(2,1)=S(2,I)*D(2,1)*S(1,J)+
     .                            S(1,I)*D(4,4)*S(2,J)
      E(3,1)=S(3,I)*D(3,1)*S(1,J)+
     .                            S(1,I)*D(6,6)*S(3,J)
      E(1,2)=S(1,I)*D(1,2)*S(2,J)+
     .                            S(2,I)*D(4,4)*S(1,J)
      E(2,2)=S(2,I)*D(2,2)*S(2,J)+
     .                            S(1,I)*D(4,4)*S(1,J)+
     .                                    S(3,I)*D(5,5)*S(3,J)
      E(3,2)=S(3,I)*D(3,2)*S(2,J)+
     .                            S(2,I)*D(5,5)*S(3,J)
      E(1,3)=S(1,I)*D(1,3)*S(3,J)+
     .                            S(3,I)*D(6,6)*S(1,J)
      E(2,3)=S(2,I)*D(2,3)*S(3,J)+
     .                            S(3,I)*D(5,5)*S(2,J)
      E(3,3)=S(3,I)*D(3,3)*S(3,J)+
     .                            S(2,I)*D(5,5)*S(2,J)+
     .                                    S(1,I)*D(6,6)*S(1,J)
      END IF
C
      IF(IF.EQ.2) THEN
      E(1,1)=S(1,I)*D(1,1)*S(1,J)+
     .                            S(2,I)*D(4,4)*S(2,J)+
     .                                    S(3,I)*D(6,6)*S(3,J)
      E(2,1)=S(1,I)*D(4,4)*S(2,J)
      E(3,1)=S(1,I)*D(6,6)*S(3,J)
      E(1,2)=S(2,I)*D(4,4)*S(1,J)
      E(2,2)=S(2,I)*D(2,2)*S(2,J)+
     .                            S(1,I)*D(4,4)*S(1,J)+
     .                                    S(3,I)*D(5,5)*S(3,J)
      E(3,2)=S(2,I)*D(5,5)*S(3,J)
      E(1,3)=S(3,I)*D(6,6)*S(1,J)
      E(2,3)=S(3,I)*D(5,5)*S(2,J)
      E(3,3)=S(3,I)*D(3,3)*S(3,J)+
     .                            S(2,I)*D(5,5)*S(2,J)+
     .                                    S(1,I)*D(6,6)*S(1,J)
      END IF
C
      DO 10 M=1,3
         DO 20 K=1,3
            A(M,K)=A(M,K)+E(M,K)*V
   20    CONTINUE
   10 CONTINUE
C
      RETURN
      END
```

6.7.4 Subroutine REINF3

```
      SUBROUTINE REINF3(IELEM,LNODS,MATNO,DMATX,ELCOD,POSGP,PROPS,
     .                  WEIGP,CARDS,GPCOS,XJACM,ESTIF,MPATT,MLAYR,
     .                  NOCAP,MBARS,VBARS,KGREF,DVOLS,TMATX)
      IMPLICIT DOUBLE PRECISION (A-H,O-Z)
      COMMON/CTRL/ NDIME,NDOFN,NECHO,NELEM,NEVAB,NGASN,NGAUS,NMATS,
     &             NNODE,NPOIN,NPROP,NREIN,NSIZE,NSTRE,NTOTG,NTOTV,
     &             NVFIX,NWKTL,NYIEL
      COMMON/FILE/ NDATA,NRESU
C***********************************************************************
C
C**** THIS SUBROUTINE EVALUATES THE CONTRIBUTION OF THE REINFORCEMENT
C     TO THE ELEMENT STIFFNESS MATRIX
C
C***********************************************************************
      DIMENSION CARDS(NDIME,NNODE,*),ELCOD(NDIME,*),
     .          DERIV(3,20),
     .          DMATX(NSTRE,*),ESTIF(NDOFN,NDOFN,*),
     .          LNODS(NNODE,*),
     .          GPCOS(NDIME,*),XJACM(NDIME,*),
     .          MATNO(*),POSGP(*),PROPS(NPROP,*),
     .          WEIGP(*),SHAPE(20),MPATT(*),
     .          NOCAP(*),MBARS(2,MLAYR,*),
     .          VBARS(3,MLAYR,*),TMATX(NDIME,NDIME,*),VECT1(3),
     .          VECT2(3),VNORM(3),DVOLS(*)
C
      KPATT=MPATT(IELEM)
      IF(KPATT.EQ.0) RETURN
      NLAYR=NOCAP(KPATT)
      IF(NLAYR.EQ.0) RETURN
      NGASS=NGAUS
C
C*** LOOP OVER THE REINFORCEMENT LAYERS
C
      DO 10 ILAYR=1,NLAYR
      IMATN=MBARS(1,ILAYR,KPATT)
      ICOOR=MBARS(2,ILAYR,KPATT)
      SPOS3=VBARS(1,ILAYR,KPATT)
      ESPES=VBARS(2,ILAYR,KPATT)
      ANGLE=VBARS(3,ILAYR,KPATT)
C
C*** ENTER LOOPS FOR AREA NUMERICAL INTEGRATION
C
      DO 50 IGAUS=1,NGASS
      SPOS1=POSGP(IGAUS)
      DO 50 JGAUS=1,NGASS
      SPOS2=POSGP(JGAUS)
C
      IF(ICOOR.NE.1) GO TO 20
      EXISP=SPOS3
      ETASP=SPOS1
      ZETSP=SPOS2
      GO TO 25
   20 IF(ICOOR.NE.2) GO TO 21
      ETASP=SPOS3
      ZETSP=SPOS1
      EXISP=SPOS2
      GO TO 25
   21 ZETSP=SPOS3
      EXISP=SPOS1
      ETASP=SPOS2
   25 CONTINUE
      KGREF=KGREF+1
```

```
C
C*** EVALUATE THE SHAPE FUNCTIONS,ELEMENTAL VOLUME,ETC.
C
      CALL     SHAPE3(DERIV,ETASP,EXISP,ZETSP,NNODE,SHAPE,NDIME)
      CALL     JACOB3(CARDS(1,1,KGREF),DERIV,DJACB,ELCOD,
     &                IELEM,NNODE,SHAPE,GPCOS(1,KGREF),NDIME,XJACM,
     .                NRESU)
C
C*** FIND THE LOCAL SYSTEM
C
      ICOOA=ICOOR+1-ICOOR/3*3
      ICOOB=ICOOA+1-ICOOA/3*3
      DO 60 IDIME=1,NDIME
      VECT1(IDIME)=XJACM(ICOOA,IDIME)
   60 VECT2(IDIME)=XJACM(ICOOB,IDIME)
      VNORM(1)=VECT1(2)*VECT2(3)-VECT1(3)*VECT2(2)
      VNORM(2)=VECT1(3)*VECT2(1)-VECT1(1)*VECT2(3)
      VNORM(3)=VECT1(1)*VECT2(2)-VECT1(2)*VECT2(1)
      DVEC1=0.
      DJAC2=0.
      DO 70 IDIME=1,NDIME
      DVEC1=DVEC1+VECT1(IDIME)*VECT1(IDIME)
   70 DJAC2=DJAC2+VNORM(IDIME)*VNORM(IDIME)
      DVEC1=SQRT(DVEC1)
      DJAC2=SQRT(DJAC2)
      VECT2(1)=VNORM(2)*VECT1(3)-VNORM(3)*VECT1(2)
      VECT2(2)=VNORM(3)*VECT1(1)-VNORM(1)*VECT1(3)
      VECT2(3)=VNORM(1)*VECT1(2)-VNORM(2)*VECT1(1)
      DVEC2=SQRT(VECT2(1)*VECT2(1)+VECT2(2)*VECT2(2)+
     .           VECT2(3)*VECT2(3))
      DO 80 IDIME=1,NDIME
      TMATX(1,IDIME,KGREF)=VECT1(IDIME)/DVEC1
      TMATX(2,IDIME,KGREF)=VECT2(IDIME)/DVEC2
   80 TMATX(3,IDIME,KGREF)=VNORM(IDIME)/DJAC2
C
C ****  EVALUATE THE D-MATRIX.
C
      CALL DREIN(DMATX,NSTRE,IELEM,PROPS,NPROP,
     .           ANGLE,IMATN,TMATX(1,1,KGREF))
C
C*** CALCULATE THE DIFFERENTIAL VOLUME
C
      DVOLS(KGREF)=DJAC2*ESPES*WEIGP(IGAUS)*WEIGP(JGAUS)
C
C     FORM THE ELEMENT STIFFNESS MATRIX
C
      INDIC=0
      KNODE=0
      DO 100 JNODE=1,NNODE
      DO 100 INODE=1,JNODE
      KNODE=KNODE+1
      CALL FORMK(INODE,JNODE,ESTIF(1,1,KNODE),CARDS(1,1,KGREF),
     .           DMATX,DVOLS(KGREF),INDIC)
  100 CONTINUE
C
   50 CONTINUE
   10 CONTINUE
      RETURN
      END
```

6.7.5 Subroutine ADDBAN

```
      SUBROUTINE ADDBAN (STIFF,MAXAI,ESTIF,LEQNS,NNODE,NDOFN)
      IMPLICIT DOUBLE PRECISION (A-H,O-Z)
      DIMENSION ESTIF(NDOFN,NDOFN,*),STIFF(*),MAXAI(*),LEQNS(NDOFN,*)
C
      DO 40 JNODE=1,NNODE
         DO 30 JDOFN=1,NDOFN
            JEQNS=LEQNS(JDOFN,JNODE)
            IF(JEQNS.NE.0) THEN
               DO 20 INODE=1,JNODE
                  MDOFN=NDOFN
                  IF(INODE.EQ.JNODE) MDOFN=JDOFN
                  KNODE=(JNODE*(JNODE-1))/2+INODE
                  DO 10 IDOFN=1,MDOFN
                     IEQNS=LEQNS(IDOFN,INODE)
                     IF(IEQNS.NE.0) THEN
                        MEQNS=MIN(IEQNS,JEQNS)
                        NEQNS=MAX(IEQNS,JEQNS)
                        NDIAG=MAXAI(NEQNS)
                        NPOS=NDIAG+NEQNS-MEQNS
                        STIFF(NPOS)=STIFF(NPOS)+ESTIF(IDOFN,JDOFN,KNODE)
                     END IF
 10               CONTINUE
 20            CONTINUE
            END IF
 30      CONTINUE
 40   CONTINUE
C
      RETURN
      END
```

6.7.6 Subroutine DTMAT

```
      SUBROUTINE DTMAT(   B,      T)
      IMPLICIT DOUBLE PRECISION (A-H,O-Z)
C
      DIMENSION B(3,3),T(6,6)
C
      DO 1 I=1,3
      DO 1 J=1,3
    1 T(I,J)=B(I,J)**2
C
      T(1,4)=B(1,1)*B(1,2)
      T(1,5)=B(1,2)*B(1,3)
      T(1,6)=B(1,3)*B(1,1)
      T(2,4)=B(2,1)*B(2,2)
      T(2,5)=B(2,2)*B(2,3)
      T(2,6)=B(2,3)*B(2,1)
      T(3,4)=B(3,1)*B(3,2)
      T(3,5)=B(3,2)*B(3,3)
      T(3,6)=B(3,3)*B(3,1)
C
      T(4,1)=B(1,1)*B(2,1)*2.
      T(4,2)=B(1,2)*B(2,2)*2.
      T(4,3)=B(1,3)*B(2,3)*2.
      T(5.1)=B(2.1)*B(3,1)*2.
```

```
      T(5,2)=B(2,2)*B(3,2)*2.
      T(5,3)=B(2,3)*B(3,3)*2.
      T(6,1)=B(3,1)*B(1,1)*2.
      T(6,2)=B(3,2)*B(1,2)*2.
      T(6,3)=B(3,3)*B(1,3)*2.
C
      T(4,4)=B(1,1)*B(2,2)+B(1,2)*B(2,1)
      T(4,5)=B(1,2)*B(2,3)+B(1,3)*B(2,2)
      T(4,6)=B(1,3)*B(2,1)+B(1,1)*B(2,3)
      T(5,4)=B(2,1)*B(3,2)+B(2,2)*B(3,1)
      T(5,5)=B(2,2)*B(3,3)+B(2,3)*B(3,2)
      T(5,6)=B(2,3)*B(3,1)+B(2,1)*B(3,3)
      T(6,4)=B(3,1)*B(1,2)+B(3,2)*B(1,1)
      T(6,5)=B(3,2)*B(1,3)+B(3,3)*B(1,2)
      T(6,6)=B(3,3)*B(1,1)+B(3,1)*B(1,3)
C
      RETURN
      END
```

6.7.7 Subroutine DREIN

```
      SUBROUTINE DREIN(DMATX,NSTRE,IELEM,PROPS,NPROP,
     .                 ANGLE,IMATN,TMATX)
      IMPLICIT DOUBLE PRECISION (A-H,O-Z)
C . . . . . . . . . . . . . . . . . . . . . . . . . . . . . .
C .                                                          .
C .    ROUTINE                                               .
C .       TO CALCULATE THE D-MATRIX FOR REINFORCEMENT        .
C . . . . . . . . . . . . . . . . . . . . . . . . . . . . . .
      DIMENSION DMATX(NSTRE,*),PROPS(NPROP,*),
     .          TMATX(3,3),T(6,6),DLOCA(6,6)
C
      DO 20 ISTRE=1,NSTRE
      DO 20 JSTRE=1,NSTRE
      DLOCA(ISTRE,JSTRE)=0.0
   20 DMATX(ISTRE,JSTRE)=0.0
C
      YOUNG=PROPS(1,IMATN)
      COEFI=YOUNG
      C=COS(ANGLE)
      S=SIN(ANGLE)
C
C*** COMPUTE THE ELASTIC D-MATRIX
C
      DLOCA(1,1)=COEFI*C*C*C*C
      DLOCA(1,2)=COEFI*S*S*C*C
      DLOCA(2,1)=COEFI*S*S*C*C
      DLOCA(2,2)=COEFI*S*S*S*S
      DLOCA(1,4)=COEFI*S*C*C*C
      DLOCA(4,1)=COEFI*S*C*C*C
      DLOCA(2,4)=COEFI*S*S*S*C
      DLOCA(4,2)=COEFI*S*S*S*C
      DLOCA(4,4)=COEFI*S*S*C*C
C
C ***BUILD UP THE SYSTEM CHANGE MATRICES
C
      CALL DTMAT (TMATX,     T)
C
      DO 12 I=1,NSTRE
      DO 12 J=1,NSTRE
```

```
      DO 12 K=1,NSTRE
      DO 12 L=1,NSTRE
   12 DMATX(I,J)=DMATX(I,J)+T(K,I)*DLOCA(K,L)*T(L,J)
      RETURN
      END
```

6.8 Effective stiffness and forces and predictor values

This section lists the routines required to evaluate the effective stiffnesses and forces and also the predictor values used in the Newmark scheme.

6.8.1 Subroutine NEWIMP

Figure 38. contains the NS - chart for subroutine NEWIMP, which generates the effective stiffnesses and loads.

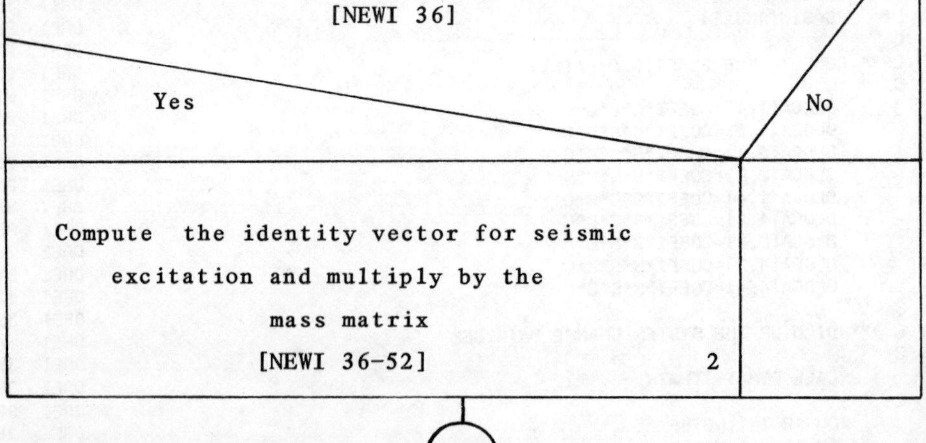

A

Compute the initial elastic resisting forces
$\underline{K}\ \underline{d}_o$ (if $\underline{d}_o \neq \underline{0}$) - calling MULTPY
[NEWI 54-62] 3

Computes the initial damping forces $\underline{C}\ \dot{\underline{d}}_o$
(Rayleigh damping is assumed)
[NEWI 64-101] 4

Compute the initial inertial forces
and initial acceleration vector $\ddot{\underline{d}}_o$
[NEWI 103-122] 5

continue 6

For first iteration calculate predictor displacement, velocity acceleration vectors, and force factors
[NEWI 124-147] 7

For all steps other than the first time step evaluate the damping forces
[NEWI 151-183] 8

Calculate and factorize effective stiffness matrix $\underline{K}^*$, if required (calling DECOMP)
[NEWI 184-199] 9

Calculate partial effective load vector
[NEWI 201-213] 10

Figure 38. NS chart for subroutine NEWIMP

```
      SUBROUTINE NEWIMP(ACCEH,ACCEI,ACCEK,ACCEL,ACCEV,DISPI,DISPL,
     .                  DISPT,IFPRE,MAXAI,RLOAD,STIFF,VELOI,VELOL,
     .                  STIFS,VELOT,YMASS)
C***********************************************************************
C
C *** GENERATES PARTIAL EFFECTIVE LOAD VECTOR
C *** AND THE EFFECTIVE STIFFNESS MATRIX K*
C
C***********************************************************************
      IMPLICIT DOUBLE PRECISION (A-H,O-Z)
      COMMON/CTRL/ NDIME,NDOFN,NECHO,NELEM,NEVAB,NGASN,NGAUS,NMATS,
     &             NNODE,NPOIN,NPROP,NREIN,NSIZE,NSTRE,NTOTG,NTOTV,
     &             NVFIX,NWKTL,NYIEL
      COMMON/RUN/  IFUNC,IPRED,KSTEP,MITER,NACCE,NOUTD,NOUTP,NREQD,
     &             NREQS,NSTEP
      COMMON/CONST/AALFA,BEETA,GAAMA,DELTA,AZERO,BZERO,OMEGA,TMAXR,
     &             DTEND,DTIME,AFACT,TOLER,ADISP,AVELO,CONSD,CONSF
      COMMON/FILE/ NDATA,NRESU
      COMMON/STAT/ IITER,ISTEP,KTOLE
      DIMENSION STIFF(*),DISPI(*),ACCEH(*),DISPL(*),IFPRE(3,*),
     .          YMASS(*),VELOI(*),ACCEV(*),VELOL(*),ACCEK(*),
     .          RLOAD(*),ACCEI(*),MAXAI(*),ACCEL(*),STIFS(*),
     .          DISPT(*),VELOT(*)
C
C      COMPUTES THE SCALAR PARAMETERS
C
        CONSA=DTIME*DTIME*(0.5-DELTA)
        CONSB=DTIME*(1.0-GAAMA)
        CONSC=DTIME*DTIME*DELTA
        CONSD=DTIME*GAAMA
        CONSF=1./CONSC
        CONSG=BEETA*GAAMA*DTIME*CONSF+1.
        CONSH=AALFA*GAAMA*DTIME*CONSF
        CONSE=CONSF+CONSH
C
      IF(ISTEP.EQ.1.AND.IITER.EQ.1) THEN
C
C      COMPUTES THE IDENTITY VECTOR FOR SEISMIC EXITATION
C      AND MULTIPLIES IT BY THE MASS MATRIX
C
        ISHOT=0
        IF(IFUNC.EQ.0) THEN
          DO 10 IPOIN=1,NPOIN
            DO 20 IDOFN=1,NDOFN
              ISIZE=IFPRE(IDOFN,IPOIN)
              IF(ISIZE.NE.0) THEN
                ACCEL(ISIZE)=0.
                IF(IDOFN.EQ.1) ACCEL(ISIZE)=YMASS(ISIZE)
              END IF
   20       CONTINUE
   10     CONTINUE
        END IF
C
C      COMPUTES THE INITIAL ELASTIC RESISTING FORCES
C
        IF(ADISP.GT.0.1E-10) THEN
          CALL MULTPY (DISPL,STIFF,DISPI,MAXAI,NSIZE,NWKTL)
        ELSE
          DO 30 ISIZE=1,NSIZE
            DISPL(ISIZE)=0.
   30     CONTINUE
        ENDIF
C
C     COMPUTES THE INITIAL DAMPING FORCES (RAYLEIGH DAMPING IS ASSUMED)
C
        IF(AVELO.GT.0.1E-10) THEN
```

```
C
C     MULTIPLIES BY THE FIRST PART OF THE DAMPING MATRIX
C
          IF(ABS(AALFA).GT.0.1E-10) THEN
             DO 40 ISIZE=1,NSIZE
             VELOL(ISIZE)=YMASS(ISIZE)*VELOI(ISIZE)
   40        CONTINUE
          ELSE
             DO 50 ISIZE=1,NSIZE
                VELOL(ISIZE)=0.0
   50        CONTINUE
          END IF
C
C     MULTIPLIES BY THE SECOND PART OF THE DAMPING MATRIX
C
          IF(ABS(BEETA).GT.0.1E-10) THEN
             CALL MULTPY (ACCEL,STIFF,VELOI,MAXAI,NSIZE,NWKTL)
          ELSE
             DO 60 ISIZE=1,NSIZE
                ACCEL(ISIZE)=0.0
   60        CONTINUE
          ENDIF
C
C     ADDS THE TWO CONTRIBUTIONS
C
          IF(ABS(AALFA)+ABS(BEETA).GT.0.1E-10) THEN
             DO 70 ISIZE=1,NSIZE
                VELOL(ISIZE)=AALFA*VELOL(ISIZE)+BEETA*ACCEL(ISIZE)
   70        CONTINUE
          END IF
       ELSE
          DO 80 ISIZE=1,NSIZE
             VELOL(ISIZE)=0.0
   80     CONTINUE
       END IF
C
C     COMPUTES THE INITIAL INERTIAL FORCE VECTOR
C
       FACTS=FUNCTS (AZERO,BZERO,DTEND,DTIME,IFUNC,     0,OMEGA,
     &              TMAXR,ACCEH,ACCEV,NACCE)
       XMODU=0.0
       DO 90 ISIZE=1,NSIZE
          ACCEI(ISIZE)=FACTS*RLOAD(ISIZE)-DISPL(ISIZE)-VELOL(ISIZE)
          XMODU=XMODU+ACCEI(ISIZE)**2
   90  CONTINUE
C
C     CALCULATES THE INITIAL ACCELERATION VECTOR
C
       IF(XMODU.GE.0.1E-10) THEN
          DO 100 ISIZE=1,NSIZE
          ACCEI(ISIZE)=ACCEI(ISIZE)/YMASS(ISIZE)
  100     CONTINUE
       END IF
       WRITE(NRESU,900)
       WRITE(NRESU,910) (ACCEI(ISIZE),ISIZE=1,NSIZE)
    END IF
C
C     CALCULATES PREDICTED DISPLACEMENT AND VELOCITY VECTOR
C
    IF(IITER.EQ.1) THEN
       DO 110 ISIZE=1,NSIZE
          IF(IPRED.NE.1) THEN
             DISPT(ISIZE)=DISPI(ISIZE)
             VELOT(ISIZE)=VELOI(ISIZE)
          END IF
          DISPI(ISIZE)=DISPI(ISIZE)+DTIME*VELOI(ISIZE)+
     &                 CONSA*ACCEI(ISIZE)
```

```
            VELOI(ISIZE)=VELOI(ISIZE)+CONSB*ACCEI(ISIZE)
            IF(IPRED.NE.2) THEN
               DISPT(ISIZE)=DISPI(ISIZE)
               VELOT(ISIZE)=VELOI(ISIZE)
            END IF
            ACCEI(ISIZE)=CONSF*(DISPT(ISIZE)-DISPI(ISIZE))
  110    CONTINUE
C
C     CALCULATE LOAD FACTORS
C
         FACTS=FUNCTS (AZERO,BZERO,DTEND,DTIME,IFUNC,ISTEP,OMEGA,
     .                 TMAXR,ACCEH,ACCEV,NACCE)
         FACTH=FUNCTA (ACCEV,AFACT,DTEND,DTIME,IFUNC,ISTEP)
      END IF
C
C     CALCULATES DAMPING FORCES (RAYLEIGH DAMPING IS ASSUMED)
C
      IF(ISTEP.NE.1) THEN
C
C     MULTIPLIES BY THE FIRST PART OF THE DAMPING MATRIX
C
         IF(ABS(AALFA).GT.0.1E-10) THEN
            DO 120 ISIZE=1,NSIZE
               VELOL(ISIZE)=YMASS(ISIZE)*VELOT(ISIZE)
  120       CONTINUE
         ELSE
            DO 130 ISIZE=1,NSIZE
               VELOL(ISIZE)=0.0
  130       CONTINUE
         END IF
C
C     MULTIPLIES BY THE SECOND PART OF THE DAMPING MATRIX
C
         IF(ABS(BEETA).GT.0.1E-10) THEN
            CALL MULTPY (ACCEL,STIFF,VELOT,MAXAI,NSIZE,NWKTL)
         ELSE
            DO 140 ISIZE=1,NSIZE
               ACCEL(ISIZE)=0.0
  140       CONTINUE
         ENDIF
C
C     ADDS THE TWO CONTRIBUTIONS
C
         IF(ABS(AALFA)+ABS(BEETA).GT.0.1E-10) THEN
            DO 150 ISIZE=1,NSIZE
               VELOL(ISIZE)=AALFA*VELOL(ISIZE)+BEETA*ACCEL(ISIZE)
  150       CONTINUE
         END IF
      END IF
C
C     COMPUTES THE K-STAR MATRIX
C
      KOUNT=(ISTEP/KSTEP)*KSTEP
      IF(KTOLE.EQ.0) KOUNT=0
      IF(ISTEP.EQ.1) KOUNT=ISTEP
      IF(KOUNT.EQ.ISTEP) THEN
         DO 160 ISIZE=1,NSIZE
            NDIAG=MAXAI(ISIZE)
            NLAST=MAXAI(ISIZE+1)-1
            DO 170 IK=NDIAG,NLAST
               STIFS(IK)=CONSG*STIFF(IK)
  170       CONTINUE
               STIFS(NDIAG)=STIFS(NDIAG)+CONSE*YMASS(ISIZE)
  160    CONTINUE
         CALL DECOMP (STIFS,MAXAI,NSIZE,ISHOT)
      END IF
```

```
C
C     CALCULATES PARTIAL EFFECTIVE LOAD VECTOR
C
      TOTAL=0.0
      DO 190 ISIZE=1,NSIZE
         IF(IFUNC.EQ.0) THEN
            TOTAL=TOTAL+RLOAD(ISIZE)*RLOAD(ISIZE)
            DISPL(ISIZE)=-VELOL(ISIZE)-FACTH*ACCEK(ISIZE)
     &                                 +RLOAD(ISIZE)
         ELSE
            TOTAL=TOTAL+RLOAD(ISIZE)*RLOAD(ISIZE)*FACTS*FACTS
            DISPL(ISIZE)=-VELOL(ISIZE)+RLOAD(ISIZE)*FACTS
         END IF
  190 CONTINUE
C
      RETURN
C
  900 FORMAT(/'  INITIAL ACCELERATION '/)
  910 FORMAT(1X,9E12.5)
      END
```

6.8.2 Function FUNCTS

```
      FUNCTION FUNCTS (AZERO,BZERO,DTEND,DTIME,IFUNC,JSTEP,OMEGA,
     .                 TMAXR,ACCEH,ACCEV,NACCE)
C*********************************************************************
C
C***  HEAVISIDE AND HARMONIC TIME FUNCTION
C
C*********************************************************************
      IMPLICIT DOUBLE PRECISION (A-H,O-Z)
      DIMENSION ACCEH(*),ACCEV(*)
C
      IF(IFUNC.EQ.0) RETURN
      FUNCTS=0.0
      IF(FLOAT(JSTEP)*DTIME.GT.DTEND) RETURN
      IF(IFUNC.EQ.4) GO TO 10
      IF(IFUNC.EQ.5) GO TO 30
      IF(IFUNC.EQ.1) FUNCTS=1.0
      IF(IFUNC.EQ.2) ARGUM=OMEGA*JSTEP*DTIME
      IF(IFUNC.EQ.2) FUNCTS=AZERO+BZERO*SIN(ARGUM)
      IF(IFUNC.EQ.3) FUNCTS=DTIME*FLOAT(JSTEP)/TMAXR
      IF(IFUNC.EQ.3.AND.FUNCTS.GT.1.0) FUNCTS=1.0
      RETURN
   10 PTIME=FLOAT(JSTEP)*DTIME
      DO 15 IACCE=1,NACCE
      TIME2=ACCEH(IACCE)
      IF(TIME2.GT.PTIME) GO TO 20
   15 CONTINUE
      RETURN
   20 TIME1=ACCEH(IACCE-1)
      FACT1=ACCEV(IACCE-1)
      FACT2=ACCEV(IACCE)
      FUNCTS=FACT1+(PTIME-TIME1)*(FACT2-FACT1)/(TIME2-TIME1)
      RETURN
   30 PTIME=FLOAT(JSTEP)*DTIME
      ARGUM=OMEGA*(PTIME-TMAXR)
      IF(PTIME.LE.TMAXR) FUNCTS=AZERO*PTIME/TMAXR
      IF(PTIME.GT.TMAXR) FUNCTS=AZERO+BZERO*SIN(ARGUM)
      RETURN
      END
```

6.8.3 Function FUNCTA

```
      FUNCTION FUNCTA (ACCER,AFACT,DTEND,DTIME,IFUNC,JSTEP)
C**********************************************************************
C
C***  ACCELERATION INTERPOLATION
C
C**********************************************************************
      IMPLICIT DOUBLE PRECISION (A-H,O-Z)
      DIMENSION ACCER(*)
      IF(IFUNC.NE.0) RETURN
      FUNCTA=0.0
      IF(JSTEP.EQ.0.OR.FLOAT(JSTEP)*DTIME.GT.DTEND) RETURN
      XGASH=(FLOAT(JSTEP)-1.0)/AFACT+1.0
      MGASH=XGASH
      NGASH=MGASH+1
      XGASH=XGASH-FLOAT(MGASH)
      FUNCTA=ACCER(MGASH)*(1.0-XGASH)+XGASH*ACCER(NGASH)
      RETURN
      END
```

6.8.4 Subroutine DECOMP

```
      SUBROUTINE DECOMP (STIFF ,MAXAI ,NEQNS ,ISHOT )
C***********************************************************************
C
C *** FACTORISES (L)*(D)*(L) TRANSPOSE OF STIFFNESS MATRIX
C
C***********************************************************************
      IMPLICIT DOUBLE PRECISION (A-H,O-Z)
      DIMENSION STIFF(*),MAXAI(*)
C
      IF(NEQNS.EQ.1) RETURN
      DO 200 IEQNS=1,NEQNS
      IMAXA=MAXAI(IEQNS)
      LOWER=IMAXA+1
      KUPER=MAXAI(IEQNS+1)-1
      KHIGH=KUPER-LOWER
      IF(KHIGH) 304,240,210
  210 KSIZE=IEQNS-KHIGH
      ICOUN=0
      JUPER=KUPER
      DO 260 JHIGH=1,KHIGH
      ICOUN=ICOUN+1
      JUPER=JUPER-1
      KMAXA=MAXAI(KSIZE)
      NDIAG=MAXAI(KSIZE+1)-KMAXA-1
      IF(NDIAG) 260,260,270
  270 NCOLM=MIN0(ICOUN,NDIAG)
      COUNT=0.
      DO 280 ICOLM=1,NCOLM
  280 COUNT=COUNT+STIFF(KMAXA+ICOLM)*STIFF(JUPER+ICOLM)
      STIFF(JUPER)=STIFF(JUPER)-COUNT
  260 KSIZE=KSIZE+1
  240 KSIZE=IEQNS
      BSUMM=0.
      DO 300 ICOLM=LOWER,KUPER
      KSIZE=KSIZE-1
      JMAXA=MAXAI(KSIZE)
```

```
      RATIO=STIFF(ICOLM)/STIFF(JMAXA)
      BSUMM=BSUMM+RATIO*STIFF(ICOLM)
  300 STIFF(ICOLM)=RATIO
      STIFF(IMAXA)=STIFF(IMAXA)-BSUMM
  304 IF(STIFF(IMAXA).GT.0.0) GO TO 200
      WRITE(6,2000) IEQNS,STIFF(IMAXA)
      STOP
  200 CONTINUE
 2000 FORMAT(//48H STOP - STIFFNESS MATRIX NOT POSITIVE DEFINITE  ,//
     .32H NONPCSITIVE PIVOT FOR EQUATION ,I4,//10H PIVOT =  ,E20.12 )
      END
```

6.8.5 Subroutine MULTPY

```
      SUBROUTINE MULTPY(C,A,B,IND,N,M)
      IMPLICIT DOUBLE PRECISION (A-H,O-Z)
      DIMENSION A(*),IND(*),B(*),C(*)
      IF(M.GT.N) GO TO 20
      DO 10 I=1,N
   10 C(I)=A(I)*B(I)
      RETURN
   20 CONTINUE
      DO 1 J=1,N
      NDIAG=IND(J)-1
      NLAST=IND(J+1)-1
      NALTO=NLAST-NDIAG
      SUMA=0.
      NBACK=J
      DO 2 L=1,NALTO
      SUMA=SUMA+B(NBACK)*A(NDIAG+L)
    2 NBACK= NBACK-1
      C(J)=SUMA
      NDIAG=NDIAG+1
      NALTO=NALTO-1
      IF(NALTO)1,1,4
    4 DO 3 K=1,NALTO
    3 C(J-K)=C(J-K)+B(J)*A(NDIAG+K)
    1 CONTINUE
      RETURN
      END
```

6.9 Internal forces routines

This section lists routines which are required to evaluate the internal resisting forces

6.9.1 Subroutine RESEVP

This subroutine organises the evaluation of the internal resisting forces and calls four subroutines STRAIN, STREC, FORMP, RESREF. The NS chart for RESEVP is given in Figure 39.

Initialise resisting forces 1

Loop over each element 2

> Initialise elemental resisting force vector 3
>
> Loop over each integration point 4
>
> > Call STRAIN to evaluate total strains 5
> >
> > Calculate elastic strains 6
> >
> > Call STREC to evaluate stresses 7
> >
> > Call FORMP to add $\underline{B}^T \underline{\sigma}$ dV to to elemental resisting forces 8
>
> Call RESREF to evaluate reinforcement contribution to the elemental resisting forces 9
>
> Assemble elemental contribution into global resisting force vector 10

Figure 39. NS chart for subroutine RESEVP

```
      SUBROUTINE RESEVP(COORD,LNODS,CRVAL,ELAST,MATNO,DVOLU,DVOLS,
     .                  CARDS,POSGP,PROPS,WEIGP,ELDIS,TMATX,TMATC,
     .                  CARTD,XJACM,STRES,DMATX,MPATT,MREIN,MLAYR,
     .                  NOCAP,MBARS,VBARS,STREF,ISTAT,ALPHI,EFFST,
     .                  DISPL,LEQNS,RESID,STRVP,STRAF,IFPRE,WORKP,
     .                  WORKF,EFFSS)
      IMPLICIT DOUBLE PRECISION (A-H,O-Z)
      COMMON/CTRL/  NDIME,NDOFN,NECHO,NELEM,NEVAB,NGASN,NGAUS,NMATS,
     &              NNODE,NPOIN,NPROP,NREIN,NSIZE,NSTRE,NTOTG,NTOTV,
     &              NVFIX,NWKTL,NYIEL
      COMMON/RUN/   IFUNC,IPRED,KSTEP,MITER,NACCE,NOUTD,NOUTP,NREQD,
     &              NREQS,NSTEP
      COMMON/CONST/AALFA,BEETA,GAAMA,DELTA,AZERO,BZERO,OMEGA,TMAXR,
     &              DTEND,DTIME,AFACT,TOLER,ADISP,AVELO,CONSD,CONSF
      COMMON/FILE/  NDATA,NRESU
      COMMON/STAT/  IITER,ISTEP,KTOLE
```

```
C.......................................................................
C
C     ROUTINE TO EVALUATE STRESSES AND EQUIVALENT RESISTING FORCES
C
C.......................................................................
      DIMENSION CARTD(NDIME,NNODE,*),COORD(NDIME,*),
     .          ELDIS(NDIME,*),ELAST(3,*),
     .          ELOAD(3,20),LNODS(NNODE,*),POSGP(*),
     .          PROPS(NPROP,*),STRAT(6),STRGP(6),
     .          WEIGP(*),STRES(NSTRE,*),
     .          DMATX(NSTRE,*),
     .          EFFST(2,*),EFFSS(2,*),
     .          DISPL(*),MATNO(*),XJACM(NDIME,*),
     .          MPATT(*),NOCAP(*),MBARS(2,MLAYR,*),
     .          VBARS(3,MLAYR,*),STREF(NSTRE,*),
     .          ISTAT(*),ALPHI(4,*),STRAN(6),
     .          LEQNS(NEVAB,*),
     .          CRVAL(4,*),RESID(*),
     .          STRVP(2,NSTRE,*),STRAF(2,NSTRE,*),
     .          IFPRE(NDOFN,*),
     .          WORKP(2,*),WORKF(2,*)
      DIMENSION DVOLS(*),DVOLU(*),CARDS(NDIME,NNODE,*),
     .          TMATX(NDIME,NDIME,*),TMATC(NDIME,NDIME,*)
C
      DO 10 ITOTV=1,NTOTV
   10 RESID(ITOTV)=0.0
C
C*** LOOP OVER THE ELEMENTS
C
      KGAST=0
      KGREF=0
      DO 20 IELEM=1,NELEM
C
C    INITIALIZE ELEMENT RESISTING FORCES
C
      DO 25 IDOFN=1,NDOFN
      DO 25 INODE=1,NNODE
      ELOAD(IDOFN,INODE)=0.0
   25 CONTINUE
C
C     SCALAR GATHER OPERATION
C
      NPOSN=0
      DO 30 INODE =1,NNODE
      DO 30 IDOFN=1,NDOFN
      NPOSN=NPOSN+1
      IEQNS=LEQNS(NPOSN,IELEM)
   30 ELDIS(IDOFN,INODE)=DISPL(IEQNS)
C
C*** ENTER LOOPS FOR AREA NUMERICAL INTEGRATION
C
      DO 50 IGAUN=1,NGASN
      KGAST = KGAST + 1
C
      DLENG=DVOLU(KGAST)**(1./3.)
C
C ****  EVALUATE THE STRAINS
C
      DO 40 ISTRE=1,NSTRE
      STRAT(ISTRE)=0.0
   40 CONTINUE
C
      CALL STRAIN(ELDIS,CARTD(1,1,KGAST),STRAT,NDIME,NNODE)
C
      DO 41 ISTRE=1,NSTRE
      STRAN(ISTRE)=STRAT(ISTRE)-STRVP(1,ISTRE,KGAST)
   41 CONTINUE
C
```

```
C*** EVALUATE STRESSES
C
      CALL STREC(IELEM,KGAST,MATNO,PROPS,NPROP,NSTRE,ELAST,
     .           ISTAT,ALPHI,DMATX,STRAT,STRGP,DLENG,STRAN,
     .           STRES,EFFST,WORKP,WORKF,CRVAL,DTIME,STRVP,KTOLE,
     .           NYIEL,TMATC(1,1,KGAST))
C
C*** CALCULATE THE EQUIVALENT NODAL FORCES AND ASSOCIATE WITH THE
C    ELEMENT NODES
C
      DO 42 INODE=1,NNODE
      CALL FORMP(CARTD(1,INODE,KGAST),STRES(1,KGAST),
     &           ELOAD(1,INODE),DVOLU(KGAST))
   42 CONTINUE
C
   50   CONTINUE
C
C*** EVALUATE NODAL FORCES DUE TO REINFORCEMENT
C
      CALL       RESREF(IELEM,ELOAD,LNODS,KGREF,DVOLS,CARDS,TMATX,
     .                  PROPS,ELDIS,STREF,DMATX,MPATT,MREIN,MLAYR,
     .                  NOCAP,MBARS,VBARS,STRAF,EFFSS)
C
C     SCALAR SCATTER OPERATION
C
      IEVAB=0
      DO 60 INODE=1,NNODE
      DO 60 IDOFN=1,NDOFN
      IEVAB=IEVAB+1
      LMVEB=LEQNS(IEVAB,IELEM)
      IF(LMVEB.EQ.0) GO TO 60
      RESID(LMVEB)=RESID(LMVEB)+ELOAD(IDOFN,INODE)
   60 CONTINUE
   20 CONTINUE
C
      RETURN
      END
```

6.9.2 Subroutine STRAIN

```
      SUBROUTINE STRAIN(E,C,S,NDIME,NNODE)
C.......................................................................
C
C     ROUTINE TO EVALUATE STRAINS
C
C.......................................................................
      IMPLICIT DOUBLE PRECISION (A-H,O-Z)
      DIMENSION E(NDIME,*),C(NDIME,*),S(*)
C
      DO 10 I=1,NNODE
         S(1)=S(1)+C(1,I)*E(1,I)
         S(2)=S(2)+C(2,I)*E(2,I)
         S(3)=S(3)+C(3,I)*E(3,I)
         S(4)=S(4)+C(2,I)*E(1,I)+C(1,I)*E(2,I)
         S(5)=S(5)+C(3,I)*E(2,I)+C(2,I)*E(3,I)
         S(6)=S(6)+C(3,I)*E(1,I)+C(1,I)*E(3,I)
 10   CONTINUE
      RETURN
      END
```

6.9.3 Subroutine FORMP

```
      SUBROUTINE FORMP(S,D,P,V)
C..............................................................
C
C                             T
C    ROUTINE TO PERFORM THE PRODUC B * SIGMA * dV
C
C..............................................................
      IMPLICIT DOUBLE PRECISION (A-H,O-Z)
      DIMENSION S(*),D(*),P(*)
C
      P(1)=P(1)+(S(1)*D(1)+S(2)*D(4)+S(3)*D(6))*V
      P(2)=P(2)+(S(2)*D(2)+S(1)*D(4)+S(3)*D(5))*V
      P(3)=P(3)+(S(3)*D(3)+S(2)*D(5)+S(1)*D(6))*V
C
      RETURN
      END
```

6.9.4 Subroutine STREC

The NS chart for this subroutine is given in Figure 40.

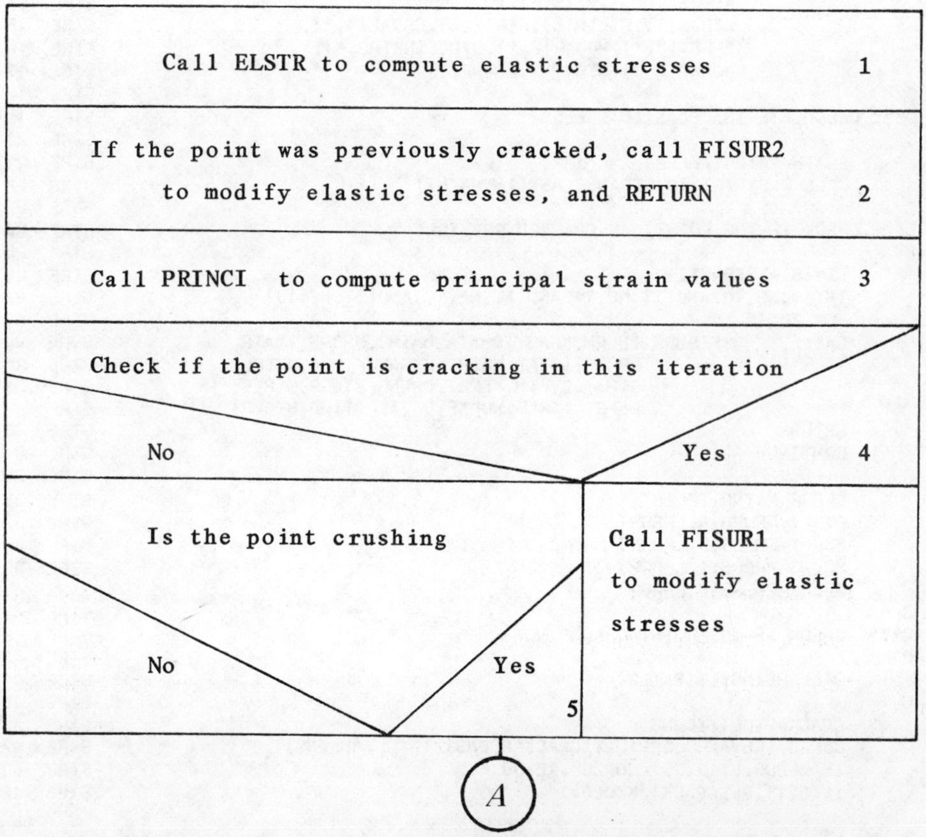

A

Call VISCOP to check for viscoplastic behaviour 6	Set all stresses equal to zero 7	8

Figure 40. NS chart for subroutine STREC

```
      SUBROUTINE STREC(IELEM,KGAST,MATNO,PROPS,NPROP,NSTRE,ELAST,
     .                 ISTAT,ALPHI,DMATX,STRAT,STRGP,
     .                 DLENG,STRAN,STRES,EFFST,WORKP,WORKF,CRVAL,
     .                 DTIME,STRVP,KTOLE,NYIEL,TMATC)
      IMPLICIT DOUBLE PRECISION (A-H,O-Z)
C . . . . . . . . . . . . . . . . . . . . . . . . . . . . . . . .
C .                                                              .
C .    ROUTINE                                                   .
C .       TO EVALUATE THE STRESSES IN  CONCRETE                  .
C .                                                              .
C . . . . . . . . . . . . . . . . . . . . . . . . . . . . . . . .
      DIMENSION DMATX(NSTRE,*),MATNO(*),ELAST(3,*),
     .          PROPS(NPROP,*),ISTAT(*),D(3),TMATC(3,3),
     .          ALPHI(    4,*),STRAT(    6),
     .          STRAN(6),STLIN(6),STRGP(6),CRVAL(4,*),
     .          EFFST(2,*),WORKP(2,*),STRES(NSTRE,*),
     .          WORKF(2,*),STRVP(2,NSTRE,*)
C
C*** CALCULATE THE ELASTIC STRESS
C
      IMATN=MATNO(IELEM)
      CALL ELSTR(STLIN,STRAN,ELAST(1,IMATN))
C
C*** CHECK IF THE POINT WAS CRACKED PREVIOUSLY
C
      IT=ISTAT(KGAST)
      IF(IT.NE.10.AND.IT.NE.11.AND.IT.NE.12.AND.IT.NE.13)
     . GO TO 15
      CALL      FISUR2(IELEM,KGAST,DMATX,MATNO,PROPS,TMATC,
     .                 NPROP,ISTAT,NSTRE,STRAN,KTOLE,NYIEL,
     .                 STRAT,STLIN,ALPHI,DLENG,STRGP,STRES,
     .                 EFFST,WORKP,WORKF,CRVAL,DTIME,STRVP)
      RETURN
   15 CONTINUE
C
      LPROP=MATNO(IELEM)
      FTULT=PROPS(4,LPROP)
      FCULT=PROPS(3,LPROP)
      YOUNG=PROPS(1,LPROP)
      GFVAL=PROPS(6,LPROP)
C
C***  CHECK IF THE POINT CRACKS NOW
C
      CALL PRINCI(STRAT,D)
C
      CRACK=FTULT/YOUNG
      CONSS=(GFVAL-0.5*FTULT*CRACK*DLENG)/(FTULT*DLENG)
      IF(CONSS.LT.0.0)  CONSS=.1E-06
      IF(D(1).GE.CRACK) KTOLE=1
```

```
      IF(D(1).GE.CRACK) WRITE(6,100) KGAST,FTULT,(D(I),I=1,3)
  100 FORMAT(5X,'KGAST=',I5,1X,'FTULT=',F10.5,'  ***  D = ',3E20.5)
      IF(D(1).GE.CRACK) GO TO 20
      GO TO 25
   20 CALL        FISUR1(IELEM,KGAST,DMATX,MATNO,PROPS,TMATC,
     .                   NPROP,ISTAT,NSTRE,STRAN,CONSS,FTULT,
     .                   STRAT,STLIN,ALPHI,DLENG,STRGP,CRACK,
     .                   EFFST,WORKP,WORKF,STRES,CRVAL,DTIME,
     .                   STRVP,KTOLE,NYIEL,D)
      RETURN
   25 CONTINUE
C
C***  NON CRACKED CONCRETE
C
      CALL INVA2(STRAT,CRUSH)
      IF(CRUSH.LT.PROPS(5,LPROP)) GO TO 50
   16 ISTAT(KGAST)=13
      DO 51 ISTRE=1,NSTRE
   51 STRES(ISTRE,KGAST)=0.0
      EFFST(2,KGAST)=0.0
      RETURN
C
C*** NON-CRUSHED CONCRETE,CHECK FOR YIELDING
C
   50 CONTINUE
      DO 60 ISTRE=1,NSTRE
   60 STRES(ISTRE,KGAST)=STLIN(ISTRE)
      CALL VISCOP (STRAN,NSTRE,DTIME,EFFST,KGAST,WORKP,WORKF,
     .             STLIN,PROPS,NPROP,LPROP,STRVP,KTOLE,NYIEL)
      RETURN
      END
```

6.9.5 Subroutine ELSTR

```
      SUBROUTINE ELSTR(SG,ST,E)
C.......................................................
C
C     ROUTINE TO EVALUATE ELASTIC STRESSES
C
C.......................................................
      IMPLICIT DOUBLE PRECISION (A-H,O-Z)
C
      DIMENSION SG(*),ST(*),E(*)
C
      SG(1)=E(1)*ST(1)+E(2)*(ST(2)+ST(3))
      SG(2)=E(1)*ST(2)+E(2)*(ST(1)+ST(3))
      SG(3)=E(1)*ST(3)+E(2)*(ST(2)+ST(1))
      SG(4)=E(3)*ST(4)
      SG(5)=E(3)*ST(5)
      SG(6)=E(3)*ST(6)
      RETURN
      END
```

6.9.6 Subroutine PRINCI

```
      SUBROUTINE PRINCI(S,D)
      IMPLICIT DOUBLE PRECISION (A-H,O-Z)
      DIMENSION S(6),D(3),X(6)
C
      S3=SQRT(3.0)
      PI=ATAN(1.0)*4.0
C
      XJ1=S(1)+S(2)+S(3)
      SM=XJ1/3.0
      X(1)=S(1)-SM
      X(2)=S(2)-SM
      X(3)=S(3)-SM
      X(4)=S(4)/2.0
      X(5)=S(5)/2.0
      X(6)=S(6)/2.0
      XJ2=(X(1)**2+X(2)**2+X(3)**2)/2.0+X(4)**2+X(5)**2+X(6)**2
      XJ3=X(1)*(X(2)*X(3)-X(5)*X(5))-
     &    X(4)*(X(4)*X(3)-X(5)*X(6))+
     &    X(6)*(X(4)*X(5)-X(2)*X(6))
      IF(XJ2.NE.0.) THEN
      ARG= -3.*S3*XJ3/(2.*XJ2**1.5)
       IF(ARG.LT.-1.) ARG=-1.0
       IF(ARG.GT.+1.) ARG=+1.0
      T=ASIN(ARG)/3.
      ELSE
      T=0.
      END IF
      CO=2.*SQRT(XJ2)/S3
      D(1)=CO*DSIN(T+2.*PI/3.)+SM
      D(2)=CO*DSIN(T         )+SM
      D(3)=CO*DSIN(T+4.*PI/3.)+SM
      RETURN
      END
```

6.9.7 Subroutine RESREF

The NS chart for this subroutine is given in Figure 41.

```
      SUBROUTINE RESREF(IELEM,ELOAD,LNODS,KGREF,DVOLS,CARDS,TMATX,
     .                  PROPS,ELDIS,STREF,DMATX,MPATT,MREIN,MLAYR,
     .                  NOCAP,MBARS,VBARS,STRAF,EFFSS)
      IMPLICIT DOUBLE PRECISION (A-H,O-Z)
      COMMON/CTRL/ NDIME,NDOFN,NECHO,NELEM,NEVAB,NGASN,NGAUS,NMATS,
     &             NNODE,NPOIN,NPROP,NREIN,NSIZE,NSTRE,NTOTG,NTOTV,
     &             NVFIX,NWKTL,NYIEL
      COMMON/FILE/ NDATA,NRESU
      COMMON/STAT/ IITER,ISTEP,KTOLE
      COMMON/CONST/AALFA,BEETA,GAAMA,DELTA,AZERO,BZERO,OMEGA,TMAXR,
     &             DTEND,DTIME,AFACT,TOLER,ADISP,AVELO,CONSD,CONSF
C***********************************************************************
C
C     ROUTINE TO EVALUATE THE STRESSES IN THE REINFORCEMENT AND
C     THE EQUIVALENT NODAL FORCES
C
C***********************************************************************
```

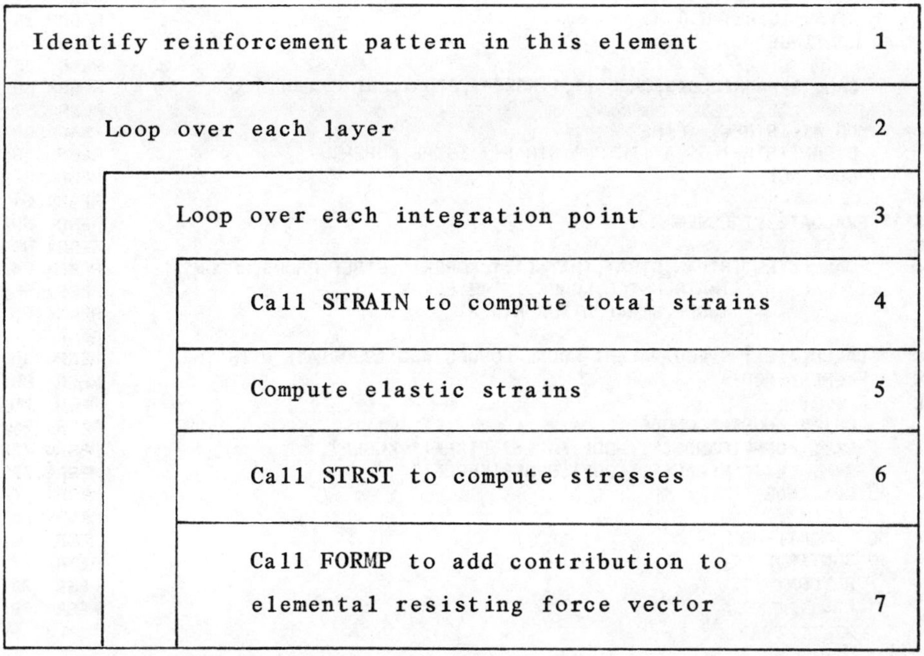

Figure 41. NS chart for the subroutine RESREF

```
      DIMENSION ELDIS(NDIME,*),
     .          ELOAD(NDIME,*),LNODS(NNODE,*),
     .          PROPS(NPROP,*),STRAT(6),STLIN(6),
     .          DMATX(NSTRE,*),EFFSS(2,*),
     .          MPATT(*),NOCAP(*),MBARS(2,MLAYR,*),
     .          VBARS(3,MLAYR,*),VECT1(3),
     .          VECT2(3),VNORM(3),STREF(NSTRE,*),
     .          STRAN(6),STRAF(2,NSTRE,*)
      DIMENSION DVOLS(*),CARDS(NDIME,NNODE,*),
     .          TMATX(NDIME,NDIME,*)
C
      KPATT=MPATT(IELEM)
      IF(KPATT.EQ.0) RETURN
      NLAYR=NOCAP(KPATT)
      IF(NLAYR.EQ.0) RETURN
C
C*** LOOP OVER THE REINFORCEMENT LAYERS
C
      DO 10 ILAYR=1,NLAYR
      IMATN=MBARS(1,ILAYR,KPATT)
      ICOCR=MBARS(2,ILAYR,KPATT)
      SPOS3=VBARS(1,ILAYR,KPATT)
      ESPES=VBARS(2,ILAYR,KPATT)
      ANGLE=VBARS(3,ILAYR,KPATT)
C
C*** ENTER LOOPS FOR AREA NUMERICAL INTEGRATION
C
      DO 50 IGAUS=1,NGAUS
      DO 50 JGAUS=1,NGAUS
C
      KGREF=KGREF+1
C
C ****  EVALUATE THE STRAINS
C
```

```
      DO 40 ISTRE=1,NSTRE
      STRAT(ISTRE)=0.0
   40 CONTINUE
C
      CALL STRAIN(ELDIS,CARDS(1,1,KGREF),STRAT,NDIME,NNODE)
C
      DO 41 ISTRE=1,NSTRE
      STRAN(ISTRE)=STRAT(ISTRE)-STRAF(1,ISTRE,KGREF)
   41 CONTINUE
C
C*** EVALUATE STRESSES
C
      CALL STRST(STRAN,STRAT,TMATX(1,1,KGREF) ,STREF,PROPS,NPROP,
     .           IMATN,NSTRE,KGREF,ISTAS,EFFSS,
     .           ANGLE,STRAF,DTIME,KTOLE)
C
C*** CALCULATE THE EQUIVALENT NODAL FORCES AND ASSOCIATE WITH THE
C    ELEMENT NODES
C
      DO 45 INODE=1,NNODE
      CALL FORMP(CARDS(1,INODE,KGREF),STREF(1,KGREF),
     &           ELOAD(1,INODE),DVOLS(KGREF))
   45 CONTINUE
C
   50   CONTINUE
   10 CONTINUE
      RETURN
      END
```

6.9.8 Subroutine STRST

```
      SUBROUTINE STRST(STRAN,STRAT,TMATX,STREF,PROPS,
     .                 NPROP,IMATN,NSTRE,KGREF,ISTAS,
     .                 EFFSS,ANGLE,STRAF,DTIME,KTOLE)
      IMPLICIT DOUBLE PRECISION (A-H,O-Z)
C . . . . . . . . . . . . . . . . . . . . . . . . . . . . .
C .                                                       .
C .   ROUTINE                                             .
C .      TO EVALUATE THE STRESSES IN REINFORCEMENT        .
C .                                                       .
C . . . . . . . . . . . . . . . . . . . . . . . . . . . . .
      DIMENSION PROPS(NPROP,*),STREF(NSTRE,*),
     .          ISTAS(1),EFFSS(2,*),
     .          STRAN(6),STRAT(6),STRIN(6),TMATX(3,3),
     .          STANO(6),STALO(6),STOLD(6),C1(3,3),
     .          T(3,3),STRAF(2,NSTRE,*),STRAS(6)
C
      YOUNG=PROPS(1,IMATN)
      YIELD=PROPS(3,IMATN)
      AZERO=PROPS(11,IMATN)
C
C   SET UP THE TRANSFORMATION MATRIX
C
      DO 10 I=1,3
      DO 10 J=1,3
      C1(I,J)=0.0
   10 T(I,J)=0.0
      C=COS(ANGLE)
      S=SIN(ANGLE)
      C1(1,1)= C
      C1(2,2)= C
      C1(1,2)=-S
      C1(2,1)= S
      C1(3,3)=1.
```

```
      DO 12 I=1,3
      DO 12 J=1,3
      DO 12 K=1,3
   12 T(I,J)=T(I,J)+TMATX(K,I)*C1(K,J)
C
C   TRANSFORM ELASTIC STRAIN TO LOCAL SYSTEM
C
      CALL TSTRN(STRAN,STANO,T,0)
C
      STRAI=STANO(1)
C
      STLIN=YOUNG*STRAI
      FLUID=AZERO
      DO 20 ISTRE=1,NSTRE
      STOLD(ISTRE)=0.0
      STALO(ISTRE)=0.0
   20 CONTINUE
C
C *** CHECK IF THE POINT IS FLOWING
C
      IF(ABS(STLIN).GT.YIELD) THEN
             KTOLE=1
         ESCUR=(ABS(STLIN)-YIELD)/YIELD
         CMULT=FLUID*ESCUR
         STALO(1)=CMULT*(STLIN/ABS(STLIN))
      ENDIF
      STOLD(1)=STLIN
C
C   TRANSFORM TO GLOBAL SYSTEM
C
      CALL TSTRN(STALO,STRIN,T,1)
      CALL TSTRS(STOLD,STRAS,T,1)
C
C   UPDATE VISCOPLASTIC STRAIN
C
      DO 60 ISTRE=1,NSTRE
      STRAF(2,ISTRE,KGREF)=STRAF(1,ISTRE,KGREF)+
     .                          DTIME*STRIN(ISTRE)
   60 STREF(ISTRE,KGREF)=STRAS(ISTRE)
      RETURN
      END
```

6.9.9 Subroutine TSTRS

```
      SUBROUTINE TSTRS(ST,SR,B,IN)
      IMPLICIT DOUBLE PRECISION (A-H,O-Z)
C
      DIMENSION ST(6),SR(6),B(3,3),S(3,3)
C
      IF(IN.EQ.0) THEN
C
C     TRANSFORMS FROM GLOBAL TO LOCAL
C
          S(1,1)=B(1,1)*ST(1)+B(2,1)*ST(4)+B(3,1)*ST(6)
          S(1,2)=B(1,1)*ST(4)+B(2,1)*ST(2)+B(3,1)*ST(5)
          S(1,3)=B(1,1)*ST(6)+B(2,1)*ST(5)+B(3,1)*ST(3)
          S(2,1)=B(1,2)*ST(1)+B(2,2)*ST(4)+B(3,2)*ST(6)
          S(2,2)=B(1,2)*ST(4)+B(2,2)*ST(2)+B(3,2)*ST(5)
          S(2,3)=B(1,2)*ST(6)+B(2,2)*ST(5)+B(3,2)*ST(3)
          S(3,1)=B(1,3)*ST(1)+B(2,3)*ST(4)+B(3,3)*ST(6)
          S(3,2)=B(1,3)*ST(4)+B(2,3)*ST(2)+B(3,3)*ST(5)
          S(3,3)=B(1,3)*ST(6)+B(2,3)*ST(5)+B(3,3)*ST(3)
C
```

```
         SR(1)=S(1,1)*B(1,1)+S(1,2)*B(2,1)+S(1,3)*B(3,1)
         SR(4)=S(1,1)*B(1,2)+S(1,2)*B(2,2)+S(1,3)*B(3,2)
         SR(6)=S(1,1)*B(1,3)+S(1,2)*B(2,3)+S(1,3)*B(3,3)
         SR(2)=S(2,1)*B(1,2)+S(2,2)*B(2,2)+S(2,3)*B(3,2)
         SR(5)=S(2,1)*B(1,3)+S(2,2)*B(2,3)+S(2,3)*B(3,3)
         SR(3)=S(3,1)*B(1,3)+S(3,2)*B(2,3)+S(3,3)*B(3,3)
      ELSE
C
C      TRANSFORM FROM LOCAL TO GLOBAL
C
         S(1,1)=B(1,1)*ST(1)+B(1,2)*ST(4)+B(1,3)*ST(6)
         S(1,2)=B(1,1)*ST(4)+B(1,2)*ST(2)+B(1,3)*ST(5)
         S(1,3)=B(1,1)*ST(6)+B(1,2)*ST(5)+B(1,3)*ST(3)
         S(2,1)=B(2,1)*ST(1)+B(2,2)*ST(4)+B(2,3)*ST(6)
         S(2,2)=B(2,1)*ST(4)+B(2,2)*ST(2)+B(2,3)*ST(5)
         S(2,3)=B(2,1)*ST(6)+B(2,2)*ST(5)+B(2,3)*ST(3)
         S(3,1)=B(3,1)*ST(1)+B(3,2)*ST(4)+B(3,3)*ST(6)
         S(3,2)=B(3,1)*ST(4)+B(3,2)*ST(2)+B(3,3)*ST(5)
         S(3,3)=B(3,1)*ST(6)+B(3,2)*ST(5)+B(3,3)*ST(3)
C
         SR(1)=S(1,1)*B(1,1)+S(1,2)*B(1,2)+S(1,3)*B(1,3)
         SR(4)=S(1,1)*B(2,1)+S(1,2)*B(2,2)+S(1,3)*B(2,3)
         SR(6)=S(1,1)*B(3,1)+S(1,2)*B(3,2)+S(1,3)*B(3,3)
         SR(2)=S(2,1)*B(2,1)+S(2,2)*B(2,2)+S(2,3)*B(2,3)
         SR(5)=S(2,1)*B(3,1)+S(2,2)*B(3,2)+S(2,3)*B(3,3)
         SR(3)=S(3,1)*B(3,1)+S(3,2)*B(3,2)+S(3,3)*B(3,3)
      END IF
C
      RETURN
      END
```

6.9.10 Subroutine TSTRN

```
      SUBROUTINE TSTRN(ST,SR,B,IN)
      IMPLICIT DOUBLE PRECISION (A-H,O-Z)
C
      DIMENSION ST(6),SR(6),B(3,3)
C
C**** TRANSFORM GLOBAL STRAINS INTO LOCAL STRAINS OR VICEVERSA
C
      ST(4)=ST(4)*0.5
      ST(5)=ST(5)*0.5
      ST(6)=ST(6)*0.5
C
      CALL TSTRS(ST,SR,B,IN)
C
      SR(4)=SR(4)*2
      SR(5)=SR(5)*2
      SR(6)=SR(6)*2
      ST(4)=ST(4)*2
      ST(5)=ST(5)*2
      ST(6)=ST(6)*2
      RETURN
      END
```

6.9.11 Subroutine FISUR1

The NS chart for this subroutine is given in Figure 42.

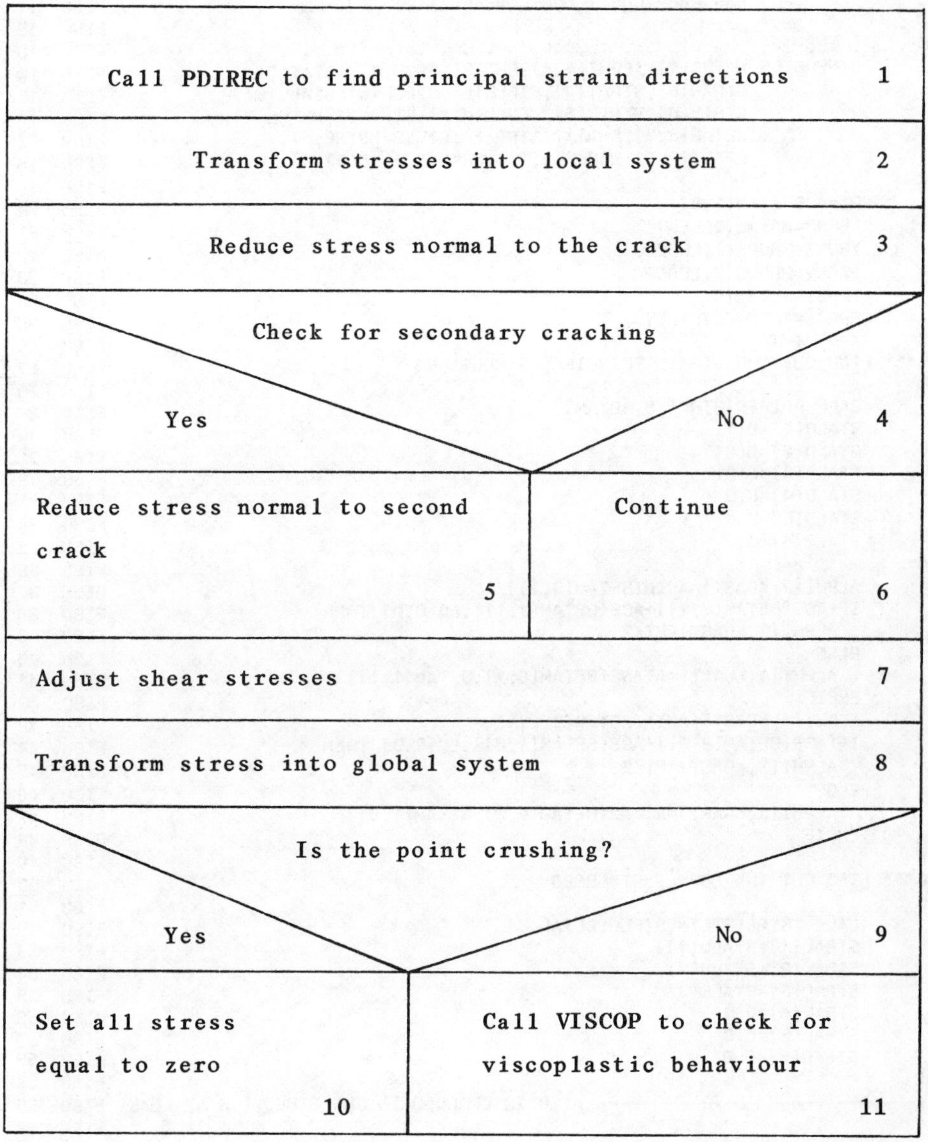

Figure 42. NS chart for the subroutine FISUR1

```
      SUBROUTINE FISUR1(IELEM,KGAST,DMATX,MATNO,PROPS,BETAM,
     .                  NPROP,ISTAT,NSTRE,STRAN,CONSS,FTULT,
     .                  STRAT,STLIN,ALPHI,DLENG,STRGP,CRACK,
     .                  EFFST,WORKP,WORKF,STRES,CRVAL,DTIME,
     .                  STRVP,KTOLE,NYIEL,D)
      IMPLICIT DOUBLE PRECISION (A-H,O-Z)
C . . . . . . . . . . . . . . . . . . . . . . . . . . . . .
C .                                                         .
C .    ROUTINE                                              .
C .       TO EVALUATE THE STRESSES IN   CONCRETE            .
C .       THAT WAS PREVIOUSLY NON-CRACKED                   .
C .                                                         .
C . . . . . . . . . . . . . . . . . . . . . . . . . . . . .
      DIMENSION MATNO(*),ALPHI(4,*),PROPS(NPROP,*),ISTAT(*),
     .          STRAN(6),STRAT(6),STRLO(6),STRGP(6),STALO(6),
     .          STRAL(6),STLIN(6),CRVAL(4,*),STRVP(2,NSTRE,*),
     .          BETAM(3,3),DMATX(NSTRE,*),STRES(NSTRE,*),
     .          EFFST(2,*),WORKP(2,*),WORKF(2,*),D(3)
C
      PI=4.0*ATAN(1.0)
      LPROP=MATNO(IELEM)
      YOUNG=PROPS(1,LPROP)
      FACK1=PROPS(7,LPROP)
      TENST=1.0E-10
      ERROR=1.0E-04*FTULT
C
C*** FIND OUT THE STRAIN PRINCIPAL DIRECTIONS
C
      CALL PDIREC(STRAT,D,BETAM)
      STALO(1)=D(1)
      STALO(2)=D(2)
      STALO(3)=D(3)
      STALO(4)=0.0
      STALO(5)=0.0
      STALO(6)=0.0
C
      ALPHI(2,KGAST)=ASIN(BETAM(3,1))
      IF(ABS(BETAM(2,1))+ABS(BETAM(1,1)).EQ.0.0) THEN
        ALPHI(1,KGAST)=PI/2.
      ELSE
        ALPHI(1,KGAST)=ATAN2(BETAM(2,1),BETAM(1,1))
      ENDIF
      ALPHI(4,KGAST)=ASIN(BETAM(3,2))
      IF(ABS(BETAM(2,2))+ABS(BETAM(1,2)).EQ.0.0) THEN
        ALPHI(3,KGAST)=PI/2.
      ELSE
        ALPHI(3,KGAST)=ATAN2(BETAM(2,2),BETAM(1,2))
      ENDIF
C
C*** FIND OUT THE LOCAL  STRESSES
C
      CALL TSTRS(STLIN,STRLO,BETAM,0)
      STRAL(1)=STALO(1)
      STRAL(2)=STALO(2)
      STRAL(3)=STALO(3)
      STRAL(4)=0.0
      STRAL(5)=0.0
      STRAL(6)=0.0
C
C----------------------------LAYER IS CRACKED IN ONE DIRECTION AT LEAST
C
      ISTAT(KGAST)=10
C
      STRAV=STALO(1)
      STREV=FTULT
      STRIV=STRAV
      CALL       TSEFF(FTULT,CRACK,CONSS,STRIV,STRAV,STREV)
```

```
      STRLO(1)=STREV
          CRVAL(1,KGAST)=STRAV
          CRVAL(2,KGAST)=STREV
          IF(STRAV.GT.TENST) TENST=STRAV
      STRAL(1)=0.0
      STRAL(4)=0.0
      STRAL(6)=0.0
C
C*** CHECK IF A SECOND CRACK IS FORMED
C
      IF(STALO(2)-CRACK) 125,125,93
C
C-------------------------------------LAYER IS CRACKED IN TWO DIRECTIONS
C
   93 ISTAT(KGAST)=12
      STRAV=STALO(2)
      STREV=FTULT
      STRIV=STRAV
      CALL      TSEFF(FTULT,CRACK,CONSS,STRIV,STRAV,STREV)
      STRAL(2)=0.0
      STRAL(5)=0.0
      STRLO(2)=STREV
              CRVAL(3,KGAST)=STRAV
              CRVAL(4,KGAST)=STREV
              IF(STRAV.GT.TENST) TENST=STRAV
C
125   CONTINUE
C
C*** ADJUST SHEAR STRESSES
C
       IF(TENST.LT.0.) TENST=0.
       COECQ=(1.0-(TENST/0.005)**FACK1)
       IF(COECQ.LT.0.1) COECQ=0.1
       STRLO(4)=COECQ*STALO(4)*YOUNG/2.
       STRLO(6)=COECQ*STALO(6)*YOUNG/2.
       IF(ISTAT(KGAST).EQ.12) STRLO(5)=COECQ*STALO(5)*YOUNG/2.
C
C***TRANSFORM STRESSES INTO GLOBAL COORDINATE SYSTEM
C
      CALL TSTRS(STRLO,STRGP,BETAM,1)
C
C***  CHECK AGAINST CRUSHING
C
      CALL INVA2(STRAL,CRUSH)
      IF(CRUSH.GT.PROPS(5,LPROP)) GO TO 203
C
C----------------------------------------------------NON CRUSHED CONCRETE
C
      DO 202 ISTRE=1,NSTRE
  202 STRES(ISTRE,KGAST)=STRGP(ISTRE)
      CALL      VISCOP (STRAN,NSTRE,DTIME,EFFST,KGAST,WORKP,
     .                  WORKF,STRGP,PROPS,NPROP,LPROP,STRVP,
     .                  KTOLE,NYIEL)
      RETURN
C
C----------------------------------------------------------CRUSHED CONCRETE
C
  203 DO 204 ISTRE=1,NSTRE
  204 STRES(ISTRE,KGAST)=0.0
      EFFST(2,KGAST)=0.0
      ISTAT(KGAST)=13
      RETURN
      END
```

6.9.12 Subroutine INVA2

```
      SUBROUTINE INVA2(SN,CRUSH)
      IMPLICIT DOUBLE PRECISION (A-H,O-Z)
C
      DIMENSION SN(6)
C
      BEETA=1.
      ALPHA=0.
      GASH1=BEETA*(SN(1)*SN(1)+SN(2)*SN(2)+SN(3)*SN(3)-
     .      SN(1)*SN(2)-SN(1)*SN(3)-SN(2)*SN(3)+
     .      0.75*(SN(6)*SN(6)+SN(4)*SN(4)+SN(5)*SN(5)))
      GESH1=ALPHA*(SN(1)+SN(2)+SN(3))*0.5
      GISH1=SQRT(GESH1*GESH1+GASH1)
      CRUSH=GESH1+GISH1
      RETURN
      END
```

6.9.13 Subroutine TSEFF

```
      SUBROUTINE TSEFF(SIGM1,DEF01,CONSS,STRIV,STRAV,STREV)
      IMPLICIT DOUBLE PRECISION (A-H,O-Z)
C
      STREV=STREV*STRAV/STRIV
      EXPUP=-(STRAV-DEF01)/CONSS
      IF(EXPUP.GT.0.5E+02) EXPUP=50.
      VALUE=SIGM1*EXP(EXPUP)
      IF(VALUE.LT.STREV)                      STREV=VALUE
      IF(STREV.GT.SIGM1)                      STREV=SIGM1
      IF(STREV.LT.0.0)                        STREV=0.0
      RETURN
      END
```

6.9.14 Subroutine PDIREC

This routine computes the principal strain directions. It calls the routine EIGVC1 to compute the eigenvector corresponding to a given eigenvalue and routine VECPRO to compute an orthonormal base from a given vector.

```
      SUBROUTINE PDIREC(S,XL,V)
      IMPLICIT DOUBLE PRECISION (A-H,O-Z)
      DIMENSION S(6),XL(3),V(3,3)
C
C       SUBROUTINE TO COMPUTE EIGENVECTORS
C
      COMP=XL(1)+XL(2)+XL(3)
      COMP2=COMP*COMP
      A3=ABS((XL(1)-XL(2))/COMP)
      A2=ABS((XL(1)-XL(3))/COMP)
      A1=ABS((XL(2)-XL(3))/COMP)
C
C       CASE-A: THREE EQUAL EIGENVALUES
C
```

```
      IF(A1.LT.1.E-10.AND.A2.LT.1.E-10) THEN
         V(1,1)=1.0
         V(2,2)=1.0
         V(3,3)=1.0
         V(1,2)=0.0
         V(1,3)=0.0
         V(2,1)=0.0
         V(2,3)=0.0
         V(3,1)=0.0
         V(3,2)=0.0
         RETURN
      END IF
C
C      CASE-B: TWO EQUAL EIGENVALUES
C
      IF(A1.LT.1.E-10) THEN
         CALL EIGVC1(S,XL(1),V(1,1),COMP2)
         CALL VECPRO(V(1,1),V(1,2),V(1,3))
         RETURN
      END IF
      IF(A2.LT.1.E-10) THEN
         CALL EIGVC1(S,XL(2),V(1,2),COMP2)
         CALL VECPRO(V(1,2),V(1,3),V(1,1))
         RETURN
      END IF
      IF(A3.LT.1.E-10) THEN
         CALL EIGVC1(S,XL(3),V(1,3),COMP2)
         CALL VECPRO(V(1,3),V(1,1),V(1,2))
         RETURN
      END IF
C
C      CASE-C: THREE DIFFERENT EIGENVALUES
C
      CALL EIGVC1(S,XL(1),V(1,1),COMP2)
      CALL EIGVC1(S,XL(2),V(1,2),COMP2)
      DOT=V(1,1)*V(1,2)+V(2,1)*V(2,2)+V(3,1)*V(3,2)
      V(1,2)=V(1,2)-DOT*V(1,1)
      V(2,2)=V(2,2)-DOT*V(2,1)
      V(3,2)=V(3,2)-DOT*V(3,1)
      XN=SQRT(V(1,2)*V(1,2)+V(2,2)*V(2,2)+V(3,2)*V(3,2))
      XN=1./XN
      V(1,2)=V(1,2)*XN
      V(2,2)=V(2,2)*XN
      V(3,2)=V(3,2)*XN
      V(1,3)=V(2,1)*V(3,2)-V(3,1)*V(2,2)
      V(2,3)=V(3,1)*V(1,2)-V(1,1)*V(3,2)
      V(3,3)=V(1,1)*V(2,2)-V(2,1)*V(1,2)
      RETURN
      END
```

6.9.15 Subroutine EIGVC1

```
      SUBROUTINE EIGVC1(S,XL,V,COM)
      IMPLICIT DOUBLE PRECISION (A-H,O-Z)
      DIMENSION S(6),V(3)
C
C     EVALUATES ONE EIGENVECTOR
C
      X1=S(1)-XL
      X2=S(2)-XL
      X3=S(3)-XL
      X4=S(4)*0.5
      X5=S(5)*0.5
      X6=S(6)*0.5
C
```

```
      DET=X1*X2-X4*X4
      IF(ABS(DET/COM).GT.1.E-10) THEN
         V1=(X4*X5-X6*X2)/DET
         V2=(X6*X4-X5*X1)/DET
         XN=SQRT(V1*V1+V2*V2+1.0)
         XN=1./XN
         V(1)=V1*XN
         V(2)=V2*XN
         V(3)=XN
         RETURN
      END IF
C
      DET=X4*X5-X6*X2
      IF(ABS(DET/COM).GT.1.E-10) THEN
         V1=(X6*X4-X5*X1)/DET
         XN=SQRT(V1*V1+1.0)
         XN=1./XN
         V(1)=XN
         V(2)=V1*XN
         V(3)=0.0
         RETURN
      END IF
C
      DET=X1*X5-X4*X6
      IF(ABS(DET/COM).GT.1.E-10) THEN
         V(1)=0.0
         V(2)=1.0
         V(3)=0.0
         RETURN
      END IF
C
      DET=X4*X3-X5*X6
      IF(ABS(DET/COM).GT.1.E-10) THEN
         V1=(X5*X5-X2*X3)/DET
         XN=SQRT(V1*V1+1.0)
         XN=1./XN
         V(1)=V1*XN
         V(2)=XN
         V(3)=0.0
         RETURN
      END IF
C
      DET=X2*X3-X5*X5
      IF(ABS(DET/COM).GT.1.E-10) THEN
         V(1)=1.0
         V(2)=0.0
         V(3)=0.0
         RETURN
      END IF
C
      V(1)=0.0
      V(2)=1.0
      V(3)=0.0
      RETURN
      END
```

6.9.16 Subroutine VECPRO

```
      SUBROUTINE VECPRO(A,B,C)
      IMPLICIT DOUBLE PRECISION (A-H,O-Z)
      DIMENSION A(3),B(3),C(3)
C
C       COMPUTES AN ORTHONORMAL BASE FROM V1
C
```

```
      XN=A(2)*A(2)+A(3)*A(3)
      IF(XN.GT.1.E-10) THEN
         B(1)=0.0
         XN=SQRT(XN)
         B(2)= A(3)/XN
         B(3)=-A(2)/XN
         C(1)= A(2)*B(3)-A(3)*B(2)
         C(2)=-A(1)*B(3)
         C(3)= A(1)*B(2)
      ELSE
         B(1)=0.0
         B(2)=1.0
         B(3)=0.0
         C(1)=0.0
         C(2)=0.0
         C(3)=1.0
      END IF
      RETURN
      END
```

6.9.17 Subroutine VISCOP

The NS chart for this subroutine is given in Figure 43.

```
      SUBROUTINE VISCOP (STRAN,NSTRE,DTIME,EFFST,KGAST,
     .                   WORKP,WORKF,STLIN,PROPS,NPROP,
     .                   LPROP,STRVP,KTOLE,NYIEL)
      IMPLICIT DOUBLE PRECISION (A-H,O-Z)
C.......................................................
C
C    ROUTINE
C       TO EVALUATE VISCOPLASTIC STRAINS
C
C.......................................................
      DIMENSION EFFST(2,*),WORKP(2,*),WORKF(2,*),
     .          PROPS(NPROP,*),STRVP(2,NSTRE,*),
     .          STRAN(6),STLIN(6),STRIN(6),AVECT(6)
C
C *** IDENTIFY MATERIAL PROPERTIES
C
      POISS=PROPS(2,LPROP)
      FCULT=PROPS(3,LPROP)
      CONST=PROPS(10,LPROP)
      AZERO=PROPS(11,LPROP)
      AONEP=PROPS(12,LPROP)
      ALFAC=PROPS(13,LPROP)
      BETA0=PROPS(14,LPROP)
      BETA1=PROPS(15,LPROP)
C
C *** EVALUATE RATE OF ELASTIC STRAIN AND GAAMA
C
      PJ2IN=(((STRAN(1)-STRAN(2))**2+(STRAN(2)-STRAN(3))**2
     .      +(STRAN(1)-STRAN(3))**2)/6.+(STRAN(4)**2+STRAN(5)**2+
     .      STRAN(6)**2)/4.)
      EEFFV=SQRT(3.*PJ2IN/(1.+POISS)**2)
      ERATE=ABS((EEFFV-EFFST(1,KGAST))/DTIME)
      IF(ERATE.LT. 1.0E-07) ERATE= 1.0E-07
      IF(ERATE.GT. 1.0E+03) ERATE=1.0E+03
      EFFST(2,KGAST)=EEFFV
      FLUID=AZERO
      IF(AONEP.NE.0.0) FLUID=FLUID*(ERATE**AONEP)
```

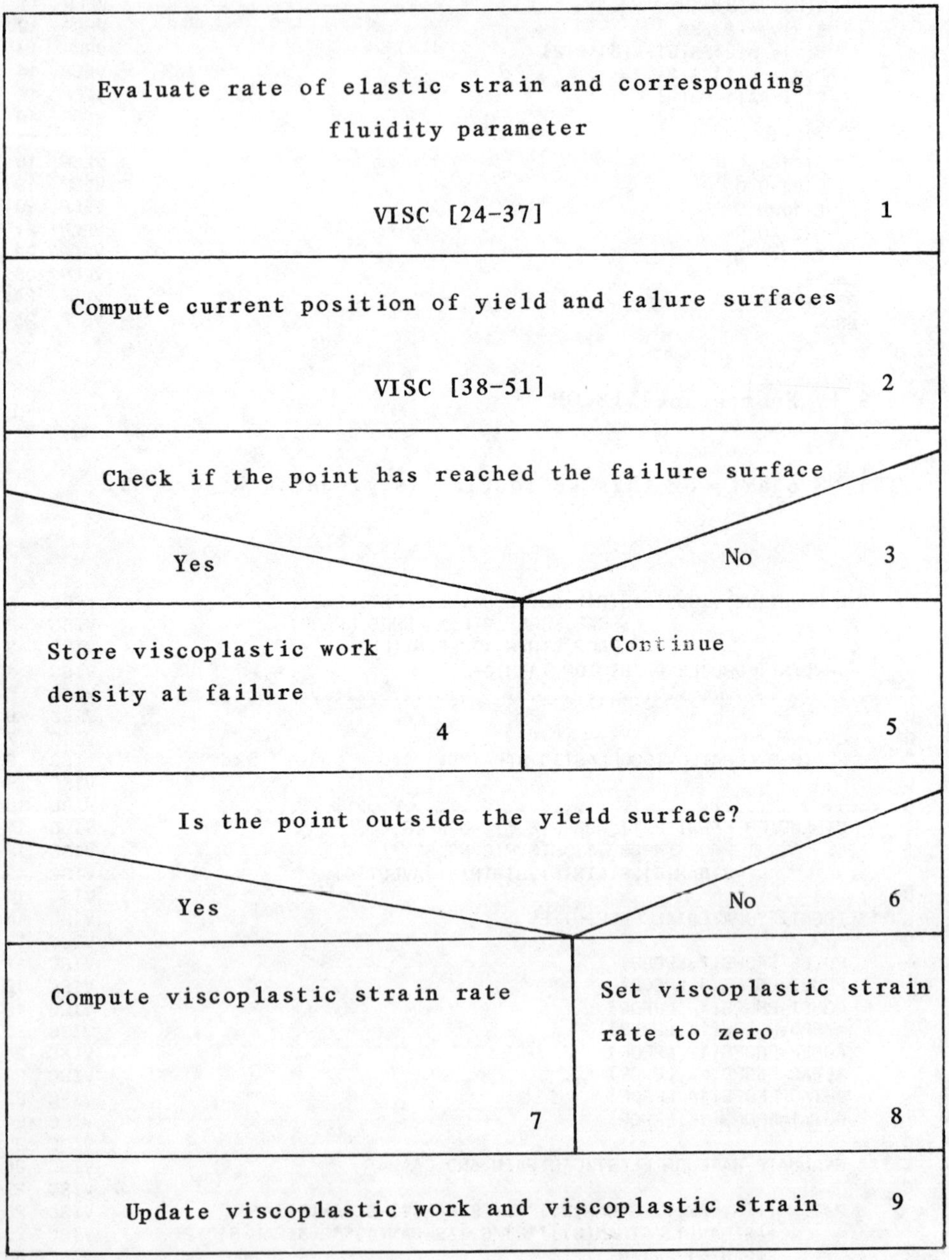

Figure 43. NS chart for the subroutine VISCOP

```
C
C *** FIND VALUE OF DISCONTINUITY AND FAILURE SURFACES
C
      TWORK=WORKP(1,KGAST)
      FWORK=WORKF(1,KGAST)
      CALL INVAR(NYIEL,STLIN,YIELD)
      PREYO=CONST*FCULT
      PREYS=PREYO
      EXPOC=-ALFAC*(TWORK-FWORK)
      IF(EXPOC.GT.0.) PRINT *,KGAST,EXPOC,TWORK,FWORK
      IF(EXPOC.LT.-100.) EXPOC=-100.
      IF(FWORK.NE.0.) PREYS=PREYO*EXP(EXPOC)
      IF(PREYS.LT.PREYO/10.) PREYS=PREYO/10.
      FAILV=BETA0*FCULT*(1.-BETA1*TWORK)
C
C *** CHECK IF THE POINT IS FAILING
C
      IF(FWORK.EQ.0.0.AND.YIELD.GT.FAILV) WORKF(2,KGAST)=TWORK
C
C *** CHECK IF THE POINT IS FLOWING
C
      IF(PREYS.GT.YIELD)  THEN
              DO 10 ISTRE=1,NSTRE
                STRIN(ISTRE)=0.
 10           CONTINUE
      ELSE
                KTOLE=1
              ESCUR=(YIELD-PREYS)/PREYO
              CMULT=FLUID*ESCUR
              CALL FLOWVP(AVECT,NYIEL,STLIN)
              DO 20 ISTRE=1,NSTRE
                STRIN(ISTRE)=CMULT*AVECT(ISTRE)
 20           CONTINUE
      ENDIF
C
C *** UPDATE VISCOPLASTIC WORK AND VP STRAINS
C
      DWORK=0.
      DO 30 ISTRE=1,NSTRE
        DWORK=DWORK+DTIME*STRIN(ISTRE)*STLIN(ISTRE)
        STRVP(2,ISTRE,KGAST)=STRVP(1,ISTRE,KGAST)+
     .                           DTIME*STRIN(ISTRE)
 30   CONTINUE
      IF(DWORK.LT.0.) PRINT *,KGAST,DWORK,TWORK,STRIN,STLIN
      WORKP(2,KGAST)=TWORK+DWORK
      RETURN
      END
```

6.9.18 Subroutine INVAR

```
      SUBROUTINE INVAR(NCRIT,STRGP,YIELD)
      IMPLICIT DOUBLE PRECISION (A-H,O-Z)
C . . . . . . . . . . . . . . . . . . . . . . . . . . . . . . .
C .                                                             .
C .   ROUTINE                                                   .
C .     CALCULATE STRESS RESULTANT                              .
C .     CONTRIBUTION TO YIELD FUNCTION                          .
C .                                                             .
C . . . . . . . . . . . . . . . . . . . . . . . . . . . . . . .
      DIMENSION STRGP(6)
C
C
C***  SELECT YIELD CRITERIA
C
      GO TO (1,3,3) NCRIT
```

```
C
C*** VON MISES
C
    1 BEETA=1.0
      ALPHA=0.0
      GO TO 4
C
C*** 3-D CONCRETE YIELD CRITERIA
C
    3 BEETA=1.355
      ALPHA=0.355
    4 GJNV2=BEETA*(STRGP(1)*STRGP(1)+STRGP(2)*STRGP(2)+
     .        STRGP(3)*STRGP(3)-STRGP(1)*STRGP(3)-STRGP(2)*STRGP(3)-
     .        STRGP(1)*STRGP(2)+3.0*(STRGP(6)*STRGP(6)+
     .        STRGP(4)*STRGP(4)+STRGP(5)*STRGP(5)))
      GINV1=ALPHA*(STRGP(1)+STRGP(2)+STRGP(3))*0.5
      GASH1=SQRT(GINV1*GINV1+GJNV2)
      YIELD=GINV1+GASH1
      RETURN
      END
```

6.9.19 Subroutine FLOWVP

```
      SUBROUTINE FLOWVP(AVECT,NCRIT,SG)
      IMPLICIT DOUBLE PRECISION (A-H,O-Z)
C . . . . . . . . . . . . . . . . . . . . . . . . . . . . . . . . . . . .
C .                                                                     .
C .      TO DETERMINE DERIVATIVE OF YIELD FUNCTION                      .
C .      1 VON MISES                                                    .
C .      3 3-D YIELD FUNCTION                                           .
C . . . . . . . . . . . . . . . . . . . . . . . . . . . . . . . . . . . .
      DIMENSION AVECT(6),SG(6)
C
C
C***  SELECT YIELD CRITERIA
C
      GO TO (1,3,3) NCRIT
C
C*** VON MISES
C
    1 BEETA=1.0
      ALPHA=0.0
      GO TO 4
C
C*** 3-D YIELD FUNCTION FOR CONCRETE
C
    3 BEETA=1.355
      ALPHA=0.355
C
    4 CONS1=ALPHA*0.5
      CONS2=CONS1*CONS1+BEETA
      CONS3=2.0*CONS1*CONS1-BEETA
      CONS4=BEETA*3.0
      AFUNC=(CONS2*(SG(1)*SG(1)+SG(2)*SG(2)+SG(3)*SG(3))+
     .        CONS3*(SG(1)*SG(2)+SG(1)*SG(3)+SG(2)*SG(3))+
     .        CONS4*(SG(6)*SG(6)+SG(4)*SG(4)+SG(5)*SG(5)))**0.5
      AFUNC=2.0*AFUNC
      AVECT(1)=CONS1+(2.0*CONS2*SG(1)+CONS3*(SG(2)+SG(3)))/AFUNC
      AVECT(2)=CONS1+(2.0*CONS2*SG(2)+CONS3*(SG(1)+SG(3)))/AFUNC
      AVECT(3)=CONS1+(2.0*CONS2*SG(3)+CONS3*(SG(1)+SG(2)))/AFUNC
      AVECT(4)=2.0*CONS4*SG(4)/AFUNC
      AVECT(5)=2.0*CONS4*SG(5)/AFUNC
      AVECT(6)=2.0*CONS4*SG(6)/AFUNC
   60 CONTINUE
      RETURN
      END
```

6.9.20 Subroutine FISUR2

The NS chart for this subroutine is given in Figure 44.

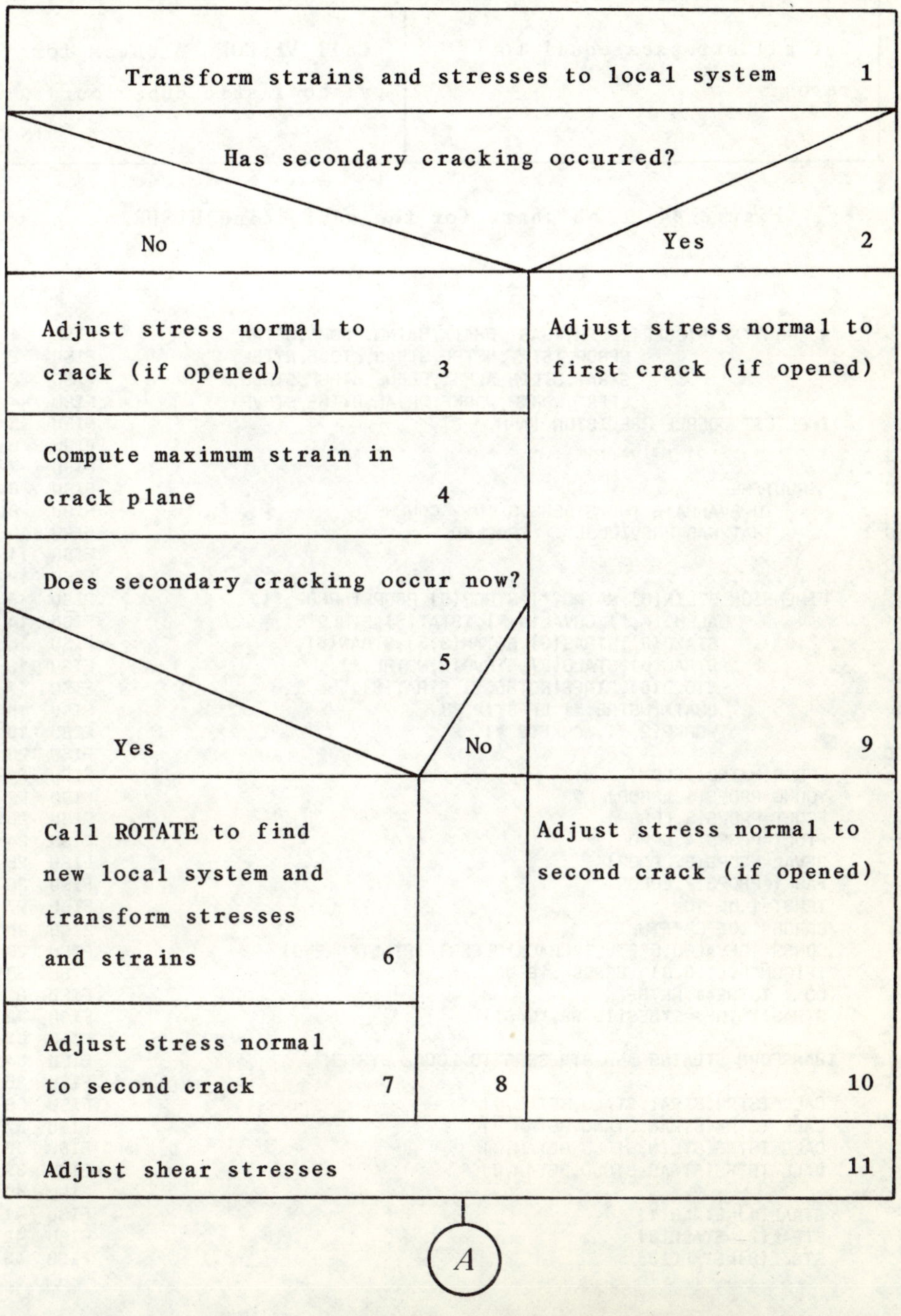

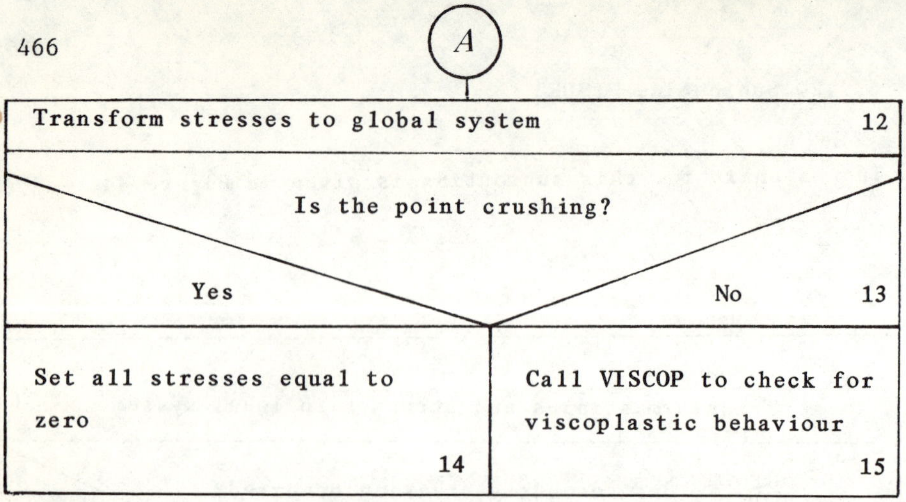

Figure 44. NS chart for the subroutine FISUR2

```
      SUBROUTINE FISUR2(IELEM,KGAST,DMATX,MATNO,PROPS,BETAM,
     .                  NPROP,ISTAT,NSTRE,STRAN,KTOLE,NYIEL,
     .                  STRAT,STLIN,ALPHI,DLENG,STRGP,STRES,
     .                  EFFST,WORKP,WORKF,CRVAL,DTIME,STRVP)
      IMPLICIT DOUBLE PRECISION (A-H,O-Z)
C . . . . . . . . . . . . . . . . . . . . . . . . . . . . .
C .                                                         .
C .    ROUTINE                                              .
C .       TO EVALUATE THE STRESSES IN   CONCRETE            .
C .       THAT WAS PREVIOUSLY   CRACKED                     .
C .                                                         .
C . . . . . . . . . . . . . . . . . . . . . . . . . . . . .
      DIMENSION STLIN(6),MATNO(*),STRGP(6),PROPS(NPROP,*),
     .          ALPHI(4,*),CRVAL(4,*),ISTAT(*),STRLO(6),
     .          STANO(6),STRAS(6),BETAM(3,3),STRAN(6),
     .          STRAL(6),STALO(6),STRVP(2,NSTRE,*),
     .          STOLD(6),STRES(NSTRE,*),STRAT(6),
     .          DMATX(NSTRE,*),EFFST(2,*),
     .          WORKP(2,*),WORKF(2,*)
C
      LPROP=MATNO(IELEM)
      YOUNG=PROPS(1,LPROP)
      FCULT=PROPS(3,LPROP)
      FTULT=PROPS(4,LPROP)
      GFVAL=PROPS(6,LPROP)
      FACK1=PROPS(7,LPROP)
      TENST=1.0E-10
      ERROR=1.0E-04*FTULT
      CONSS=(GFVAL-0.5*FTULT*CRACK*DLENG)/(FTULT*DLENG)
      IF(CONSS.LT.0.0)  CONSS=.1E-06
      DO 1 ISTRE=1,NSTRE
    1 STRAS(ISTRE)=STRES(ISTRE,KGAST)
C
C*** TRANSFORM STRAINS AND STRESSES TO LOCAL SYSTEM
C
      CALL TSTRN(STRAT,STALO,BETAM,0)
      CALL TSTRN(STRAN,STANO,BETAM,0)
      CALL TSTRS(STLIN,STRLO,BETAM,0)
      CALL TSTRS(STRAS,STOLD,BETAM,0)
C
      STRAL(1)=STALO(1)
      STRAL(2)=STALO(2)
      STRAL(3)=STALO(3)
```

```
      STRAL(4)=0.0
      STRAL(5)=STALO(5)
      STRAL(6)=0.0
C
C*** IS THE LAYER DOUBLY-CRACKED? (YES GO TO 100)
C
      IT=ISTAT(KGAST)
      IF(IT.EQ.12.OR.IT.EQ.13) GO TO 100
C
C*** SINGLY-CRACKED CONCRETE LAYER
C
      ISTAT(KGAST)=10
      IF(STALO(1)) 15,15,11
C
C-----------------------------------------------------CRACK IS OPEN
C
   11 STRAL(1)=0.0
      IF(STANO(1)) 12,12,19
   12 STRLO(1)=CRVAL(2,KGAST)*STALO(1)/CRVAL(1,KGAST)
      GO TO 15
   19 CONTINUE
      STRAV=STALO(1)
      STREV=CRVAL(2,KGAST)
      STRIV=CRVAL(1,KGAST)
      CALL        TSEFF(FTULT,CRACK,CONSS,STRIV,STRAV,STREV)
      STRLO(1)=STREV
C
   15 CONTINUE
          IF(STALO(1).GT.CRVAL(1,KGAST)) THEN
             CRVAL(1,KGAST)=STALO(1)
             CRVAL(2,KGAST)=STRLO(1)
          ENDIF
C
C*** CHECK IF A SECOND CRACK IS FORMED
C
C **** FIRST COMPUTE MAXIMUM STRAIN PARALLEL TO CRACK
C
      S11=STALO(2)
      S22=STALO(3)
      S12=STALO(5)/2.
      P1=(S11+S22)/2.+SQRT(0.25*(S11-S22)**2+S12**2)
C
      CRACK=FTULT/YOUNG
C
      IF(P1-CRACK) 150,150,20
C
C-----------------------------------THE SECOND CRACK SET DOES FORM
C
   20 ISTAT(KGAST)=12
      WRITE(6,900) KGAST,STALO(2)
  900 FORMAT(5X,'KGAST=',I5,'  ***  D2=',E20.3)
C
C     TRANSFORM TO NEW SYSTEM
C
      CALL        ROTATE(STRLO,BETAM,ALPHI,KGAST,STRAT,
     .                   STALO,STRAN,STANO,STLIN,STRAS,STOLD,
     .                   STRAL)
      STRAV=STALO(2)
      STRIV=STRAV
      STREV=FTULT
      CALL        TSEFF(FTULT,CRACK,CONSS,STRIV,STRAV,STREV)
      IF(STREV.GT.FTULT) STREV=FTULT
      STRLO(2)=STREV
              CRVAL(3,KGAST)=STALO(2)
              CRVAL(4,KGAST)=STRLO(2)
      STRAL(2)=0.0
      STRAL(5)=0.0
      GO TO 150
```

```
C
C*** DOUBLY-CRACKED CONCRETE LAYER
C
  100 IT=ISTAT(KGAST)
C--------------------IF THE LAYER IS COMPLETELY DEGRADATED,DO NOTHING
      STRAL(5)=0.0
C
      IF(STALO(1).LT.0.0.AND.STALO(2).LT.0.0) GO TO 150
      IF(STALO(1).LT.0.0.AND.STALO(2).GE.0.0) GO TO 105
C
C------------------------------------------- FIRST CRACK IS OPENED
C
      STRAL(1)=0.0
      IF(STANO(1)) 62,62,69
 62   DESIG=CRVAL(2,KGAST)*STALO(1)/CRVAL(1,KGAST)
      GO TO 65
 69   STRAV=STALO(1)
      STREV=CRVAL(2,KGAST)
      STRIV=CRVAL(1,KGAST)
      CALL      TSEFF(FTULT,CRACK,CONSS,STRIV,STRAV,STREV)
      DESIG=STREV
C
  65  STRLO(1)=DESIG
           IF(STALO(1).GT.CRVAL(1,KGAST)) THEN
              CRVAL(1,KGAST)=STALO(1)
              CRVAL(2,KGAST)=STRLO(1)
           ENDIF
      IF(STALO(2).LT.0.0) GO TO 150
C
C-----------------------------------------------SECOND CRACK IS OPENED
105   STRAL(2)=0.0
      IF(STANO(2)) 63,63,68
 63   DESIG=CRVAL(4,KGAST)*STALO(2)/CRVAL(3,KGAST)
      GO TO 66
 68   STRAV=STALO(2)
      STREV=CRVAL(4,KGAST)
      STRIV=CRVAL(3,KGAST)
      CALL      TSEFF(FTULT,CRACK,CONSS,STRIV,STRAV,STREV)
      DESIG=STREV
 66   STRLO(2)=DESIG
          IF(STALO(2).GT.CRVAL(3,KGAST)) THEN
              CRVAL(3,KGAST)=STALO(2)
              CRVAL(4,KGAST)=STRLO(2)
          ENDIF
 150  CONTINUE
C
C*** ADJUST SHEAR STRESSES
C
        TENST=MAX(CRVAL(1,KGAST),CRVAL(3,KGAST))
         COECQ=(1.-(TENST/0.005)**FACK1)
         IF(COECQ.LT.0.1) COECQ=0.1
         STRLO(4)=COECQ*STALO(4)*YOUNG*0.5
         STRLO(6)=COECQ*STALO(6)*YOUNG*0.5
         IF(ISTAT(KGAST).EQ.12) STRLO(5)=COECQ*STALO(5)*YOUNG*0.5
C
C***TRANSFORM STRESSES TO GLOBAL COORDINATE SYSTEM
C
      CALL TSTRS(STRLO,STRGP,BETAM,1)
C
C***  CHECK AGAINST CRUSHING
C
      CALL INVA2(STRAL,CRUSH)
      IF(CRUSH.GT.PROPS(5,LPROP)) GO TO 203
C
C---------------------------------------------------NON CRUSHED CONCRETE
C
      DO 202 ISTRE=1,NSTRE
```

```
  202 STRES(ISTRE,KGAST)=STRGP(ISTRE)
      CALL       VISCOP (STRAN,NSTRE,DTIME,EFFST,KGAST,WORKP,
     .                   WORKF,STRGP,PROPS,NPROP,LPROP,STRVP,
     .                   KTOLE,NYIEL)
  210 CONTINUE
      RETURN
C
C-----------------------------------------CRUSHED OR TOO CRACKED CONCRETE
C
  203 ISTAT(KGAST)=13
  200 EFFST(2,KGAST)=0.0
      DO 251 ISTRE=1,NSTRE
  251 STRES(ISTRE,KGAST)=0.0
      RETURN
      END
```

6.9.21 Subroutine ROTATE

```
      SUBROUTINE ROTATE(STRLO,BETAM,ALPHI,KGAST,STRAT,
     .                  STALO,STRAN,STANO,STLIN,STRAS,STOLD,
     .                  STRAL)
      IMPLICIT DOUBLE PRECISION (A-H,O-Z)
      DIMENSION STRLO(6),BETAM(3,3),BETA2(3,3),BETAO(3,3),
     .          STANO(6),STOLD(6),STALO(6),STRAT(6),
     .          STRAN(6),STLIN(6),STRAS(6),STRAL(6),
     .          ALPHI(4,*)
C
      PI=4.0*ATAN(1.0)
      ERROR=1.E-10
C
C   FIND DIRECTION OF MAXIMUM STRAIN
C
      STR11=STALO(2)
      STR22=STALO(3)
      STR12=STALO(5)*0.5
      DENTA=STR11-STR22
      IF(ABS(STR12).GT.ERROR) GO TO 90
      ANGLE=0.0
      IF(DENTA.LT.0.0) ANGLE=PI/2.
      GO TO 80
   90 IF(ABS(DENTA).GT.ERROR) GO TO 70
      ANGLE=PI/4.
      IF(STR12.LT.0.0) ANGLE=-PI/4.
      GO TO 80
   70 ANGLE=0.5*ATAN(2.*STR12/DENTA)
      CA=COS(ANGLE)
      SA=SIN(ANGLE)
      PSTR1=CA*CA*STR11+SA*SA*STR22+2.*SA*CA*STR12
      PSTR2=SA*SA*STR11+CA*CA*STR22-2.*SA*CA*STR12
      IF(PSTR1.GE.PSTR2)  GO TO 80
      ANGLE=ANGLE+PI/2.
   80 CONTINUE
C
C   FIND NEW TRANSFORMATION MATRIX
C
      DO 1 I=1,3
      DO 1 J=1,3
      BETA2(I,J)=0.0
      BETAO(I,J)=BETAM(I,J)
    1 BETAM(I,J)=0.0
C
```

```
      BETA2(1,1)= 1.
      BETA2(2,2)= COS(ANGLE)
      BETA2(3,3)= COS(ANGLE)
      BETA2(2,3)=-SIN(ANGLE)
      BETA2(3,2)= SIN(ANGLE)
C
      DO 2 I=1,3
      DO 2 J=1,3
      DO 2 K=1,3
    2 BETAM(I,J)=BETAM(I,J)+BETA0(I,K)*BETA2(K,J)
C
      ALPHI(4,KGAST)=ASIN(BETAM(3,2))
      IF(ABS(BETAM(2,2))+ABS(BETAM(1,2)).EQ.0.0)
     .ALPHI(3,KGAST)=PI/2.
      IF(ABS(BETAM(2,2))+ABS(BETAM(1,2)).NE.0.0)
     .ALPHI(3,KGAST)=ATAN2(BETAM(2,2),BETAM(1,2))
C
      CALL ODIREC(ALPHI,BETAM,KGAST,    0)
C
C   TRANSFORM STRESS AND STRAIN TO NEW SYSTEM
C
      STREV=STRLO(1)
      CALL TSTRN(STRAT,STALO,BETAM,0)
      CALL TSTRN(STRAN,STANO,BETAM,0)
      CALL TSTRS(STLIN,STRLO,BETAM,0)
      CALL TSTRS(STRAS,STOLD,BETAM,0)
C
      STRLO(1)=STREV
C
      STRAL(1)=0.0
      STRAL(2)=STALO(2)
      STRAL(3)=STALO(3)
      STRAL(4)=0.0
      STRAL(5)=STALO(5)
      STRAL(6)=0.0
C
      RETURN
      END
```

6.9.22 Subroutine ODIREC

```
      SUBROUTINE ODIREC(ALPHI,BETAM,KGAST,INDEX)
      IMPLICIT DOUBLE PRECISION (A-H,O-Z)
C
      DIMENSION ALPHI(4,*),BETAM(3,3),A(3,3)
C
      SA1=SIN(ALPHI(1,KGAST))
      CA1=COS(ALPHI(1,KGAST))
      SB1=SIN(ALPHI(2,KGAST))
      CB1=COS(ALPHI(2,KGAST))
      SA2=SIN(ALPHI(3,KGAST))
      CA2=COS(ALPHI(3,KGAST))
      SB2=SIN(ALPHI(4,KGAST))
      CB2=COS(ALPHI(4,KGAST))
C
      BETAM(1,1)=CB1*CA1
      BETAM(2,1)=CB1*SA1
      BETAM(3,1)=SB1
      BETAM(1,2)=CB2*CA2
      BETAM(2,2)=CB2*SA2
      BETAM(3,2)=SB2
      BETAM(1,3)=BETAM(2,1)*BETAM(3,2)-BETAM(3,1)*BETAM(2,2)
      BETAM(2,3)=BETAM(1,2)*BETAM(3,1)-BETAM(1,1)*BETAM(3,2)
      BETAM(3,3)=BETAM(1,1)*BETAM(2,2)-BETAM(2,1)*BETAM(1,2)
C
```

```
      IF(INDEX.EQ.0) RETURN
      DO 1 I=1,3
      DO 1 J=1,3
    1 A(J,I)=BETAM(I,J)
      DO 2 I=1,3
      DO 2 J=1,3
    2 BETAM(I,J)=A(I,J)
      RETURN
      END
```

6.10 Corrector values and convergence check

This section list the routines needed to evaluate corrected values for displacements, velocities and accelerations and to check convergence.

6.10.1 Subroutine ITRATE

The NS chart for this subroutine is given in Figure 45.

Computes inertial forces	1
Computes total effective load vector	2
Call REDBAK to find corrector displacements	3
Update displacements, velocities and accelerations	4
Check convergence	5

Figure 45. NS chart for the subroutine ITRATE

```
      SUBROUTINE ITRATE(ACCEI,ACCEL,YMASS,DISPI,DISPL,DISPT,MAXAI,
     .                  NCHEK,RESID,STIFS,VELOI,VELOL,VELOT,SUMP1,
     .                  RATIO)
C***********************************************************************
C
C***  CALCULATES CORRECTOR VALUES AND CHECKS CONVERGENCE
C
C***********************************************************************
      IMPLICIT DOUBLE PRECISION (A-H,O-Z)
      COMMON/CTRL/ NDIME,NDOFN,NECHO,NELEM,NEVAB,NGASN,NGAUS,NMATS,
     &             NNODE,NPOIN,NPROP,NREIN,NSIZE,NSTRE,NTOTG,NTOTV,
     &             NVFIX,NWKTL,NYIEL
      COMMON/RUN/  IFUNC,IPRED,KSTEP,MITER,NACCE,NOUTD,NOUTP,NREQD,
     &             NREQS,NSTEP
      COMMON/CONST/AALFA,BEETA,GAAMA,DELTA,AZERO,BZERO,OMEGA,TMAXR,
     &             DTEND,DTIME,AFACT,TOLER,ADISP,AVELO,CONSD,CONSF
      COMMON/STAT/ IITER,ISTEP,KTOLE
C
      DIMENSION DISPI(*),VELOI(*),ACCEI(*),RESID(*),MAXAI(*),
     .          DISPL(*),VELOL(*),ACCEL(*),STIFS(*),DISPT(*),
     .          YMASS(*),VELOT(*)
C
      NCHEK=0
C
C *** COMPUTE INERTIAL FORCES
C
      DO 10 ISIZE=1,NSIZE
        ACCEL(ISIZE)=YMASS(ISIZE)*ACCEI(ISIZE)
   10 CONTINUE
C
C *** CALCULATES TOTAL EFFECTIVE LOAD VECTOR
C
      SUMRS=0.0
      DO 660 ISIZE=1,NSIZE
      ACCEL(ISIZE)=DISPL(ISIZE)-ACCEL(ISIZE)-RESID(ISIZE)
        SUMRS=SUMRS+ACCEL(ISIZE)*ACCEL(ISIZE)
  660 CONTINUE
       SUMRS=SQRT(SUMRS)
       IF(IITER.EQ.1)  SUMP1=SUMRS
       RATI1=RATIO
       RATIO=0.0
       IF(SUMP1.NE.0.0)  RATIO=SUMRS/SUMP1
       ALPHA=1.
C
C *** CALCULATES DELTA DISPLACEMENT
C
  210 CALL REDBAK (STIFS,ACCEL,MAXAI,NSIZE)
C
C *** CORRECT DISPLACEMENTS, ACCELERATION AND VELOCITIES
C
      DO 670 ISIZE=1,NSIZE
      DISPT(ISIZE)=DISPT(ISIZE)+ACCEL(ISIZE)*ALPHA
      ACCEI(ISIZE)=CONSF*(DISPT(ISIZE)-DISPI(ISIZE))
  670 VELOT(ISIZE)=VELOI(ISIZE)+CONSD*ACCEI(ISIZE)
C
C *** CHECK CONVERGENCE
C
      TOLE1=2.
      IF(KTOLE.EQ.1) TOLE1=TOLER
      IF(RATIO.GT.TOLE1) GO TO 550
      NCHEK=1
      GO TO 240
  550 IF(IITER.LT.MITER) GO TO 230
  240 DO 540 ISIZE=1,NSIZE
      VELOI(ISIZE)=VELOT(ISIZE)
  540 DISPI(ISIZE)=DISPT(ISIZE)
  230 CONTINUE
      RETURN
      END
```

6.10.2 Subroutine REDBAK

```
      SUBROUTINE REDBAK (STIFF ,FORCE ,MAXAI ,NEQNS )
      IMPLICIT DOUBLE PRECISION (A-H,O-Z)
      DIMENSION FORCE(*),STIFF(*),MAXAI(*)
C
      DO 400 IEQNS=1,NEQNS
      LOWER =MAXAI(IEQNS)+1
      KUPER=MAXAI(IEQNS+1)-1
      IF(KUPER-LOWER) 400,410,410
  410 JEQNS=IEQNS
      SUMCC=0.0
      DO 420 ICOLM=LOWER,KUPER
      JEQNS=JEQNS-1
  420 SUMCC=SUMCC+STIFF(ICOLM)*FORCE(JEQNS)
      FORCE(IEQNS)=FORCE(IEQNS)-SUMCC
  400 CONTINUE
C
      DO 480 IEQNS=1,NEQNS
      KMAXA=MAXAI(IEQNS)
  480 FORCE(IEQNS)=FORCE(IEQNS)/STIFF(KMAXA)
      IF(NEQNS.EQ.1) RETURN
      JEQNS=NEQNS
      DO 500 IEQNS=2,NEQNS
      LOWER=MAXAI(JEQNS)+1
      KUPER=MAXAI(JEQNS+1)-1
      IF(KUPER-LOWER) 500,510,510
  510 KEQNS=JEQNS
      DO 520 ICOLM=LOWER,KUPER
      KEQNS=KEQNS-1
  520 FORCE(KEQNS)=FORCE(KEQNS)-STIFF(ICOLM)*FORCE(JEQNS)
  500 JEQNS=JEQNS-1
      RETURN
      END
```

6.11 Output routines

6.11.1 Subroutine OUTDYN

This routine records the converged values of the viscoplastic state variables and outputs displacements, stresses and material state variables if required.

```
      SUBROUTINE OUTDYN(DISPT,NGRQS,NPRQD,MGPCO,TDISP,ISTAT,IFPRE,
     .                  STRES,EFFST,WORKP,WORKF,GPCOD,STRVP,STRAF,
     .                  ALPHI,EFFSS)
C***********************************************************************
C
C *** OUTPUT ROUTINE
C
C***********************************************************************
      IMPLICIT DOUBLE PRECISION (A-H,O-Z)
      COMMON/CTRL/ NDIME,NDOFN,NECHO,NELEM,NEVAB,NGASN,NGAUS,NMATS,
     &             NNODE,NPOIN,NPROP,NREIN,NSIZE,NSTRE,NTOTG,NTOTV,
     &             NVFIX,NWKTL,NYIEL
```

```
      COMMON/RUN/  IFUNC,IPRED,KSTEP,MITER,NACCE,NOUTD,NOUTP,NREQD,
     &             NREQS,NSTEP
      COMMON/FILE/ NDATA,NRESU
      COMMON/STAT/ IITER,ISTEP,KTOLE
      COMMON/CONST/AALFA,BEETA,GAAMA,DELTA,AZERO,BZERO,OMEGA,TMAXR,
     &             DTEND,DTIME,AFACT,TOLER,ADISP,AVELO,CONSD,CONSF
C
      DIMENSION DISPT(*),NPRQD(*),TDISP(*),
     .          IFPRE(NDOFN,*),EFFST(2,*),NGRQS(*),
     .          EFFSS(2,*),WORKP(2,*),ISTAT(*),
     .          STRES(NSTRE,*),STRVP(2,NSTRE,*),
     .          STRAF(2,NSTRE,*),WORKF(2,*),
     .          ALPHI(4,*),GPCOD(NDIME,*)
C
      DO 5 ITOTG=1,NTOTG
        EFFST(1,ITOTG)=EFFST(2,ITOTG)
    5 CONTINUE
      IF(KTOLE.NE.0) THEN
        DO 10 ITOTG=1,NTOTG
          WORKP(1,ITOTG)=WORKP(2,ITOTG)
          WORKF(1,ITOTG)=WORKF(2,ITOTG)
            DO 20 ISTRE=1,NSTRE
              STRVP(1,ISTRE,ITOTG)=STRVP(2,ISTRE,ITOTG)
   20       CONTINUE
   10   CONTINUE
        NTOTS=NELEM*MGPCO
          DO 30 ITOTG=1,NTOTS
           EFFSS(1,ITOTG)=EFFSS(2,ITOTG)
            DO 40 ISTRE=1,NSTRE
              STRAF(1,ISTRE,ITOTG)=STRAF(2,ISTRE,ITOTG)
   40       CONTINUE
   30   CONTINUE
      END IF
C
C *** REARRANGE DISPLACEMENT VECTOR
C
        DO 50 ITOTV=1,NTOTV
          TDISP(ITOTV)=0.0
   50   CONTINUE
C
        KOUNT=0
        DO 60 IPOIN=1,NPOIN
          DO 70 IDOFN=1,NDOFN
            IEQNS=IFPRE(IDOFN,IPOIN)
            KOUNT=KOUNT+1
            IF(IEQNS.NE.0) TDISP(KOUNT)=DISPT(IEQNS)
   70     CONTINUE
   60   CONTINUE
C
      TTIME=DTIME*FLOAT(ISTEP)
      KOUND=(ISTEP/NOUTP)*NOUTP
      IF(KOUND.EQ.ISTEP) THEN
C
C *** OUTPUT DISPLACEMENTS
C
        WRITE(NRESU,900)  TTIME,ISTEP
        IF(NREQD.NE.0) THEN
          WRITE(NRESU,910)
          DO 80 IPOIN=1,NPOIN
            DO 90 IREQD=1,NREQD
              IF(IPOIN.EQ.NPRQD(IREQD)) THEN
              NPOSN=(IPOIN-1)*NDOFN+1
              NPOSM=IPOIN*NDOFN
              WRITE(NRESU,920) IPOIN,(TDISP(IPOSN),IPOSN=NPOSN,NPOSM)
              END IF
   90       CONTINUE
   80     CONTINUE
        END IF
      END IF
```

```
C
C *** OUTPUT STRESSES
C
      IF(NREQS.NE.0) THEN
          WRITE(NRESU,930)
          DO 100 ITOTG=1,NTOTG
              DO 110 IREQS=1,NREQS
                IF(ITOTG.EQ.NGRQS(IREQS))
     &          WRITE(NRESU,940) ITOTG,(STRES(ISTRE,ITOTG),ISTRE=1,NSTRE)
  110         CONTINUE
  100     CONTINUE
      END IF
C
C*** OUTPUT TO TAPE FOR PLOTTING
C
      IF(NOUTD.EQ.0) RETURN
      KOUND=IABS((ISTEP/NOUTD)*NOUTD)
      IF(KOUND.NE.ISTEP) RETURN
      IF(KTOLE.EQ.0.AND.NOUTD.GT.0) RETURN
C
      IINCS=IINCS+1
      WRITE(10,950) IINCS,TTIME
C
C *** OUTPUT DISPLACEMENTS
C
      IF(NOUTD.LT.0) THEN
          WRITE(10,955)
          DO 115 IPOIN=1,NPOIN
              NPOSN=(IPOIN-1)*NDOFN+1
              NPOSM=NPOSN+NDOFN-1
              WRITE(10,956) IPOIN,(TDISP(IPOSN),IPOSN=NPOSN,NPOSM)
  115     CONTINUE
      END IF
C
C ***  WRITE OUT MATERIAL STATE
C
     DO 120 IELEM=1,NELEM
       WRITE(10,960) IELEM
       PI=4.0*ATAN(1.0)
       DO 130 IGAUS = 1, NGASN
         IGAUG=(IELEM-1)*NGASN+IGAUS
         ALPH1=ALPHI(1,IGAUG)*180./PI
         ALPH2=ALPHI(2,IGAUG)*180./PI
         ALPH3=ALPHI(3,IGAUG)*180./PI
         ALPH4=ALPHI(4,IGAUG)*180./PI
         WRITE(10,970) IGAUS,ISTAT(IGAUG),ALPH1,ALPH2,ALPH3,ALPH4,
    &      (GPCOD(IDIME,IGAUG),IDIME=1,NDIME)
  130  CONTINUE
  120 CONTINUE
C
C     FORMATS
C
  900 FORMAT(5X, 'RESULTS AT TIME ',F10.5,5X,'ISTEP =',I5)
  910 FORMAT(5X, 'DISPLACEMENTS',/1X,'NNODE',3X,
     .          'X-DISP',6X,'Y-DISP',6X,'Z-DISP',/)
  920 FORMAT(2(1X,I5,3E12.5))
  930 FORMAT(5X,'STRESSES',/,1X,' G.P.',3X,'X-STRE',6X,'Y-STRES',
     .       6X,'Z-STRES',6X,'XZ-STR',6X,'YZ-STR',6X,'XY-STR',/)
  940 FORMAT(1X,I5,6E12.5)
  950 FORMAT(//5X,'INCREMENT NUMBER ',I5,5X,'AT TIME',F10.5)
  955 FORMAT(//10X,'DISPLACEMENTS')
  956 FORMAT(1H0,5X,I5,10X,3F12.5)
  960 FORMAT(1H0,10X,'ELEMENT NUMBER',I5/9X,19('*')/' G.P.',
     . '         ISTAT        ALPHI1         ALPHI2          ALPHI3 ',
     . '        ALPHI4',4X,'G.P. X   G.P. Y   ',
     . 'G.P. Z   ')
  970 FORMAT(1H ,I3,1X,I12,4(1X,F12.5),1X,3F9.3)
      RETURN
      END
```

7. USE OF PROGRAM DARC3

7.1 Input instructions for DARC3

There now follows a set of user instructions for program DARC3.

Data set 1 - problem title

format (40A2) - one record

cols. 01-80	TITLE	title of problem

Data set 2 - control data

format (8I5) - one record

cols. 01-05	NPOIN	number of nodal points
06-10	NELEM	number of elements
11-15	NVFIX	number of constrained nodes with one or more degree of freedom constrained to zero
16-20	NNODE	number of nodes per element
21-25	NMATS	number of different materials
26-30	NECHO	parameter to control printing = 0, then print all data = 1, then don't print load data = 2, then don't print any data
31-35	NREIN	number of reinforcement patterns

Data set 2 - element data

format (13I5/15X,10I5) - two records per element

first record

cols. 01-05	NUMEL	element number
06-10	MATNO(NUMEL)	material set number

11-15	MPATT(NUMEL)	reinforcement pattern number
16-20	LNODS(NUMEL,1)	1st. nodal connection number
.		
.		
66-70	LNODS(NUMEL,10)	10th. nodal connection number

<u>second record</u>

cols. 01-15	blank	
16-20	LNODS(NUMEL,11)	11th. nodal connection number
.		
.		
66-70	LNODS(NUMEL,20)	20th. nodal connection number

<u>Data set 4 - nodal coordinates</u>

format(I5,3F10.5) - one record per node

cols. 01-05	IPOIN	nodal point number
06-15	COORD(IPOIN,1)	x-coordinate
16-25	COORD(IPOIN,2)	y-coordinate
26-35	COORD(IPOIN,3)	z-coordinate

<u>Data set 5 - restrained nodes</u>

format(1X,I4,7X,3I1) - one record per restrained node

cols. 02-05	IPOIN	nodal point number
13	IFPRE(1)	constraint on u displacement = 0 for free variable = 1 for restrained variable
14	IFPRE(2)	constraint on v displacement = 0 for free variable = 1 for restrained variable
15	IFPRE(3)	constraint on w displacement = 0 for free variable = 1 for restrained variable

Data set 6 - material properties

format(I5/5E10.4/5E10.4/5E10.4) - four records per material

first record

cols.	01-05	NUMAT	material set number

second record

cols.	01-10	PROPS(1,NUMAT)	elastic modulus, E
	11-20	PROPS(2,NUMAT)	poisson's ratio, (*)
	21-30	PROPS(3,NUMAT)	compressive strength,
	31-40	PROPS(4,NUMAT)	tensile strength, (*)
	41-50	PROPS(5,NUMAT)	crushing strain in concrete, (*)

third record

cols.	01-10	PROPS(6,NUMAT)	fracture energy, (*)
	11-20	PROPS(7,NUMAT)	shear retention factor, (*)
	21-30	PROPS(8,NUMAT)	not used
	31-40	PROPS(9,NUMAT)	material density, (*)
	41-50	PROPS(10,NUMAT)	elasticity limit indicator, (*)

fourth record

cols.	01-15	PROPS(11,NUMAT)	fluidity parameter,
	16-30	PROPS(12,NUMAT)	fluidity parameter, (*)
	31-45	PROPS(13,NUMAT)	post-failure-softening parameter. (*)
	46-60	PROPS(14,NUMAT)	failure surface parameter, (*)
	61-75	PROPS(15,NUMAT)	failure surface parameter, (*)

(*) implies that the property is not used for reinforcement materials

Data set 7

format(2I5/2I5,3F10.5) - NREIN*NLAYR(IREIN) records

first record (control data)

cols.	01-05	KREIN	pattern identification number
	06-10	NLAYR	number of layers in the pattern

second record set (layer definition data)

cols.	01-05	INMAT	material number
	06-10	ICOOR	number of local coordinate to which reinforcement layer is perpendicular i.e. 1,2 or 3
	11-20	COORD	value of local coordinate at which layer is located, note that -1<COORD<+1
	21-30	THICK	thickness of the layer
	31-40	ANGLE	angle between bars and local x-axis

Note that there are (1 + number of layers in pattern) records are repeated for each pattern.

Data set 8 - time integration control data

format(11I5) - one record

cols.	01-05	NSTEP	total number of time steps
	06-10	NOUTD	displacement and stress history at required points written to file every NOUTD steps
	11-15	NOUTS	displacements and stresses written at required points every NOUTP steps
	16-20	NREQD	number of nodes for selective output of displacement every NOUTD steps

21-25	NREQS	number of sampling points for selective output of stresses every NOUTS steps
26-30	NACCE	number of acceleration or load history ordinates (note that if IFUNC.NE.0 and and IFUNC.NE.4, then NACCE is not used and this record may left equal to zero)
31-35	IFUNC	time function code = 0, acceleration time history = 1, Heaviside function, f(t) = 1.0 = 2, harmonic excitation, f(t)=a0 + b0 sinω t = 3, linear-constant function = 4, arbitrary load history = 5, linear-harmonic function
36-40	IFIXD	not used
41-45	MITER	maximum number of iterations allowed per time step
46-50	KSTEP	number of steps after which the stiffness matrix is reformed
51-55	IPRED	= 1, standard predictor values = 2, modified predictor values

<u>Data set 9 - time integration parameters</u>

format(7F10.3/4F10.3)

<u>first record</u>

cols. 01-10	DTIME	time step length
11-20	DTEND	time at which the excitation force is removed
21-30	DTREC	time step of acceleration records
31-40	AALFA	= damping paramter
41-50	BEETA	= damping parameter

51-60	DELTA	Newmark's integration parameter
61-70	GAAMA	Newmark's integration parameter
71-80	AZERO	constant for harmonic excitation a0

<u>second record</u>

cols. 01-10	BZERO	constant for harmonic excitation b0
11-20	OMEGA	constant for harmonic excitation ω
21-30	TOLER	specified tolerance
31-40	TMAXR	time for end of linear raise used when IFUNC = 3 or 5

<u>Data set 10 - nodal displacement history output data</u>

format(16I5/16I5/....) - NREQD/16 records

<u>first record</u>

cols. 01-05	NPRQD(1)	1st. node at which displacement history is required
06-10	NPRQD(2)	2nd. node at which displacement history is required
	.	
	.	
76-80	NPRQD(16)	16th. node at which displacement history is required

Note that further records are included as required

Data set 11 - sampling point stress history output data

format(16I5/16I5/.....) - NREQS/16 records

first record

cols. 01-05	NGRQS(1)	1st. integrating point at which stresses are required
06-10	NGRQS(2)	2nd. integrating point at which stresses are required
.		
.		
76-80	NGRQS(16)	16th. integrating point at which stresses are required

Data set 12 - initial displacement data

format(I5,3F10.5) - one record for each node, if all displacements are zero then read last node

cols. 01-05	NGASH	nodal point
06-15	XGASH	initial x-displacement
16-25	YGASH	initial y-displacement
26-35	ZGASH	initial z-displacement

Data set 13 - initial velocity data

format(I5,3F10.5) - one record for each node, if all velocities are zero then read last one

cols. 01-05	NGASH	nodal point
06-15	XGASH	initial x-displacement
16-25	YGASH	initial y-displacement
26-35	ZGASH	initial z-displacement

Data set 14 - load title

format(40A2) - one record

cols. 01-80	TITLE	title of applied load

Data set 15 - load indicator data

format(3I5) - one card

cols. 01-05	IPLOD	point load indicator
06-10	IGRAV	gravity load indicator
11-15	IFACE	face load indicator

Data set 16 - point load data

format(I5,3F10.5) - one record for loaded node note that this data must be terminated by a record for the highest node whether it is loaded or not

cols. 01-05	LODPT	node number
06-15	PVECT(1)	load in x-direction
16-25	PVECT(2)	load in y-direction
26-35	PVECT(3)	load in z-direction

Data set 17 - gravity load data

format(4F10.5) - one record

cols. 01-10	GVECT(1)	x-component of gravity direction vector
11-20	GVECT(2)	y-component of gravity direction vector
21-30	GVECT(3)	z-component of gravity direction vector
31-40	GCONS	gravity constant

Data set 18 - pressure load control data

format(I5) - one record (note if NFECS = 0 then omit record)

cols.	01-05	NFECS	number of loaded faces

Data set 19 - face identification record

format(9I5) - one record for each face total of NFECS records

cols.	01-05	NEASS	number of the element with loaded face
	06-10	NOPRS(1)	1st. edge node
	11-15	NOPRS(2)	2nd. edge node
		.	
		.	
	41-45	NOPRS(8)	8th. edge node

Data set 20 - face pressure data

format NFECS*(4(6F10.3/)) - four records for each face IFECS

first record

cols.	01-10	PRESS(IFECS,1)	local x-component of applied pressure for node ifecs
	11-20	PRESS(IFECS,2)	local y-component of applied pressure for node ifecs
	21-30	PRESS(IFECS,3)	local z-component of applied pressure for node ifecs
	31-40	PRESS(IFECS+1,1)	local x-component of applied pressure for node ifecs+1
	41-50	PRESS(IFECS+1,2)	local y-component of applied pressure for node ifecs+1
	51-60	PRESS(IFECS+1,3)	local z-component of applied pressure for node ifecs+1

<u>second record</u>

cols. 01-10 PRESS(IFECS+2,1) local x-component of applied
pressure for node ifecs+2

etc.

7.2 Test example - simply supported beam

The dynamically-loaded, simply supported beam described in Section 5.2 is now adopted as a test example to demonstrate the use of DARC3. Typical input and output data for this example is given in Figures 46 and 47 respectively.

```
   ADINA REINFORCED BEAM
68     5    11    20     2     2     0     1
 1     1     1     1     2     3     5     8     7     6     4     9    10
                  12    11    13    14    15    17    20    19    18    16
 2     1     1    13    14    15    17    20    19    18    16    21    22
                  24    23    25    26    27    29    32    31    30    28
 3     1     1    25    26    27    29    32    31    30    28    33    34
                  36    35    37    38    39    41    44    43    42    40
 4     1     1    37    38    39    41    44    43    42    40    45    46
                  48    47    49    50    51    53    56    55    54    52
 5     1     1    49    50    51    53    56    55    54    52    57    58
                  60    59    61    62    63    65    68    67    66    64
 1       0.000       6.000      11.000
 2       0.000       3.000      11.000
 3       0.000       0.000      11.000
 4       0.000       6.000       5.500
 5       0.000       0.000       5.500
 6       0.000       6.000       0.000
 7       0.000       3.000       0.000
 8       0.000       0.000       0.000
 9       9.999       6.000      11.000
10       9.999       0.000      11.000
11       9.999       6.000       0.000
12       9.999       0.000       0.000
13      19.999       6.000      11.000
14      19.999       3.000      11.000
15      19.999       0.000      11.000
16      19.999       6.000       5.500
17      19.999       0.000       5.500
18      19.999       6.000       0.000
19      19.999       3.000       0.000
20      19.999       0.000       0.000
21      28.999       6.000      11.000
22      28.999       0.000      11.000
23      28.999       6.000       0.000
24      28.999       0.000       0.000
25      37.998       6.000      11.000
26      37.998       3.000      11.000
27      37.998       0.000      11.000
28      37.998       6.000       5.500
29      37.998       0.000       5.500
```

Figure 46 Typical input for program DARC3

```
 30    37.998    6.000     0.000
 31    37.998    3.000     0.000
 32    37.998    0.000     0.000
 33    43.996    6.000    11.000
 34    43.996    0.000    11.000
 35    43.996    6.000     0.000
 36    43.996    0.000     0.000
 37    49.994    6.000    11.000
 38    49.994    3.000    11.000
 39    49.994    0.000    11.000
 40    49.994    6.000     5.500
 41    49.994    0.000     5.500
 42    49.994    6.000     0.000
 43    49.994    3.000     0.000
 44    49.994    0.000     0.000
 45    54.495    6.000    11.000
 46    54.495    0.000    11.000
 47    54.495    6.000     0.000
 48    54.495    0.000     0.000
 49    58.997    6.000    11.000
 50    58.997    3.000    11.000
 51    58.997    0.000    11.000
 52    58.997    6.000     5.500
 53    58.997    0.000     5.500
 54    58.997    6.000     0.000
 55    58.997    3.000     0.000
 56    58.997    0.000     0.000
 57    63.498    6.000    11.000
 58    63.498    0.000    11.000
 59    63.498    6.000     0.000
 60    63.498    0.000     0.000
 61    68.000    6.000    11.000
 62    68.000    3.000    11.000
 63    68.000    0.000    11.000
 64    68.000    6.000     5.500
 65    68.000    0.000     5.500
 66    68.000    6.000     0.000
 67    68.000    3.000     0.000
 68    68.000    0.000     0.000
  6       11            0.000     0.000     0.000
  7       11            0.000     0.000     0.000
  8       11            0.000     0.000     0.000
 61      110            0.000     0.000     0.000
 62      110            0.000     0.000     0.000
 63      110            0.000     0.000     0.000
 64      110            0.000     0.000     0.000
 65      110            0.000     0.000     0.000
 66      110            0.000     0.000     0.000
 67      110            0.000     0.000     0.000
 68      110            0.000     0.000     0.000
  1
 .61E+04         .00  .374E+01  .915E+00   .35E-02
 0.6E-03    .00E-00          .  .217E-06   0.1E+01
.3055E+00  .760E+00   0.1E+02  .184E+01  .109E+01
  2
 0.3E+05         .00   .44E+02   0.1E+10   0.3E+03
 0.1E+04      .00000         .   0.1E+01   0.1E+01
.1000E-02  .971E+00   0.1E+10   0.1E+10   0.1E+10
  1    1
  2    2       1.      .33         .0
500    0    1    4    0    0    1    0   50 2000    2    0
 .00050        1000.         0.         0.         0.        .25        .5
    1.           .1       .02
 62   66   67   68
 68
 68
 PAIR OF POINT LOADS
  1    0    0
 37          .          .     -1.125
 38          .          .     -4.500
 39          .          .     -1.125
 68          .          .          .
```

Figure 46 Typical input for program DARC3 contd...

TITLE OF RUN.   ADINA REINFORCED BEAM

=============

ECHO OF INPUT DATA.

TOTAL NUMBER OF NODAL POINTS............ 68

TOTAL NUMBER OF ELEMENTS................ 5

TOTAL NUM. OF RESTRAINED BOUNDARY NDS... 11

NUMBER OF NODES PER ELEMENT............ 20

NUMBER OF DIFFERENT MATERIALS........... 2

NUMBER OF YIELD CRITERION SELECTED...... 2

NUM OF DIFFERENT REINFORCEMENT PATTERNS. 1

NODAL CONNECTION   ANTI-CLOCKWISE AROUND ELEMENT. RIGHT HAND SCREW RULE
****

ELEMENT NUMBER.	PROPERTY SET.	REINFORC. PATTERN	NODE NUMBERS. N1	N2	N3	N4	N5	N6	N7	N8	N9	N10
1	1	1	1	2	3	5	8	7	6	4	9	10
			12	11	13	14	15	17	20	19	18	16
2	1	1	13	14	15	17	20	19	18	16	21	22
			24	23	25	26	27	29	33	31	30	28
3	1	1	25	26	27	29	32	31	30	28	33	34
			36	35	37	38	39	41	44	43	42	40
4	1	1	37	38	39	41	44	43	42	40	45	46
			48	47	49	50	51	53	56	55	54	52
5	1	1	49	50	51	53	56	55	54	52	57	58
			60	59	61	62	63	65	68	67	66	64

NODAL CO-ORDINATES DATA.
****

NODE NUMBER	X CO-ORDINATE.	Y CO-ORDINATE.	Z CO-ORDINATE.
1	0.000	6.000	11.000
2	0.000	3.000	11.000
3	0.000	0.000	11.000
4	0.000	6.000	5.500
5	0.000	0.000	5.500
6	0.000	0.000	0.000
7	0.000	3.000	0.000
8	0.000	0.000	0.000
9	9.999	6.000	11.000
10	9.999	0.000	11.000
11	9.999	6.000	0.000
12	9.999	0.000	0.000
13	19.999	6.000	11.000
14	19.999	3.000	11.000
15	19.999	0.000	11.000
16	19.999	6.000	5.500
17	19.999	0.000	5.500
18	19.999	6.000	0.000
19	19.999	3.000	0.000
20	19.999	0.000	0.000

Figure 47 Typical output from program DARC3

21	28.999	6.000	11.000
22	28.999	0.000	11.000
23	28.999	6.000	0.000
24	28.999	0.000	0.000
25	37.998	6.000	11.000
26	37.998	3.000	11.000
27	37.998	0.000	11.000
28	37.998	6.000	5.500
29	37.998	0.000	5.500
30	37.998	6.000	0.000
31	37.998	3.000	0.000
32	37.998	0.000	0.000
33	43.996	6.000	11.000
34	43.996	0.000	11.000
35	43.996	6.000	0.000
36	43.996	0.000	0.000
37	49.994	6.000	11.000
38	49.994	3.000	11.000
39	49.994	0.000	11.000
40	49.994	6.000	5.500
41	49.994	0.000	5.500
42	49.994	6.000	0.000
43	49.994	3.000	0.000
44	49.994	0.000	0.000
45	54.495	6.000	11.000
46	54.495	0.000	11.000
47	54.495	6.000	0.000
48	54.495	0.000	0.000
49	58.997	6.000	11.000
50	58.997	3.000	11.000
51	58.997	0.000	11.000
52	58.997	6.000	5.500
53	58.997	0.000	5.500
54	58.997	6.000	0.000
55	58.997	3.000	0.000
56	58.997	0.000	0.000
57	63.498	6.000	11.000
58	63.498	0.000	11.000
59	63.498	6.000	0.000
60	63.498	0.000	0.000
61	68.000	6.000	11.000
62	68.000	3.000	11.000
63	68.000	0.000	11.000
64	68.000	6.000	5.500
65	68.000	0.000	5.500
66	68.000	6.000	0.000
67	68.000	3.000	0.000
68	68.000	0.000	0.000

RESTRAINED NODES REL. TO THE X-Y-Z CO-ORD. SYSTEM AND THE ORIG. POSITION
****

NODE	X RESTRAINT	Y RESTRAINT	Z RESTRAINT
6	0	1	1
7	0	1	1
8	0	1	1
61	1	1	0
62	1	1	0
63	1	1	0
64	1	1	0
65	1	1	0
66	1	1	0
67	1	1	0
68	1	1	0

Figure 47 Typical output from program DARC3 contd...

MATERIAL PROPERTY SETS.
****

	SET 1	SET 2
YOUNG MODULUS..................................	0.6100E+04	0.3000E+05
POISSON RATIO..................................	0.0000E+00	0.0000E+00
COMPRESSION FLOW STRESS........................	0.3740E+01	0.4400E+02
CRACKING STRESS (YOUNG*CRACKING STRAIN)....	0.9150E+00	0.1000E+10
CRUSHING STRAIN................................	0.3500E-02	0.3000E+03
FRACTURE ENERGY................................	0.6000E-03	0.1000E+04
FACTOR FOR SHEAR REDUCTION.....................	0.0000E+00	0.0000E+00
NOT USED.......................................	0.0000E+00	0.0000E+00
MATERIAL DENSITY...............................	0.2170E-06	0.1000E+01
FACTOR FOR END OF ELASTICITY...................	0.1000E+01	0.1000E+01
A0 FOR FLUIDITY PARAMETER......................	0.3055E+00	0.1000E-02
A1 FOR FLUIDITY PARAMETER......................	0.7600E+00	0.9710E+00
ALFA-C FOR STRAIN-SOFTENING....................	0.1000E+02	0.1000E+10
BETA0 FOR MONITORING SURFACE...................	0.1840E+01	0.1000E+10
BETA1 FOR MONITORING SURFACE...................	0.1090E+01	0.1000E+10

REINFORCEMENT SETS.
****

REINFORCEMENT SET NO. 1

	LAYER 1
MATERIAL NUMBER.........................	2
COORDINATE NUMBER.......................	2
COORDINATE POSITION.....................	1.00000
THICKNESS...............................	0.33000
ANGLE FROM EXI-AXIS.....................	0.00000

TIME STEPPING PARAMETERS
****

NSTEP= 500	NOUTD= 0	NOUTP= 1
NREQD= 4	NREQS= 0	NACCE= 0
IFUNC= 1	IFIXD= 0	MITER= 50
KSTEP= 2000	IPRED= 2	
DTIME= 0.5000E-03	DTEND= 1000.	DTREC= 0.0000E+00
AALFA= 0.0000E+00	BEETA= 0.0000E+00	DELTA= 0.2500
GAAMA= 0.5000	AZERO= 0.0000E+00	BZERO= 1.000
OMEGA= 0.1000	TOLER= 0.2000E-01	TMAXR= 0.0000E+00

SELECTIVE OUTPUT REQUESTED FOR FOLLOWING
****

NODES 62 66 67 68

NODE	INITIAL X-DISP.	INITIAL Y-DISP.	INITIAL Z-DISP.
****	***************	***************	***************
68	0.00000E+00	0.00000E+00	0.00000E+00

Figure 47 Typical output from program DARC3 contd...

```
NODE    INITIAL X-VELO.    INITIAL Y-VELO.    INITIAL Z-VELO.
****    ***************    ***************    ***************

68      0.00000E+00        0.00000E+00        0.00000E+00

NEQNS=  182     NWKTL=   6765

TITLE      PAIR OF POINT LOADS

APPLIED LOADING TO STRUCTURE.
*****************************

POINT LOAD PARAMETER......................   1

GRAVITY LOAD PARAMETER....................   0

FACE LOADS PARAMETER......................   0

POINT LOADING.
**************

 NODE               PX                   PY                  PZ
  37              0.000                0.000              -1.125
  38              0.000                0.000              -4.500
  39              0.000                0.000              -1.125
  68              0.000                0.000               0.000


      RESULTS AT TIME     0.00050      ISTEP =     1
      DISPLACEMENTS
  NNODE     X-DISP        Y-DISP       Z-DISP
     62 0.00000E+00 0.00000E+00-0.14759E-02
     66 0.00000E+00 0.00000E+00-0.14830E-02
     67 0.00000E+00 0.00000E+00-0.14879E-02
     68 0.00000E+00 0.00000E+00-0.14830E-02

      RESULTS AT TIME     0.00100      ISTEP =     2
      DISPLACEMENTS
  NNODE     X-DISP        Y-DISP       Z-DISP
     62 0.00000E+00 0.00000E+00-0.67187E-02
     66 0.00000E+00 0.00000E+00-0.67202E-02
     67 0.00000E+00 0.00000E+00-0.67234E-02
     68 0.00000E+00 0.00000E+00-0.67202E-02

      RESULTS AT TIME     0.00150      ISTEP =     3
      DISPLACEMENTS
  NNODE     X-DISP        Y-DISP       Z-DISP
     62 0.00000E+00 0.00000E+00-0.14573E-01
     66 0.00000E+00 0.00000E+00-0.14577E-01
     67 0.00000E+00 0.00000E+00-0.14575E-01
     68 0.00000E+00 0.00000E+00-0.14577E-01

      RESULTS AT TIME     0.00200      ISTEP =     4
      DISPLACEMENTS
  NNODE     X-DISP        Y-DISP       Z-DISP
     62 0.00000E+00 0.00000E+00-0.23933E-01
     66 0.00000E+00 0.00000E+00-0.23938E-01
     67 0.00000E+00 0.00000E+00-0.23944E-01
     68 0.00000E+00 0.00000E+00-0.23938E-01
```

Figure 47 Typical output from program DARC3 contd...

```
    RESULTS AT TIME     0.00250       ISTEP =      5
    DISPLACEMENTS
NNODE    X-DISP         Y-DISP         Z-DISP
   62 0.00000E+00 0.00000E+00-0.36293E-01
   66 0.00000E+00 0.00000E+00-0.36294E-01
   67 0.00000E+00 0.00000E+00-0.36294E-01
   68 0.00000E+00 0.00000E+00-0.36294E-01

    RESULTS AT TIME     0.00300       ISTEP =      6
    DISPLACEMENTS
NNODE    X-DISP         Y-DISP         Z-DISP
   62 0.00000E+00 0.00000E+00-0.51238E-01
   66 0.00000E+00 0.00000E+00-0.51246E-01
   67 0.00000E+00 0.00000E+00-0.51248E-01
   68 0.00000E+00 0.00000E+00-0.51246E-01

    RESULTS AT TIME     0.00350       ISTEP =      7
    DISPLACEMENTS
NNODE    X-DISP         Y-DISP         Z-DISP
   62 0.00000E+00 0.00000E+00-0.68243E-01
   66 0.00000E+00 0.00000E+00-0.68242E-01
   67 0.00000E+00 0.00000E+00-0.68244E-01
   68 0.00000E+00 0.00000E+00-0.68242E-01


    RESULTS AT TIME     0.00400       ISTEP =      8
    DISPLACEMENTS
NNODE    X-DISP         Y-DISP         Z-DISP
   62 0.00000E+00 0.00000E+00-0.86275E-01
   66 0.00000E+00 0.00000E+00-0.86286E-01
   67 0.00000E+00 0.00000E+00-0.86283E-01
   68 0.00000E+00 0.00000E+00-0.86286E-01

    RESULTS AT TIME     0.00450       ISTEP =      9
    DISPLACEMENTS
NNODE    X-DISP         Y-DISP         Z-DISP
   62 0.00000E+00 0.00000E+00-0.10483E+00
   66 0.00000E+00 0.00000E+00-0.10482E+00
   67 0.00000E+00 0.00000E+00-0.10483E+00
   68 0.00000E+00 0.00000E+00-0.10482E+00

    RESULTS AT TIME     0.00500       ISTEP =     10
    DISPLACEMENTS
NNODE    X-DISP         Y-DISP         Z-DISP
   62 0.00000E+00 0.00000E+00-0.12473E+00
   66 0.00000E+00 0.00000E+00-0.12475E+00
   67 0.00000E+00 0.00000E+00-0.12474E+00
   68 0.00000E+00 0.00000E+00-0.12475E+00

    RESULTS AT TIME     0.00550       ISTEP =     11
    DISPLACEMENTS
NNODE    X-DISP         Y-DISP         Z-DISP
   62 0.00000E+00 0.00000E+00-0.14518E+00
   66 0.00000E+00 0.00000E+00-0.14517E+00
   67 0.00000E+00 0.00000E+00-0.14517E+00
   68 0.00000E+00 0.00000E+00-0.14517E+00

    RESULTS AT TIME     0.00600       ISTEP =     12
    DISPLACEMENTS
NNODE    X-DISP         Y-DISP         Z-DISP
   62 0.00000E+00 0.00000E+00-0.16644E+00
   66 0.00000E+00 0.00000E+00-0.16642E+00
   67 0.00000E+00 0.00000E+00-0.16643E+00
   68 0.00000E+00 0.00000E+00-0.16642E+00
```

Figure 47 Typical output from program DARC3 contd...

```
      RESULTS AT TIME      0.00650       ISTEP =    13
      DISPLACEMENTS
 NNODE    X-DISP         Y-DISP        Z-DISP
    62 0.00000E+00 0.00000E+00-0.18684E+00
    66 0.00000E+00 0.00000E+00-0.18687E+00
    67 0.00000E+00 0.00000E+00-0.18686E+00
    68 0.00000E+00 0.00000E+00-0.18687E+00

      RESULTS AT TIME      0.00700       ISTEP =    14
      DISPLACEMENTS
 NNODE    X-DISP         Y-DISP        Z-DISP
    62 0.00000E+00 0.00000E+00-0.20466E+00
    66 0.00000E+00 0.00000E+00-0.20462E+00
    67 0.00000E+00 0.00000E+00-0.20463E+00
    68 0.00000E+00 0.00000E+00-0.20462E+00

      RESULTS AT TIME      0.00750       ISTEP =    15
      DISPLACEMENTS
 NNODE    X-DISP         Y-DISP        Z-DISP
    62 0.00000E+00 0.00000E+00-0.22203E+00
    66 0.00000E+00 0.00000E+00-0.22205E+00
    67 0.00000E+00 0.00000E+00-0.22204E+00
    68 0.00000E+00 0.00000E+00-0.22205E+00

      RESULTS AT TIME      0.00800       ISTEP =    16
      DISPLACEMENTS
 NNODE    X-DISP         Y-DISP        Z-DISP
    62 0.00000E+00 0.00000E+00-0.23971E+00
    66 0.00000E+00 0.00000E+00-0.23969E+00
    67 0.00000E+00 0.00000E+00-0.23969E+00
    68 0.00000E+00 0.00000E+00-0.23969E+00

      RESULTS AT TIME      0.00850       ISTEP =    17
      DISPLACEMENTS
 NNODE    X-DISP         Y-DISP        Z-DISP
    62 0.00000E+00 0.00000E+00-0.25675E+00
    66 0.00000E+00 0.00000E+00-0.25675E+00
    67 0.00000E+00 0.00000E+00-0.25674E+00
    68 0.00000E+00 0.00000E+00-0.25675E+00

      RESULTS AT TIME      0.00900       ISTEP =    18
      DISPLACEMENTS
 NNODE    X-DISP         Y-DISP        Z-DISP
    62 0.00000E+00 0.00000E+00-0.27290E+00
    66 0.00000E+00 0.00000E+00-0.27289E+00
    67 0.00000E+00 0.00000E+00-0.27290E+00
    68 0.00000E+00 0.00000E+00-0.27289E+00

      RESULTS AT TIME      0.00950       ISTEP =    19
      DISPLACEMENTS
 NNODE    X-DISP         Y-DISP        Z-DISP
    62 0.00000E+00 0.00000E+00-0.28709E+00
    66 0.00000E+00 0.00000E+00-0.28708E+00
    67 0.00000E+00 0.00000E+00-0.28708E+00
    68 0.00000E+00 0.00000E+00-0.28708E+00

      RESULTS AT TIME      0.01000       ISTEP =    20
      DISPLACEMENTS
 NNODE    X-DISP         Y-DISP        Z-DISP
    62 0.00000E+00 0.00000E+00-0.29775E+00
    66 0.00000E+00 0.00000E+00-0.29776E+00
    67 0.00000E+00 0.00000E+00-0.29775E+00
    68 0.00000E+00 0.00000E+00-0.29776E+00
```

Figure 47 typical output from program DARC3 contd...

```
    RESULTS AT TIME     0.01050      ISTEP =    21
    DISPLACEMENTS
NNODE    X-DISP        Y-DISP       Z-DISP
   62 0.00000E+00 0.00000E+00-0.30530E+00
   66 0.00000E+00 0.00000E+00-0.30527E+00
   67 0.00000E+00 0.00000E+00-0.30528E+00
   68 0.00000E+00 0.00000E+00-0.30527E+00

    RESULTS AT TIME     0.01100      ISTEP =    22
    DISPLACEMENTS
NNODE    X-DISP        Y-DISP       Z-DISP
   62 0.00000E+00 0.00000E+00-0.31115E+00
   66 0.00000E+00 0.00000E+00-0.31115E+00
   67 0.00000E+00 0.00000E+00-0.31114E+00
   68 0.00000E+00 0.00000E+00-0.31115E+00

    RESULTS AT TIME     0.01150      ISTEP =    23
    DISPLACEMENTS
NNODE    X-DISP        Y-DISP       Z-DISP
   62 0.00000E+00 0.00000E+00-0.31598E+00
   66 0.00000E+00 0.00000E+00-0.31595E+00
   67 0.00000E+00 0.00000E+00-0.31596E+00
   68 0.00000E+00 0.00000E+00-0.31595E+00

    RESULTS AT TIME     0.01200      ISTEP =    24
    DISPLACEMENTS
NNODE    X-DISP        Y-DISP       Z-DISP
   62 0.00000E+00 0.00000E+00-0.31861E+00
   66 0.00000E+00 0.00000E+00-0.31862E+00
   67 0.00000E+00 0.00000E+00-0.31861E+00
   68 0.00000E+00 0.00000E+00-0.31862E+00

    RESULTS AT TIME     0.01250      ISTEP =    25
    DISPLACEMENTS
NNODE    X-DISP        Y-DISP       Z-DISP
   62 0.00000E+00 0.00000E+00-0.31788E+00
   66 0.00000E+00 0.00000E+00-0.31785E+00
   67 0.00000E+00 0.00000E+00-0.31786E+00
   68 0.00000E+00 0.00000E+00-0.31785E+00

    RESULTS AT TIME     0.01300      ISTEP =    26
    DISPLACEMENTS
NNODE    X-DISP        Y-DISP       Z-DISP
   62 0.00000E+00 0.00000E+00-0.31434E+00
   66 0.00000E+00 0.00000E+00-0.31435E+00
   67 0.00000E+00 0.00000E+00-0.31433E+00
   68 0.00000E+00 0.00000E+00-0.31435E+00

    RESULTS AT TIME     0.01350      ISTEP =    27
    DISPLACEMENTS
NNODE    X-DISP        Y-DISP       Z-DISP
   62 0.00000E+00 0.00000E+00-0.30700E+00
   66 0.00000E+00 0.00000E+00-0.30700E+00
   67 0.00000E+00 0.00000E+00-0.30700E+00
   68 0.00000E+00 0.00000E+00-0.30700E+00

    RESULTS AT TIME     0.01400      ISTEP =    28
    DISPLACEMENTS
NNODE    X-DISP        Y-DISP       Z-DISP
   62 0.00000E+00 0.00000E+00-0.29706E+00
   66 0.00000E+00 0.00000E+00-0.29703E+00
   67 0.00000E+00 0.00000E+00-0.29703E+00
   68 0.00000E+00 0.00000E+00-0.29703E+00
```

Figure 47 typical output from program DARC3 contd...

REFERENCES

1. Zienkiewicz, O.C.
'The Finite Element Method', 3rd Edn.
McGraw-Hill, London, 1977.

2. Koslov, D. and Frazier, G.A.
'Treatment of hourglass patterns in low order finite element codes',
Int. Num. Anal. Meth. Geom., 2, 57-72, 1978.

3. Flanagan, D.P. and Belytschko, T.
'A uniform strain hexahedron and quadrilateral with orthogonal hourglass control',
Int. J. Num. Meth. Engng., 17, 679-706, 1981.

4. Halquist, J.O.
'Theoretical manual for DYNA-3D',
Lawrence Livermore Laboratory, 1982.

5. Crisfield, M.A.
'Some recent research on numerical techniques for structural analysis',
NUMETA 85, 565-575, 1985.

6. Irons, B.M.
'Quadrature rules for brick based finite elements',
Int. J. Num. Meth. Engng., 3, 293-294, 1971.

7. Buyukozturk, O. and Shareef, S.S.
'Constitutive modeling of concrete in finite element analysis',
Computers and Structures, 21, 581-610, 1985.

8. Phillips, D.V. and Zienkiewicz, O.C.
'Finite element nonlinear analysis of concrete structures',
Proc. Inst. Civ. Engng., 61, 59-98, 1976.

9. Zienkiewicz, O.C., Owen, D.R.J. and Phillips, D.V.
'Finite element analysis of reactor vessels',
Nuclear Engng. and Design, 20, 507-541, 1972.

10. Cook, R.D.
'Concepts and application of finite element analysis',
2nd Edn., Wiley, Chichester, 1981.

11. Cook, R.D.
'Remarks about diagonal mass matrices',
Int. J. Num. Meth. Engng., 17, 1427-1429, 1981.

12. Clough, R.W.
'Analysis of structural vibrations ad dynamic response',
in Recent Advances in Math. Meth. of Struct. Anal. and Design, 441-485, ed. R.H. Gallagher et al (eds.),
University of Alabama Press, 1971.

13. Hinton, E., Rock, T. and Zienkiewicz, O.C.
'A note on mass lumping and related processed in the finite element method',
Earthquake Engng. Struct. Dyn., 4, 246-249, 1976.

14. Shantaram, D., Owen, D.R.J. and Zienkiewicz, O.C.
'Dynamic transient behaviour of two and three dimensional structures including plasticity, large deformation effects and fluid interaction',
Earthquake Engng. Struct. Dyn., 4, 561-578, 1976.

15. Rock, T. and Hinton, E.
'Free vibration and transient response of thick and thin plates using the finite element method',
Earthquake Engng. Struct. Dyn., 3, 51-63, 1974.

16. Liu, C.Q.
'Nonlinear and transient finite element analysis of general reinforced concrete plates and shells',
Ph.D. Thesis, University of Wales, Swansea, 1985.

17. Fullard, K.
'Thermal transient analysis involving large temperature gradients',
C.E.G.B. Report RD/B/N/ 3831, 1976.

18. Fried, I. and Malkus, D.S.,
'Finite element mass matrix lumping by numerical integration without convergence rate loss',
Int. J. Solid Struct., 11, 461-466, 1976.

19. Bićanić, N.
'Nonlinear finite element transient response of concrete structures',
Ph.D. Thesis, University of Wales, Swansea, 1978.

20. Surana, K.S.
'Lumped mass matrices with non-zero inertia for general shell and axisymmetric shell elements',
Int. J. Num. Meth. Engng., 12, 1635-1650, 1978.

21. Wilson, E.L. and Penzien, J.
'Evaluation of orthogonal damping matrices',
Int. J. Num. Meth. Engng., 4, 5-10, 1972.

22. Watstein, D.
'Effect of straining rate on the compressive strength and elastic properties of concrete',
ACI Journal, 24, 729-744, 1953.

23. Mainstone, R.J.
'Properties of material at high rates of straining or loading',
Materiaux et Constructions, 8, 102-116, 1975.

24. Spooner, D.C.
'Stress-strain-time relationships for concrete',
Magazine of Concrete Research, 23,73-76, 1971.

25. Sparks, D.R. and Menzies, J.B.
'The effect of rate of loading in plain concrete',
Magazine of Concrete Research, 25, 73-80, 1973.

26. Hatano, T. and Tsutsumi, H.
'Dynamical compressive deformation and failure of concrete under earthquake load',
Proc. 2nd WCEE, Tokyo, 3, 1963-1978, 1960.

27. Hatano, T.
'Relations between strength of failure, strain ability elastic modulus and failure time of concrete',
Central Research Institute of Electric Power Industry, C-6001, Tokyo, 1960.

28. Hatano, T.
'Dynamical behaviour of concrete under impulsive tensile load',
Central Research Institute of Electric Power Industry, C-6002, Tokyo, 1960.

29. Hatano, T.
'Dynamic behaviour of concrete under periodical compressive load',
Central Research Institute of Electric Power Industry, C-6104, Tokyo, 1962.

30. Hatano, T. and Watanabe, H.
'Fatigue failure of concrete under periodic compressive load',
Transactions JSCE, 3, 106-107, 1971.

31. Nelissen, L.J.M.
'Biaxial testing of normal concrete',
Heron, 18, No.1, Delft, 1972.

32. Bićanić, N.
'Nonlinear finite element transient response of concrete structures',
Ph.D. Thesis, University of Wales, Swansea, 1978.

33. Bićanić, N. and Zienkiewicz, O.C.
'Constitutive model for concrete under dynamic loading',
Earthquake Engng. and Struct. Dyn., 11, 689-710, 1973.

34. Albertini, C. and Montagnani
'Testing techniques based on the split Hopkinson bar'
in 'Mechanical properties at high rates of strain',
(eds. Hardings, J.), Conference series No.21,
The Institute of Physics, London, 1974.

35. Hardings, J.
'Effect of high strain rate on the room-temperature strength and ductility of five alloy steels',
J. of the Iron and Steel Institute, 435-432, June, 1972.

36. Perzyna, P.
'Fundamental problems in viscoplasticity',
Adv. Appl. Mech., 9, 243-377, 1966.

37. Argyris, J.H., Krempl, E. and Willam, K.J.
'Constitutive models and finite element solution of inelastic behaviour',
in 'Formulations and computational algorithms in finite element analysis', (eds. K.J. Bathe, J.T.Oden and W. Wunderlich), 1977.

38. Zienkiewicz, O.C., Fejzo, R. and Bićanić, N.
'Experience in analysing plain concrete structures using a rate sensitive model with crack monitoring capabilities', Int. Conf. on Constitutive Laws for Engng. Materials, University of Arizona, 1983.

39. Kupfer, H., Hilsdorf, K.H. and Rush, H.
'Behaviour of concrete under biaxial stresses', Proc. ACI, 66, 656-666, 1969.

40. Ngo, D. and Scordelis, A.C.
'Finite element analysis of reinforced concrete beams', ACI Journal, 64, 152-163, 1967.

41. Saouma, V.E. and Ingraffea, A.R.
'Fracture mechanics analysis of discrete cracking', IABSE Colloq., Delft, 393-416, 1981.

42. Nilsson, L. and Oldenburg, M.
'Nonlinear wave propagation in plastic fracturing materials - a constitutive modelling and finite element analysis', IUTAM Symp. on 'Nonlinear Deformation Waves', Tallin, 1982.

43. Jiang, J.J.
'Finite element techniques for statical analysis of structures in reinforced concrete', Ph.D. Thesis, Dept. of Struct. Mech., Chalmers Univ. of Tech., Pub 83:2, 1983.

44. Bažant, Z.P. and Oh, B.H.
'Crack band theory for fracture of concrete', RILEM, Materiaux et Constructions, 16, 155-177, 1983.

45. Glemberg, R.
'Dynamic analysis of concrete structures', Ph.D. Thesis, Dept. of Struct. Mech., Chalmers Univ. of Tech., Pub 84:1, 1984.

46. Rots, J.G., Nauta, P., Kusters, G.M.A. and Blaauwendraad, J.
'Smeared crack approach and fracture localization in concrete',
HERON, 30, No. 1, Delft, 1985.

47. Bergan, P.G.
'Some aspects of interpolation and integration in nonlinear finite element analysis of reinforced concrete structures',
in 'Computer aided analysis and design of concrete structures' (F. Damjanic et al., eds.) , 301-316,
Pineridge Press, Swansea, 1984.

48. Gustafsson, J.
'Fracture mechanics studies of non-yielding materials like concrete',
Ph.D. Thesis, Univ. of Lund, 1985.

49. Cope, R.J., Rao, P.V., Clark, L.A. and Norris, P.
'Modelling of reinforced concrete behaviour for finite element analysis of bridge decks',
in 'Proceedings of Int. Conf. on Num. Meth. for Non-Linear Problems' (C. Taylor et al., eds.),
Pineridge Press, Swansea, 1980.

50. Bažant, Z.P.
'Discussion on Session 2 - Structural modelling for numerical analysis',
IABSE Colloq., Final Report, 482, Delft, 1981.

51. Scanlon, A. and Murray, D.W.
'Time-dependent reinforced concrete slab deflections',
ASCE, J. Struct. Div., 100, 1911-1924, 1974.

52. Gilbert, R.I. and Warner, R.F.
'Tension stiffening in reinforced concrete slabs',
ASCE, J. Struct. Div., 104, 1885-1900, 1978.

53. Hillerborg, A., Modeer, H. and Petersson, P.E.
'Analysis of crack formation and crack growth in concrete by means of fracture mechanics and finite elements',
Cement and Concrete Research, 6, 773-781, 1976.

54. Bažant, Z.P. and Cedolin, L.
'Fracture mechanics of reinforced concrete',
ASCE, J. Mech. Div., 106, 1207-1306

55. Willam, K.J. and Sture, S.
'A composite fracture model for localized fracture in cementitious materials',
Second Symp. on the interaction of non-nuclear munitions with structures, Florida, 1985.

56. Willam, K.J.
'Experimental and computational aspects of concrete fracture',
in 'Computer aided analysis and design of concrete structures' (F.Damjanic et al., eds.), 33-70,
Pineridge Press, Swansea, 1984.

57. Willam, K.J., Bićanić, N. and Sture, S.
'Constitutive and computational aspects of strain-softening and localization in solids',
ASME-WAM'84 Symposium on 'Constitutive equations: micro, macro and computational aspects',
New Orleans, 1984.

58. Petersson, P.E.
'Crack growth and development of fracture zones in plain concrete and similiar materials',
Ph.D. Thesis, Univ. of Lund, 1981.

59. Červenka, V.
'Constitutive model for cracked reinforced concrete',
ACI Journal, 82, 877-882, 1985.

60. Zienkiewicz, O.C. and Cormeau, I.C.
'Visco-plasticity-plasticity and creep in elastic solids- a unified numerical solution approach',
Int. J. Num. Meth. Engng., 8, 821-845, 1974.

61. Cormeau, I.C.
'Viscoplasticity and plasticity in the finite element method',
Ph.D. Thesis, University of Wales, Swansea, 1976.

62. Newmark, N.M.
'A method of computation for structural dynamics',
J. Engng. Mech. Div., ASCE, 85, 67-94, 1959.

63. Belytschko, T.
'Explicit time integration of structure-mechanical systems',
in 'Advanced Structural Dynamics', ed. by J. Donea, 97-122, 1978.

64. Zienkiewicz, O.C., Wood, W.L. and Taylor, R.L.
'An alternative single step algorithm for parabolic boundary value problems',
Int. J. Earthquake Engng. Struct. Dyn., 8, 31-40, 1980.

65. Zienkiewicz, O.C., Wood, W.L., Hine, N.W. and Taylor, R.L.
'A unified set of single step algorithm',
Int. J. Num. Meth. Engng., 20, 1524-1552, 1984.

66. Collatz, L.
'The numerical treatment of differential equations'
Springer Verlag, New York, 1966.

67. Houbolt, J.C.
'A recurrent matrix solution for the dynamic response of an elastic aircraft',
J. Aeron. Sci., 17, 540-550, 1950.

68. Wilson, E.L., Farhoomand, I. and Bathe, K.J.
'Nonlinear dynamic analysis of complex structures'
Int. J. Earthquake Engng. Struct. Dyn., 1, 241-252, 1973.

69. Hughes, T.J.R. and Belytschko, T.
'A precis of developments in computational methods for transient analysis',
J. Appl. Mech., 45, 371-374, 1978.

70. Hine, N.W.
'Starting conditions and procedure for the solution of a 1-D dynamic elastic bar problem using the SS22 and Newmark single step time integration methods',
I.N.M.E., University College of Swansea, C/R/530/85, 1985.

71. Hughes, T.J.R. and Liu, W.K.
'Implicit-explicit finite elements in transient analysis: stability theory',
J. Appl. Mech., 45, 371-374, 1978.

72. Hughes, T.J.R. and Liu, W.K.
'Implicit-explicit finite elements in transient analysis: implementation and numerical examples',
J. Appl. Mech., 45, 375-378, 1978.

73. Hughes, T.J.R., Pister, K.S. and Taylor, R.L.
'Implicit-explicit finite elements in nonlinear transient analysis',
Comp. Meth. Appl. Mech. Engng., 17/18, 159-182, 1979.

74. Owen, D.R.J. and Hinton, E.
'Finite elements in plasticity: theory and practice',
Pineridge Press, Swansea, 1980.

75. ADINA system verification manual.
ADINA Engineering, Inc., Watertown, Mass., 1983.

76. Rebora, B. and Zimmermann, T.
'Dynamic rupture analysis of reinforced concrete shells',
Nuclear Engng. and Design, 37, 269-297, 1976.

77. Liu, G.Q.
'Nonlinear and transient finite element analysis of general reinforced concrete plates and shells',
Ph.D. Thesis, University College of Swansea, C/Ph/84/85, 1985.

78. Crutzen, Y., Reyneu, J. and Vellafane, E.
'Impulsive loading on concrete structures',
SMIRT 6, paper J10/1, Paris, 1981.

79. Crutzen, Y. and Reyneu J.
'Disintegration of concrete shell structures under violent dynamic loading conditions',
SMIRT 7, paper J7/1*, Chicago, 1983.

80. Karnil, H., Korst, G., Sharpe, R.L., Krutzik, N. and Shankar, S.
'Analysis of critical structures and contained equipment for aircraft impact loading'
SMIRT 5, paper J9/1, Berlin, 1979.

81. Johnson, G.R. and Epstein, H.I.
'Short duration analysis earthquake'
ASCE, Struct. Div., 102, 993-1000, 1976.

ADDITIONAL NOTES

E. HINTON* and BAHAA S. AL JANABI**

* Department of Civil Engineering, University College of Swansea, U.K.

** Faculty of Civil Engineering, MTC, Baghdad, Iraq

These additional notes are intended to supplement the material presented in some of the chapters of this book. Note that the number before the decimal point in the square brackets corresponds to a specific chapter in the book.

[A1.1] INCLUSION OF ROTATORY INERTIA EFFECTS IN THE CLOSED FORM SOLUTION

The closed form solution presented in Chapter 1 dealt with the free vibrations of simply supported rectangular plates of uniform thickness with dimensions a and b, and resting on elastic Winkler foundations. It is possible to obtain the following set of homogeneous equations that may be solved for the natural frequencies of vibration

$$\begin{bmatrix} (P_{11} - \omega_{mn}^2 I) & P_{12} & P_{13} \\ P_{12} & (P_{22} - \omega_{mn}^2 I) & P_{23} \\ P_{13} & P_{23} & (P_{33} - \omega_{mn}^2 P) \end{bmatrix} \begin{bmatrix} A_{mn} \\ B_{mn} \\ C_{mn} \end{bmatrix} = \begin{bmatrix} 0 \\ 0 \\ 0 \end{bmatrix} \qquad (A1.1)$$

If the rotatory interia (I) is neglected, only one eigenvalue and its eigenvector results for each m, n. The frequency of vibration is given as

$$\omega_{mn}^2 = (QP_{33} + 2P_{12}P_{23}P_{13} - P_{22}P_{13}^2 - P_{11}P_{23}^2)/(PQ) \qquad (A1.2)$$

where $Q = (P_{11}P_{22} - P_{12}^2)$ and the eigenvectors associated with the natural frequency are

$$A_{mn} = C_{mn}(P_{12}P_{23} - P_{22}P_{13})/(P_{11}P_{22} - P_{12}^2) \qquad (A1.3a)$$

$$B_{mn} = C_{mn}(P_{12}P_{13} - P_{11}P_{23})/(P_{11}P_{22} - P_{12}^2) \qquad (A1.3b)$$

when normalised to C_{mn}.

However, if rotatory inertia effects are not neglected, then three eigenvalues and their respective eigenvectors result for each m, n pair. To find the eigenpairs, (A1.1) must be solved — this implies finding the conditions for which the determinant of the matrix on the left hand side of (A1.1) vanishes — which in turn leads to a cubic equation of the form

$$-\lambda^3 + c_1\lambda^2 + c_2\lambda + c_3 = 0 \qquad (A1.4)$$

where

$$\begin{aligned}
\lambda &= \omega_{mn}^2 \\
c_1 &= q_1/A \\
c_2 &= f/A \\
c_3 &= e/A \\
q_1 &= P_{11}PI + P_{22}PI + P_{33}I^2 \\
A &= PI^2 \\
f &= (P_{23}^2 + P_{13}^2 - P_{11}P_{33} - P_{22}P_{33})I + (P_{12}^2 - P_{11}P_{22})P \\
e &= P_{11}P_{22}P_{33} - P_{11}P_{23}^2 - P_{33}P_{12}^2 + 2P_{12}P_{13}P_{23} - P_{22}P_{13}^2 \\
P &= \int_{-h/2}^{h/2} \rho dz \\
I &= \int_{-h/2}^{h/2} \rho z^2 dz \\
\rho &= \text{mass density per unit volume}
\end{aligned}$$

As the coefficients c_i are functions of m and n, a set of three frequencies can be computed from (A1.4) corresponding to each pair (m, n). Usually, two of these frequencies are several orders of magnitude higher than the lowest frequency and hence are not of immediate interest. Note that the lowest frequency is associated with flexural vibration whereas the other frequencies are associated with shear vibration modes.

Newton's method may be used to find the roots of (A1.4). This has been implemented in program TRAM and the main changes are now reviewed. The main segment and subroutines DATA, COEF and EIGEN are modified and a new subroutine called SOLV is incorporated.

In subroutine DATA a new variable KTYPE is added to control the type of analysis required:

KTYPE=0 frequency without rotatory inertia effects

KTYPE=1 frequency with rotatory inertia effects

The remaining subroutines, which were described in Chapter 1, remain unchanged. The new and modified subroutines are now listed.

Main segment

```
C     PROGRAM TRAM
C
C     ***********************************************************
C     *                                                         *
C     *             DYNAMIC ANALYSIS OF MINDLIN PLATES          *
C     *                   CLOSED FORM SOLUTION                  *
C     *            ( WITH OR WITHOUT ROTARY INERTIA EFFECTS)    *
C     *                                                         *
C     *                                                         *
C     *                                                         *
C     ***********************************************************
C
      IMPLICIT REAL*8(A-H,O-Z)
      DIMENSION  BMX(140),BMY(140),BMXY(140),CX(140),CY(140),CXY(140),
     .           FCR(20,20),QX(140),QY(140),TITLE(20),W(140),WMN(20,20),
     .           WUX(140),WUY(140),XCORD(140),YCORD(140)
      DATA MPON/140/
      DATA LPON/20/
      DATA MITER/25/
C
      CALL DATA (AA,ALFA,BB,BETA,D11,D22,D21,D12,D66,DP,ETA,ETB,FO,F2,
     .           FX,FY,G1,GFS,IP,IQ,IT,J,KP,MPON,NPON,NUM,NUMF,PI,PM,
     .           PZ,S44,S55,T1,T2,T3,TIN,TITLE,U,V,XCORD,YCORD,
     .           H,KTYPE)
      CALL OUTD (AA,ALFA,BB,BETA,D11,D22,D21,D12,D66,DP,ETA,ETB,FO,F2,
     .           FX,FY,GFS,G1,IP,IQ,IT,J,KP,MPON,NPON,NUM,NUMF,PM,PZ,
     .           S44,S55,T1,T2,T3,TIN,TITLE,U,V,XCORD,YCORD,KTYPE)
      IF(KP.EQ.2) GO TO 20
C
C*** FREE VIBRATION, INITIALY STRESSED VIBRATION AND BUCKLING ANALYSIS
C
      II=0
      DO 15 M=1,NUMF
      DO 15 N=1,NUMF
      CALL COEF (AA,BB,D11,D22,D12,D66,FX,FY,G1,GFS,M,N,
     .           P11,P12,P13,P22,P23,P33,PI,S44,S55,
     .           H,C1,C2,C3,PM,KTYPE)
      CALL SOLV (C1,C2,C3,X1,MITER,KTYPE)
      CALL EIGEN(AA,ALFA,AMN1,BB,BETA,BMN1,CMN1,FCR,G1,GFS,II,LPON,M,N,
     .           PI,P11,P12,P13,P22,P23,P33,PM,S44,S55,WMN2,WMN,X1,
     .           KTYPE)
   15 CONTINUE
      IF(KP.EQ.1)GO TO 30
C
C*** TRANSIENT DYNAMIC ANALYSIS
```

```
C
   20 DO 10 II=1,J
      T=FLOAT(II)*TIN
      CALL INIT(BMX,BMY,BMXY,CX,CY,CXY,MPON,NPON,QX,QY,W,WUX,WUY)
      DO 5 M=1,NUM,IT
      DO 5 N=1,NUM,IT
      CALL COEF (AA,BB,D11,D22,D12,D66,FX,FY,G1,GFS,M,N,
     .           P11,P12,P13,P22,P23,P33,PI,S44,S55,
     .           H,C1,C2,C3,PM,KTYPE)
      CALL SOLV (C1,C2,C3,X1,MITER,KTYPE)
      CALL EIGEN(AA,ALFA,AMN1,BB,BETA,BMN1,CMN1,FCR,G1,GFS,II,LPON,M,N,
     .           PI,P11,P12,P13,P22,P23,P33,PM,S44,S55,WMN2,WMN,X1,
     .           KTYPE)
      CALL CONS (AA,BB,ETA,ETB,IQ,M,N,PI,PZ,QMN,U,V)
      CALL CONIN(DP,FO,F2,IP,PI,T,T1,T2,T3,W2,WMN2)
      CALL SUMS (AA,AMN1,BB,BMN1,BMX,BMY,BMXY,CMN1,CX,CY,CXY,D11,D22,
     .           D12,D66,G1,M,MPON,N,NPON,PM,QMN,QX,QY,PI,S44,S55,W,
     .           W2,WMN2,WUX,WUY,XCORD,YCORD)
    5 CONTINUE
      CALL OUTP (BMX,BMY,BMXY,MPON,NPON,NUM,QX,QY,T,W,WUX,WUY)
   10 CONTINUE
      IF(KP.EQ.2)GO TO 35
   30 CALL OUTF(ALFA,BETA,FCR,LPON,NUMF,WMN)
   35 CONTINUE
      STOP
      END
```

Subroutine DATA

```
      SUBROUTINE DATA (AA,ALFA,BB,BETA,D11,D22,D21,D12,D66,DP,ETA,ETB,
     .                 FO,F2,FX,FY,G1,GFS,IP,IQ,IT,J,KP,MPON,NPON,NUM,
     .                 NUMF,PI,PM,PZ,S44,S55,T1,T2,T3,TIN,TITLE,U,V,
     .                 XCORD,YCORD)
C
C***  THIS SUBROUTINE READS IN ALL DATA
C
      IMPLICIT REAL*8(A-H,O-Z)
      DIMENSION         TITLE(20),XCORD(MPON),YCORD(MPON)
C
      READ(5,900)TITLE
  900 FORMAT(20A4)
      READ(5,905)AA,BB
  905 FORMAT(2F10.5)
      READ(5,910)D11,D22,D12,D66
  910 FORMAT(4F10.5)
      D21=D12
      READ(5,915)S44,S55
```

```
915  FORMAT(2F10.5)                                                    DATA  19
     READ(5,920)PZ,GFS,G1,FX,FY,PM                                     DATA  20
920  FORMAT(6F10.5)                                                    DATA  21
     READ(5,925)KP                                                     DATA  22
925  FORMAT(I5)                                                        DATA  23
     IF(KP.EQ.1) GO TO 15                                              DATA  24
     READ(5,930)NUM,NPON                                               DATA  25
930  FORMAT(2I5)                                                       DATA  26
     DO 5 IPON=1,NPON                                                  DATA  27
     READ(5,935)JPON,XCORD(IPON),YCORD(IPON)                           DATA  28
935  FORMAT(I5,2F10.5)                                                 DATA  29
  5  CONTINUE                                                          DATA  30
     READ(5,940)IQ,IT                                                  DATA  31
940  FORMAT(2I5)                                                       DATA  32
     IF(IQ.LT.2) GO TO 10                                              DATA  33
     READ(5,945)ETA,ETB                                                DATA  34
945  FORMAT(2F10.5)                                                    DATA  35
     IF(IQ.LT.3) GO TO 10                                              DATA  36
     READ(5,950)U,V                                                    DATA  37
950  FORMAT(2F10.5)                                                    DATA  38
 10  CONTINUE                                                          DATA  39
     READ(5,955) IP,FO,F2,DP,T1,T2,T3                                  DATA  40
955  FORMAT(I5,6F10.5)                                                 DATA  41
     READ(5,960)J,TIN                                                  DATA  42
960  FORMAT(I5,F10.5)                                                  DATA  43
     IF(KP.EQ.2) GO TO 20                                              DATA  44
 15  READ(5,965)NUMF,ALFA,BETA                                         DATA  45
965  FORMAT(I5,2F10.5)                                                 DATA  46
 20  CONTINUE                                                          DATA  47
     PI=3.141592654                                                    DATA  48
     RETURN                                                            DATA  49
     END                                                               DATA  50
```

Subroutine COEF

```
      SUBROUTINE COEF (AA,BB,D11,D22,D12,D66,FX,FY,G1,GFS,M,           COEF   1
     .                N,P11,P12,P13,P22,P23,P33,PI,S44,S55,            COEF   2
     .                H,C1,C2,C3,PM,KTYPE)                             COEF   3
      IMPLICIT REAL*8(A-H,O-Z)                                         COEF   4
C                                                                      COEF   5
C*** THIS SUBROUTINE CALCULATES THE COEFFICIENTS                       COEF   6
C*** (P11,P12,P13,P22,P23,P33,C1,C2,C3)                                COEF   7
C                                                                      COEF   8
      P11=D11*(FLOAT(M)*PI/AA)*(FLOAT(M)*PI/AA)                        COEF   9
     .+D66*(FLOAT(N)*PI/BB)*(FLOAT(N)*PI/BB)+G1*S55                    COEF  10
      P12=(D12+D66)*(FLOAT(M)*PI/AA)*(FLOAT(N)*PI/BB)                  COEF  11
      P13=G1*S55*(FLOAT(M)*PI/AA)                                      COEF  12
```

```fortran
      P22=D66*(FLOAT(M)*PI/AA)*(FLOAT(M)*PI/AA)
     .+D22*(FLOAT(N)*PI/BB)*(FLOAT(N)*PI/BB)+G1*S44
      P23=G1*S44*(FLOAT(N)*PI/BB)
      P33=(G1*S55+FX)*(FLOAT(M)*PI/AA)*(FLOAT(M)*PI/AA)
     .+(G1*S44+FY)*(FLOAT(N)*PI/BB)*(FLOAT(N)*PI/BB)+GFS
C
      IF(KTYPE.EQ.0) RETURN
      P=PM
      T=H
      ROT=P*T*T/12.
      E = P11*P22*P33 - P11*P23*P23 - P33*P12*P12 +
     .2.*P12*P13*P23 - P22*P13*P13
      F = (P23*P23 + P13*P13 - P11*P33 - P22*P33)*ROT +
     .(P12*P12 - P11*P22)*P
      Q1=(P11*P*ROT + P22*P*ROT + P33*ROT*ROT)
      A = P*ROT*ROT
      C1= Q1/A
      C2= F/A
      C3= E/A
      RETURN
      END
```

Subroutine EIGEN

```fortran
      SUBROUTINE EIGEN(AA,ALFA,AMN1,BB,BETA,BMN1,CMN1,FCR,G1,GFS,II,
     .                 LPON,M,N,PI,P11,P12,P13,P22,P23,P33,PM,S44,S55,
     .                 WMN2,WMN,X1,KTYPE)
C
C*** EVALUATES EIGENVALUES, EIGENVECTORS AND BUCKLING FORCES
C
      IMPLICIT REAL*8(A-H,O-Z)
      DIMENSION FCR(LPON,LPON),WMN(LPON,LPON)
C
C
      IF(KTYPE.EQ.1) GO TO 20
C
      Q=(P11*P22)-(P12*P12)
      WMN2=((Q*P33)+(2.0*P12*P23*P13)-(P22*P13*P13)-(P11*P23*
     .P23))/(PM*Q)
      GO TO 30
 20   S1=X1
      WMN2=S1
 30   CONTINUE
      IF(II.EQ.0) GO TO 5
C
C*** EIGENVECTORS
C
```

```
      CMN1=1.0
      AMN1=(((P12*P23)-(P22*P13))/((P11*P22)-(P12*P12)))*CMN1
      BMN1=(((P12*P13)-(P11*P23))/((P11*P22)-(P12*P12)))*CMN1
      GO TO 10
C
C*** EIGENVALUES
C
    5 WMN(M,N)=SQRT(WMN2)
      IF(ALFA.NE.0.0) GO TO 15
      IF(BETA.EQ.0.0) GO TO 10
C
C*** BUCKLING FORCES
C
   15 FCR(M,N)=-(((2.0*P12*P23*P13)-(P22*P13*P13)-(P11*P23*P23))/
     .((P11*P22)-(P12*P12))+
     .((G1*S55*(FLOAT(M)*PI/AA)*(FLOAT(M)*PI/AA))+
     .(G1*S44*(FLOAT(N)*PI/BB)*(FLOAT(N)*PI/BB))+GFS))/
     .((ALFA*(FLOAT(M)*PI/AA)*(FLOAT(M)*PI/AA))+
     .(BETA*(FLOAT(N)*PI/BB)*(FLOAT(N)*PI/BB)))
   10 CONTINUE
      RETURN
      END
```

Subroutine SOLV

```
      SUBROUTINE SOLV (C1,C2,C3,X1,MITER,KTYPE)
C**
C**   OT SOLV EQUATION BY NEWTONS METHOD
      IMPLICIT REAL*8(A-H,O-Z)
C
      IF(KTYPE.EQ.0)RETURN
      X1=1.
      FTOLE = 0.00001
      DO 10 J=1,MITER
      FX= -X1*X1*X1 + C1*X1*X1 +C2*X1 + C3
      DRFX = -3.*X1*X1 +2.*C1*X1 + C2
      DELX = FX/DRFX
      S = X1-DELX
      X1= S
      IF(ABS(FX).LT.FTOLE) RETURN
 10   CONTINUE
C*****EVALUTTE THE SECOND AND THIRD ROOTS
      Y1= (C1-X1)
      Y2= C2 + (C1-X1)*X1
      F1=SQRT(Y1*Y1 +4.*Y2)
      X2=(Y1+F1)/2.0
      X3=(Y1-F1)/2.0
```

```
60    CONTINUE                                                      SOLV  23
      RETURN                                                        SOLV  24
      END                                                           SOLV  25
```

In Tables A1.1 and A1.2, the natural frequency parameters are shown for square simply supported plates with thickness-to-span ratios of $h/a = 0.1$ and $h/a = 0.01$. The results listed in the tables highlight the effect of including rotatory inertia effects.

Table A1.1 Frequency parameters Ω_{mn} for a simply supported square plate: $h/a = 0.1$, $k^2 = 0.833$, $\nu = 0.3$

		Ω_{mn}		
m	n	3D closed form	Mindlin closed form.	thin plate c. form
1	1	0.932	0.930	0.963
2	1	2.226	2.219	2.408
2	2	3.421	3.406	3.853
3	1	4.171	4.149	4.816
3	2	5.239	5.206	6.261
4	1	—	6.731	—
3	3	6.889	6.834	8.668
4	2	7.511	7.446	9.632
4	3	9.268	8.896	12.521

Table A1.2 Frequency parameters Ω_{mn} for a simply supported square plate: $h/a = 0.01$, $k^2 = 0.833$, $\nu = 0.3$

m n	Ω_{mn} Mindlin closed form	Ω_{mn} thin plate c. form
1 1	0.09629	0.09632
2 1	0.2406	0.2408
2 2	0.3848	0.3853
3 1	0.4809	0.4816
3 2	0.6249	0.6261
4 1	0.8167	0.8187
3 3	0.8647	—
4 2	0.9605	—
4 3	1.1997	—

[A1.2] CLOSED FORM SOLUTION FOR CLAMPED PLATES

The closed form solution presented in Chapter 1 for the free vibration and transient dynamic analysis of simply supported rectangular plates has been recently extended by Ramakumar and co-workers [A1.1-2] to deal with clamped boundaries using a Lagrangian multiplier technique. The method uses the same expressions for the lateral displacement and normal rotations as those used for the simply supported plate. However, corrections in the form of constraints are made on the clamped boundaries using Lagrangian multipliers. Program TRAM can thus be used as a basis for the free vibration and transient dynamic analysis of Mindlin plates with clamped boundaries.

A further Rayleigh-Ritz procedure for clamped plates and plates with other boundary conditions has been presented by Dawe and Roufaeil [A1.3].

REFERENCES

(A1.1) R.L. Ramkumar, P.C. Chen and W.J. Sanders,
Free vibration solution for clamped orthotropic plates using
using Lagrangian multiplier technique,
AIAA J, **25**, 146-151, 1987.

(A1.2) P.C. Chen and R.L. Ramkumar,
Static and dynamic analysis of clamped orthotropic plates using
Lagrangian multiplier technique,
AIAA J, **25**, 316-323, 1987.

(A1.3) D.J. Dawe and O.L. Roufaeil,
Rayleigh-Ritz vibration analysis of Mindlin plates,
J. Sound Vib., **69**, 345-359, 1980.

[A2.1] EXTENSIONS OF MINDLIN STRIP METHOD TO SHELLS AND FOLDED PLATE STRUCTURES

Onate and Suarez [A2.1] have demonstrated that the Mindlin strip formulation described in Chapter 2 can be extended to shells and folded plate structures — see Figure A2.1. Some examples will now be presented which have been analysed with the linear strip element with a single point integration of all terms of the stiffness and mass matrices.

Example 1 - Slab/beam structure

For the slab/beam structure shown Figure A2.2, the transverse section is discretised using 24 linear strips. Some of the vibration modes for the first and second harmonic term are shown in Figure A2.2 together with the natural frequencies for the first three harmonics are shown. Note that numerical results obtained compare well with those obtained by Cheung [A2.2] also plotted in the same figure.

Example 2 - Box girder bridge with circular planform

In this example a two-cell box girder bridge of circular planform is analyzed. The geometry and material properties of the problem are shown in Figure A2.3 Thirty six linear strips are used to discretise the structure. Various modes of vibration are illustrated in Figure A2.3 which also shows the values of the natural frequencies for the first four harmonics. Some numerical results obtained by Cheung [A2.2] are also plotted.

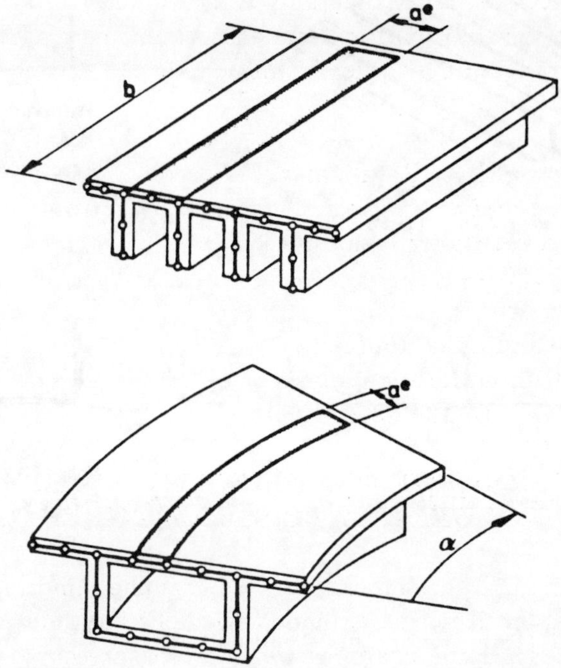

Figure A2.1 Further finite strip models

Example 3 - Cylindrical shell

Details of the geometry and material properties of a cylindrical shell are shown in Figure A2.4. The curved geometry of the shell is modelled using 48 flat, linear strips. The first three vibration modes for the first harmonic term are plotted in Figure A2.4 where a plot of the natural frequencies for the two first harmonics is also shown. Comparisons with results obtained by Morris and Dawe using curved strips [A2.3] are also plotted in the same figure.

Example 4 - Cylindrical tank with spherical dome

The final example analyzed is a cylindrical tank with a spherical dome as shown in Figure A2.5. The meridional section of the structure is discretised using 15 and 34 strips for the cylindrical wall and the dome respectively. Results for the first vibration modes corresponding to harmonic terms zero and one, are plotted in Figure A2.5. The natural frequencies corresponding to the first mode for different harmonic terms are presented in Figure A2.5 where results obtained by Feijoo et al [A2.4] using curved elements are also plotted. Good agreement between both sets of results is again obtained.

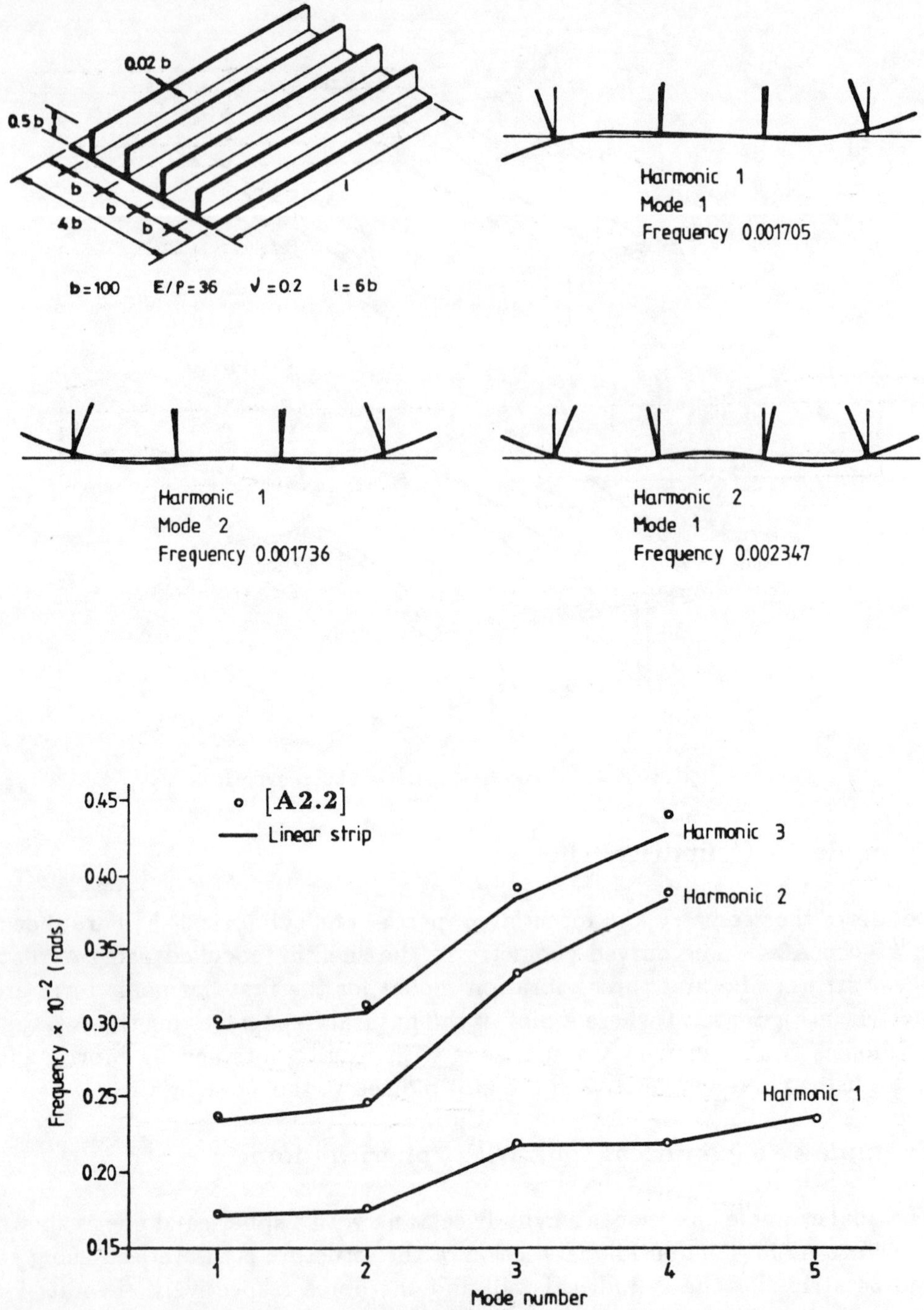

Figure A2.2 Geometry, modes and frequencies for a slab/beam structure

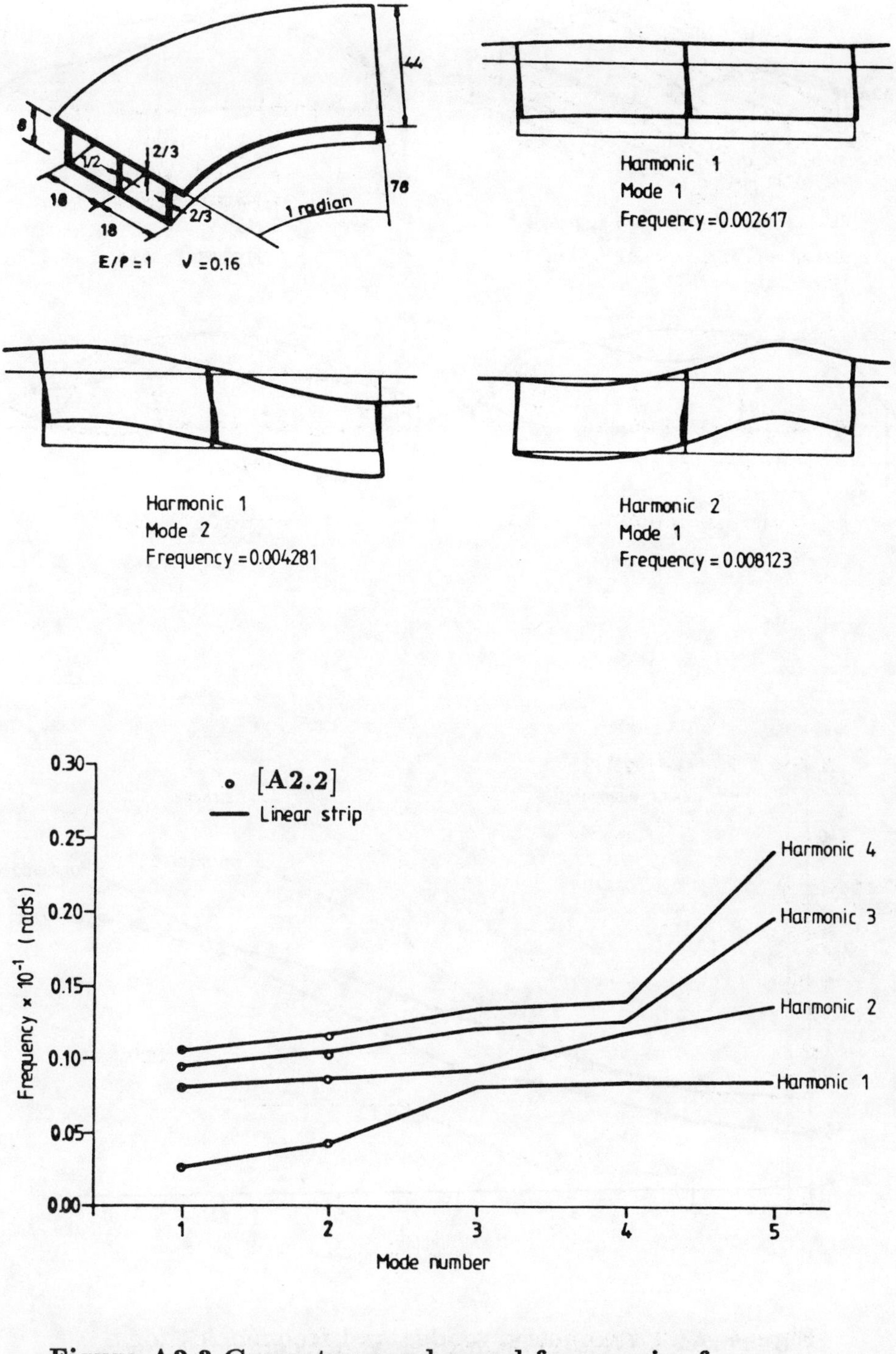

Figure A2.3 Geometry, modes and frequencies for a curved box girder

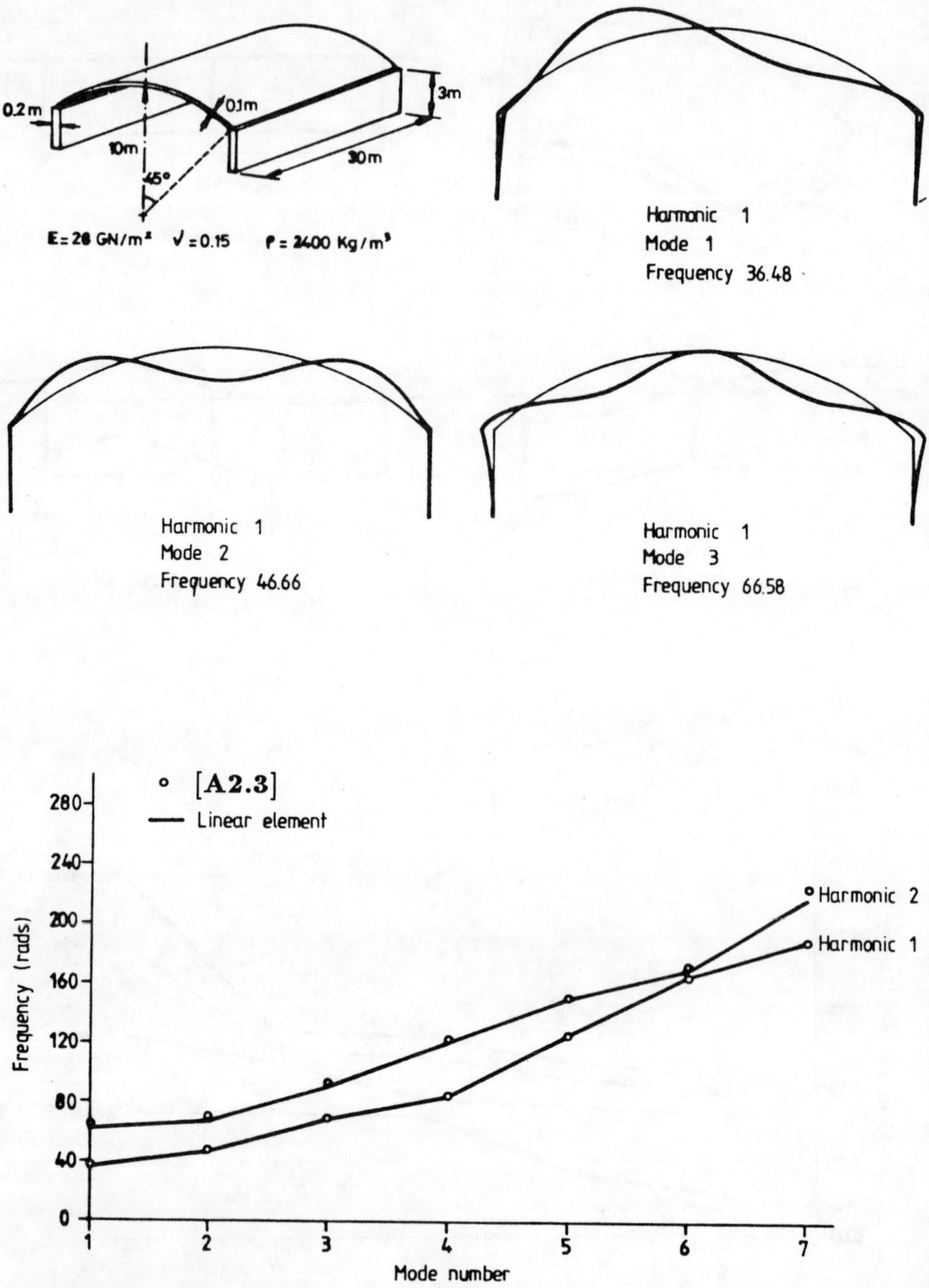

Figure A2.4 Geometry, modes and frequencies for a cylindrical shell

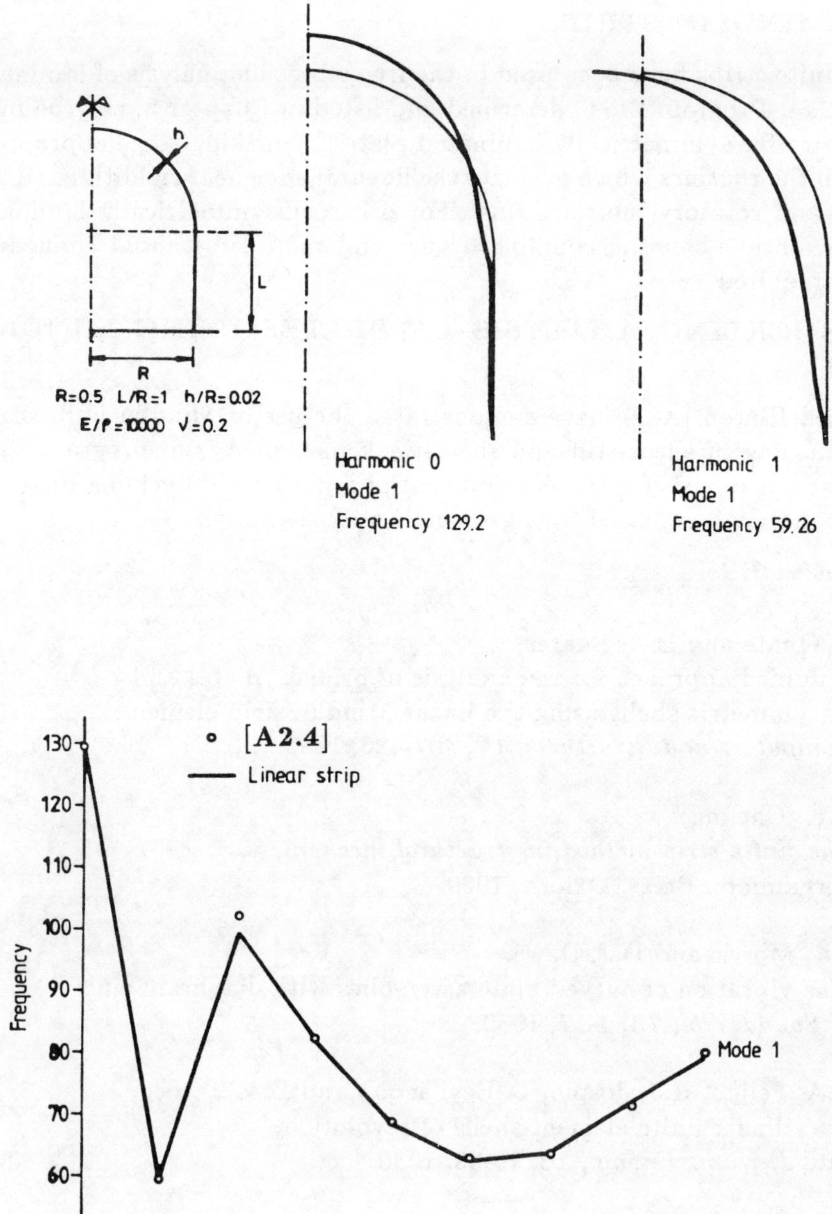

Figure A2.5 Geometry, modes and frequencies for cylindrical tank with spherical dome

[A2.2] FREE VIBRATION ANALYSIS OF LAMINATED PLATES USING MINDLIN STRIPS

Mindlin finite strips have been used in the free vibration analysis of laminated plates [A2.5]. Program FIST, described and listed in Chapter 2, may be modified to cater for symmetrically laminated plates by making some appropriate changes to the routines which evaluate the flexural and shear rigidities and also the mass and rotatory inertia terms. For other, unsymmetrically laminated plates, membrane-bending coupling occurs and more substantial changes to FIST are required.

[A2.3] BUCKLING ANALYSIS OF PLATES USING MINDLIN STRIPS

Benson and Hinton [A2.6] have demonstrated the use of Mindlin finite strips for the buckling of shear-stiff and shear-weak plates. Again, program FIST may be used as a basis for the development of a finite strip buckling program. The mass matrix is replaced by a geometric stiffness matrix.

REFERENCES

(A2.1) E. Oñate and B.A. Suarez,
A unified approach for the analysis of bridges, plates and axisymmetric shells using the linear Mindlin strip element,
Computers and Structures, **17**, 407-426, 1983.

(A2.2) Y.K. Cheung,
The finite strip method in structural mechanics,
Pergammon Press, Oxford, 1969.

(A2.3) J.R. Morris and D.J. Dawe,
Free vibration of curved plate assemblies with diaphram ends,
J. Sound Vib., **73**, 1-17, 1980.

(A2.4) R.A. Feijoo, R.J. Jospin, L. Bevilacqua and E.A. Taroco,
Curvilinear finite element shells of revolution,
Int. J. Num. Engng., **16**, 19-33, 1980.

(A2.5) E. Hinton,
A note on a thick finite strip method for the free vibration of laminated plates,
Earthqu. Engng. Struct. Dyn., **4**, 511-520, 1976.

(A2.6) P.R. Benson and E. Hinton,
A thick finite strip solution for static, free vibration and stability problems,
Int. J. Num. Meth. Engng., **10**, 665-678, 1976.

[A3.1] FREE VIBRATIONS OF PLATES WITH CONCENTRATED MASSES

The finite element program VIBUK presented in Chapter 3 dealt with the free vibrations of Mindlin plates has been extended to deal with concentrated masses.

Tables A3.1 and A3.2 show the natural frequency parameters for square simply supported plates of thickness-to-span ratios $h/a = 0.0001$ and $h/a = 0.01$. In each plate there is a central concentrated mass $\mu = m_i/\rho a^2 = 0.25$. The results listed in the tables provide comparsions with closed form solutions [A3.1]. In the finite element studies, both lumped and consistent mass representations are considered.

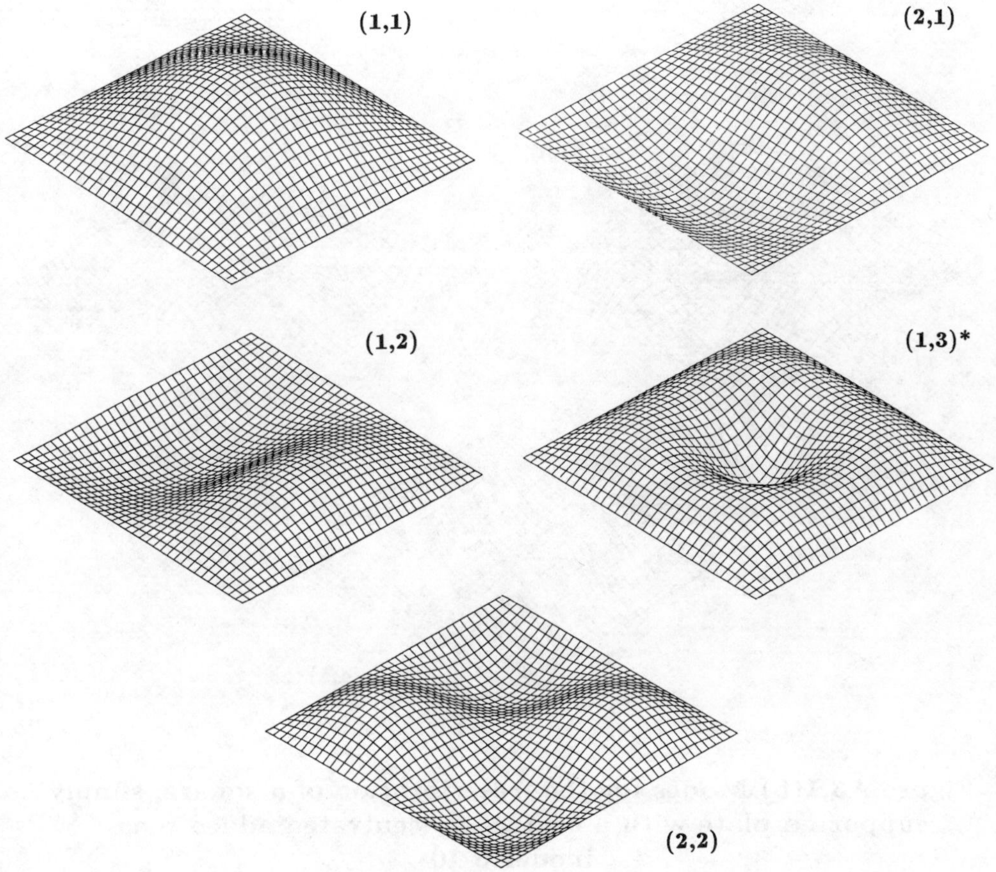

Figure A3.1(a) Modes for the free vibration of a square, simply supported plate with a central concentrated added mass: modes 1-5

Some differences between the modes predicted by the finite element solutions and those given by the closed form solution can be detected. The finite element modes are illustrated in Figure A3.1. The sixth mode obtained using finite el-

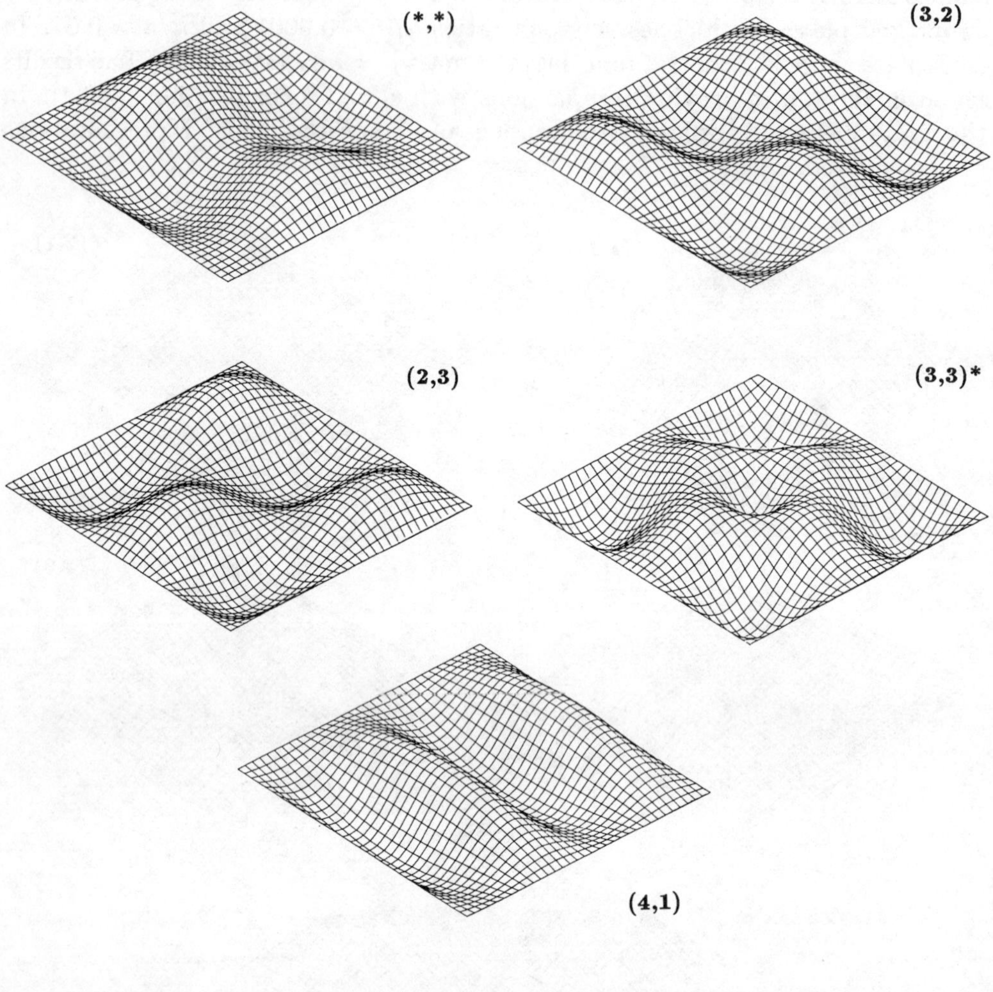

Figure A3.1(b) Modes for the free vibration of a square, simply supported plate with a central concentrated added mass: modes 6-10

ements does not have a counterpart in the closed form solution. Furthermore, the (3,1), (3,3) and (5,10) form modes have a different shape for the corresponding frequency in the finite element solution. These are highlighted with an asterisk (*) in Tables A3.1 and A3.2. Apart form the sixth mode the closed form and finite element frequency predictions are in excellent agreement.

Further studies of the vibrations of skew plates carrying a concentrated mass have been presented by Mizusawa [A3.2]. This analysis is based on thin plate theory and uses the spline element method, which is the Rayleigh-Ritz discretisation procedure with B-spline functions. Various boundary conditions are considered in this work.

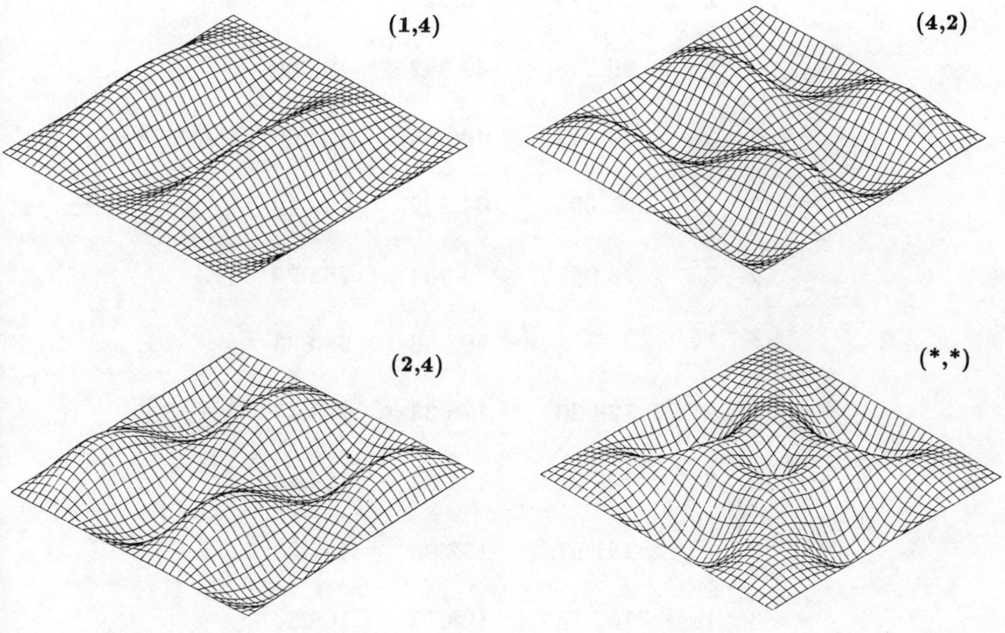

Figure A3.1(c) Modes for the free vibration of a square, simply supported plate with a central concentrated added mass: modes 11-15

Table A3.1 Frequency parameters Ω_{mn} for a simply supported square plate with a concentrated mass:
$h/a = 0.0001$, $k^2 = 0.833$, $\nu = 0.3$

		Ω_{mn}		
m	n	Mindlin closed form	f.e. lumped mass	f.e. consis. c.mass
1	1	13.729	13.727	13.727
2	1	49.348	49.352	49.360
1	2	49.348	49.352	49.360
3	1	65.005	64.992	65.012
*	*			
2	2	78.957	78.954	78.979
*	*	—	98.756	98.833
3	2	128.30	128.33	128.45
2	3	128.30	128.33	128.45
3	3	151.97	152.06	152.25
*	*			
4	1	167.78	168.15	168.54
1	4	167.78	168.15	168.54
4	2	197.39	197.64	198.13
2	4	197.39	197.64	198.13
5	1	211.73	212.33	212.93
*	*			

Table A3.2 Frequency parameters Ω_{mn} for a simply supported square plate with a concentrated mass: $h/a = 0.01$, $k^2 = 0.833$, $\nu = 0.3$

		Ω_{mn}		
m	n	Mindlin closed form	f.e. lumped mass	f.e. consis. c.mass
1	1	13.719	13.719	13.719
2	1	49.303	49.307	49.315
1	2	49.303	49.307	49.315
3 *	1 *	64.718	64.757	64.776
2	2	78.841	78.840	78.864
*	*	—	98.577	98.653
3	2	128.00	128.02	128.14
2	3	128.00	128.02	128.14
3 *	3 *	151.16	151.27	151.46
4	1	167.26	167.63	168.02
1	4	167.26	167.63	168.02
4	2	196.67	196.93	197.41
2	4	196.67	196.93	197.41
5 *	1 *	210.38	210.94	211.52

[A3.2] NATURAL FREQUENCIES AND MODES OF RHOMBIC MINDLIN PLATES

Kanaka Raju and Hinton [A3.3] have carried out a parametric study of the natural frequencies and mode shapes of thin and moderately thick rhombic plates using a 9-noded Lagrangian, isoparametric, quadrilateral plate element based in Mindlin's theory. A wide range of skew angles and boundary conditions are considered and comparisons with earlier published work are provided where possible. A brief sample of these results is now presented.

Figure A3.2 shows the rhombic plates and combinations of boundary conditions considered. The skew angle ($\alpha = 90 - \beta$) is varied from 0 to 60 degrees in steps of 15 degrees.

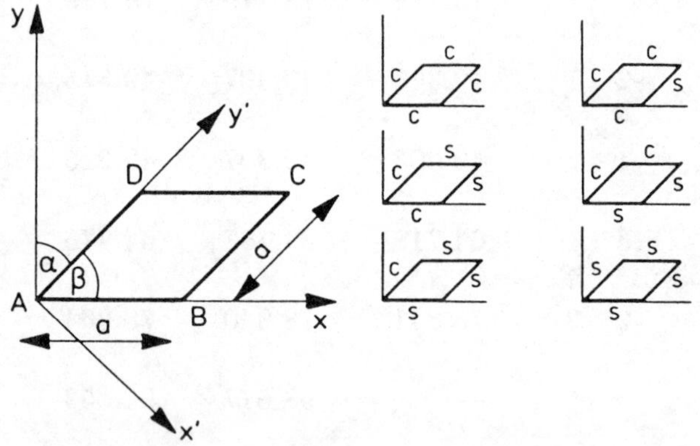

Figure A3.2 Rhombic plate geometry and boundary conditions

Combinations of two types of boundary condition are included in these studies:

(a) clamped (C) boundaries in which ($w = \theta_x = \theta_y = 0$),

(b) simply-supported (S) boundaries in which $w = \theta_t = 0$ (where θ_t is the rotation in the plane normal to the plate edge).

The 9-node Lagrangian element has been used to evaluate frequencies and mode shapes for a series of thin rhombic plates with various boundary conditions and angles of skew. For problems in which the plate is simply supported on all edges a 5×5 mesh is adopted. Otherwise a 6×6 mesh is used.

In Table A3.3 the results obtained using the finite element method are compared with those of Nair and Durvasula [A3.4] for various boundary conditions and skew angles. The frequencies are expressed in terms of the parameter $\lambda = [\omega(\rho t)^{1/2}/D](l^2/\pi^2)$ and there is good agreement between the two sets of results.

Table A3.3 Frequency parameters λ for thin rhombic plates with various edge conditions and skew angles $h/a = 0.001$, $\nu = 0.3$

			λ		
boundary			$\alpha =$		
conditions	60	45	30	15	0
CCCC	12.408	6.665	4.674	3.872	3.648
	—	6.680	4.675	3.870	3.647
CCSC	10.773	5.843	4.119	3.421	3.226
	—	5.973	4.151	3.425	3.225
CSCS	9.887	5.330	3.750	3.112	2.935
	—	5.511	3.797	3.121	2.933
CCSS	8.635	4.829	3.457	2.895	2.742
	—	5.213	3.570	2.922	2.741
CSSS	8.037	4.328	3.047	2.537	2.396
	—	4.578	3.120	2.550	2.396
SSSS	7.058	3.666	2.548	2.117	2.001
	—	3.525	2.524	2.115	2.000

Mode shapes for the particular case of the plate with clamped boundary conditions in which the thickness/span ratio is 0.1 are shown in Figure A3.3.

[A3.3] NONLINEAR VIBRATIONS OF MINDLIN PLATES

Kanaka Raju and Hinton [A3.5] have presented a study of the large amplitude vibrations of Mindlin plates using Lagrangian, isoparametric, quadrilateral elements. Square, rectangular, circular and elliptical plates with clamped and simply supported boundary conditions were considered. The results for simply supported square plates of thickness to span ratios $h/b = 0.001$ and $h/b = 0.1$ are shown in Tables A3.4 and A3.5 respectively a Poisson's ratio of 0.3. These results are presented in the form of a linear frequency parameter λ and nonlinear to linear period ratios for various values of c/h (amplitude to thickness) ratios. These results are compared with results obtained earlier by Kanaka Raju [A3.6]. A 2×2 mesh of elements was used in a symmetric quadrant of the plate

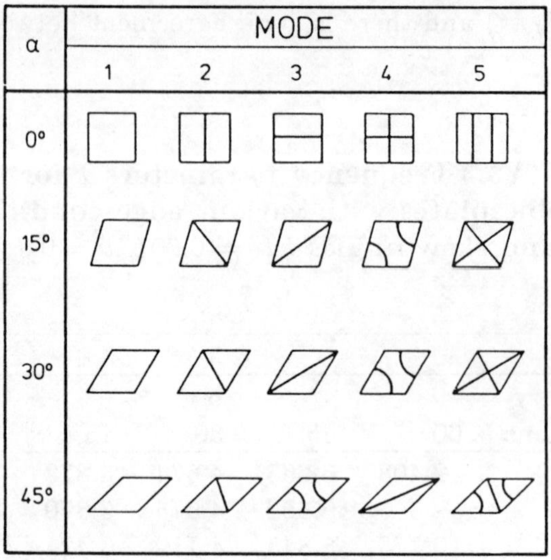

Figure A3.3 Modal patterns of CCCC rhombic plates

Note that two different types of simply supported boundary condition are used in these studies: SS_1 and SS_2

Table A3.4 Frequency parameters λ and T_{NL}/T_L values for the nonlinear vibrations of a simply supported square plate: $h/b = 0.001$

		T_{NL}/T_L	
c/h	SS_1	SS_2	c.f.
0.0	1.0000	1.0000	1.0000
0.2	0.9811	0.9818	0.9818
0.4	0.9309	0.9332	0.9327
0.6	0.8631	0.8672	0.8652
0.8	0.7905	0.7959	0.7916
1.0	0.7210	0.7272	0.7199
λ	0.9499×10^{-5}	0.9638×10^{-5}	0.9633×10^{-5}

Table A3.5 Frequency parameters λ and T_{NL}/T_L values for the nonlinear vibrations of a simply supported square plate: $h/b = 0.1$

	T_{NL}/T_L		
c/h	SS_1	SS_2	c.f.
0.0	1.0000	1.0000	1.0000
0.2	0.9788	0.9809	0.9788
0.4	0.9233	0.9301	0.9226
0.6	0.8504	0.8620	0.8475
0.8	0.7746	0.7895	0.7681
1.0	0.7036	0.7204	0.6931
λ	0.0894	0.0931	0.0895

[A3.4] MASS REPRESENTATION IN MINDLIN PLATE FINITE ELEMENT ANALYSIS

Much interesting work has been carried out on mass representation in finite element analysis. For example, Hinton et al [A3.7] have presented a special technique for lumping masses to nodal points. This method has been studied in the context of Mindlin plates by Hinton and Bićanić [A3.8]. More recently, Malkus and Plesha [A3.9] have discussed the implications of using zero and negative masses in finite element vibration and transient dynamic analysis.

REFERENCES

(A3.1) J.W. Nicholson and L.A. Bergman,
Vibration of thick plates carrying concentrated masses,
J. Sound Vib., **103**, 357-369, 1985.

(A3.2) T. Mizusawa,
Vibrations of skew plates carrying a concentrated mass,
J. Sound Vib., **116**, 561-572, 1987.

(A3.3) K. Kanaka Raju and E. Hinton
Natural frequencies and modes for rhombic Mindlin plates,
Earthqu. Engng. Struct. Dyn., **8**, 55-62, 1980.

(A3.4) P.S. Nair and S. Durvasula,
Vibration of skew plates,
J. Sound Vib., **26**, 1-19, 1973.

(A3.5) K. Kanaka Raju and E. Hinton,
Nonlinear vibrations of thick Mindlin plate elements,
Int. J. Num. Meth. Engng., **15**, 249-257, 1980.

(A3.6) K. Kanaka Raju, G. Venkateswara and I.S. Raju,
Effect of geometric nonlinearity on the free flexural vibrations of moderately thick rectangular plates,
Computers and Structures, **9**, 441-444, 1978.

(A3.7) E. Hinton, T. Rock and O.C. Zienkiewicz,
A note on mass lumping and related processes in the finite element metl
Earthqu. Engng. Struct. Dyn., **4**, 245-249, 1976.

(A3.8) E. Hinton and N. Bićanić,
A comparison of Lagrangian and Serendipity Mindlin plate elements for free vibration analysis,
Computers and Structures, **10**, 483-493, 1979.

(A3.9) D.S. Malkus and M.E. Plesha,
Zero and negative masses in finite element vibration and transient analysis,
Comp. Meth. Appl. Mech. Engng., **59**, 281-306, 1986.

[A5.1] CRITICAL TIME STEP ESTIMATES

The usual method for obtaining stable time steps in explicit finite element programs (e.g. DYNAM) is by computing or estimating the maximum eigenvalues for individual elements and then by making use of the element inequality [A5.1]

$$\omega_{max} \leq \max_e \omega^e_{max} \tag{A5.1}$$

so that the stable time step is bounded by the expression

$$\Delta t \leq 2/\omega_{max} \tag{A5.2}$$

For 4-noded Mindlin plate elements with uniform reduced integration (i.e. 1×1 Gauss-Legendre rule for shear and bending terms), selective reduced integration (2 × 2 for bending and 1 × 1 for shear) or one-point integration with a stabilization procedure, Beltyschko and Lin [A5.2] have shown that for isotropic material

$$\omega_{max} = \{4[\max(\lambda_1, \lambda_5)]/(\rho A h \alpha)\}^{1/2} \tag{A5.3}$$

in which

$$\lambda_1 = c\alpha \hat{a}_{11}/A + cA/4 \tag{A5.4}$$

$$\lambda_5 = D\{R_1 + [R_1^2 - 4(1-\nu^2)R_2^2]^{1/2}\}^{1/2}/4A \tag{A5.5}$$

and

$$\begin{aligned}
\alpha &= h^2/12 \\
c &= \kappa G h \\
D &= Eh^3/12(1-\nu^2) \\
\hat{a}_{11} &= (R_1 + R_3)/4 \\
R_1 &= y_{24}^2 + y_{31}^2 + x_{24}^2 + x_{31}^2 \\
R_2 &= y_{31}x_{24} - y_{24}x_{31} \\
R_3 &= (R_1^2 - 4R_2^2)^{1/2}
\end{aligned}$$

Note also that $y_{24} = y_2 - y_4$ etc. where the nodes are numbered in an anticlockwise manner.

Beltyschko and Lin also provide formulae for anisotropic plates. These expressions are more accurate for the 4-node Mindlin plate elements than the critical time step estimate given in Chapter 5. An alternative is to use Gerschgorin's bounds for each element. Beltyschko and Lin [A5.2] demonstrate this approach for anisotropic Mindlin plate examples.

[A5.2] TRANSIENT DYNAMIC ANALYSIS OF A SIMPLY SUPPORTED SQUARE PLATE SUBJECTED TO A CONCENTRATED CENTRAL PATCH LOAD

Program DYNAM, which was described in Chapter 5, is now used to demonstrate the behaviour of a simply supported square plate subjected to a Heaviside, concentrated patch load. In the analysis the following parameters are adopted: side length $a = 1.0$, thickness $h = 0.1$, elastic modulus $E = 10920.0$, density $\rho = 100.0$ and pressure intensity $q = 0.16$. The pressure acts over a central square area of side length $b = 0.2$. Using the estimate given in Chapter 5, the time step length is taken as $\Delta t = 0.0025$ in order to avoid instability

Figure A5.1 shows the deflected plate profiles at time stations $t = 25\Delta t, 50\Delta t, 100\Delta t, 250\Delta t, 400\Delta t, 425\Delta t, 450\Delta t$ and $475\Delta t$. To provide a check on the finite element solution, program TRAM of Chapter 1 (suitably modified to allow for rotatory inertia — see Section [A1.1]) is also used to produce deflected plate profiles at the same time stations and as can be seen from Figure A5.1, excellent agreement is obtained.

Central displacement and bending moment time histories are shown in Figures A5.2 and A5.3 respectively for the Heaviside load.

The effect of suddenly removing the concentrated patch load is now examined. Cut-off times for the applied load of $t_c = T, T/2, T/4, T/10$ and $T/20$ are considered where T is the fundamental period of the plate. Central displacement and bending moment time histories are shown in Figures A5.4-A5.13 respectively. Again, excellent agreement between the closed form and finite element solutions is detected.

For the Heaviside load, where $t_c = \infty$, the central deflection ranges from 1.02 to 0.0 and the central bending moment ranges from 19.7 to 0.0. However, for a cut-off time of $t_c = T/2$, the central deflection ranges from 0.98 to -0.97 and the central bending moment ranges from 18.0 to -14.9.

REFERENCES

(A5.1) I. Fried,
Discretization and round-off errors in the finite element analysis of elliptic boundary value problems,
Ph.D. thesis, MIT, 1971.

(A5.2) T. Belytschko and J.I. Lin,
Eigenvalues and stable time steps for the bilinear Mindlin plate element
Int. J. Num. Meth. Engng., **21**, 1729-1745, 1985.

closed form solution **finite element solution**

Figure A5.1(a) Deflected plate profiles for a simply supported square plate subjected to a central concentrated patch load time stations $t = 25\Delta t, 50\Delta t, 100\Delta t, 250\Delta t$

closed form solution

finite element solution

Figure A5.1(b) Deflected plate profiles for a simply supported square plate subjected to a central concentrated patch load time stations $t = 400\Delta t, 425\Delta t, 450\Delta t, 475\Delta t$

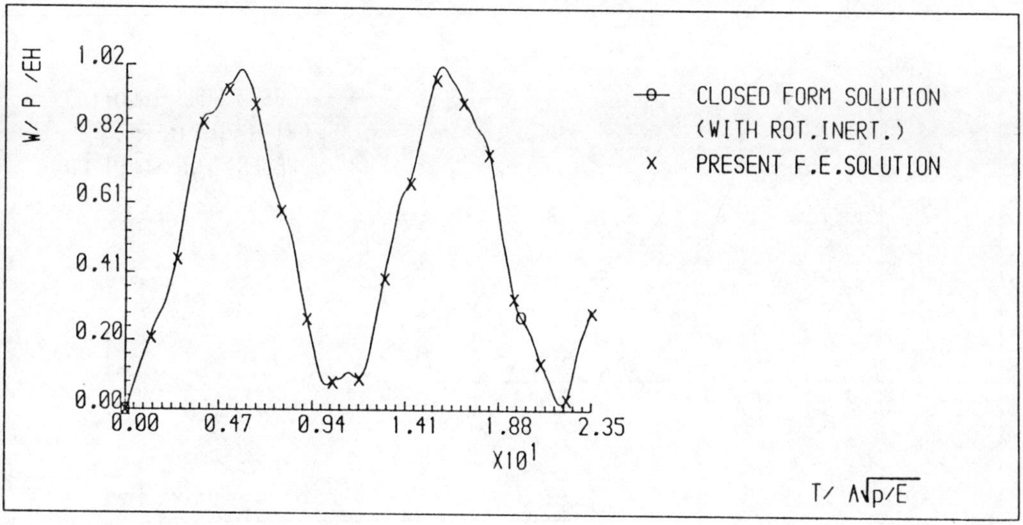

Figure A5.2 Central deflection time histories for a simply supported, square plate subjected to a central concentrated patch load: closed form and finite element solutions Heaviside load i.e. cut-off time: $t_c = \infty$

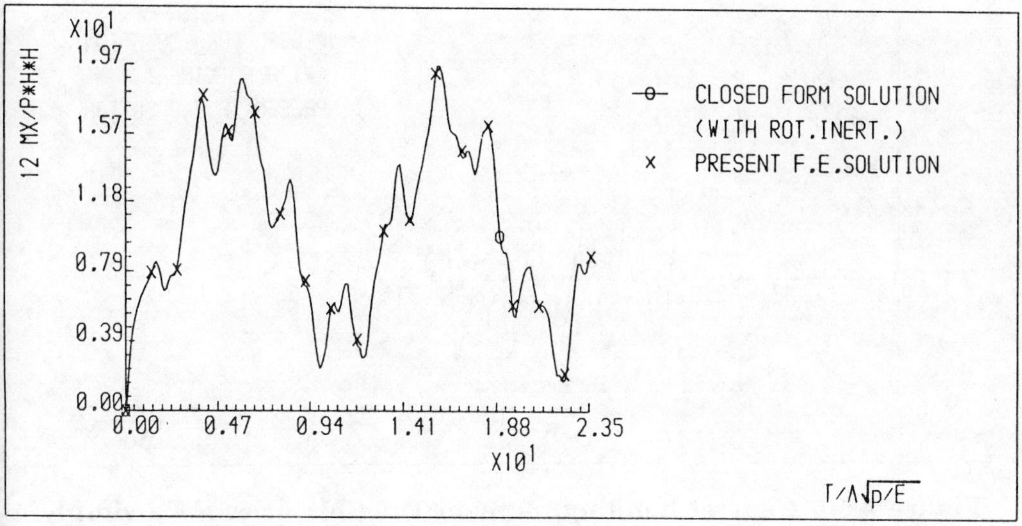

Figure A5.3 Central bending moment time histories for a simply supported, square plate subjected to a central concentrated patch load: closed form and finite element solutions Heaviside load i.e. cut-off time: $t_c = \infty$

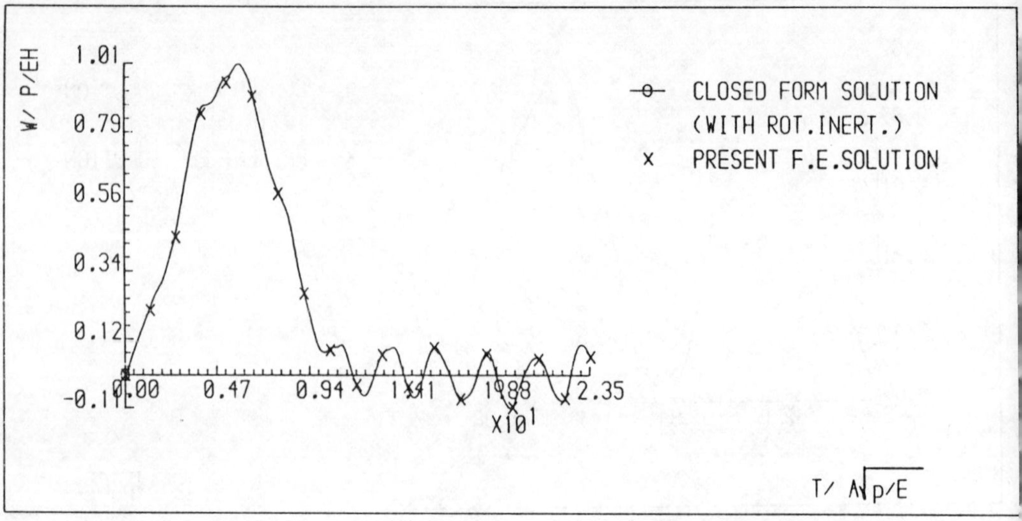

Figure A5.4 Central deflection time histories for a simply supported, square plate subjected to a central concentrated patch load: closed form and finite element solutions cut-off time: $t_c = T$

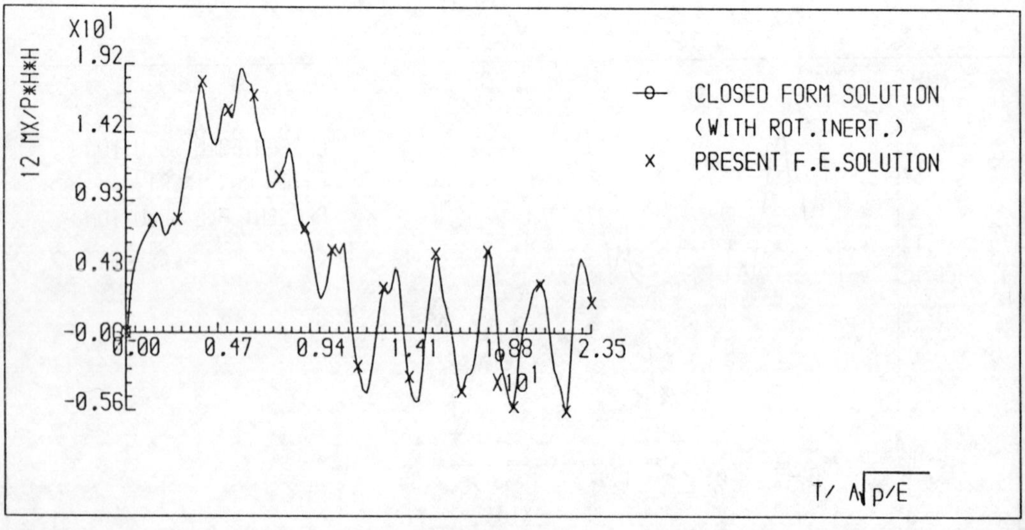

Figure A5.5 Central bending moment time histories for a simply supported, square plate subjected to a central concentrated patch load: closed form and finite element solutions cut-off time: $t_c = T$

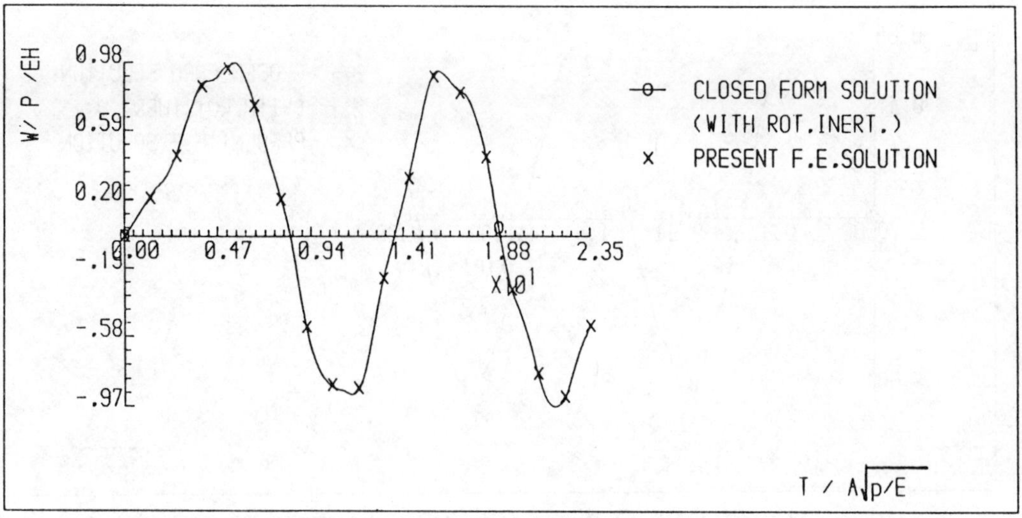

Figure A5.6 Central deflection time histories for a simply supported, square plate subjected to a central concentrated patch load: closed form and finite element solutions cut-off time: $t_c = T/2$

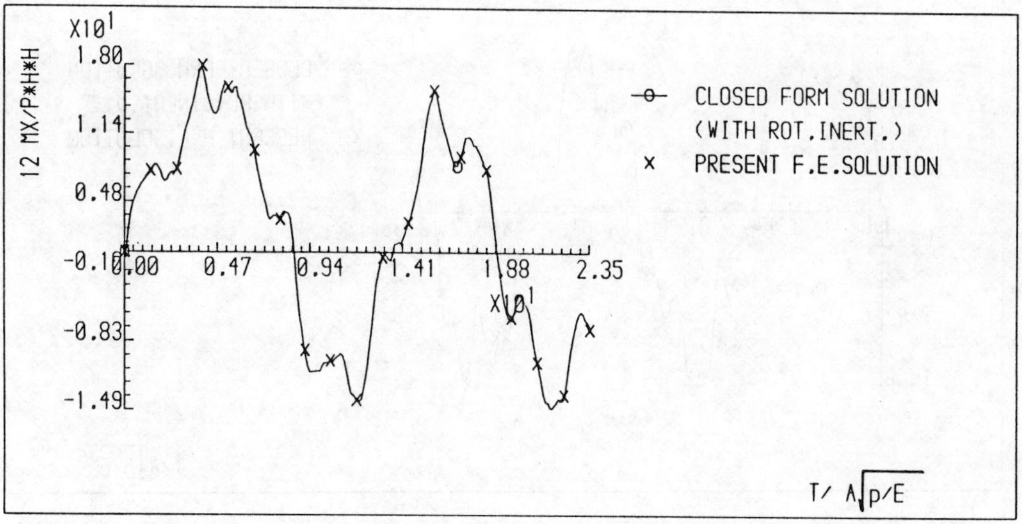

Figure A5.7 Central bending moment time histories for a simply supported, square plate subjected to a central concentrated patch load: closed form and finite element solutions cut-off time: $t_c = T/2$

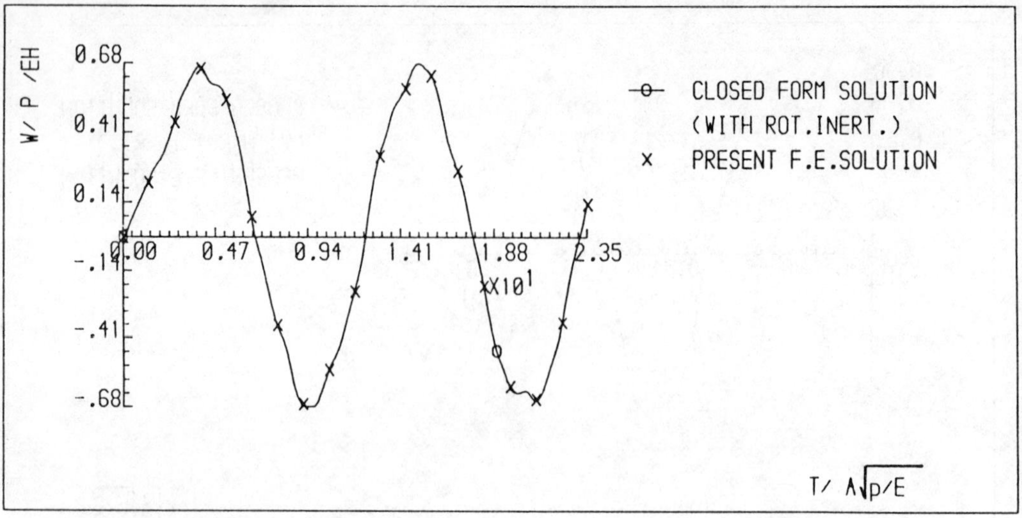

Figure A5.8 Central deflection time histories for a simply supported, square plate subjected to a central concentrated patch load: closed form and finite element solutions cut-off time $t_c = T/4$

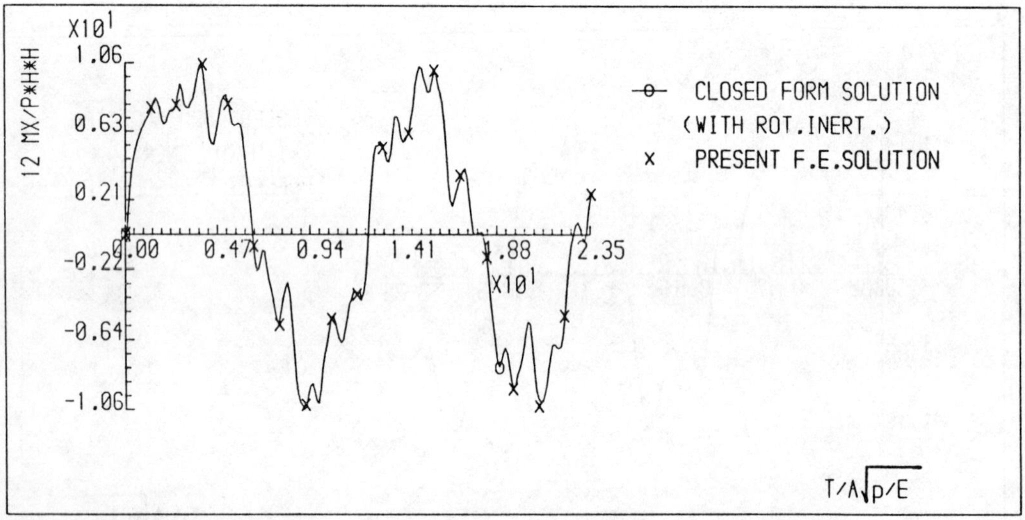

Figure A5.9 Central bending moment time histories for a simply supported, square plate subjected to a central concentrated patch load: closed form and finite element solutions cut-off time: $t_c = T/4$

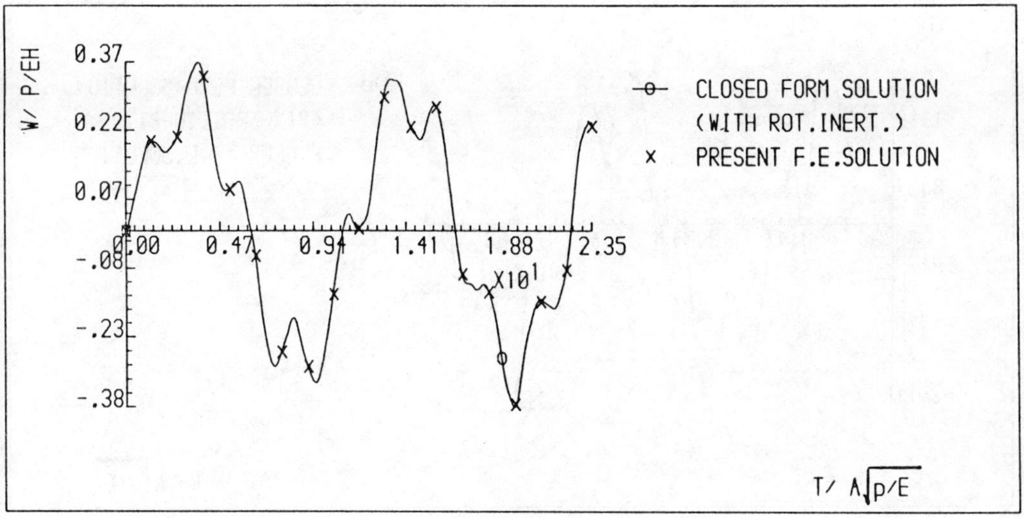

Figure A5.10 Central deflection time histories for a simply supported, square plate subjected to a central concentrated patch load: closed form and finite element solutions cut-off time: $t_c = T/10$

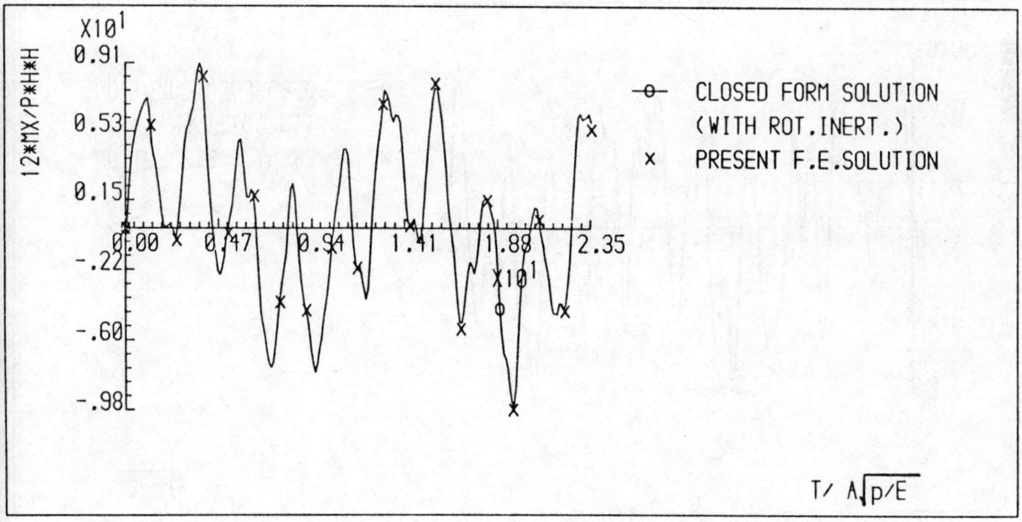

Figure A5.11 Central bending moment time histories for a simply supported, square plate subjected to a central concentrated patch load: closed form and finite element solutions cut-off time: $t_c = T/10$

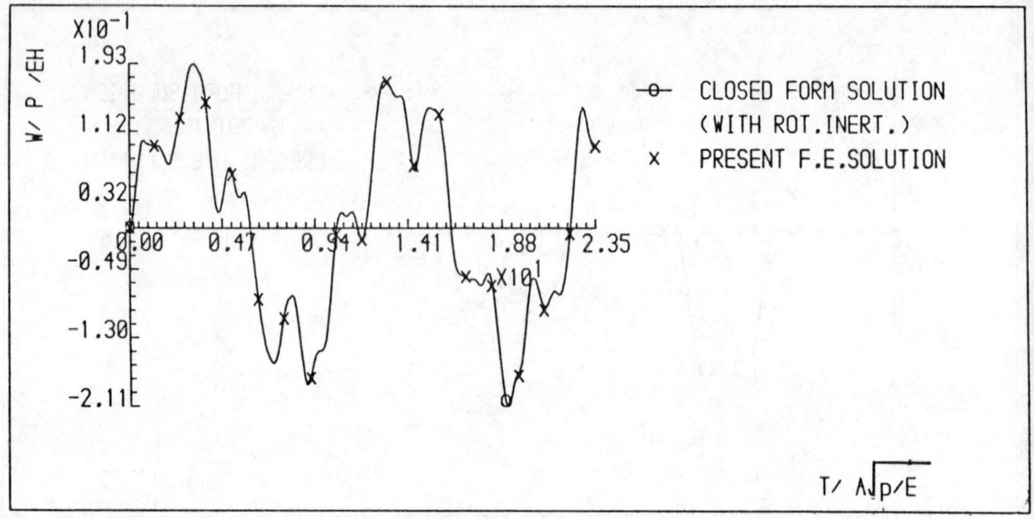

Figure A5.12 Central deflection time histories for a simply supported, square plate subjected to a central concentrated patch load: closed form and finite element solutions cut-off time: $t_c = T/20$

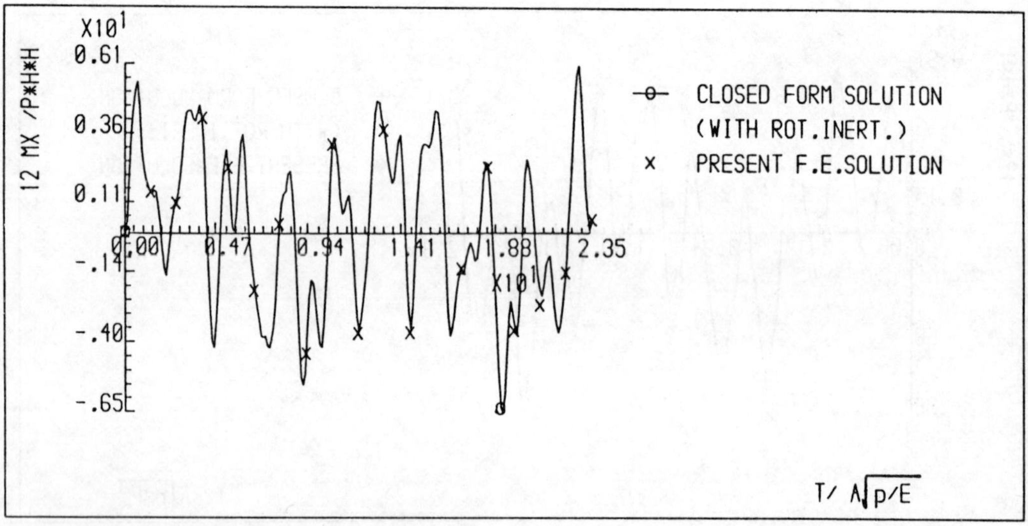

Figure A5.13 Central bending moment time histories for a simply supported, square plate subjected to a central concentrated patch load: closed form and finite element solutions cut-off time: $t_c = T/20$

AUTHOR INDEX

SUBJECT INDEX